THE Chemistry OF Acrylonitrile

Second Edition

THE Chemistry OF Acrylonitrile

Second Edition

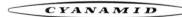

AMERICAN CYANAMID COMPANY

PETROCHEMICALS DEPARTMENT

30 Rockefeller Plaza

New York 20, N. Y.

FOREWORD

The "CHEMISTRY OF ACRYLONITRILE" *was first published in 1951. Since that time acrylonitrile has continued to grow in importance as an industrial chemical. New applications in the fields of plastics and surface coatings have been developed. The use of acrylonitrile as a basic material in the synthetic fiber industry has shown spectacular growth. Its application as a modifier for natural polymers —cyanoethylation of cellulose, proteins and starch—has introduced many new and promising applications.*

As a result of these increased activities, American Cyanamid has felt it necessary to expand and revise its book, the "CHEMISTRY OF ACRYLONITRILE." *The literature appearing since the publication of the first edition has been examined and a large number of references added, resulting in a twofold increase of the bibliography. A major addition is a new section containing tables of reaction conditions, yields, and literature references for many known reactions of acrylonitrile.*

American Cyanamid invites comments and questions on any phase of acrylonitrile chemistry.

TABLE OF CONTENTS

INTRODUCTION

In his discovery of acrylonitrile (1893) Moureu showed it to be the nitrile of acrylic acid having the structure $CH_2=CHCN$. From its first synthesis until just before World War II, acrylonitrile remained a laboratory curiosity. Because of the need for oil resistant rubber for military purposes, acrylonitrile was then produced commercially in the United States and in Germany for copolymerization with butadiene to form the so-called nitrile rubbers.

At the conclusion of hostilities, nitrile rubber requirements slackened and it became necessary to seek new uses for acrylonitrile. First and foremost of these was the acrylic fibers. This development grew rapidly so that at the present time the manufacture of acrylic fibers represents one of the major consuming industries for acrylonitrile. Additional uses have also developed in the plastics, surface coatings, and adhesives industries. Moreover, a variety of promising applications have been found using acrylonitrile as a chemical intermediate and as a modifier for natural polymers.

Because of its highly polar nitrile group and its activated double bond, acrylonitrile can undergo a wide variety of chemical reactions. For example, practically all compounds having a labile hydrogen atom will add across acrylonitrile's double bond. This permits the introduction of the cyanoethyl group into a large variety of molecules. Moreover, the nitrile group itself can be converted into an acid, ester, amide, or amine.

Perhaps the best known reaction is polymerization. Acrylonitrile can be polymerized or copolymerized with a large number of vinyl monomers using a variety of polymerization techniques. Its introduction into copolymers generally results in greater hardness as well as improved oil, chemical, and heat resistance.

These improvements in copolymer properties are the principal reasons for acrylonitrile's commercial utility in the textile, rubber, and plastics fields previously mentioned. Furthermore, as a chemical intermediate it can be used in the synthesis of antioxidants, pharmaceuticals, dyes, surface active agents, etc.

American Cyanamid invites correspondence concerning the application of acrylonitrile in all fields, and will gladly make available its wealth of experience in the chemistry and applications of this reactive compound.

THE Chemistry OF Acrylonitrile

Syntheses of Acrylonitrile

Physical Properties

Chemical Properties

Methods

Toxicity

Bibliography

SYNTHESES OF ACRYLONITRILE

SYNTHESES

The first synthesis of acrylonitrile (1893) involved the removal of water from (a) ethylene cyanohydrin, or (b) acrylamide, by reaction with phosphorus pentoxide (802):

$$\text{(a)} \quad 3HOCH_2CH_2CN + P_2O_5$$
$$3CH_2\text{=}CHCN + 2H_3PO_4$$
$$\text{(b)} \quad 3CH_2\text{=}CHCONH_2 + P_2O_5$$

Currently acrylonitrile is produced commercially from either ethylene cyanohydrin or acetylene and hydrocyanic acid.

Manufacture from Ethylene Cyanohydrin

To effect the decomposition of ethylene cyanohydrin into acrylonitrile and water it is not necessary to remove the evolved water by the use of a dehydrating agent such as phosphorus pentoxide. The decomposition of the cyanohydrin proceeds spontaneously and rapidly in the presence of suitable catalysts, and under the proper conditions (390). The wet acrylonitrile which is produced may be dried by azeotropic distillation, either by itself (214), or with dichloromethane (146), or chloroform (1080).

Manufacture from Acetylene

An early German patent (92) discloses that acrylonitrile is formed when a mixture of acetylene and hydrocyanic acid is passed over the proper catalysts at 400°C. to 500°C.:

$$C_2H_2 + HCN \longrightarrow CH_2\text{=}CHCN$$

There have been numerous improvement patents on this process (202, 443, 473, 474, 475, 849, 884, 978, 1013, 1015, 1231, 1232).

The reaction also proceeds readily in an aqueous solution of ammonium chloride and cuprous chloride (511, 992, 993). Excess acetylene is used and the acrylonitrile distills from the reactor. It is recovered and refined, largely by additional fractionation.

Other Methods of Synthesis

	Reference
1 Acetonitrile and Formaldehyde	134, 495
2 Acrolein, Ammonia and Oxygen	103, 104, 331, 332, 333, 334
3 Acrolein Oxime	1101
4 Acrylic Acid and Ammonia	64, 914, 915
5 3-Alkoxypropionamides	975, 976
6 3-Alkoxypropionitriles	599
7 Allylamine	746
8 Lactonitrile	644, 922, 1048, 1450
9 3,3′,3″-Nitrilotrispropionamide	871

(*Other Methods of Synthesis—Continued*)   Reference

10	Propionitrile	98, 151, 351, 457, 706
11	Vinyl Chloride	352
12	Miscellaneous	

Still other methods reported in the literature include the synthesis of acrylonitrile from various hydrocarbons and hydrocyanic acid (884, 979), from ethylene and cyanogen chloride (35), and from various olefins with ammonia and oxygen (201, 274, 320, 1016).

PHYSICAL PROPERTIES

The important physical properties of acrylonitrile are listed below.

A) *Physical Constants*

Appearance	Colorless liquid
Burning Velocity (1122)	47.0 cm./sec. (in air)
Critical Pressure (1)	34.9 atms.
Critical Temperature (1)	246°C.
Cryoscopic Constant (341, 611, 1164)	2.7 mole %/°C.
Density (1, 312, 341, 641, 1113, 1120)	0.8060 (20°C.)
	0.8004 (25°C.)
	$d = 0.8281 - 0.001106t$ (0-30°C.)
Dielectric Constant (1, 312)	38 (33.5 megacycles)
Dipole Moment (559, 621, 930, 1150)	3.3×10^{-18} e.s.u.-cm. (in CCl_4)
	3.51×10^{-18} e.s.u.-cm. (in C_6H_6)
	3.88×10^{-18} e.s.u.-cm. (vapor phase)
Explosive Limits (554, 614)	3.05 to $17.0 \pm 0.5\%$ (by volume in air at 25°C.)
Flash Point (Tagliabue Open Cup—1, 312)	0°C. (32°F.)
Freezing Point (341, 611, 1164)	-83.55 ± 0.05°C.
Ignition Temperature (1)	481°C. (898°F.)
Ionization Potential (792)	10.75 electron-volts
Molar Polarization (930)	266.0 cc. (25°C.)
Molar Refraction (341, 930, 1120)	15.67 (D line)
Molecular Weight (theory)	53.06
Odor	Faintly pungent
Parachor (341, 1120)	150.1 (15.1°C.)
	151.1 (40.6°C.)
Refractive Index (1, 95, 312, 341, 1120)	$n_D^{25} = 1.3888$
Surface Tension (1, 341, 1120)	27.3 dynes/cm. (24°C.)
Surface Tension of Aqueous Solutions (145)	$C = 0.223d - 0.0018d^2 + 0.00013d^3$ (C = 0 − 6 weight percent, d = dynes/cm.)
Vapor Density (theoretical)	1.83 (Air = 1.0)
Vapor Pressure (95, 312, 341, 477, 1038)	See also Figure 1

(Physical Constants of Acrylonitrile—Continued)

Pressure, mm. Hg	Temperature, °C.
50	8.7
100	23.6
250	45.5
500	64.7
760	77.3

Vapor Pressure, Partial
  Water Azeotrope (1, 477)

$$\text{Log } p = 7.518 - \frac{1644.7}{T}$$

Aqueous Solutions   See Figure 7

Viscosity (1, 341)   0.34 centipoises (25°C.)

B) Azeotropes

	B.P., °C.	Wt. % Acrylonitrile
Benzene (547)	73.3	47
Carbon Tetrachloride (547)	66.2	21
Chlorotrimethylsilane (951)	57	7
Methyl Alcohol (547)	61.4	39
Isopropyl Alcohol (547)	71.7	56
Tetrachlorosilane (950, 951)	51.2	89
Water (1, 126, 312, 547)	71	88

C) Solubilities   (1, 312, 341, 403, 611)

	Temp., °C.	% H_2O in Acrylonitrile	% Acrylonitrile in H_2O
Water	0	2.1	7.2
	20	3.1	7.35
	40	4.8	7.9

Organic Solvents   Miscible with most organic solvents including acetone, benzene, carbon tetrachloride, ether, ethyl acetate, ethyl alcohol, ethylene cyanohydrin, liquid carbon dioxide, methyl alcohol, petroleum ether, toluene, xylene, and some kerosenes.

Aqueous Bases and Alkali Salts (1213, 1305)
Three-Component System, Styrene-acrylonitrile-water (585)
Solubility Parameter, 10.5 [cal./cc.]$^{1/2}$ (972)

D) Spectra

Infrared (1, 82, 315, 459, 1003, 1088, 1095)   See Figure 2
Raman (1, 459, 911, 1091)   See Figure 3
Ultraviolet (1, 312, 930, 1051)   See Figure 4
Microwave (1150)
Proton Magnetic (769)

Mass Spectrum (1)

m/e	Intensity*	m/e	Intensity*	m/e	Intensity*
12	7.9	26	94.7	39	2.4
13	3.6	26.5	0.3	40	0.3
14	4.3	27	20.0	50	8.6
15	0.4	28	4.6	51	33.6
24	4.5	36	3.0	52	76.7
25	11.5	37	5.2	53	100.0
25.5	0.3	38	8.1	54	3.6

*Consolidated Model No. 21-103 spectrometer. Relative intensities at 70 ionizing volts and ion-source temperature of 270°C. Only peaks greater than 0.2% of base peak are listed. Ratio of sensitivity of acrylonitrile at mass 53 to sensitivity of *n*-butane at mass 43 is 0.55.

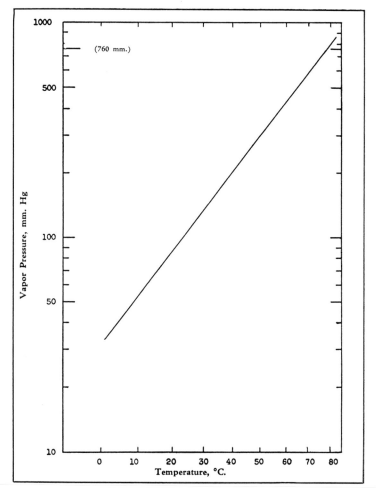

Figure 1 Vapor Pressure of Acrylonitrile.

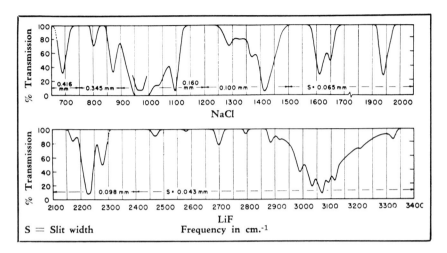

Figure 2   Infrared Spectrum of Liquid Acrylonitrile.

(Cell Length = 0.1 mm.; Temperature = 25°C.)

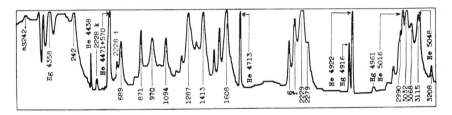

Figure 3   Raman Spectrum of Liquid Acrylonitrile Excited by Hg 4358 Å.

(The strongest lines also appear excited by Hg 4358 Å [f], Hg 4339 Å [g], Hg 4078 Å [i] and Hg 4047 Å [k]. The Raman lines are given in wave-numbers [cm.⁻¹].)

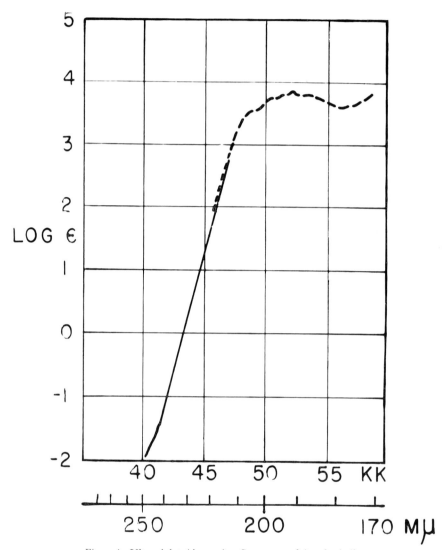

Figure 4   Ultraviolet Absorption Spectrum of Acrylonitrile

The logarithm of the molar absorptivity is plotted against linear energy in kilokaysers
(10^3 cm.$^{-1}$) and a non-linear wavelength scale in millimicrons. The molar absorptivity is
equal to the absorbance divided by the product of the cell light path length in centimeters
and concentration in moles per liter. The solid line represents undiluted liquid acrylonitrile examined in cells of various light path lengths down to 0.05 mm., versus water.
The dashed line represents the spectrum of acrylonitrile in solution in heptane, examined
with heptane in the comparison cell, and is reproduced from H. B. Klevens and J. R.
Platt, "Survey of Vacuum Ultraviolet Spectra of Organic Compounds in Solution,"
Tech. Report ONR Contract N6ORI-20, Task Order IX, Project NR 019 101 (1954),
by permission of the authors.

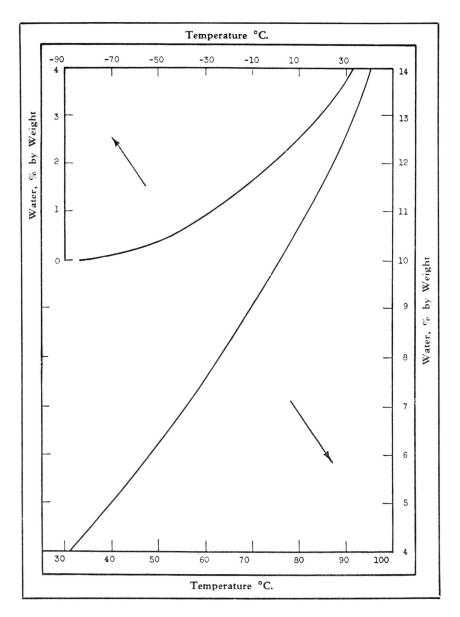

Figure 5 The Solubility of Water in Acrylonitrile.

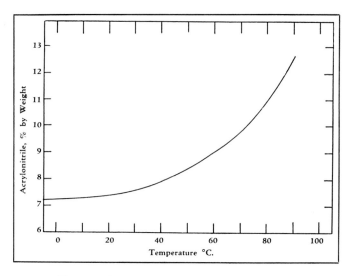

Figure 6 The Solubility of Acrylonitrile in Water.

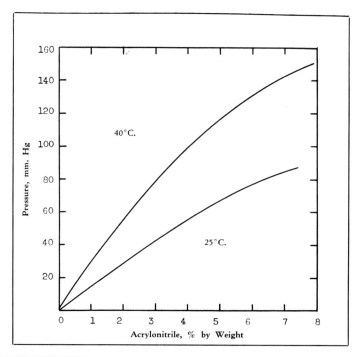

Figure 7 Partial Vapor Pressure of Acrylonitrile over its Aqueous Solutions at 25° and 40°C.

E) Structure

The infrared and Raman spectra of liquid acrylonitrile shown in Figures 2 and 3 and the microwave spectra of acrylonitrile vapor (1150) are compatible with a planar structure and the assumed bond distances given in Figure 8 ($\alpha \sim 120°$). Assignments of the vibrational frequencies are available in the literature together with calculations of the thermodynamic functions for the vapor over the temperature range 25-727°C. (459, 647). Combination of these data with the measured heats of vaporization and combustion, assuming perfect gas behavior, yields the thermodynamic data reported in Section F.

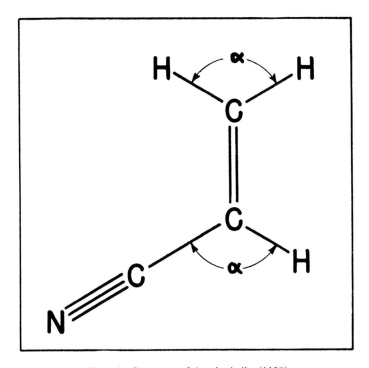

Figure 8 Structure of Acrylonitrile (1150)

$$\begin{aligned}
\text{C–C} &\sim 1.46 \text{ Å} \\
\text{C=C} &\sim 1.38 \text{ Å} \\
\text{C–H} &\sim 1.09 \text{ Å} \\
\text{C=N} &\sim 1.16 \text{ Å} \\
\alpha &\sim 120°
\end{aligned}$$

F) Thermodynamic Data (1, 341, 459, 611)

Entropy (vapor), S	65.47 cal./deg./mole (25°C., 1 atm.)
Free Energy of Formation (vapor), ΔF	+45.37 kcal./mole (25°C.)
Heat of Combustion (liquid), ΔH	−420.8 kcal./mole (25°C.)
Heat of Formation (liquid), ΔH	+36.20 ± 0.13 kcal./mole (25°C.)

(Thermodynamic Data for Acrylonitrile—Continued)

Heat of Vaporization, ΔH	7.8 kcal./mole (0-77°C.)
Molar Heat Capacity (liquid), Cp.	26.5 ± 1.5 cal./mole/deg.
Molar Heat Capacity (vapor), Cp.	$6.75 + 33.27 \times 10^{-3}$ T
	-10.91×10^{-6} T² cal./mole/deg.
	(77-1000°C., 1 atm.)
Molar Heat of Fusion	$1585 \pm$ kcal./mole

G) Stability

Highly purified acrylonitrile may polymerize spontaneously, particularly in the absence of oxygen or on exposure to visible light. This may be prevented by the incorporation of traces of ammonia, ammonium carbonate, or one of the products resulting from the reaction of ammonia with acrylonitrile (313, 314). Other stabilizing agents have been claimed in the literature (123, 217, 260, 493, 673, 744, 745, 824, 1005, 1119, 1167).

Acrylonitrile polymerizes violently in the presence of concentrated alkali (1). Extreme caution should be exercised if it is found necessary to treat acrylonitrile with strongly alkaline materials. Alkali is used as a catalyst for many of the reactions of acrylonitrile, especially the cyanoethylation reactions, but the amounts involved are small and the cyanoethylation reactions are almost always rapid. It is customary, however, to add the acrylonitrile gradually to the alkaline reaction mixture in order to prevent the accumulation of appreciable amounts of unreacted acrylonitrile. In this manner violent polymerization is avoided.

On standing, acrylonitrile may slowly develop a yellow color particularly after excessive exposure to light. This is prevented by the addition of a small amount of water (36, 213). It is also reported that aluminum, ammonium, cadmium, mercuric and zinc chlorides inhibit color development (749).

H) Handling Precautions (138, 880)

In its technical bulletin entitled, "Handling–Storage–Analyses of Acrylonitrile," American Cyanamid has presented detailed procedures for the proper handling and storage of acrylonitrile. This section summarizes these procedures. For additional details the reader is referred to the above bulletin.

During the time of its large-volume commercial use, acrylonitrile has enjoyed a good record of safe handling. This record has been achieved in spite of the fact that acrylonitrile is explosive, flammable and toxic. It is toxic by ingestion, inhalation, and absorption of vapors or liquids through the skin. It has a low flash point (0°C.), and will form explosive mixtures with air over a range of 3 to 17 volume-percent of acrylonitrile vapor.

Because of these hazards, acrylonitrile should be stored and used in closed systems wherever possible. Work areas should be adequately ventilated, and should be free from open lights, flames, and equipment that is not explosion-proof. Workers should be instructed in the proper handling procedures, and should be provided with the necessary protective clothing and equipment.

CHEMICAL PROPERTIES

Acrylonitrile is an exceptionally versatile chemical intermediate. Its easy introduction into a large variety of compounds affords convenient syntheses of 3-substituted propionitriles, propionamides, propionic acids and esters, and propylamines. Under proper conditions acrylonitrile polymerizes, either by itself or with other monomers.

These chemical properties are discussed briefly in this section. Tables are provided which systematically outline the known reactions of acrylonitrile, giving reaction conditions, yields, and physical properties of products. Where more than one reference describes the same reaction, only the conditions claiming the best yield are listed, although all the pertinent additional references are cited.

REACTIONS OF THE NITRILE GROUP

Hydration and Hydrolysis (See Table 1)

Acrylonitrile is hydrated rapidly at 100°C. by 84.5% sulfuric acid ($H_2SO_4 \cdot H_2O$) to produce acrylamide sulfate, which upon neutralization yields free acrylamide (9, 30):

$$CH_2=CHCN + H_2O + H_2SO_4 \longrightarrow CH_2=CHCONH_2 \cdot H_2SO_4$$

$$CH_2=CHCONH_2 \cdot H_2SO_4 + CaO \longrightarrow CH_2=CHCONH_2 + CaSO_4 + H_2O$$

When acrylonitrile is heated with less concentrated sulfuric acid, or when acrylamide sulfate is heated with additional water, acrylic acid and ammonium bisulfate are formed:

$$CH_2=CHCONH_2 \cdot H_2SO_4 \longrightarrow CH_2=CHCOOH + NH_4HSO_4$$

The rate of hydrolysis of acrylonitrile with aqueous alkali has been studied (737):

$$CH_2=CHCN + 2H_2O \xrightarrow[OH^-]{H^+ \text{ or}} CH_2=CHCOOH + NH_3$$

When hydrochloric acid is used to catalyze the hydration- and hydrolysis-reactions, addition of hydrogen chloride also occurs. Good yields of either 3-chloropropionamide or 3-chloropropionic acid may be obtained (80, 580):

$$CH_2=CHCN + HCl + H_2O \longrightarrow ClCH_2CH_2CONH_2$$

$$CH_2=CHCN + HCl + 2H_2O \longrightarrow ClCH_2CH_2COOH + NH_4Cl$$

The reaction of acrylonitrile with alcohols in the presence of concentrated sulfuric acid may be used to prepare esters of acrylic acid (518, 1156). Acrylamide sulfate is formed as the intermediate:

$$CH_2=CHCN + H_2SO_4 \cdot H_2O \longrightarrow CH_2=CHCONH_2 \cdot H_2SO_4$$

$$CH_2=CHCONH_2 \cdot H_2SO_4 + ROH \longrightarrow CH_2=CHCOOR + NH_4HSO_4$$

Imido ethers have been prepared by reacting acrylonitrile with alcohols in the presence of anhydrous hydrogen halides (890):

$$CH_2=CHCN + ROH + HX \longrightarrow XCH_2CH_2\overset{\underset{\displaystyle \|}{NH \cdot HX}}{C}OR$$

Reactions with Olefins and with Alcohols (*See* Table IIa *and* IIb)

Acrylonitrile reacts with olefins in concentrated sulfuric acid to produce N-substituted acrylamides. In a typical example, acrylonitrile is added to a solution of olefin in sulfuric acid. After a short holding period at 30-40°C., the product is precipitated by pouring the reaction mixture into water. Thus 2-methyl-2-butene and acrylonitrile form N-(1,1-dimethylpropyl)-acrylamide (923, 924):

$$CH_2=CHCN + CH_3-\overset{\overset{\displaystyle CH_3}{\displaystyle |}}{C}=CHCH_3 \xrightarrow[\text{(2) } H_2O]{\text{(1) } H_2SO_4} CH_2=CHCONHC(CH_3)_2$$
$$\underset{\displaystyle C_2H_5}{|}$$

Acrylonitrile will also react with tertiary alcohols to give N-substituted acrylamides. Thus *tert*-butyl alcohol treated with acrylonitrile in sulfuric acid gives excellent yields of N-*tert*-butylacrylamide (879):

$$CH_2=CHCN + HOC(CH_3)_3 \xrightarrow{H_2SO_4} CH_2=CHCONHC(CH_3)_3$$

Secondary alcohols such as isopropyl alcohol and cyclohexanol also react to give the corresponding N-substituted acrylamides (879).

Reactions with Aldehydes and Methylol Compounds (*See* Table III)

Anhydrous formaldehyde (meta- or paraformaldehyde) reacts exothermically with acrylonitrile in the presence of catalytic amounts of concentrated sulfuric acid to produce 1,3,5-triacrylylhexahydro-s-triazine (1137):

$$3CH_2=CHCN + 3CH_2O \xrightarrow{H_2SO_4} \text{ring structure}$$

with ring:
NCOCH=CH₂ at top, CH₂ and CH₂ below it, CH₂=CHCON and NCOCH=CH₂, and CH₂ at bottom

The reaction of acrylonitrile with formaldehyde in the presence of excess 85%-sulfuric acid produces N,N'-methylenebisacrylamide, a good cross linking agent (735):

$$2CH_2=CHCN + CH_2O + H_2O \xrightarrow{H_2SO_4} CH_2=CHCONH^*$$
$$\underset{\displaystyle CH_2=CHCONH}{\overset{\displaystyle |}{\underset{\displaystyle |}{CH_2}}}$$

*American Cyanamid Co., New Product Bulletin No. 24

An analogous reaction is observed with chloral (735):

$$2CH_2\!\!=\!\!CHCN + Cl_3CCHO + H_2O \xrightarrow{\text{H}_2\text{SO}_4} \begin{array}{c} CH_2\!\!=\!\!CHCONH \\ | \\ CHCCl_3 \\ | \\ CH_2\!\!=\!\!CHCONH \end{array}$$

N-Methylol compounds, such as N-methylolbenzamide (804), yield mixed bisamides when allowed to react with acrylonitrile in the presence of sulfuric acid:

CH₂=CHCN + ⟨benzene ring⟩-CONHCH₂OH $\xrightarrow{\text{H}_2\text{SO}_4}$ ⟨benzene ring⟩-CONHCH₂NHCOCH=CH₂

REACTIONS OF THE DOUBLE BOND

Diels-Alder and Related Reactions (*See Table* IV)

Acrylonitrile is a member of a class of organic compounds having activated double bonds which act as dienophiles in the Diels-Alder reaction. Upon heating with aliphatic or alicyclic compounds containing a system of conjugated carbon-to-carbon double bonds, it reacts to form cyclic products. A typical example is the reaction of 1,3-butadiene with acrylonitrile to produce 3-cyclohexene-1-carbonitrile, an intermediate in the synthesis of pimelic acid (873):

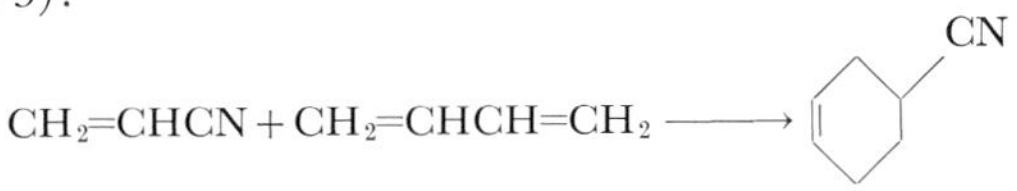

CH₂=CHCN + CH₂=CHCH=CH₂ ⟶ ⟨cyclohexene ring with CN⟩

The reaction of acrylonitrile with piperylene is particularly interesting because of the possibility of forming two pairs of *cis-trans* isomers (45, 404, 530, 763, 866, 1076):

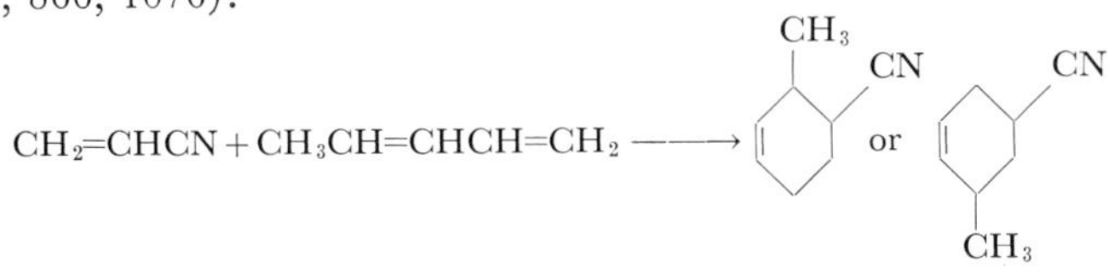

CH₂=CHCN + CH₃CH=CHCH=CH₂ ⟶ ⟨ring with CH₃ and CN⟩ or ⟨ring with CN and CH₃⟩

The chief, but not exclusive, product is the *cis-ortho* isomer (763). With 1-phenyl-1,3-butadiene the *trans-ortho* adduct is the principal product (762).

In most examples of Diels-Alder reactions of acrylonitrile, hydroquinone or another polymerization inhibitor is used. Temperatures of 100-150°C. are commonly maintained from 5 to 24 hours.

Several reactions related to the Diels-Alder reaction have been carried out with acrylonitrile, but with acrylonitrile acting as the diene rather than the dienophile. Prolonged heating of acrylonitrile with tetrafluoroethylene at 125-130°C. produces 2,2,3,3-tetrafluorocyclobutanecarbonitrile (258):

$$CH_2\!\!=\!\!CHCN + F_2C\!\!=\!\!CF_2 \longrightarrow \begin{array}{c} F_2C\!-\!CH_2 \\ |\quad\ | \\ F_2C\!-\!CHCN \end{array}$$

The dimerization of acrylonitrile at 190-200°C. under pressure is another reaction of this type (284):

$$2CH_2{=}CHCN \longrightarrow \begin{array}{c} CH_2{-}CHCN \\ |\qquad\ | \\ CH_2{-}CHCN \end{array}$$

Both the *cis*- and *trans*-cyclobutanedicarbonitriles are obtained.

On the other hand, chlorotrifluoroethylene and water react under similar conditions to yield 2,2-difluoroglutaric acid (1202):

$$CH_2{=}CHCN + CF_2{=}CFCl + H_2O \longrightarrow HOOCCF_2CH_2CH_2COOH$$

An interesting cycloaddition-reaction occurs on refluxing acrylonitrile with the N-oxide of benzonitrile in ether, giving 3-phenyl-2-isoxazoline-5-carbonitrile (301):

$$CH_2{=}CHCN + C_6H_5C{=}N{\rightarrow}O \longrightarrow$$

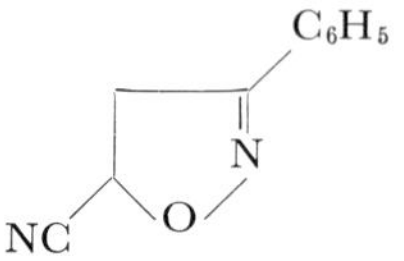

Hydrogenation (*See Table* v)

The hydrogenation of acrylonitrile may be accomplished in excellent yields by the use of either copper (913), rhodium (503), or nickel (1, 159) catalysts to give propionitrile. This may be further hydrogenated to propylamine:

$$CH_2{=}CHCN + H_2 \xrightarrow{\text{Catalyst}} CH_3CH_2CN \xrightarrow{2H_2} CH_3CH_2CH_2NH_2$$

The synthesis of allylamine by the hydrogenation of acrylonitrile has not been reported. However, allylamine may be prepared by reduction of the Diels-Alder adduct of acrylonitrile and anthracene, followed by thermal cleavage of the adduct (822):

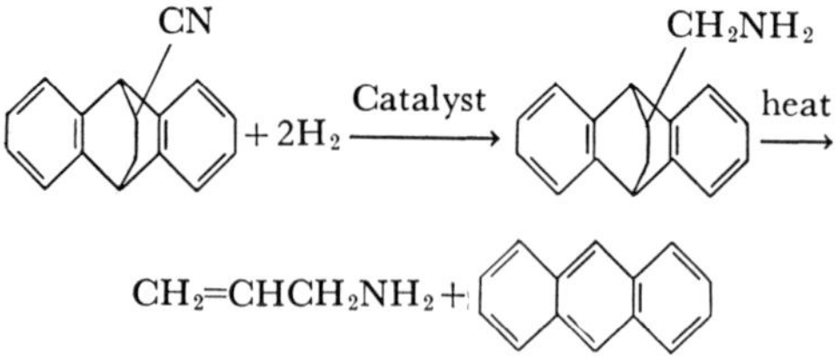

$$CH_2{=}CHCH_2NH_2 +$$

Chemical reduction under alkaline conditions as, for example, with methyl alcohol and magnesium in an anhydrous medium (687), or with sodium amalgam in aqueous solution (589), produces adiponitrile in low yields. In the latter case, hydrolysis to adipic acid occurs concurrently:

$$2CH_2{=}CHCN + 2CH_3OH + Mg \longrightarrow \begin{array}{c} CH_2CH_2CN \\ | \\ CH_2CH_2CN \end{array} + (CH_3O)_2Mg$$

Halogenation (See Table VI)

The halogenation of acrylonitrile at low temperatures proceeds via the addition of a molecule of halogen to produce 2,3-dihalopropionitriles:

$$CH_2=CHCN + X_2 \longrightarrow XCH_2CHXCN$$

At elevated temperatures and in the absence of ultraviolet light, the addition reaction is accompanied by evolution of hydrogen halide followed by the addition of a second molecule of halogen to produce 2,2,3-trihalopropionitrile:

$$XCH_2CHXCN \longrightarrow CH_2=CXCN + HX$$

$$CH_2=CXCN + X_2 \longrightarrow XCH_2CX_2CN$$

In the presence of ultraviolet light both the 2,2,3- and 2,3,3-isomers are obtained.

The simple, uncatalyzed addition of a halogen to acrylonitrile is a slow reaction at ordinary temperatures (368, 494, 674). After a considerable induction period the reaction spontaneously accelerates, possibly as a result of catalysis by the hydrogen halide which is formed as a by-product. Rate measurements for the chlorination and bromination of acrylonitrile in dilute acetic acid solution have been reported, and catalysis of bromination by added hydrobromic acid has been demonstrated (368).

A catalyzed reaction involving chlorine and acrylonitrile in pyridine solution has been reported to give almost quantitative yields of 2,3-dichloropropionitrile (140). Reactions illuminated by a 200-watt lamp are also reported to proceed readily (1039).

If acrylonitrile is chlorinated in aqueous solution the hypochlorous acid present reacts to form 2-chlorohydracrylonitrile (324, 1100):

$$CH_2=CHCN + HOCl \longrightarrow HOCH_2CHClCN$$

A dichloroglutaronitrile derivative also may be obtained by the action of chlorine on aqueous solutions of acrylonitrile (1121):

$$2CH_2=CHCN + Cl_2 \longrightarrow \underset{\overset{|}{CH_2CH_2CN}}{ClCH_2CClCN}$$

Simultaneous alcoholysis and chlorination occur to give 2,3-dichloropropionic acid esters when acrylonitrile is reacted with chlorine in aqueous alcoholic solutions containing sulfuric acid (325):

$$CH_2=CHCN + Cl_2 + ROH \xrightarrow[H_2O]{H_2SO_4} ClCH_2CHClCOOR + NH_4HSO_4$$

The methyl, ethyl, propyl and isopropyl esters have been prepared in this manner (325).

Formation of 1,2,2,3-tetrachloro-N-2-chloroethylpropylidenimine is observed when a mixture of acrylonitrile and ethylene is reacted with chlorine (200);

$$CH_2=CHCN + CH_2=CH_2 + 3Cl_2 \longrightarrow ClCH_2CH_2N=CClCCl_2CH_2Cl + HCl$$

When nitryl chloride, a pseudohalogen, is added to cold acrylonitrile the principal product is 2-chloro-3-nitropropionitrile (139, 991):

$$CH_2=CHCN + NO_2Cl \longrightarrow NO_2CH_2CHClCN$$

When the reaction is carried out in ether, 3-nitroacrylonitrile is the principal product (991).

The various halogenated propionitriles may be dehydrohalogenated by the action of tertiary amines (696, 697, 1014), sodium acetate (1, 140), potassium cyanide (141), phosphorus pentoxide (140), or heat (140, 251, 697, 1160), or dehalogenated by metals (247) to produce a variety of halogen-substituted acrylonitriles.

2-Chloroacrylonitrile may be prepared by simultaneous chlorination and dehydrohalogenation of acrylonitrile. This results when acrylonitrile and chlorine are passed over activated carbon at high temperatures (707).

A particularly interesting reaction of 2,3-dichloroacrylonitrile involves treatment with ammonia or various amines to give 3-amino-2-chloroacrylonitrile or derivatives (363, 781):

$$CHCl=CClCN + 2NH_3 \longrightarrow H_2NCH=CClCN + NH_4Cl$$

A more detailed description of the reactions of acrylonitrile with halogens is presented in Cyanamid's Petrochemical Department Bulletin PD-5 entitled "The Reaction of Acrylonitrile with Halogens."

Reactions with Diazo Compounds (See Table VII)

2-Halo-3-arylpropionitriles may be prepared by the Meerwein reaction of diazonium chlorides and bromides with acrylonitrile at low temperatures:

$$CH_2=CHCN + C_6H_5N_2^+Cl^- \xrightarrow[\text{acetone}]{Cu^{++}} C_6H_5CH_2CHClCN + N_2$$

The reaction is conducted in aqueous acetone solutions in which the diazotized amine solution has been neutralized with sodium acetate. Catalytic amounts of cupric chloride are necessary for the reaction (654).

An unusual reaction occurs between 9-diazofluorene and acrylonitrile in the absence of a catalyst to produce a cyanocyclopropane derivative (537, 538):

Reactions with Alcohols and Carbon Monoxide (*See Table* VIII)

A process for the preparation of 3-cyanopropionaldehyde acetals has been reported (86). This reaction involves the treatment of acrylonitrile with an alcohol, carbon monoxide, hydrogen, and a cobalt hydrogenation catalyst at temperatures of 100-200°C. and pressures of 1200 atmospheres:

$$CH_2=CHCN + 2ROH + CO + H_2 \xrightarrow{Co} \begin{array}{c} RO \\ \diagdown \\ CHCH_2CH_2CN + H_2O \\ \diagup \\ RO \end{array}$$

When cobalt octacarbonyl is employed (458), a mixture of C_{15} amines is obtained.

Reactions with Miscellaneous Compounds (*See Table* IX)

Acrylonitrile is reported to react with ozone to give a product which will catalyze the polymerization of ethylene (721).

Trifluoroiodomethane reacts with acrylonitrile under the influence of ultraviolet light to produce 4,4,4-trifluoro-2-iodobutyronitrile (484):

$$CH_2=CHCN + CF_3I \longrightarrow F_3CCH_2CHICN$$

CYANOETHYLATION REACTIONS

There are a great many compounds possessing the grouping HA (wherein H is a reactive hydrogen atom) which add readily to the carbon-carbon double bond of acrylonitrile. In each case a 3(or β)-substituted propionitrile is the primary reaction product. Although little kinetic evidence for the reaction mechanism has been presented, it is reasonable to assume that in most cases this reaction proceeds by attack of the anion of HA on the positively polarized β-carbon atom. This is followed by the transfer of a proton from a neutral HA molecule (or from solvent) to the α-carbon atom:

$$CH_2=CHC\equiv N \longleftrightarrow [CH_2CH=C=\ddot{N}] + A^- \longrightarrow$$

$$\begin{bmatrix} ACH_2CH=C=\ddot{N} \\ \uparrow \\ ACH_2\ddot{C}HC\equiv N \end{bmatrix} + HA \longrightarrow ACH_2CH_2CN + A^-$$

It has not been determined whether the proton adds to the nitrogen atom (1,4-addition), followed by rearrangement, or whether the proton adds directly to the α-carbon atom (1,2-addition).

The compounds that have been added to acrylonitrile to produce cyanoethyl derivatives may be classified according to the atom attached to the reactive hydrogen. Thus, examples of cyanoethylation of compounds containing As-H, B-H, Br-H, C-H, Cl-H, N-H, O-H, P-H, S-H, Si-H and Sn-H bonds have been reported. Among the specific classes of compounds that readily undergo the cyanoethylation reaction are a variety of alcohols, aldehydes, amines, amides, esters, ketones, mercaptans and inorganic acids and their salts. In nearly every case a strong base is used to catalyze the reaction. However, in the case of most N-H, P-H and As-H compounds, no catalyst is required, while aryl amines (e.g., aniline) require an acidic catalyst.

Carbon-Cyanoethylation

ALDEHYDES (*See Table* x)

The reaction of acrylonitrile with aldehydes containing at least one hydrogen atom on the 2(or α)-carbon atom leads to formation of derivatives of 4-cyanobutyraldehyde:

$$CH_2=CHCN + RR'CHCHO \longrightarrow NCCH_2CH_2CRR'CHO$$

If there is more than one hydrogen atom at the α-position, a mixture of the mono- and di-cyanoethylated derivatives is usually obtained (1124).

Particular care must be taken to prevent aldolization when working with aldehydes such as acetaldehyde, isobutyraldehyde and propionaldehyde (180, 182). Good yields of the cyanoethylated products are obtained, at least in the case of isobutyraldehyde, by the use of alkali cyanide as the condensing agent (587, 916, 1084).

The reaction of acrylonitrile with 2-ethyl-2-hexenal (180, 183) is interesting because no α-hydrogen is immediately available for reaction. The mechanism evidently involves a preliminary allylic rearrangement under the influence of the basic catalyst (180):

$$C_2H_5CH_2CH=CCHO \underset{}{\overset{OH^-}{\rightleftharpoons}} C_2H_5CH=CHCHCHO$$
$$\overset{|}{C_2H_5} \qquad\qquad \overset{|}{C_2H_5}$$

$$CH_2=CHCN + C_2H_5CH=CHCHCHO \longrightarrow C_2H_5CH=CHC(CHO)CH_2CH_2CN$$
$$\overset{|}{C_2H_5} \qquad\qquad\qquad \overset{|}{C_2H_5}$$

The 4-cyanobutyraldehyde derivatives obtained by the cyanoethylation of aldehydes are interesting and useful chemical intermediates. They can be converted by hydrolysis to the aldehydo-acids and, by subsequent oxidation, to the glutaric acid derivatives (180), or they may be oxidized directly to 4-cyanobutyric acids (180). By catalytic hydrogenation the aldehydo-acids may be cyclized to δ-lactones (180):

$$RR'C\overset{\displaystyle CHO}{\underset{\displaystyle CH_2CH_2COOH}{<}} + H_2 \longrightarrow RR'C\overset{\displaystyle CH_2OH}{\underset{\displaystyle CH_2CH_2COOH}{<}} \longrightarrow RR'C\overset{\displaystyle CH_2-O}{\underset{\displaystyle CH_2-CH_2}{<}}CO$$

KETONES (*See Table* xi)

Ketones containing at least one α-hydrogen atom can be cyanoethylated by reaction with acrylonitrile in the presence of basic catalysts:

$$CH_2=CHCN + RR'CHCOR'' \longrightarrow RR'CCH_2CH_2CN$$
$$\overset{|}{OCR''}$$

In general, where more than one α-hydrogen is present on the same carbon atom, the second cyanoethyl group adds with greater ease than the first, and the third with greater ease than the second:

$$CH_2=CHCN + RCOCH_3 \longrightarrow RCOCH_2CH_2CH_2CN$$

$$CH_2=CHCN + RCOCH_2CH_2CH_2CN \longrightarrow RCOCH(CH_2CH_2CN)_2$$

Use of excess ketone favors the formation of the less highly cyanoethylated products (93). Monocyanoethylation of cyclohexanone in high yield has been accomplished by conversion of the ketone to its pyrrolidine enamine prior to cyanoethylation (1033):

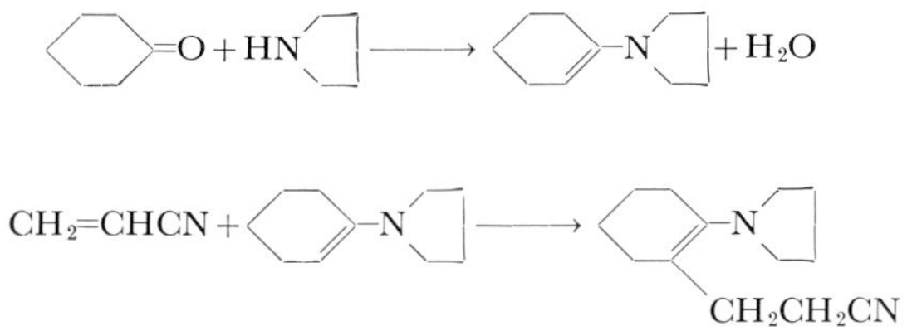

This enamine can be hydrolyzed readily to the ketonitrile:

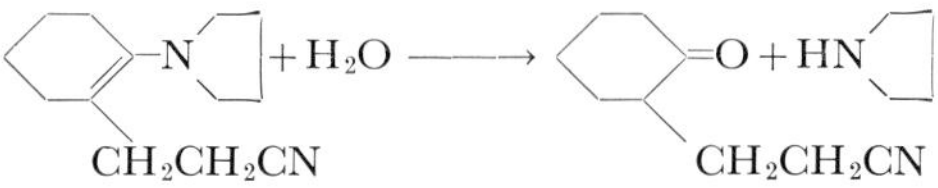

This product, in turn, can be hydrolyzed readily to the corresponding acid. This method thus presents an excellent path by which to prepare 4-acylbutyric and 4-acylpimelic nitriles or acids. The method is applicable to compounds containing more than one ketone group as indicated in Table XI.

ESTERS AND AMIDES* (*See Table* XII)

Apparently the hydrogen atoms in the α-position of esters and amides are not sufficiently activated by these groups alone to permit cyanoethylation by acrylonitrile. In cases in which the α-position is also activated by one or more other negative groups the reaction proceeds smoothly. The other activating groups may be keto (acetoacetic esters), carbalkoxy (malonic esters), cyano (cyanoacetic esters), aromatic (9-carbalkoxy fluorene) or phosphono (phosphonoacetic esters). The products of these reactions are derivatives of glutaric acid or pimelic acid:

$$2CH_2{=}CHCN + XCH_2COOC_2H_5 \longrightarrow \underset{\underset{CH_2CH_2CN}{|}}{\overset{\overset{CH_2CH_2CN}{|}}{X\overset{|}{C}COOC_2H_5}}$$

$$CH_2{=}CHCN + XYCHCOOC_2H_5 \longrightarrow \underset{\underset{CH_2CH_2CN}{|}}{XY\overset{}{C}COOC_2H_5}$$

(X = negative substituent, Y = any organic group.)

The cyanoethylation of cyanoacetic ester (931) is of particular interest, as it presents evidence that lower temperatures favor polycyanoethylation and higher temperatures favor monocyanoethylation. Thus at 40°C. the dicyano-

*The Nitrogen-cyanoethylation of amides is discussed on page 24 ethylated cyanoacetic ester is the exclusive product, while at 150-165°C. the monocyanoethylated ester predominates:

$$CH_2=CHCN + NCCH_2CO_2R \underset{\xrightarrow{150\text{-}165°C.}}{\overset{40°C.}{\xrightarrow{\hspace{2cm}}}} \begin{array}{l} (NCCH_2CH_2)_2C(CN)CO_2R \\ \\ NCCH_2CH_2CH(CN)CO_2R \end{array}$$

NITRILES (See Table XIII)

The cyano group, like the ester and amide groups, does not by itself exert a sufficient activating influence to cause reaction with acrylonitrile except in the case of hydrocyanic acid. However, if the carbon atom bonded to the cyano group is attached to a second activating group, reaction will occur. Cyanoacetic esters and amides (*Table* XII), phenylacetonitriles, phosphonacetonitriles, and unsaturated nitriles (*Table* XIII) are examples of nitriles which will react with acrylonitrile. The monocyanoethylated products of these reactions are derivatives of glutaronitrile:

$$CH_2=CHCN + XYCHCN \longrightarrow \underset{|}{XYCCN} \atop CH_2CH_2CN$$

It is interesting to note that 3-butenenitrile and crotononitrile produce the same two products in roughly the same proportions (162, 178). This is evidence for a tautomeric shift of the allylic type:

$$\begin{array}{l} CH_3CH=CHCN \quad CH_2=CHCN \\ \quad\quad\text{or} \quad\quad\quad\quad\quad\quad\quad\quad\quad\quad\quad\quad\quad\quad CH_2=CHCN \\ CH_2=CHCH_2CN \end{array} \longrightarrow \underset{CH_2CH_2CN}{CH_3CH=CCN} \longrightarrow \underset{C(CH_2CH_2CN)_2CN}{CH_2=CH}$$

Similar reactions occur with 3-methyl-3-butenenitrile and cyclohexylidene-acetonitrile (162, 178).

The tendency, mentioned previously (p. 19), of increasing temperature favoring monocyanoethylation over dicyanoethylation has been studied in the case of phenylacetonitrile (931). As the temperature of the reaction is increased from 40°C. to 225°C., the yield of monocyanoethylated product increases from 0% to 80% while that of the dicyanoethylated material decreases from 93% to 0%:

$$CH_2=CHCN + C_6H_5CH_2CN \underset{\xrightarrow{40°C.}}{\overset{225°C.}{\xrightarrow{\hspace{2cm}}}} \begin{array}{l} C_6H_5CH(CH_2CH_2CN)CN \\ \\ C_6H_5C(CH_2CH_2CN)_2CN \end{array}$$

NITRO COMPOUNDS (See Table XIV)

The nitro group is strongly electron-withdrawing, and the hydrogen atom on the adjoining carbon atom will react at moderate temperatures with acrylonitrile. Mono-, di- and tri-cyanoethylated products have been obtained (1089):

$$CH_2=CHCN + CH_3NO_2 \longrightarrow \begin{array}{l} NCCH_2CH_2CH_2NO_2 \\ \\ (NCCH_2CH_2)_2CHNO_2 \\ \\ (NCCH_2CH_2)_3CNO_2 \end{array}$$

Cyanoethylation of dinitromethane or 2,2-dinitro-1,3-propanediol leads to 4,4-dinitropimelonitrile (383). In the latter case, the loss of formaldehyde to give dinitromethane occurs before reaction with acrylonitrile:

$$2CH_2=CHCN + CH_2(NO_2)_2 \longrightarrow (NCCH_2CH_2)_2C(NO_2)_2$$

SULFONES (See Table XV)

A sulfone group activates the hydrogen on an α-carbon atom sufficiently for cyanoethylation to occur if the α-carbon is also attached to either 1) a second sulfone group, 2) a vinyl group, or 3) a benzene ring. Dicyanoethylation is always observed except with sulfones containing a benzyl moiety which bears an ortho substituent. In this latter case only monocyanoethylation occurs because of the steric interference exerted by the substituent (1300):

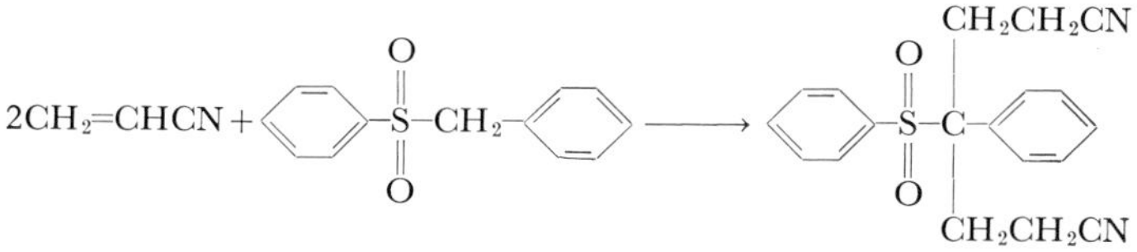

AROMATIC HYDROCARBONS (See Table XVI)

Cyclopentadiene and 6,6-dimethylfulvene react with acrylonitrile in the absence of catalyst to form adducts of the Diels-Alder type (See Table IV). However, in the presence of a basic catalyst only cyanoethylated products are obtained (158).

Fluorene and substituted fluorenes undergo cyanoethylation at the methylene group. With 9-fluorenol, carbon-cyanoethylation rather than oxygen-cyanoethylation occurs (205):

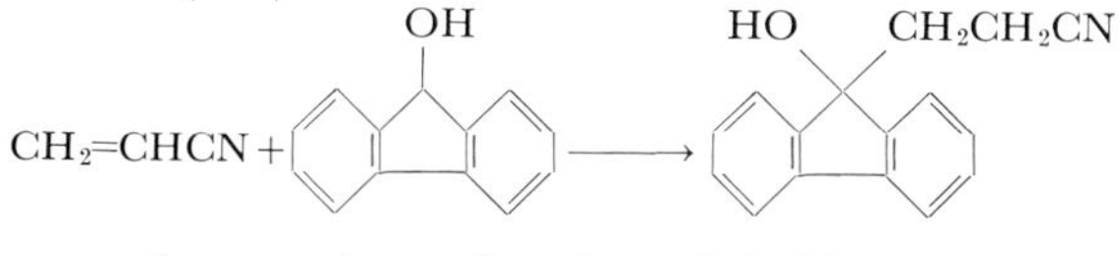

Reaction occurs at the α-carbon when 2-naphthol is treated with acrylonitrile in the presence of an equivalent amount of base (467, 468):

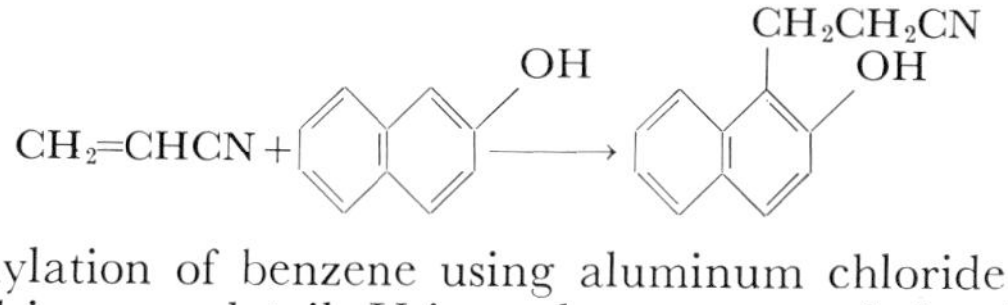

The cyanoethylation of benzene using aluminum chloride as a catalyst has been studied in some detail. Using a large excess of aluminum chloride only a low yield of dihydrocinnamonitrile is obtained. Better yields are obtained by first saturating the reaction mixture with hydrochloric acid to form 3-chloropropionitrile (442):

$$CH_2=CHCN + HCl \longrightarrow ClCH_2CH_2CN$$

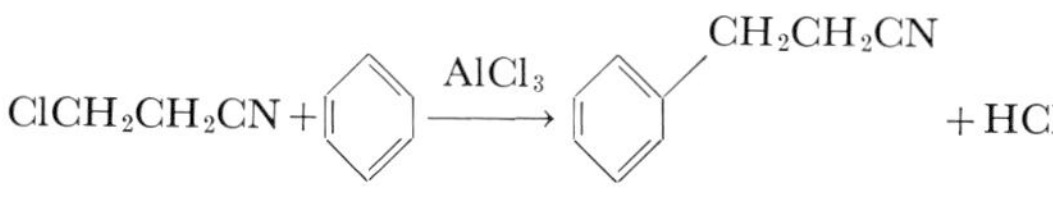

Nuclear cyanoethylation is also observed with various phenols, such as resorcinol, in the presence of zinc chloride and hydrogen chloride (681):

$$CH_2{=}CHCN + \underset{\text{(resorcinol)}}{\text{HO}\bigcirc\text{OH}} \xrightarrow[\text{HCl}]{ZnCl_2} \text{HO}\bigcirc\text{OH} \\ CH_2CH_2CN$$

Under the above conditions, 4,6-diethylresorcinol reacts with acrylonitrile to produce a stable compound possessing an unsubstituted imino chloride group:

$$CH_2{=}CHCN + \underset{C_2H_5 \quad C_2H_5}{\text{HO}\bigcirc\text{OH}} \xrightarrow[\text{HCl}]{ZnCl_2} \underset{C_2H_5 \quad C_2H_5}{\overset{\overset{\displaystyle Cl}{\underset{CH_2CH_2\overset{|}{C}{=}NH}{|}}}{\text{HO}\bigcirc\text{OH}}}$$

ALIPHATIC HYDROCARBONS (*See Table* XVII)

Under ordinary conditions of temperature and pressure simple olefins fail to undergo cyanoethylation.

However, it has been reported recently that olefins such as isobutylene will react with acrylonitrile at pressures of 500-1000 atmospheres and 200-300°C. to give fair yields of cyanoethylated products (15, 1194):

$$CH_2{=}CHCN + CH_3{-}\overset{CH_3}{\underset{|}{C}}{=}CH_2 \xrightarrow[\text{585-1020 atm.}]{235°C.} CH_2{=}\overset{CH_3}{\underset{|}{C}}{-}CH_2CH_2CH_2CN$$

Acetylene reacts with acrylonitrile at lower temperatures and pressures in the presence of triphenyl phosphine and nickel-cyanide complex to give 2,4,6-heptatrienenitrile (199, 620):

$$CH_2{=}CHCN + 2HC{\equiv}CH \xrightarrow[\text{150-200 p.s.i.}]{65-70°C.} CH_2{=}CHCH{=}CHCH{=}CHCN$$

Since variation of the mole ratio of acrylonitrile to acetylene produces only the 1:2 adduct, a stepwise-reaction mechanism is considered unlikely (199).

HALOFORMS (*See Table* XVIII)

Bromoform and chloroform have been cyanoethylated to give 4,4,4-trihalobutyronitriles (175, 827):

$$CH_2{=}CHCN + X_3CH \longrightarrow X_3CCH_2CH_2CN$$

Under similar conditions, iodoform fails to react (175).

Nitrogen-Cyanoethylation (*See Table* XIX)

The cyanoethylation of amines produces 3-alkylaminopropionitriles. In most cases a catalyst is not required. At low temperatures primary amines react with acrylonitrile to produce the monocyanoethylated product; at higher temperatures a second cyanoethyl group may be added, yielding the tertiary amines, the 3,3′-alkyliminodipropionitriles (173):

$$CH_2=CHCN + RNH_2 \longrightarrow RNHCH_2CH_2CN$$

$$CH_2=CHCN + RNHCH_2CH_2CN \longrightarrow RN(CH_2CH_2CN)_2$$

The cyanoethylation of ammonia leads to three products:

$$CH_2=CHCN + NH_3 \begin{cases} \longrightarrow H_2NCH_2CH_2CN \\ \longrightarrow HN(CH_2CH_2CN)_2 \\ \longrightarrow N(CH_2CH_2CN)_3 \end{cases}$$

The relative proportions of the three products are determined by the molar ratio of reactants used (173). The reaction is of most importance in the preparation of β-alanine (207) and 3,3′-iminodipropionitrile (33). Nitrilotrispropylamine is formed in small amounts only.

An aromatic nucleus attached to an amino group tends to hinder cyanoethylation. However, the cyanoethylation of aniline and substituted anilines may be carried out in good yield in the presence of acetic acid, or cupric acetate, yielding 3-anilinopropionitrile (1279):

$$CH_2=CHCN + \langle \rangle -NH_2 \xrightarrow{\text{acetic acid}} \langle \rangle -NHCH_2CH_2CN$$

The list of amines which have been cyanoethylated includes aliphatic, alicyclic, aromatic, and heterocyclic bases. The 3-alkylaminopropionitriles so produced are valuable intermediates (31) for many chemical processes. They may be hydrolyzed, esterified or hydrogenated, or they may be condensed with aromatic systems in the Hoesch synthesis. The diamines obtained through hydrogenation are particularly useful in the synthesis of various pharmaceuticals (31).

The reaction with cyanamide (485) produces an interesting trinitrile, bis(2-cyanoethyl)cyanamide:

$$2CH_2=CHCN + H_2NCN \rightleftharpoons NCN(CH_2CH_2CN)_2$$

Other amines which have been cyanoethylated include hydrazine (520), hydroxylamine (520) and cyanoguanidine (486).

The cyanoethylation of alkali-metal salts of α-amino acids proceeds smoothly for the acidic or neutral amino acids (728). Histidine and arginine are said to be inert to acrylonitrile under cyanoethylation conditions.

It has been reported that 4,5-dimethyl-2-thiazolethiol reacts with acrylonitrile to effect cyanoethylation of the nitrogen, rather than the sulfur atom (1029):

The cyanoethylation of phenylhydrazine is especially interesting since cyanoethylation with a basic catalyst yields a cyanoethylation product substituted on the α-nitrogen atom:

$$CH_2=CHCN + \langle \rangle -NHNH_2 \xrightarrow{\text{base}} \langle \rangle -N(NH_2)CH_2CH_2CN$$

whereas an acid catalyst yields a product substituted on the β-nitrogen atom (870):

$$CH_2=CHCN + \langle \rangle -NHNH_2 \xrightarrow{\text{acid}} \langle \rangle -NHNHCH_2CH_2CN$$

The cyanoethylation of amides is similar to that of amines except that strongly basic catalysts are usually necessary (1135):

$$CH_2=CHCN + RCONH_2 \longrightarrow RCONHCH_2CH_2CN$$

$$CH_2=CHCN + RCONHCH_2CH_2CN \longrightarrow RCON(CH_2CH_2CN)_2$$

It is interesting that N-methylformamide does not react with acrylonitrile (1135). In general, carboxylic acid amides, imides and lactams, and the aliphatic- and aromatic-sulfonamides will react readily in the presence of basic catalysts.

Oxygen-Cyanoethylation (See Table xx)

Alcohols and other hydroxy compounds are cyanoethylated by acrylonitrile, producing 3-alkoxypropionitriles:

$$CH_2=CHCN + ROH \rightleftharpoons ROCH_2CH_2CN$$

The reaction has been applied to a large number of aliphatic monohydric and polyhydric alcohols, to alcohols containing ether, tertiary-amino, and other non-reacting groups, and to phenols. The 3-alkoxypropionitriles produced may be hydrolyzed, hydrogenated, esterified or condensed with various reagents (31).

The reaction with primary and secondary alcohols occurs at 20-80°C. in the presence of basic catalysts. Tertiary alcohols require more drastic treatment; in fact, they may be used as solvents for cyanoethylation of primary and secondary alcohols at lower temperatures.

The cyanoethylation of alcohols by acrylonitrile is an equilibrium reaction (173), being more favorable for the cyanoethylation of primary than of secondary or tertiary alcohols. It is probable, therefore, that polyhydric alcohols such as starch, cellulose and viscose are first cyanoethylated at the primary hydroxyl groups.

The cyanoethylation of water produces 3,3'-oxydipropionitrile:

$$2CH_2=CHCN + H_2O \rightleftharpoons O(CH_2CH_2CN)_2$$

The reaction probably involves ethylene cyanohydrin as an intermediate, as it has been found that the dipropionitrile is more readily prepared from this intermediate. Aqueous formaldehyde or "methylene glycol" ($HOCH_2OH$) and the higher glycols react in the same manner:

$$2CH_2=CHCN + HO(CH_2)_nOH \longrightarrow (CH_2)_n(OCH_2CH_2CN)_2$$

However, if formaldehyde is cyanoethylated in the presence of an alcohol, the reaction occurs as if the first step were hemiformal formation (185):

$$ROH + CH_2O \longrightarrow ROCH_2OH$$

$$CH_2=CHCN + ROCH_2OH \longrightarrow ROCH_2OCH_2CH_2CN$$

The reaction of acrylonitrile with phenols requires the use of elevated temperatures (120-140°C.) (58, 268, 1104):

$$CH_2=CHCN + C_6H_5OH \longrightarrow C_6H_5OCH_2CH_2CN$$

The cyanoethylation of phenols at the o- or p-positions has been discussed earlier (page 22).

Aldoximes and ketoximes may be cyanoethylated in excellent yield at room temperature:

$$CH_2=CHCN + R_2C=NOH \longrightarrow R_2C=NOCH_2CH_2CN$$

The cyanoethylation of organic hydroperoxides has been reported (476):

$$CH_2=CHCN + C_2H_5OOH \longrightarrow C_2H_5OOCH_2CH_2CN$$

Sulfur-Cyanoethylation (See Table XXI)

The reaction of acrylonitrile with sulfhydryl compounds is analogous to that with hydroxy compounds. The products are 3-(alkylthio)propionitriles:

$$CH_2=CHCN + RSH \longrightarrow RSCH_2CH_2CN$$

These cyanoethylations proceed readily at temperatures below 50°C., and in the presence of basic catalysts. The reaction has been made the basis for a quantitative analytical method for acrylonitrile (page 61).

Hydrogen sulfide (421) and sodium sulfide (1, 526) are cyanoethylated to 3,3'-thiodipropionitrile:

$$2CH_2=CHCN + H_2S \longrightarrow S(CH_2CH_2CN)_2$$

Acrylonitrile reacts in a similar fashion with sodium polysulfide in aqueous solutions to form 3,3'-dithiodipropionitrile (1037):

$$CH_2=CHCN + NaS_x \longrightarrow NCCH_2CH_2SSCH_2CH_2CN$$

Sodium and potassium bisulfites readily add to acrylonitrile to produce the corresponding salts of 3-sulfopropionitrile (209, 958):

$$CH_2=CHCN + NaHSO_3 \longrightarrow NaO_3SCH_2CH_2CN$$

Kinetic studies of this reaction in dilute aqueous solution (795) indicate that a bimolecular reaction between sulfite ion and acrylonitrile is the rate-determining step.

The reaction of thioacetic acid with acrylonitrile gives the acetate of 3-mercaptopropionitrile in good yields (288, 289):

$$CH_2=CHCN + CH_3\overset{\overset{\displaystyle O}{\|}}{C}SH \longrightarrow CH_3\overset{\overset{\displaystyle O}{\|}}{C}SCH_2CH_2CN$$

The relative susceptibility of sulfhydryl and hydroxyl groups to cyano-ethylation is indicated by the reaction of acrylonitrile with 2-mercapto-ethanol which forms the sulfur-cyanoethylation product in high yield (422):

$$CH_2=CHCN + HOCH_2CH_2SH \longrightarrow HOCH_2CH_2SCH_2CH_2CN$$

The cyanoethylation of diethylphosphorodithioic acid has also been reported (87):

$$CH_2=CHCN + (C_2H_5O)_2\overset{\overset{\displaystyle S}{\uparrow}}{P}SH \longrightarrow (C_2H_5O)_2\overset{\overset{\displaystyle S}{\uparrow}}{P}SCH_2CH_2CN$$

The reaction of acrylonitrile with sulfhydryl compounds has also been extended to include a variety of thiazolethiols (557), and thiophenols (557). Alkali-metal salts of dithiocarbamic acids react readily with acrylonitrile to form the corresponding cyanoethyl esters (469):

$$CH_2=CHCN + R_2N\overset{\overset{\displaystyle S}{\|}}{C}SNa + H_2O \longrightarrow R_2N\overset{\overset{\displaystyle S}{\|}}{C}SCH_2CH_2CN + NaOH$$

Miscellaneous Cyanoethylations (See Table XXII)

ARSINES

Aryl arsines are readily cyanoethylated by reacting them with refluxing acrylonitrile without the use of catalysts (269). Methyl arsine has been reacted with acrylonitrile in the presence of a basic catalyst at room temperature (270):

$$2CH_2=CHCN + RAsH_2 \longrightarrow RAs(CH_2CH_2CN)_2$$

PHOSPHINES AND PHOSPHONATES

Organic phosphorus derivatives may be cyanoethylated easily without a catalyst or in the presence of acidic or basic catalysts. With phenyl phosphine the best yields were obtained in the absence of catalyst (739). With alkyl phosphonates good yields were obtained using a basic catalyst (893):

$$2CH_2=CHCN + RPH_2 \longrightarrow RP(CH_2CH_2CN)_2$$

BORANES

The reaction of diborane with acrylonitrile at room temperature in the absence of a catalyst has been reported (1032) although the structure of the isolated products has not been determined.

SILANES

The cyanoethylation of trichlorosilane has recently been reported (836) to proceed readily at 160°C. in the presence of pyridine, platinum, or benzyltrimethylammonium chloride to give 3-trichlorosilylpropionitrile:

$$CH_2=CHCN + Cl_3SiH \longrightarrow Cl_3SiCH_2CH_2CN$$

In the presence of both pyridine and stainless steel however, the only product isolated was 2-trichlorosilylpropionitrile (837):

$$CH_2=CHCN + Cl_3SiH \longrightarrow CH_3CHCN$$
$$\underset{SiCl_3}{|}$$

This is the only reported case of reverse or α-addition in which hydrogen adds to the β-carbon in acrylonitrile, and the remainder of the molecule adds to the α-carbon.

TIN HYDRIDES

Tri-n-butyl- and triphenyltin hydrides react with acrylonitrile in the absence of catalysts to give the 3-substituted propionitriles (1115):

$$CH_2=CHCN + R_3SnH \longrightarrow R_3SnCH_2CH_2CN$$

Hydrogen Halide Cyanoethylation (*See Table* XXIII)

Anhydrous hydrogen chloride (800) and hydrogen bromide (803) react exothermically in the cold to give 3-halopropionitriles. This reaction is catalyzed by aliphatic amines, or by quaternary ammonium salts (364, 800) although apparently, good yields can be obtained with no catalyst (388):

$$CH_2=CHCN + HX \longrightarrow XCH_2CH_2CN$$

Reaction with Natural and Synthetic Polymers

Many natural and synthetic polymers that contain labile hydrogen atoms react with acrylonitrile under suitable conditions to give cyanoethyl derivatives. In general, aqueous caustic has been used to catalyze these reactions. Since the extent of cyanoethylation of the polymer can be varied by suitable choice of reaction conditions, a variety of products may be obtained from one starting material. Under certain conditions cyanoethylation is accompanied by hydrolysis; in these cases many of the nitrile groups are hydrolyzed to carboxylic acid salts, thereby producing a polyelectrolyte.

As might be expected, the physical properties of polymers change when they are cyanoethylated. Hydrophilic polymers become more hydrophobic, and when cyanoethylated to a high degree, may become soluble in organic solvents.

Cyanoethylation may be carried out either in a homogeneous manner (e.g., on cellulose xanthate as in viscose dope) or in a heterogeneous system (such as on cotton yarn immersed in aqueous caustic solution). For a given polymer, homogeneous-phase cyanoethylation appears to result in the most uniform distribution of cyanoethyl residues.

References to articles and patents describing methods of cyanoethylation of natural and synthetic polymers are given in the accompanying outline. The properties of many of these cyanoethylated products are given in the appropriate parts of the Application Section. The process variables and economics for the commercial-scale cyanoethylation of cotton are described in the industry report "Cyanoethylation of Cotton" (1243).

I. NATURAL POLYMERS

    A. Carbohydrates

        1. Cellulose

            a. Cotton (fabric, staple, yarn) (232, 439, 600, 1018, 1197, 1213, 1237, 1272, 1274, 1294, 1304, 1443, 1446)
(for reviews see 261, 310, 1243)

            b. Flax (1394)

            c. Jute (1)

            d. Manila (1)

            e. Pulp (linters, wood cellulose) (127, 414, 551, 561, 776, 1116, 1235, 1451)

            f. Regenerated Cellulose (127, 290, 551, 676, 715, 1018, 1324, 1451)

            g. Sisal (1)

            h. Wood (1)

        2. Dextran (1)

        3. Dextrin (1)

        4. Gums

            a. Galactomannon: guar, locust bean, honey locust, flame tree, tara (783, 784, 785)

            b. Glucomannon: iles mannon (783, 784, 785)

            c. Arabic, tragacanth, karaya (784)

        5. Starch

            a. Corn, potato, tapioca, wheat (1, 126, 427, 549, 719)

        6. Tylose (427)

    B. Lignin (1441)

    C. Proteins (650)

        1. Blood albumen (651)

        2. Casein (279, 651, 1335)

        3. Gelatin (306, 416, 651)

        4. Glue (651)

        5. Gluten (256)

        6. Soybean (279)

            a. Fibers (279)

        7. Wool (732, 1212)

        8. Zein (279, 306, 651)

            a. Fibers (279)

II. Modified Natural Polymers

    A. Cellulose Xanthate (278, 527, 529, 710, 711, 712, 714, 717, 718, 719)
    B. Dimethylthiourethane of Cellulose (1196)
    C. Ethylcellulose (551)
    D. Ethylthiourethane of Cellulose (1196)
    E. Hydroxyethylcellulose (713, 1117)
    F. Methylcellulose (713)
    G. Phenylthiourethane of Cellulose (1196)

III. Synthetic Polymers

    A. Acetone-formaldehyde condensate (1108)
    B. Acetone-isobutyraldehyde condensate (1108)
    C. Methyl ethyl ketone-formaldehyde condensate (1108)
    D. Poly(allyl alcohol) (1143)
    E. Poly(crotyl alcohol) (1145)
    F. Poly(3-chloroallyl alcohol) (1143)
    G. Polyketone from ethylene and carbon monoxide (794)
    H. Polyketone from propylene, ethylene and carbon monoxide (794)
    I. Poly(methallyl alcohol) (1143)
    J. Poly(methyl vinyl ketone) (794)
    K. Poly(vinyl alcohol) (427, 550, 1049, 1098, 1174, 1251, 1319, 1320, 1324)

POLYMERIZATION REACTIONS

The most important property of acrylonitrile is its ability to undergo additional polymerization to form high molecular-weight products. Physical studies (22) indicate that this reactivity is due to the relatively high polarity of the acrylonitrile molecule. These same studies also indicate that acrylonitrile will copolymerize best with other highly active monomers, and that if the comonomer has an electron-rich bond, there will be a tendency toward alternation of monomer units in the chain.

This monomer polarity also gives rise to the unique properties of acrylonitrile polymers. Strong van der Waals forces and close packing of adjacent chains are responsible for high heat distortion temperatures, good resistance to chemicals, excellent outdoor durability, and hard, strong, tough surfaces.

The utilization of these properties is discussed in the Applications Section. The present section discusses polymerization methods, monomer reactivity ratios, chemical modifications, and the physical properties of acrylonitrile polymers.

Homopolymerization

Pure acrylonitrile may be polymerized rapidly and spontaneously at room temperature if inhibitors such as oxygen, water, hydroquinones, and amines are excluded. Less pure monomer exhibits a variable induction period, and may be stable for a long time at fairly high temperatures. Traces of oxygen produce a pronounced inhibiting effect by reacting with active radicals (842, 984, 1005). Acetylene polymers also inhibit the polymerization (539).

Rapid polymerization takes place in the presence of substances capable of producing free radicals. Peroxides such as hydrogen peroxide (995) and benzoyl peroxide (1291), azo compounds such as 2,2'-azobis(isobutyronitrile) (539, 1011, 1190) and 2,2'-azobis(2,4-dimethylvaleronitrile) (1011), and tetra-alkyldiarylethanes (1191) have been used as a source of free radicals for initiation of acrylonitrile polymerization.

Radiation has been employed successfully to bring about acrylonitrile polymerization. Ultraviolet light acting on pure acrylonitrile (610) and on solutions of acrylonitrile containing ferric salts (369, 371, 947, 948), or H_2O_2 (297), will initiate polymerization. Visible light may be used if a dye, a reducing agent, and oxygen are all present (847, 1369). Polymerization by γ-rays (112, 225, 226, 238, 259, 888, 889, 1208, 1209, 1221, 1226, 1380, 1432), X-rays (259, 297, 298, 299, 886, 887, 888), high energy electrons (965, 1268), and ultrasonic vibrations (703) have been reported.

Because of the electron-deficient character of the double bond in acrylonitrile, acid catalysts such as aluminum chloride have very little catalytic effect (455). Silver salts dissolved in acrylonitrile will promote polymerization, but a free radical rather than a cationic mechanism is indicated (945). A variety of basic catalysts such as sodium and sodamide, on the other hand, cause vigorous polymerization of acrylonitrile (367, 536, 862, 1072, 1169).

The polymerization of acrylonitrile is rapid (681) and exothermic [17.3±0.5 k.cal. per mole (1094)], making bulk polymerization difficult to control. Since polyacrylonitrile is insoluble in the monomer, a heterogeneous polymerization with unusual kinetic features results (71, 72, 73, 641, 1087). The polymer insolubility leads to a thick paste from which heat is not easily removed.

It is possible to polymerize acrylonitrile in the vapor phase (596, 615) or, if a suitable solvent is employed, in the homogeneous liquid phase (670, 671, 889, 1036, 1086). The use of concentrated zinc chloride solutions is satisfactory for producing a polymer solution, suitable for direct film casting or fiber spinning (670, 671). Ordinarily, however, the polymer will be insoluble in the reacting medium, and will precipitate as it is formed (1036).

Acrylonitrile is conveniently polymerized in aqueous solution. Advantages of this system are economy, ease of temperature control, and adaptability to certain redox catalyst systems. These allow for rapid polymerization at relatively low temperatures (20-60°C.). Molecular weight is controlled by the catalyst content and the temperature. Chain transfer agents, such as alcohols, also may be used (308, 850). The color of polymer made by low-temperature redox initiation is often better than that obtained by the use of other catalyst systems.

Redox catalyst systems (51, 61, 94, 152, 271, 516, 597, 603, 627, 750, 801, 846, 853, 984, 985) contain at least two components, an oxidizing agent and a reducing agent, and for acrylonitrile, are usually effective only in acid solutions (1). In addition, the ions of certain metals, such as copper, silver and iron, may be employed at very small concentrations (e.g., 5 to 200 p.p.m.) to increase further the rate of initiation (62, 252). However, uncontrolled contamination by metallic ions should be avoided since in many systems polymerization may be retarded or totally inhibited (1). The marked inhibiting effect of oxygen on the polymerization of acrylonitrile by redox systems has been investigated in detail (1005). The catalytic activity of redox systems depends on the fact that some oxidation—reduction reactions progress at a convenient rate via a free-radical mechanism, these radical intermediates being the actual initiators of polymerization. Examples of such systems are ammonium persulfate-sodium bisulfate, and hydrogen peroxide-ferrous sulfate. In the latter system it has been shown that hydroxyl radicals are the chain initiators (94). Many other useful systems have been found, most of them comprising a peroxy compound and an oxidizable sulfoxy compound.

Aqueous solution-polymerization also may be initiated by peroxides alone, by azo compounds, or by radiation. It has been reported that X-rays and gamma rays are effective because of the intermediate formation of hydroxyl radicals (296).

Initially monomer may be present in excess of the solubility limit (152). In the absence of emulsifying agents and with a water-soluble catalyst the reaction appears to occur chiefly in the aqueous phase, while with an organic-solvent soluble catalyst the reaction proceeds in the organic phase (1011).

Acrylonitrile may be polymerized in emulsion (152, 386, 630, 743, 840, 892) using either conventional or redox catalyst systems, and by either batch- or continuous-methods (661). It is somewhat difficult to prepare stable polyacrylonitrile emulsions, particularly with high solids content. However, if the proper concentration of an emulsifier such as lauryl sodium sulfate is used, and if the reaction temperature is kept within certain limits, stable emulsions of 20-25% solids content may be prepared (1). It also has been shown that if the polymerization is effected in the presence of a halogenated hydrocarbon, such as ethylene dichloride, the resulting latex is stable (476). A comparison of the emulsion polymerization of acrylonitrile with that of methyl methacrylate has been made (630).

The ease with which polymerization of acrylonitrile is initiated has led to the use of the monomer as a means of detecting free-radical intermediates in various inorganic and organic reactions (321, 343, 539, 540, 541, 626, 659, 1046, 1390, 1415).

Suitable methods of polymerizing acrylonitrile are indicated more specifically by the following examples. The procedure of Example 1 or some modification of it is ordinarily preferred.

Example 1—Slurry Polymerization with a Redox Catalyst System (61)

The following system is heated at 30°C. under nitrogen with slow stirring:

Water	200	grams
Acrylonitrile	10.0	grams
Potassium persulfate	0.4	gram
Sodium bisulfite	0.15	gram

Polymer begins to form immediately, and after an hour the yield is 86.3%. It is important that the pH be maintained below 5, and it is preferable to operate at about pH 3. The initial pH is 3.6; after an hour it is 3.2.

Example 2—Continuous Slurry Polymerization with a Redox Catalyst (37).

The following system is stirred at 35°C.:

Water	1150 grams
Polyacrylonitrile	450 grams
Sulfuric acid	To give pH 3

A stream of acrylonitrile containing 3.1% water, a stream of catalyst solution containing 2.93 grams of sodium chlorate and 10.5 grams of sodium sulfite per liter of water, and a stream of aqueous sulfuric acid (5 grams per liter) are fed simultaneously to the reactor. Each of the feed streams is run continuously at a rate of 236 ml. per hour. The slurry continuously overflows through a side arm at the 1600 ml. level in the reactor. The average residence time is thus 2.2 hours. After 7.5 hours the pH of the reaction mixture is 2.5 and an 89% yield of polymer having an average molecular weight of about 75,000 is obtained; hence the polymer concentration in the reaction mixture at this time is 24.8% by weight, and the monomer concentration by difference is 3.1%.

Copolymerization

When polymerization is initiated in a mixture of acrylonitrile with another monomer, the two monomers ordinarily enter into the copolymer at different rates. Accordingly, the copolymer is always richer in the more reactive monomer than is the mixture of the monomers from which it is forming. Since the monomers are being used at different rates the composition of the copolymer being formed changes continuously during a batch reaction. For many applications the uniformity of the copolymer composition is not critical. Sometimes, however, it becomes important to prepare an acrylonitrile copolymer with a relatively narrow range of chain compositions, e.g., to improve the strength or clarity of the copolymer (2, 223, 1001) or, in the case of thermoplastic copolymers, to reduce the flow temperature (346, 1056).

Obviously, the composition of the copolymer from a batch-polymerization will be more uniform if the reaction is stopped before the change in the composition of the residual monomer mixture becomes great. However, in practice this involves recovering and recycling a large proportion of the original monomer mixture. This can be avoided if an additional feed of the more reactive monomer (or a mixture of the monomers rich in the more reactive monomer) is continuously fed during the polymerization. The rate should be sufficient to maintain the ratio of concentrations of unreacted monomers substantially constant during the whole period of polymerization. The reflux temperature may be used as an indicator of the relative monomer concentrations (223, 461).

In order to obtain initial production of copolymer of a predetermined composition it is usually necessary to start with a monomer mixture which has a different composition. While the proper composition for the mixture may be determined by trial and error, it can also be calculated from the reactivity ratios r_1 and r_2 for the two monomers (M_1 and M_2) if these ratios are known. The ratios are defined as follows:

$$r_1 = \frac{k_{11}}{k_{12}}, r_2 = \frac{k_{22}}{k_{21}}$$

k_{11} = rate constant for the reaction between a copolymer chain ending in M_1 and an M_1 monomer

k_{12} = rate constant for the reaction between a copolymer chain ending in M_1 and an M_2 monomer

k_{22} and k_{21} are the rate constants for the reactions of a copolymer chain ending in M_2 with monomers M_2 and M_1, respectively

For a more detailed discussion see reference 759.

Reactivity ratios for the copolymerization of acrylonitrile with various monomers are listed in Table xxiv.

The following is an illustrative calculation of the monomer composition required to make a copolymer of acrylonitrile of definite composition:

Copolymer desired: Acrylonitrile (M_1) 75% by weight

Methyl acrylate (M_2) 25% by weight

One may use the following equation:

$$C = \frac{P-1 + \sqrt{(1-P)^2 + 4Pr_1r_2}}{2r_1}$$

where C = mole ratio of M_1 to M_2 charged

P = mole ratio of M_1 to M_2 in copolymer = $\dfrac{\frac{75}{53}}{\frac{25}{86}} = 4.84$

from Table xxiv, $r_1 = 1.26$ and $r_2 = 0.67$

Substituting, $C = \dfrac{(4.84-1) + \sqrt{(1-4.84)^2 + 4(4.84)\,(1.26)\,(0.67)}}{2(1.26)}$

$C = 3.7$ moles M_1 per mole M_2

In terms of weight, this means that the monomer mixture should consist of 70% acrylonitrile and 30% methyl acrylate.

It should be emphasized that with this monomer charge, only the initial copolymer will have the desired composition. If, however, the calculated charge (i.e., 70:30) is placed in the reactor and polymerization initiated at reflux, one may then begin adding a mixture of monomers having the same composition as that of the polymer first formed (i.e., 75:25). This addition is done at such a rate as to maintain a constant reflux temperature. Thus the monomers are being added at the same rate at which they are being reacted, keeping the concentrations of unreacted monomers constant. As soon as all the feed has been added, the polymerization is stopped and unreacted monomers are recovered for reuse.

TABLE XXIV

Monomer-Reactivity Ratios for Copolymerization with Acrylonitrile (M_1) at ca. 60°C. (unless otherwise noted)

Comonomer (M_2)	r_1	r_2
1-Acetoxy-1,3-butadiene (456)	0.0	0.7
2-Acetoxystyrene (224)	0.08 ± 0.01	0.4 ± 0.05
Acrylamide (904)	0.875	1.357
Allyl alcohol (1369)	3.96 ± 0.53	0.11 ± 0.10
Allyl chloride (224)	3.0 ± 0.2	0.05 ± 0.01
1,1-Bis(p-anisyl)ethylene (337)	0.014 ± 0.002	0
1,1-Bis(p-chlorophenyl)ethylene (337)	0.024 ± 0.003	0
Bis(trimethylsiloxy)vinylmethylsilane (1376)	8.0	0.1
Butadiene (501)	0.0 ± 0.04	0.35 ± 0.08
Butyl acrylate (809)	1.003 ± 0.012	1.005 ± 0.005
Chloroprene (501)	0.01 ± 0.01	6.07 ± 0.53
Crotonic acid (337)	21 ± 10	0
2,5-Dichlorostyrene (434)	0.19	0.07
Diethyl fumarate (758)	8	0
Diethyl maleate (758)	12	0
Diphenylacetylene (337)	13.6 ± 1.0	0
1,1-Diphenylethylene (337)	0.028 ± 0.003	0
$trans$-1,2-Di(2-pyridyl)ethylene (1333)	0.95 ± 0.05	0.02 ± 0.05
Ethyl β-ethoxyethylacrylate (1382)	10.5 ± 1.5	0.02 ± 0.02
Ethyl vinyl ether (1382)	0.7 ± 0.2	0.03 ± 0.02
2-Fluorobutadiene (1368)	0.07 ± 0.03	0.59 ± 0.10
1-Hexene (337)	12.2 ± 2.4	0
1-Hexyne (337)	5.4 ± 0.5	0
Isobutylene (841)	1.02	0
Isoprene (501)	0.03 ± 0.03	0.45 ± 0.05
Maleic anhydride (758)	6	0
Methacrolein (456)	0.06	2.0
Methacrylonitrile (841)	0.32	2.68
Methacryloxymethylpentamethyldisiloxane (1340)	0.19 ± 0.04	1.44 ± 0.15
Methyl acrylate (1) (30°)	1.26 ± 0.1	0.67 ± 0.1
Methyl 2-chloroacrylate (21)	0.15	2.0
Methyl cinnamate (300, 337)	6 ± 2	0
Methyl methacrylate (693)	0.15 ± 0.07	1.2 ± 0.14
α-Methylstyrene (400)	0.06 ± 0.02	0.1 ± 0.02
(460)	0.06 ± 0.02	0.055 ± 0.005
o-Methylstyrene (1)	0.06 ± 0.05	0.33 ± 0.1
m-Methylstyrene (1)	0.07 ± 0.04	0.43 ± 0.1
p-Methylstyrene (1)	0.05 ± 0.02	0.33 ± 0.1
Methyl vinyl ketone (694)	0.61 ± 0.04	1.78 ± 0.22
Phenylacetylene (337)	0.26 ± 0.03	0.33 ± 0.05
Styrene (619)	0.04 ± 0.04	0.41 ± 0.08
Tetrachloroethylene (336)	470	0
Trichloroethylene (758)	67	0
3,3,3-Trichloropropene (337)	12.2 ± 1.2	0.10 ± 0.015
Trimethyl aconitate (1332)	5.50 ± 0.5	0
Trimethylsiloxyvinyldimethylsilane (1376)	8.0	0.1
Tris(trimethylsiloxy)vinylsilane (1376)	8.0	0.1
Vinyl acetate (760)	4.05 ± 0.3	0.061 ± 0.013
(102)	6.0	0.07
Vinyl benzoate (224)	5.0 ± 0.05	0.05 ± 0.005
Vinyl chloride (694)	3.28 ± 0.06	0.02 ± 0.02
Vinyl ethyl ether (758)	5	0
Vinyl 2-ethylhexoate (224)	12 ± 2	0.01 ± 0.01
Vinyl formate (224)	3.03 ± 0.05	0.04 ± 0.005
Vinylidene chloride (693)	0.91 ± 0.1	0.37 ± 0.1
Vinyltrimethoxysilane (1427)	6.0	0
Vinyl stearate (1448)	4.3	0.03

In Table xxv there are listed reactivity values of a somewhat different nature, reported in the earlier literature (833). In these experiments, equimolar quantities of acrylonitrile and a second monomer were copolymerized. The mole ratios of monomers in the resulting polymers are given:

TABLE XXV
Reactivity of Monomers with Acrylonitrile (M_1) (833)

Comonomer (M_2)	Mole Ratio M_1/M_2 in Copolymer
Allyl acetate	9.63
1,1-Diphenylethylene	0.662
Methyl acrylate	1.06
Methyl 2-chloroacrylate	0.345
Indene	1.20
Stilbene	2.53

The arrangement of monomer units in acrylonitrile copolymers will vary with the comonomer used. A random arrangement of the two units appears to be most common. If the product of the monomer reactivity ratios $r_1r_2 = 1$, the two types of monomer units are arranged completely at random in the chain. If r_1r_2 is less than 1, the structure deviates from the random in the direction of regular alternation. It is seldom if ever found that r_1r_2 is greater than 1 (759).

Special techniques may be used to achieve "block" copolymers of acrylonitrile wherein a substantial number of acrylonitrile units occur in succession, and are followed by a substantial number of comonomer units (513, 514, 515, 834, 835, 1200, 1290, 1343).

Another structural variation may be achieved by grafting branches onto a preformed polymer (1200, 1227, 1290, 1342, 1434). For example, when acrylonitrile is polymerized in the presence of natural rubber polymer, a portion of the polyacrylonitrile formed attaches to mid-chain sites on the rubber giving it increased solvent resistance (685, 1299).

Graft copolymers of acrylonitrile and poly(N-acrylylmorpholine) have been prepared by heating an aqueous mixture of acrylonitrile and the preformed polymer with potassium persulfate (1239).

Vinyl acetate polymer has been grafted onto polyacrylonitrile by heating polyacrylonitrile latex with vinyl acetate monomer and potassium persulfate (483). Solubility studies indicated that about 50% of the vinyl acetate had become grafted onto the polyacrylonitrile.

Flame resistant, spinnable polymers have been produced by grafting acrylonitrile onto poly(vinyl chloride) or poly(vinylidene chloride) (1238).

A different type of graft copolymer is presumably formed when acrylonitrile is copolymerized with poly(vinylsiloxanes) (556, 558), since here the preformed polymer has vinyl groups which may enter either at the end, or in the middle of the polyacrylonitrile chains.

Radiation has been used successfully as an initiator in the preparation of block and graft copolymers (1200, 1201, 1210, 1275, 1342, 1343, 1378, 1411). Irradiation of polymers produces free radical sites which are capable of initiating vinyl polymerizations. Whether a block- or graft-copolymer is formed depends on the location of the radical site.

Several excellent reviews have been published on the techniques employed in block- and graft-polymerization (1267, 1290, 1377, 1378).

Acrylonitrile has been copolymerized with more than 400 different co-monomers. A tabulation of these copolymers, together with a summary of properties, uses and typical laboratory procedures is given in an American Cyanamid Company technical bulletin entitled "Polymers and Copolymers of Acrylonitrile."

Modification of Acrylonitrile Polymers

Polymers and copolymers of acrylonitrile are capable of undergoing further transformation through chemical reactions of the nitrile group. For example, polyamines are said to be obtained when polyacrylonitrile (257, 602, 851) and its copolymers (257, 639, 734, 1142) are hydrogenated.

Polymers and copolymers of acrylonitrile can be hydrolyzed by aqueous alkali to give water-soluble materials containing carboxylate groupings (563, 628, 737, 788, 1203). If polyacrylonitrile is heated above about 80°C. with concentrated alkali, the pasty mixture passes through a thick, red stage and eventually becomes clear, viscous, yellow and water-soluble (628). The product is chiefly the salt of polyacrylic acid.

Solutions of hydrolyzed polyacrylonitrile are interesting for a number of applications (1). They may be stored at elevated temperatures without change in viscosity, and they are apparently not susceptible to the action of molds or bacteria. The solutions are stable from about pH 4 to 12, or higher. At lower pH's coagulation tends to occur. Solutions of hydrolyzed polyacrylonitrile have good tolerance for both anions and cations, and for hydrophilic solvents.

Partial hydration of polyacrylonitrile with concentrated sulfuric acid has been reported to give a solution from which fibers may be spun (883). Reaction of polyacrylonitrile with hydroxylamine introduces amidoxime groups (969, 1400) and hydroxamic acid groups (1399). The resulting polymer is said to have increased dye affinity (969).

Polyacrylonitrile in dilute solutions in dimethylformamide undergoes extremely rapid random chain scission if a strong base such as sodium hydroxide is added (723). The intrinsic viscosity may be reduced to 5 to 10% of its original value. Polymethacrylonitrile does not behave in this way indicating that the α-hydrogen atoms of polyacrylonitrile appear to be involved in the chain cleavage.

Butadiene-acrylonitrile and styrene-acrylonitrile copolymers are reported to become cross-linked when irradiated with high-energy electrons (684).

Properties of Acrylonitrile Polymers

The structure of polyacrylonitrile is usually represented as that of a linear paraffin with nitrile groups on alternate carbon atoms:

$$----CH_2-CH-CH_2-CH-CH_2-CH-CH_2-CH----$$
$$\qquad\quad CN \qquad\quad CN \qquad\quad CN \qquad\quad CN$$

The infrared spectrum of the polymer indicates that by far the major portion of the polymer possesses this head-to-tail structure (552). The absence of ketene-imine absorption, in the infrared spectrum of the polymer, indicates that 1-4 addition does not occur to an appreciable extent, as it does in the polymerization of methacrylonitrile (1050). The extent of chain branching which occurs depends upon the method of polymerization, with high temperatures leading to more branching.

Polyacrylonitrile from bulk polymerization contains trapped-free radicals (75, 76). These radicals are destroyed in a matter of minutes after contact with air.

The unique properties of polyacrylonitrile are attributed to its strong, compact $-$CN dipoles. Close packing of adjacent chains produces a crystalline structure with powerful intermolecular forces. The specific gravity of the polymer is 1.17, corresponding to a 31% shrinkage on polymerization (641, 825). Only specific, and highly polar liquids are able to solvate the nitrile dipoles, separate the chains and effect solution (197, 409, 552, 869, 1044, 1125). By way of contrast, polymethacrylonitrile, which has the bulky methyl group in place of hydrogen, softens at 115°C., and dissolves in a variety of solvents.

Fractionations of solutions of acrylonitrile polymers (119, 504, 552, 1307) and copolymers (219) by solvent precipitation have been reported. The crystalline nature of the polymer is unfavorable for good fractionation (119). A relationship between viscosity average molecular weight and intrinsic viscosity has been developed by Cleland and Stockmayer (246):

$$[\eta] = 2.43 \times 10^{-4} \, M_2^{0.75}$$

where $[\eta]$ is the intrinsic viscosity in deciliters per gram. This equation, based on light-scattering measurements of unfractionated samples, is in good agreement with similar measurements of other investigators (1). Other equations have been given by Houtz (552), Bisschops (119) and Onyon (1367). In the case of copolymers of acrylonitrile some anomalous effects have been noted; for example, certain liquids dissolve copolymers having a limited range of composition, but will not dissolve either homopolymer (95).

Concentrated solutions of polyacrylonitrile (such as a 20% solution in dimethylformamide) will undergo reversible gelation. The phenomenon is strongly dependent on temperature and concentration, and has been ascribed to the formation of crystalline nuclei (118, 120).

When polyacrylonitrile is heated it softens somewhat, but does not flow except under high pressure. At temperatures above about 130°C. the polymer yellows slowly. Between 200°C. and 300°C. rapid decomposition occurs. Ammonium cyanide, hydrocyanic acid and acrylonitrile are formed in small amounts as a result of pyrolysis between 175°C. and 300°C. (534). The thermal degradation of copolymers of acrylonitrile has been studied (440, 675).

Polyacrylonitrile fibers have been reported to retain more than half their strength after heating 16 hours at 200°C. at which time they are said to be jet black (552). Additives that inhibit color development in heated acrylonitrile polymers have been discovered (982). The exact cause of such color development is unknown, although formation of condensed heterocyclic rings has been postulated (552, 646). The color stability of polyacrylonitrile varies with the method of preparation. The initiating system chosen is particularly important (1). This suggests that color may develop only at special points such as end groups or double bonds, rather than randomly in the molecule.

The second-order transition-temperature of polyacrylonitrile has been given as >100°C. based on dielectric measurements (1177), and as 130°C. from extrapolation of dilatometer measurements (420). This transition temperature has also been determined for several copolymers of acrylotrile (420, 498, 1153).

Because of the difficulties encountered in obtaining perfect molded specimens from polyacrylonitrile, data on mechanical properties are very limited (964). Numerous reports on mechanical properties of polyacrylonitrile fibers (198, 463, 489, 552, 960, 1043) and of copolymers (389, 829, 1092) have appeared.

Some of the electrical properties of polyacrylonitrile (505, 959, 1177, 1178) and acrylonitrile copolymers (190, 357, 358, 505, 959) have been determined.

The permeabilities of polyacrylonitrile films to water vapor (789) and organic vapors (999) have been studied. The diffusion rates of hydrogen and nitrogen through butadiene-acrylonitrile rubber have also been reported (83).

Polyacrylonitrile cannot be spread at an air-water interface to form a monomolecular film, but is said to give a film of the "condensed type" at an oil-water interface (548).

At 25°C. and 50% relative humidity, polyacrylonitrile is stated to absorb only 0.8% water (624). However, Houtz reports that polyacrylonitrile absorbs 1.5 to 2% moisture very rapidly at moderate humidities (552).

The crystallinity of polyacrylonitrile is reported to be evident from X-ray studies of the polymer and of the drawn fibers (552). The presence of 3-mole percent vinyl acetate is said to reduce crystallinity (623).

When examined under the electron microscope, an emulsion or latex of polyacrylonitrile appears to consist of spheroidal particles ranging from 500 to 1000 Ångstroms in diameter (927). These particles are frequently aggregated or joined by fibrous connectors. This appears to be a manifestation of fibrillation. A peculiar property of polyacrylonitrile is this tendency of the "latex" or emulsion particle to persist after molding. An electron micrograph of a fractured surface of molded polyacrylonitrile (Figure 11) shows the presence of particles corresponding in size and shape to the particles of the powder from which it was molded.

Polyacrylonitrile has been studied with regard to its macromolecular texture. Thin films were cast on glass from a 0.5% solution in ethylene carbonate. They were metalized at an angle to improve photographic contrast of the top surface of the film, and were subsequently examined in the electron microscope. Electron micrographs (Figure 11) showed a still finer particulate texture than was observed in the fracture surface. These are probably the ultimate particles, i.e., the macromolecules. Not only are they pictured in size and shape, about 20 to 100 Ångstroms in diameter, but it is possible to estimate their molecular weight from their measured sizes (926). Figure 11 also shows the tendency of the macromolecules to aggregate (appearing as raised areas in picture). This can better be appreciated when depicted at lower magnification, as in Figure 12, which, for maximum effect, should be viewed at arm's length. These aggregates correspond approximately in size and shape with the spheroidal particles shown in Figures 9 and 10. A typical aggregate is indicated in Figure 12 by the arrow.

Secondary aggregates, visible with the optical microscope (1), usually appear spherical or oval (Figure 13); but under some conditions the structure is that of a dried gel (Figure 14). These secondary aggregates usually can be broken down mechanically and are probably dependent on such factors as rate of agitation, kind and quantity of electrolyte, and the presence of copolymers and dispersing agents.

Summary

Acrylonitrile is a monomer capable of imparting unique properties to polymeric materials, both by polymerization and copolymerization. Special characteristics of polyacrylonitrile include:

> Hardness
> Heat resistance and slow burning
> Resistance to most solvents and chemicals
> Resistance to sunlight and exposure
> Ability to form oriented fibers and films
> Reactivity toward nitrile group reagents
> Compatibility with certain polar substances

Some of the more important commercial developments in which these properties have been utilized are summarized in the next section of this book.

APPLICATIONS

This section is based, for the most part, on numerous references to the patent literature. While the information contained in these references is thought to be accurate and reliable, American Cyanamid is not in a position to refute or support their claims. This section merely presents the data, claims, and statements of the literature cited. For additional details on specific items, it is recommended that the reader consult the original sources.

Adhesives

Acrylonitrile-butadiene rubbers can be formulated into adhesives with characteristically high strength, excellent aging properties, and good chemical resistance, including resistance to aliphatic and aromatic solvents, and to most plasticizers that cause bond failure of other adhesives. These adhesives are especially suited to bonding synthetic rubber stocks to metal (555).

Acrylonitrile-butadiene rubber and phenolic resins can be dissolved together in solvents, such as methyl ethyl ketone, to form extremely useful cements (43, 286, 339, 354, 392, 431, 436, 821, 872, 905, 961, 1158). These cements have the flexibility of nitrile rubber and the cured adhesive strength of phenolic resins. Metals, plastics, rubber, leather, wood, fabrics, glass fiber, Nylon and resin-coated materials may be cemented to themselves, and to each other (392, 1407).

Among the other modifying ingredients in reported adhesive formulations based on nitrile rubber are various vinyl polymers and copolymers (372, 401, 560, 799, 863, 905, 986, 1061), wood rosin products (96, 239, 339, 393, 479, 499, 757), polychloroprene (393), chlorinated rubbers (179, 415, 609), butadiene-styrene rubber (104), natural rubber (105, 609), and coumarone resins (372).

Treating acrylonitrile-butadiene resins with dilute sulfuric acid (949) or with concentrated phosphoric acid (330) gives oil-resistant rubber cements. Another modification of the copolymer is achieved by heating with maleic anhydride. This product, compounded with polychloroprene and dehydroabietic acid, is particularly useful in bonding polymer films to metal surfaces (393).

An acrylonitrile-butadiene emulsion, prepared in the presence of dodecyl mercaptan, provides a pressure-sensitive adhesive film with excellent aging characteristics (1247).

Among the specific applications mentioned for the various rubber-based adhesives are: joining leather parts in shoe manufacture (328, 431, 757, 863), bonding an abrasive coating to foam rubber (354), adhesive for resealable waxed paper wrappings (479), subcoat for adhesive tapes (105, 361, 499), adhesives for waterproof plywood lamination (401), bonding glass fibers into insulating board (436), attaching magnetic tape to flexible backing (961), bonding brake linings to brake shoe (43), joining pile fibers to fabric backing (372), attaching patches to plastic film (986), and bonding abrasive materials to form grinding wheels (1379).

Other copolymers of acrylonitrile which have been found useful in adhesive applications are acrylonitrile-ethyl acrylate copolymers for pigment coating of paper (810); acrylonitrile-vinylidene chloride copolymers in conjunction with casein for book binding (1184); and acrylonitrile-acrylic acid -alkyl acrylate terpolymers as coatings for fabric and paper, undercoatings for poly(vinyl chloride) top coats, and as pigment binders for leather (1328).

Antioxidants

3-Thiopropionic acids and esters of the type $RSCH_2CH_2COOR'$ are effective antioxidants for edible oils, fats, waxes, and soap (448, 449). These esters may be prepared by esterification of the nitriles resulting from the cyanoethylation of mercaptans. Thiodipropionic acid, the product of hydrolysis of 3,3'-thiodipropionitrile (33), is useful in preventing the rancidification of fats and edible oils (448).

Chemotherapy

Acrylonitrile has been employed in two multi-step syntheses of an antimalarial Hydrangea alkaloid (69) as well as in the synthesis of adrenal cortical hormones (1171, 1172).

Several 3-alkylaminopropylamines, which are prepared by hydrogenation of the alkylamine-acrylonitrile adduct, have been condensed with heterocyclic compounds to yield antimalarials (41, 195, 272, 293, 525, 632, 1000, 1023, 1055, 1105):

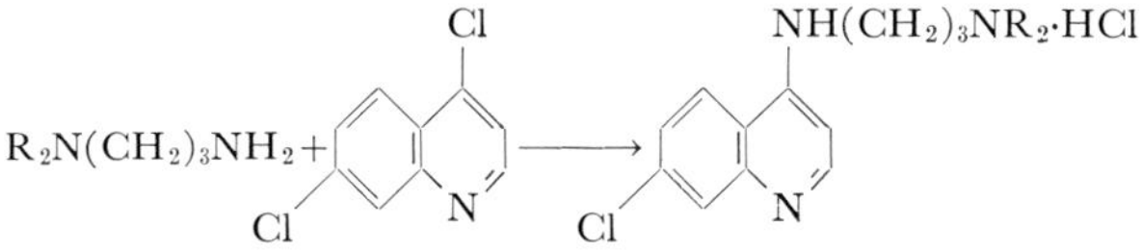

$$R_2N(CH_2)_3NH_2 + \quad \overset{Cl}{\underset{Cl}{\bigcirc\bigcirc_N}} \longrightarrow \quad \overset{NH(CH_2)_3NR_2 \cdot HCl}{\underset{Cl}{\bigcirc\bigcirc_N}}$$

Derivatives of dialkylaminopropylamines, for example N-(3-diethylaminopropyl)-1,8-naphtholimide, have shown activity as local anesthetics, but in most cases their toxicities are relatively high (101, 751).

The synthesis of the pellagra-preventive factor, pantothenic acid, usually involves β-alanine. This intermediate may be prepared in one step from acrylonitrile, ammonia and water (207). Alternatively, β-alanine may be synthesized by hydrolyzing the reaction product from phthalimide and acrylonitrile (412), or from acetamide and acrylonitrile (843).

Ethyl 3-ethoxypropionate, prepared by alcoholysis of 3-ethoxypropionitrile, can be used in the preparation of vitamin B_1 (1012). Among the amino acids which have been synthesized from acrylonitrile are dl-cystine (454), dl-glutamic acid (254), and dl-ornithine (14):

CYSTINE:

$$CH_2=CHCN + Cl_2 \longrightarrow CH_2ClCHClCN \longrightarrow CH_2=CClCN + HCl$$

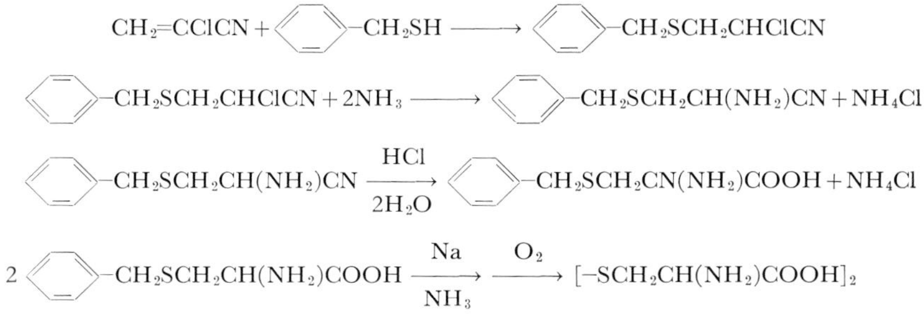

$$CH_2=CClCN + \bigcirc-CH_2SH \longrightarrow \bigcirc-CH_2SCH_2CHClCN$$

$$\bigcirc-CH_2SCH_2CHClCN + 2NH_3 \longrightarrow \bigcirc-CH_2SCH_2CH(NH_2)CN + NH_4Cl$$

$$\bigcirc-CH_2SCH_2CH(NH_2)CN \xrightarrow[2H_2O]{HCl} \bigcirc-CH_2SCH_2CN(NH_2)COOH + NH_4Cl$$

$$2 \bigcirc-CH_2SCH_2CH(NH_2)COOH \xrightarrow[NH_3]{Na} \xrightarrow{O_2} [-SCH_2CH(NH_2)COOH]_2$$

GLUTAMIC ACID:

$$CH_2=CHCN + NH_2CH(CO_2C_2H_5)_2 \xrightarrow{KOH} NCCH_2CH_2C(NH_2)(CO_2C_2H_5)_2$$

$$NCCH_2CH_2C(NH_2)(CO_2C_2H_5)_2 + H_2O \xrightarrow{H_2SO_4} HO_2CCH_2CH(NH_2)COOH$$

ORNITHINE:

$$CH_2=CHCN + CH_3CONHCH(CO_2C_2H_5)_2 \xrightarrow{Na} \underset{\overset{|}{CH_2CH_2CN}}{CH_3CONHC(CO_2C_2H_5)_2}$$

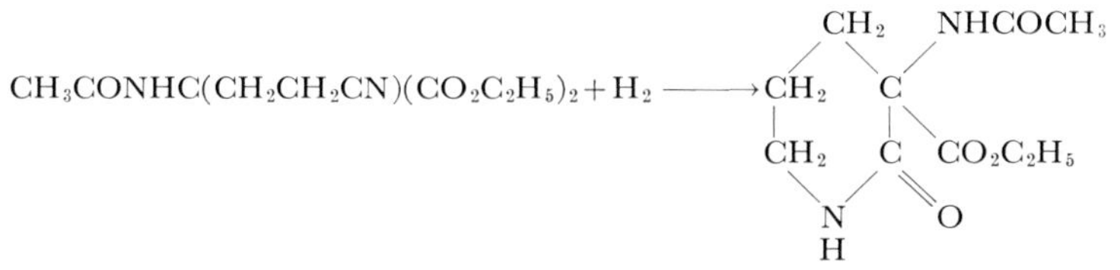

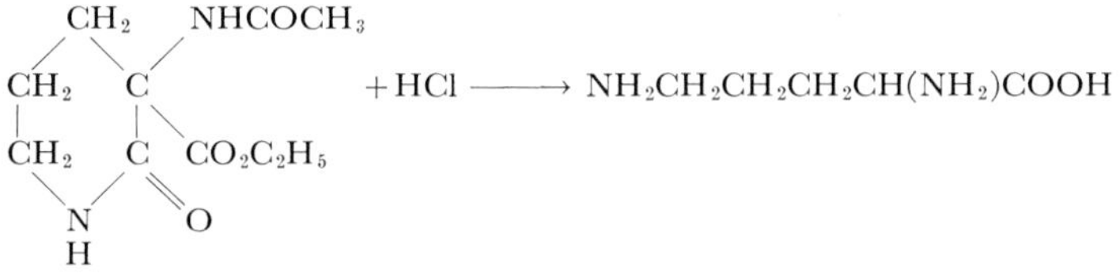

$$CH_3CONHC(CH_2CH_2CN)(CO_2C_2H_5)_2 + H_2 \longrightarrow$$

$$\begin{array}{c} CH_2 \quad NHCOCH_3 \\ CH_2 \quad C \\ CH_2 \quad C \quad CO_2C_2H_5 \\ N \quad O \\ H \end{array}$$

$$\begin{array}{c} CH_2 \quad NHCOCH_3 \\ CH_2 \quad C \\ CH_2 \quad C \quad CO_2C_2H_5 \\ N \quad O \\ H \end{array} + HCl \longrightarrow NH_2CH_2CH_2CH_2CH(NH_2)COOH$$

Dyes

Many of the various nitriles, amides, acids, and esters prepared via cyanoethylation reactions may prove useful as intermediates in the synthesis of dyes (664, 1078). Scarlet dyes, which are particularly useful for the dyeing of cellulose acetate fibers, and which are exceptionally fast to the action of light and gas, may be prepared from the product of the cyanoethylation of N-(2-hydroxyethyl)aniline (327).

Two such dyes have the following structures:

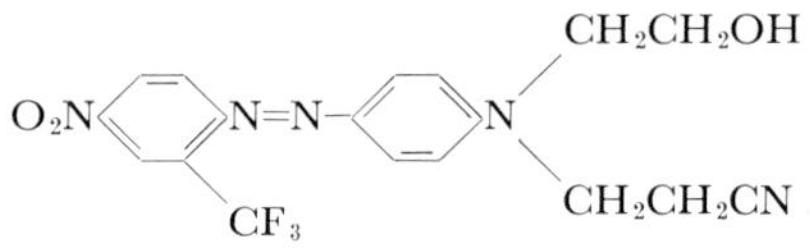

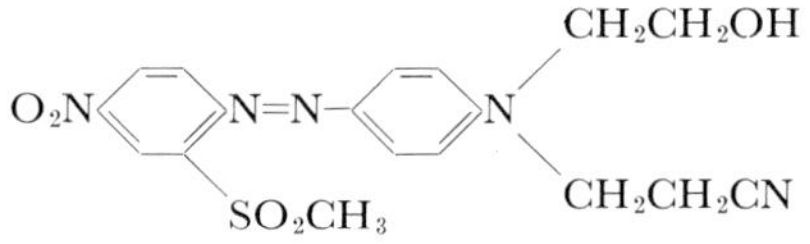

Compounds made by the intramolecular condensation of aromatic aminopropionitriles are also of interest in the dye industry (571). Compounds of the type, RCH_2CH_2CN, where R is phenylmethylamino, 1-carbazolyl or 1-(1,2,3,4-tetrahydro)quinolyl residues, can be used for these syntheses.

Electrical Industries

Cable and wire insulation can be made from acrylonitrile-alkyl acrylate copolymers (1393) as well as from acrylonitrile-butadiene rubbers alone (725, 831), or blended with poly(vinyl chloride) (3, 65), poly(vinylidene chloride) (425), poly(isobutylene) (144), or vinyl chloride-vinyl acetate copolymer (1127). Insulating materials can be obtained from polyacrylonitrile blended with polyacrylates, from acrylonitrile-halogenated styrene copolymers (150), from acrylonitrile-vinyl ester copolymers after treatment with an aldehyde or ketone (302), from a heated mixture of a polyacrylate and polyacrylonitrile (832), or from a heated mixture of a polyacrylate, polyacrylonitrile, and an alkyd or phenol-aldehyde resin.

An acrylonitrile-butyl acrylate-methacrylic acid terpolymer, blended with a urea- or melamine-formaldehyde resin, is useful as an insulating coating for magnetic wire (1396).

A styrene-based thermoplastic casting composition, for the potting of electrical components, is improved by incorporating from 1 to 30% acrylonitrile (686). The electrical properties of the resin have been reported for 5% acrylonitrile content (358).

A dielectric paper, made of cyanoethylated wood cellulose, can be used in capacitors (776). Highly cyanoethylated cellulose, an amorphous, thermoplastic material, has an unusually high dielectric constant (13.3 at 60 cycles and 25°C.) (1324). Polyacrylonitrile fibers are finding use for electrical insulation (349).

An electrically conductive rubber can be prepared by incorporating a conductive carbon black into a solution of acrylonitrile-butadiene copolymer in methyl ethyl ketone, evaporating the ketone, and curing (653).

Emulsifying Agents

The cyanoethyl ethers obtained by the reaction of cellulose (127), starch (126) or gums (784) with acrylonitrile are useful as thickening, emulsifying and dispersing agents. Their use in textile sizes and insecticidal sprays has been recommended (126, 127). Oxidized cyanoethylated casein can be used as a substitute for gelatin in peptizing silver-halide dispersions (1325). The use of cyanoethylated proteins as emulsion stabilizers for butadiene-styrene coating compositions has been reported (1335).

The preparation of quaternary ammonium compounds, having the general structure $RCONH(CH_2)_3NR_3Cl$, involves the cyanoethylation of a dialkylamine as an intermediate step in their synthesis. They have excellent wetting, emulsifying and germicidal properties (265).

Polyacrylonitrile is useful as a thickening agent for organic detergents (858).

It has been discovered (32) that 3-methoxypropylamine, which is prepared by hydrogenation of the methyl alcohol-acrylonitrile addition product, is useful in preparing soaps from fatty acids in which the amine serves as the basic constituent. These soaps show excellent emulsifying and dispersing action for certain natural and synthetic resins and waxes. Such emulsions and dispersions are useful in floor finishes, water paints, textile finishes and in similar fields of application. The use of this amine is particularly advantageous for these purposes because its aqueous solutions do not change greatly in composition on evaporation. Approximately constant alkalinity is thus maintained as films containing these materials are allowed to dry.

Fibers

ACRYLIC FIBERS

The importance of acrylonitrile in the synthetic fiber industry is indicated by the fact that approximately 100 million pounds were consumed in 1957. Outstanding physical properties together with moderate cost, have enabled these fibers to find increasingly broader application.

A list of properties and an outline of the uses these properties suggest follow (895, 910, 1336):

Properties

Resistance to stretch

Resistance to heat

Resistance to sunlight and outdoor exposure

Resistance to microorganisms

Resistance to insects

Resistance to chemical attack

High strength

Dimensional stability to dry- and wet-cleaning

Low moisture absorption

Rapid drying

High flex life

Good recovery from wrinkling

Silk-like luster, hand, and drape

Warm feel or "hand"

Adaptability to standard equipment

Excellent bonding to rubber and resins

Good electrical properties

Ability to be set by heat

High covering power and bulk

Uses

Acid resistant clothing

Anode bags

Aprons

Auto tops

Awnings

Bags for chemicals

Bathing suits

Blankets

Blouses

Bristles

Carpets

Conveyor aprons

Electrical insulation

Felts

Filtration cloths

Fish nets

Hosiery

Jersey fabrics

Laundry nets

Lingerie

Linings

Outdoor furniture

Overcoats

Paint-roller covers

Pile fabrics

Pipe covering

Rainwear

Sewing thread

Sheets for hospital beds

Shirts

Shock-resistant rope

Shower curtains

Suits and dresses

Sweaters

Tarpaulins

Tire cords

Tropical clothing

Umbrellas

Uniforms

Upholstery

Yacht sails

Polyacrylonitrile itself does not dissolve in the usual spinning solvents. Therefore, some of its more soluble copolymers were first used, e.g., those with a high proportion of vinyl chloride, which are soluble in acetone. The resulting fibers are better than the older vinyl chloride-vinyl acetate fibers with respect to resistance to solvents, dye affinity, and shrinking and softening temperatures (161, 941).

In the form of staple fibers the vinyl chloride-acrylonitrile copolymers have many advantages over wool. They are strong and resilient, warm, dyeable, and resistant to combustion. Moreover, they are unattacked by moths or mildew, are non-shrinkable, and are resistant to solvents, acids and alkalis.

With the discovery of solvents suitable for spinning polyacrylonitrile and its copolymers, the development of a number of commercial fibers of high acrylonitrile content has taken place. A great many patents have issued within the past few years on new copolymers containing about 85-90% acrylonitrile. The comonomers have usually been added to increase dye or moisture affinity of the fiber. In general, the copolymers retain the desirable physical properties of polyacrylonitrile. Several excellent reviews have covered this rapidly expanding acrylic fiber field (462, 648, 649, 1083).

It has been reported that mixtures of acrylonitrile copolymers and fully cyanoethylated cellulose can be spun from a common solvent (1365).

Natural Fibers

An important chemical modification of cotton may be achieved by cyanoethylation of the hydroxyl groups to such an extent that a nitrogen content of 3 to 4% is obtained (261). Fiber appearance, tensile strength, and elongation are not appreciably changed. However, a marked improvement in resistance to microorganisms, heat degradation and acid degradation is obtained. In general, the affinity for most direct dyes decreases as the nitrogen content of cyanoethylated cotton increases, whereas the affinity for acetate and acid dyes increases (261, 1261).

It is expected that cyanoethylated cotton will find uses in thread, cord, rope, nets and textiles where its improved chemical, physical, and biological properties are needed (1236, 1243). Some of the end uses which are being considered for this modified cotton are:

Enameling duck	Ironing-board covers
Filter fabrics	Sand bags
Fishing lines and nets	Tents and tarpaulins
Industrial belting	Tobacco shade-cloth

Other cellulosic fibers such as manila, sisal and jute can be made rot resistant by cyanoethylation, and may find applications in marine uses (1, 1228, 1236).

Cyanoethylation increases the affinity of wool for cationic and direct dyes (1212).

Graphic Arts

Copolymers of acrylamide, acrylic acid, and the acrylates with acrylonitrile can be used as gelatin replacements in making photographic emulsions (97, 570, 708). A copolymer of acrylonitrile with vinylidene chloride and itaconic acid is useful as a layer between gelatin-silver halide emulsions and the paper-film backing (1045). In addition, a black, opaque, paper backing for film is obtained, by coating with an acrylonitrile-vinylidene chloride copolymer in which carbon black is dispersed (652).

Terpolymers of acrylonitrile, acrylic esters, and vinylpyridines or vinyl quinolines are reported to be useful mordants for acid-photographic dyes. The terpolymers are used in layers or coatings to prevent diffusion of the dyes (1263). Acrylonitrile-butyl acrylate-N-methyl methacrylamide terpolymers can be used as protective coatings on the viewing surface of photographic elements such as prints, negatives and positive transparencies (1404, 1406).

A process for printing designs on fabric by a decalcomania technique employs an emulsion of polyacrylonitrile on the fabric to be printed (1173).

Mixtures of polyacrylonitrile and polystyrene (510), as well as copolymers of acrylonitrile and styrene (509), are reported to be useful for making solvent-resistant printing plates. Acrylonitrile-butadiene rubber has been suggested as a facing for offset printing blankets (618) and other rolls or plates subjected to the action of printing inks (619).

An acrylonitrile-styrene emulsion which has been subjected to alkaline hydrolysis is useful as a thickener for printing pastes (535).

A resin vehicle for fast-drying printing inks can be obtained by heating an esterified mixture of tall oil and polycarboxylic acid with styrene and acrylonitrile monomers (967). Acrylonitrile-butadiene (752) or acrylonitrile-styrene copolymers (968) can be incorporated into printing ink compositions (752).

Insecticides

Acrylonitrile and several of its derivatives are excellent fumigants for use against a variety of insects (356, 631, 771, 1052). Either alone, or mixed with carbon tetrachloride, acrylonitrile gives high penetration and kill against the tobacco moth and cigarette beetle in stored tobacco (78, 79, 1052, 1060), and against the confused flour beetle in stored grain (275, 276, 429, 701, 920, 1004, 1052). Acrylonitrile is also an effective fumigant for combatting rice weevil (275, 771). It is reportedly useful for Aphis rumicis (771), citrus red spider (771), resistant California red scale (771), citrus mealy bug (771), southern army worm (771), oriental fruit fly (70, 700), and the common household insects (428, 429, 771) such as the carpet beetle, cockroach and clothes moth. However, it should be noted that there was some damage to the plants involved in these experiments. A mixture of acrylonitrile and carbon tetrachloride also is valuable in the fumigation of stored seeds. The fumigant appears to kill effectively without any injurious effect upon the germination (430).

The cyanoethyl ester of diethylphosphorodithioic acid is an effective insecticide for the German roach, the milkweed bug, the American roach and the common housefly (87). A large number of halogenated derivatives of acrylonitrile, such as 2-chloroacrylonitrile, have been tested and found to be effective as fumigants for grain-infesting- and household-insects (311). Polyacrylonitrile, 3,3′-oxydipropionitrile (from water and acrylonitrile), and 4-acetyl-4-(2-cyanoethyl)pimelonitrile (from acetone and acrylonitrile) are said to be effective against pea aphids (756).

Leather

Leather-like sheets can be prepared from a blend of acrylonitrile-butadiene copolymer, clay and polyvinyl chloride (973); from a mat of non-woven fibers such as polyacrylonitrile fibers plus a binder, such as an acrylonitrile copolymer (439); or from a blend of phenol-formaldehyde resin and butadiene-acrylonitrile copolymer (1183). Acrylonitrile-butadiene rubber, after heating with a blowing agent and then leaching, gives a moisture- and vapor-permeable leather substitute (845).

Acrylonitrile-butadiene latex is claimed to be a useful finishing agent (115, 374) for natural leather.

Paper

Acrylonitrile rubbers are useful for imparting water and oil resistance to paper, and for providing paper with increased burst factors, tensile strength, elongation, stiffness and sizing resistance. Porosity is decreased (844). Acrylonitrile-butadiene latices can be incorporated into paper, either before sheet formation (28, 55, 115, 121, 683, 854, 1093, 1401) or afterwards (115, 282, 292, 1093, 1109). In the former case, treatment may be effected by the use of alum, or by some other means of precipitation of the latex, so that the rubber particles adhere firmly to the cellulose filaments. Sheets produced from the paper treated in this way are hard and tough and have high density. Incorporation of a mixture of acrylonitrile-butadiene latex and phenol-aldehyde resin, before sheet formation, is said to produce a paper with exceptional stiffness (1401). Paper sheets impregnated by either dry- or wet-web saturation techniques are soft and possess high edge tear resistance, excellent wet strength, low density, high elongation and good fold and drape properties (115). The BARDAC Process can be used for stock addition of synthetic rubber latices to paper and paperboard (28). Mineral pigments and clays can be dispersed in the latex when coating paper sheet (747, 1031).

Papers containing acrylonitrile rubber are very useful as gasket material (1093), protective wrappings, shelf coverings, imitation leather bases, tape backing and other specialized uses (115). A further advantage lies in their compatibility with other vinyl resins. Coatings of these vinyl latices can, therefore, be applied to paper saturated with acrylonitrile-butadiene rubber without the use of additional adhesives (115).

Paper made from polyacrylonitrile fibers is three to ten times as strong as paper made from pulp or rags and may, therefore, find specialized uses (839).

Paper which possesses valuable dielectric properties for capacitor construction (776) has been made from cyanoethylated wood pulp. Cyanoethylation also improves the dimensional stability (1228) and printability (1235) of paper, and renders it rotproof (1).

Acrylonitrile can be polymerized on the surface of paper to impart a beneficial polyacrylonitrile coating (227).

Plastics

Polyacrylonitrile itself is difficult to mold because of its lack of flow. Copolymers of acrylonitrile, on the other hand, have been prepared with good molding characteristics. In general, introduction of acrylonitrile into copolymers increases hardness, solvent resistance and softening temperature. Lack of flow in the high-nitrile copolymers may be overcome by the use of plasticizers.

Copolymers with Acrylates

Copolymers of acrylonitrile with ethyl acrylate have been suggested for impregnating filling material for upholstery (510), and for covering gloves for amputees (291, 689, 828), while those with methyl methacrylate are useful in oilcloth, linoleum, wall panels, etc. (564).

The bulk copolymerization of acrylonitrile and methyl methacrylate gives a thermoplastic product with unusual mechanical endurance. This property makes it outstandingly useful, for example, in arch supports, or in shuttles (566).

A three-component copolymer of acrylonitrile, butyl acrylate and vinyl acetate, blended by milling with vinyl acetate-butyl acrylate copolymer, produces flexible films particularly suited for rainwear, shoe soles, and food wrapping. Reportedly, the blend has good stiffness-temperature characteristics (222). A product of similar properties and applications results from ternary copolymerization of acrylonitrile, 2-ethylhexyl acrylate and vinyl chloride (955).

Blends of acrylonitrile-ethyl acrylate copolymers with melamine-formaldehyde resins yield tough, dimensionally-stable molded products resistant to crazing and possessing good electrical properties. Low mold shrinkage (e.g., 5.1 mils per inch) and low water absorption also are claimed (1165).

A three-component copolymer of acrylonitrile, methyl methacrylate and methacrylamide has excellent tensile and impact strength as well as good solvent resistance (91).

Copolymers with Butadiene

The rubbery acrylonitrile-butadiene copolymers have proved to be highly valuable modifying ingredients in both thermoplastic and thermosetting resins.

Acrylonitrile-butadiene copolymers containing larger amounts of acrylonitrile than are used in synthetic rubbers are tough, leathery and oil resistant (496, 983). By blending these copolymers with acrylonitrile-styrene copolymers, a thermoplastic product of considerable versatility is produced (286, 304, 305, 1112, 1129, 1269). This material can be pigmented, molded, cemented, riveted, drilled, sawed, turned, cold-punched, buffed and polished. It has high-impact strength and is resistant to solvents and to most alkalis and acids. It is waterproof, mildew-proof, vermin-proof, odorless, washable, and light in weight, and it is warm to the touch even at low temperatures. Its use in golf-club heads, luggage, radio and typewriter cases, molded cams, gears, pipe fittings, door knobs, golf-bag bottoms, sun helmets, instrument cases, refrigerator strips, panels and food trays has been recommended (286, 1112, 1129). When natural rubber (Hevea) is added to the above blend of copolymers the resulting ternary blend is particularly useful in relatively heavy, semi-rigid sheetings. These can be used as flat panels, or post-formed into curved panellings for automotive interiors, automotive wheel housings and formed luggage shells, as well as sinks, drainboards and counter tops. The finished articles are tough, dimensionally stable and impact resistant (907).

When an acrylonitrile-butadiene elastomer is blended with polystyrene the product exhibits low acid- and water-absorption and high impact strength. Storage-battery containers molded from this blend withstand cycles of hot-and-cold exposure well, and have an impact strength ten times that of containers made from polystyrene alone (335). The addition of a peroxide during the blending of the elastomer with the polystyrene improves the tensile- and impact-strength of the product (329). Instead of blending polystyrene with acrylonitrile-butadiene elastomer, the latter can be dissolved in monomeric styrene and the mixture polymerized. The product is a homogenous interpolymer which can easily be molded (40).

A lower-density thermoplastic copolymer of acrylonitrile, butadiene, and styrene has high tensile and impact strength (782).

Improved mechanical properties of films and molded articles of poly(vinyl chloride) are obtained when butadiene-acrylonitrile copolymers are used as plasticizers (855, 919, 996, 1262). Films of such a blend are eminently suitable for food wrapping (996). The insolubility and inertness of the elastomer are particularly advantageous in this application (688). Suitable food-wrapping films are also obtained with a ternary blend of acrylonitrile-butadiene copolymer, acrylonitrile-vinyl chloride copolymer and polychloroprene (997), and with a blend of acrylonitrile-butadiene copolymer with vinyl chloride-vinylidene chloride copolymer (212). When acrylonitrile-butadiene elastomer is compounded with vinyl chloride-vinyl acetate copolymer, and other additives, a long-wearing phonograph-record composition results (852). A tear-resistant porous-sheet material, used in shoe inner soles, is obtained with a blend of acrylonitrile-butadiene elastomer and poly(vinyl chloride) (1262).

A blend of rubber hydrochloride, butadiene-acrylonitrile rubber and a plasticizer is said to be particularly useful for preparing packaging film for oily foodstuffs, such as lard or margarine (1118).

Molded parts made with phenolic resins, although strong, are inherently brittle. Nitrile rubbers, unlike most other rubbers, are compatible with phenolic resins. Blends of acrylonitrile-butadiene rubber (containing about 90% acrylonitrile) with highly modified phenolic resins have found many commercial uses (286, 724, 823, 1163, 1199). Low-cost, "low-impact" fillers, such as wood flour and asbestos, can be used to give high-impact moldings using these phenolic-rubber blends. The use of mineral fillers permits manufacture of parts with exceptionally good electrical and other physical properties (286). Employment of the nitrile rubber permits phenolic moldings of greater hardness than can usually be obtained without excessive pigment loading (392). The products are more resistant to the effects of high temperature and oxidation, and have much better low-temperature flexibility than the highly loaded compounds of equivalent hardness. Other properties, such as impact strength and water absorption, are also improved (392, 1199). The use of these blends in pipe and pipe fittings is growing. The material can be cut and threaded using standard equipment (724).

High-density molded articles can be formed from blends of nitrile rubber and cork (245, 1155). A joint-sealing composition composed of coal-tar pitch, nitrile rubber and polymerized castor oil has high resistance to jet fuels, as well as high solvent resistance generally (773).

Copolymers with Isobutylene

Copolymerization of acrylonitrile with isobutylene gives products containing 70% acrylonitrile having a flow temperature of 105°C. These copolymers are suitable for molding, and for the impregnation and coating of textiles (346, 1107).

A three-component copolymer of acrylonitrile, isobutylene and vinylidene chloride is extrudable at 150°C. under 50 pounds pressure. With a plasticizer, this copolymer may be pressed at 180°C. to give a clear disk which does not become brittle on prolonged storage (1022). Acrylonitrile-isobutylene copolymers can be plasticized with ketone-aldehyde condensation products, thereby reducing the flow temperature. Other physical properties are unimpaired (1056).

Copolymers with Styrene and Substituted Styrenes

Acrylonitrile-styrene copolymers are easily molded (67) to give products which have much better tensile strength than ordinary polystyrene (221, 223, 303, 451, 524, 742). The flexural and impact strengths are also improved. These copolymers possess improved resistance to abrasion and heat, greater outdoor durability and better resistance to oils and solvents. They also exhibit less after-crazing due to unrelieved molding stresses, and improved insert reduction (1140). Printing plates prepared from acrylonitrile-styrene copolymers show good hardness, great toughness, complete insolubility in benzene, and good stability to motor fuel (509).

Cyanamid's Cymac* 201 methylstyrene and acrylonitrile copolymer is reported to give moldings with high tensile and flexural strengths, high heat-distortion temperature, and good craze-, abrasion-, and chemical-resistance (223, 1338, 1339).

Acrylonitrile-isopropenyltoluene copolymers have also been reported to be desirable molding materials (669).

A third monomer such as p-vinylbiphenyl (987), maleic anhydride (988), acrylic acid (1217), or acenaphthylene (1225), can be included to produce thermoplastic molding compositions. A thermosetting material, useful as a binder for mica, results from the four-component copolymerization of acrylonitrile, styrene, maleic anhydride and diallyl phthalate (777).

Copolymers with Other Monomers

Thermoplastic molding compounds may be prepared from copolymers of acrylonitrile with vinyl acetate (461), vinyl acetate plus methacrylonitrile (896), vinyl chloride (417), vinylidene chloride (379, 480, 616, 790, 908), allyl isocyanate (955) and α-methylstyrene (1111).

Copolymers of acrylonitrile and N-2-norcamphanylacrylamide are useful in the preparation of tough, high melting films, sheets and molded products (1220).

Cyanoethylated Cellulose

With the introduction of two or more cyanoethyl groups per anhydroglucose unit, cellulose is converted into an amorphous, thermoplastic prod-

---
*Reg. U. S. Pat. Off.

uct. This material is soluble in organic solvents such as acetone, acrylonitrile, dimethylformamide and pyridine. It can be molded, spun into fibers and cast into films (1, 551, 714, 1324, 1365). It has an unusually high dielectric constant (1324).

Plasticizers

Acrylonitrile-butadiene elastomers are plasticizers for polyvinyl and polyvinylidene chlorides and other vinyl polymers (3, 131, 340, 384, 392, 423, 613, 899, 918, 919, 977, 1182). Problems of staining, plasticizer bloom, and of evaporation or lacquer lifting are avoided when this plasticizer is used (392). Nitrile rubber is also useful as a modifier for phenol-, urea-, and melamine-formaldehyde resins (574). Polyacrylonitrile also can be used as a modifier for these same resins (348, 466, 672). Other copolymers of acrylonitrile reportedly useful in plasticizing vinyl polymers are: acrylonitrile-butadiene-isobutylene terpolymer (77), acrylonitrile-ethyl acrylate copolymer (901), and a three-component polymer of acrylonitrile, butyl acrylate and nitropropane (385).

Acrylonitrile and succinonitrile have been suggested as flow promoters for a blend of epoxy resin and poly(vinyl acetate) (1151). Alkoxypropionitriles plasticize vinyl chloride-vinylidene chloride copolymers (377, 378), and the esters derived from these nitriles also have plasticizing properties. 4-Acylbutyric esters, made by the cyanoethylation of various ketones (130, 176, 395, 898), are particularly useful as plasticizers for vinyl resins such as poly(vinyl chloride). Plasticizers also result from esterification of cyanoethylated alcohols of various types (31). The cyanoethylation products of substituted malonic esters can be used to plasticize vinyl resins (397), while cyanoethylated rosin amines plasticize synthetic rubbers (625). The product of cyanoethylation of ketone-aldehyde condensates can be used to plasticize acrylonitrile-isobutylene copolymers (1056). The reaction products of acrylonitrile with α- and β-tung oil fatty acids are secondary plasticizers for vinyl chloride-vinyl acetate copolymers (1286).

Rubber

Production of rubber goods from acrylonitrile-butadiene copolymers constitutes one of the most important end uses for acrylonitrile. Methods of compounding such rubbers, and descriptions of their properties and uses, are detailed at great length in the patent literature, and are summarized in a number of books and articles (114, 191, 362, 392, 741, 819, 939, 1144).

The rubbers are usually made from acrylonitrile-butadiene copolymers which contain 15-55% by weight acrylonitrile. These rubbers possess high resistance to the swelling action of solvents, oils and greases, far surpassing natural rubber or GR-S products in this respect. In addition, they possess excellent resistance to heat, aging and sunlight (392). Depending upon the methods of compounding, a great variety of rubbers characterized by high tensile strength, excellent elongation, and low-compression set can be produced. Certain formulations provide a combination of low-temperature flexibility and oil resistance, and so are particularly useful for rubber parts operating in coolants. Acrylonitrile rubbers also can be made to have high abrasion resistance, low coefficients of friction, non-corrosiveness to metals, non-adherence to metals, good electrical conductivity and compatibility with vinyl and phenolic resins. It is not possible to have maximum values for all of these properties in one single rubber; but, by proper mixing and compounding, many valuable combinations of these properties can be achieved.

Acrylonitrile-butadiene rubbers are suitable for use at temperatures as high as 250°F., and, if operation in the presence of oxygen is not required, they may be used at temperatures above 300°F. However, elevated temperatures combined with long exposure tend to harden the rubber and reduce its elongation. Low temperatures cause nitrile rubber to become brittle. However, by using certain plasticizers, such as dioctyl adipate, the freeze point can be extended down to as low as −60°F. Long immersion in oil, gasoline, vegetable- and animal-fats and oils, paint- and ink-driers, alcohol or glycol, even at 250°F. or higher, causes little or no change in volume, or in other physical properties of the rubber. For these reasons the acrylonitrile rubbers have found extensive use in parts exposed to petroleum products, coolants, hydraulic fluids and similar liquids. They have been found to be particularly useful for (392):

Gaskets	Non-slip, non-marking soles
Grommets	and heels
Industrial hose of all kinds	Creamery equipment
Mountings for machinery	Rubber-covered rolls for
Vibration-damping	textile, leather, printing,
equipment mountings	paper industries
and couplings	Printing blankets and mats
Shock-absorbing equipment	Special parts for machinery
Adhesives	requiring resistance to
Jackets for electric cables,	oils or fats
connectors and terminal	Pump and valve linings
fittings	Kitchen and plumbing
Conveyor belting	accessories

Protective clothing

Acrylonitrile-butadiene copolymers can be compounded into either hard- or sponge-rubbers. It is even possible to produce a rubber which is both hard and cellular, and which possesses some very unusual properties (392). This material weighs only 6-8 pounds per cubic foot, yet it has a compressive strength of several hundred pounds per square inch. Water, oil, gasoline and many other liquids are not absorbed, and it will withstand temperatures of 200°F. Its strength-to-weight ratio is one of the highest among commercial materials. It is particularly valuable as insulation against heat, sound, and electricity (392).

Compounding an acrylonitrile-butadiene rubber with a vinyl chloride-vinyl acetate copolymer results in a unicellular foam-rubber with excellent shock-absorbing properties (1381).

Acrylonitrile-butadiene rubbers with special chemical or physical properties may be obtained by polymerizing vinyl monomers within the rubber during cold mastication (1198). Free radicals produced by chain rupture during mastication act as initiators for the polymerization.

The properties of acrylonitrile-butadiene rubbers can be modified by blending the copolymers with natural or synthetic polymers before vulcanization. For example, blending with an equal weight of ethoxyethylcellulose gives vulcanizates with excellent oil and sunlight resistance (424).

Chloroprene and fluoroprene produce rubbery, vulcanizable products when copolymerized with acrylonitrile. The freeze resistance and resilience of the fluoroprene vulcanizate is superior to the corresponding chloroprene formulation (780).

Vulcanizable copolymers of acrylonitrile and acrylic esters also have been obtained. While the tensile strengths of the vulcanizates are lower than those from acrylonitrile-butadiene copolymers, the strengths are still well above the serviceable minimum. The heat resistance of several of these compositions is good, judging from the fact that only small changes in the brittle point take place on aging 72 hours at 350°F. (389).

Rubbery materials which resist swelling in fluorinated (as well as non-fluorinated) solvents can be prepared by copolymerization of acrylonitrile with 1,1-dihydroperfluorobutyl acrylate (10).

A number of rubbery three-component polymers have been prepared which are said to possess advantages over acrylonitrile-butadiene copolymers. A terpolymer of acrylonitrile, butadiene and vinylidene chloride has a better combination of tensile- and elongation-characteristics and lower permanent-set values than acrylonitrile-butadiene rubbers. This three-component polymer also has good resistance to aromatic hydrocarbons, good tear strength and desirable electrical properties (1020). A mixture of vinyl esters of soya-bean-oil acids has been used as a modifying third monomer in acrylonitrile-butadiene rubber compositions (1130). Acrylonitrile-butadiene rubber copolymers of controlled gel content (as indicated by the portion insoluble in methyl ethyl ketone) can be prepared by adding small amounts of divinylbenzene to the partially polymerized mixture of monomers. The rubbery product is particularly suitable for blending with thermoplastic polymers, such as polystyrene or styrene-acrylonitrile copolymer, to improve the impact strength (936). Cross-linking is prevented or retarded during the copolymerization of acrylates with dienes by the addition of small amounts of acrylonitrile which acts as a polymerization regulator. The products can be vulcanized to give synthetic rubbers (394). A three-component copolymer of acrylonitrile, butadiene and 2-methyl-5-vinylpyridine, quaternized during vulcanization, is said to possess better oil- and chemical-resistance and better tensile strength characteristics than acrylonitrile-butadiene copolymers (1414).

Soil Aggregating Agents

Partial alkaline hydrolysis of polyacrylonitrile produces a polyelectrolyte which is predominantly a salt of polyacrylic acid. When the sodium, ammonium or calcium salts of hydrolyzed polyacrylonitrile are added to certain soils of poor structure, aggregation of soil particles occurs. Such additives are said to improve soil aeration, moisture retention, rate of germination of seeds and yield of crops (88, 132, 228, 410, 490, 491, 492, 748, 805, 806, 1010, 1058, 1204, 1353, 1444). In addition, erosion of soil during run-off of rainfall is greatly reduced (229, 1010, 1132).

Outdoor piles of finely-divided mineral matter frequently create a dust problem. This can be avoided by spraying the piles with a solution of hydrolyzed polyacrylonitrile. A thin crust is formed which is resistant to erosion by wind and rainfall (38). Aqueous suspensions of mineral fines may be flocculated by the same product (770).

Calcium acrylate, which can be prepared from acrylonitrile via acrylic acid, has been polymerized in soil to improve load-bearing characteristics (236).

Solvents

The solubilizing characteristics of the nitrile and ester groups, either of which can be introduced into a molecule by cyanoethylation, make acrylonitrile a particularly valuable intermediate for the preparation of solvents. Acrylonitrile itself is a polar solvent, largely water-insoluble, and should be considered for the extraction of polar molecules from aqueous solutions. Propene and propane can be separated by a solvent composed of acetonitrile, acrylonitrile and water (1082). The alkoxypropionitriles and alkylaminopropionitriles, obtained by the cyanoethylation of alcohols and amines, possess excellent solvent properties (31, 716). They are miscible with all the common organic solvents. Alkoxypropionitriles will dissolve poly(vinyl acetate), poly(vinyl chloride), polymethacrylates and vinyl chloride-vinyl acetate copolymers, as well as other polymeric materials. Cyanoethylated ethanolamines dissolve nitrocellulose and similar substances (521).

3,3'-Oxydipropionitrile, 3,3'-iminodipropionitrile and 3,3'-thiodipropionitrile are particularly useful solvents (953). They have the property of selectively dissolving aromatic or other highly unsaturated materials in the presence of aliphatics. The use of the thio- and oxydipropionitriles in this application has been investigated in detail, and their superiority to diethylene glycol has been demonstrated in several systems (1002).

Surface Coatings

Acrylonitrile will copolymerize in emulsion with a wide variety of other monomers to produce film-forming resins, useful in surface-coating compositions. The properties which the introduction of acrylonitrile exerts upon the film characteristics of polymers and copolymers are the following (294):

Tack freeness	Very low elongation
Hardness and toughness	Very low water absorption
Very high tensile strength	High resistance to saponification

Many applications in the surface-coatings field have been found for copolymers of acrylonitrile with a few specific comonomers, as discussed below.

COPOLYMERS WITH BUTADIENE

Coating Compositions for Fabrics

A blend of an acrylonitrile-butadiene copolymer with a chlorinated polyethylene and polychloroprene is the essential ingredient in a coating composition for upholstery fabrics. The coating is flexible at low temperatures, shows good abrasion resistance and does not exhibit tackiness at elevated temperatures (380). A composition similar to the above is suitable for coating one side of a flexible base (350).

Compositions recommended for coating glass fibers contain an acrylonitrile-butadiene copolymer alone (208) or combined with poly(tetrafluoroethylene) (1223). The coated fibers are heated to set the copolymer, and then are treated with a water-repellent. Fabric made from these fibers can be washed, dry-cleaned and handled similarly to common fabrics.

Acrylonitrile-butadiene copolymers are useful in making printing pastes for glass fabrics (682).

Acrylonitrile-butadiene latex, following reaction with sulfur dioxide, is useful as a coating resin for textiles, paper and wood (553).

Thermoplastic binders containing copolymers of acrylonitrile and butadiene find use in a surface coating applied by a specifically designed roller-coating apparatus (793).

Synthetic fabrics of a leather-like nature can be prepared from glass fibers, butadiene-acrylonitrile copolymer, a phenolic resin and methyl phenyl-polysiloxane (116).

Coating Compositions for Metals

Water suspensions of a vinyl chloride polymer and an acrylonitrile-butadiene rubber form strong films on many materials when dried at room temperature. Their use as protective coatings for non-ferrous metals and alloys has been suggested (401).

Metal surfaces are protected from corrosive attack and abrasion by a strippable coating comprising an inner rubbery layer 0.002-0.1 inch thick (such as acrylonitrile-butadiene copolymer) and a thicker outer layer of asphaltic material (981).

Coatings for Miscellaneous Surfaces

A coating composition for use on floors and similar surfaces is made from shellac, a terpene phenolic resin, butadiene-acrylonitrile copolymer and a dispersing agent (66).

Non-porous films can be made self-sealing by applying a blend of butadiene-acrylonitrile elastomer and natural rubber (488).

Cracking problems associated with poly(tetrafluoroethylene) dispersion coatings disappear when butadiene-acrylonitrile copolymer is added to the dispersion (518).

An enamel composition having a uniform drying rate is obtained with acrylonitrile-butadiene copolymer, a dispersed pigment, a heavy metal soap dryer and calcium oxide (658).

Acrylonitrile-butadiene copolymers are reportedly useful for mixing with proteins for coatings which are set with ammonia (612).

Priming coats for various surfaces can be formulated by mixing acrylonitrile-butadiene elastomer, another vinyl copolymer and a protein (1141).

Acrylonitrile and butadiene, polymerized in the presence of large mercaptan concentrations, give viscous liquid or semisolid sulfur-containing products useful as drying oils or binding agents (977).

COPOLYMERS WITH STYRENE

Acrylonitrile can be used as a partial replacement for styrene or methylstyrene in styrenated alkyds. The following effects have been shown to result from this replacement: a marked improvement in the resistance of films to mineral spirits and an increased speed of drying. Furthermore, film clarity is better, bronzing and chalking (in pigmented films) is less and resin viscosity is increased (307, 865). Resins of this type are commercially available from American Cyanamid Company under the trademark Cycopol* 320-5.

Three-component polymers of acrylonitrile, styrene and a conjugated diolefin have been incorporated into a recipe for coating paper and fabrics and for blending with asphalts and waxes (1114). These terpolymers are also useful in lacquers and enamels and for coating metal tanks to prevent corrosion.

Coating compositions prepared from a three-component polymer of acrylonitrile, α-methylstyrene and ethyl acrylate have good adhesion to rubber articles, dry tack-free, are flexible and are not rapidly deteriorated by sunlight, ozone or weathering (956).

Nylon fabrics coated with a formulation containing styrene-acrylonitrile copolymer have good gloss, flexibility, surface hardness and wearing ability (856).

When tall oil is heated with a polybasic acid (e.g. maleic or fumaric acid), a polyhydric alcohol (e.g., pentaerythritol), and acrylonitrile- and styrene-monomers, resins are obtained. These resins are useful in paints, lacquers and printing inks (966).

A dispersion of styrene-acrylonitrile copolymer blended with a dispersion of rubbery butadiene-acrylonitrile copolymer gives a highly effective grease-proofing finish to paper. These are applied over a priming coat of a different copolymer (280, 281).

COPOLYMERS WITH VINYLIDENE CHLORIDE

Acrylonitrile-vinylidene chloride resins have a low transfer rate for water and a very low transfer rate for gases such as CO_2 and O_2. Their chemical resistance is, in general, good. When sprayed they form tough, semi-elastomeric, non-flammable films with good hydrocarbon resistance. These coatings have been virtually unaffected in more than two years' service on the interiors and exteriors of oil refinery equipment, including tanks and pipes (810, 909).

Copolymers of acrylonitrile and vinylidene chloride are used in latex paints, and are outstanding for their resistance to a great variety of chemicals and for their toughness. Paints containing these copolymers, plasticized by dibutyl phthalate, exhibit excellent wear. The paints are outstanding for

---

*Reg. U. S. Pat. Off.

brushability, levelling, and absence of foam. They show promise for use in industrial maintenance and in food processing plants and dairies where grease and food acids cause trouble (7, 502).

A three-component polymer of acrylonitrile, vinylidene chloride and ethyl acrylate has valuable film-forming properties. The films are tough, flexible, moisture-impervious and greaseproof. The lattices may be used to form coatings by electrodeposition in a manner similar to that employed with rubber latex (1021).

Fuel-Resistant Coatings

A Saran-type coating of acrylonitrile-vinylidene chloride copolymer in methyl ethyl ketone was tested for preventing corrosion of the steel cargo tanks of Navy carriers when successive cargoes of gasoline were carried. The coating was brushed on in several coats to a thickness of 0.008 inch. The coatings were estimated from test data to be adequate protection against the corrosion caused by moisture, salt-water ballast, and gasoline for four years, and it was estimated that life expectancy could be extended indefinitely by touch-ups at four-year intervals (285). Other authors have also reported (283, 811, 906) that acrylonitrile-vinylidene chloride copolymers are acceptable as linings for fuel tanks. The copolymers may be applied as such to steel. In lining concrete, it is best utilized as an overcoating for a more extensible material such as polysulfide rubber.

Moistureproof Coatings

Coatings of acrylonitrile-vinylidene chloride copolymers on rubber hydrochloride film increase the resistance to passage of gases such as oxygen, nitrogen and carbon dioxide. This coated film is especially suitable for packaging coffee, milk powder, egg powder, dried yeast, dried fruits, smoked meat and tobacco wherein low oxygen-permeability is desired (215).

Acrylonitrile-vinylidene chloride copolymer, when applied to regenerated cellulose film, gives an excellent moisture-resistant, heat-sealable, durable, flexible, transparent coating (110, 111, 143, 482, 523, 877). The cellulose film can be given a curable base coating before application of the acrylonitrile copolymer (472).

Other similar coating compositions are described as follows:

(a) A water-sensitive, non-fibrous organic material is waterproofed by an aqueous dispersion of a copolymer of vinylidene chloride and acrylonitrile (848).

(b) A moistureproof, heat-sealable, flexible, transparent film is produced by treating regenerated cellulose with a coating of a three-component polymer of acrylonitrile, vinylidene chloride and itaconic acid (876).

(c) A hydrolyzed three-component polymer of acrylonitrile, vinylidene chloride and vinyl acetate gives a strongly adhering coating on regenerated cellulose film without the use of an anchoring subcoat (875).

An acrylonitrile-vinylidene chloride copolymer, formulated with a halogenated hydrocarbon and methyl ethyl ketone, produces film with good heat-sealability at moderately low temperatures (481).

When a vinyl chloride-vinyl acetate copolymer is modified with an acrylonitrile-vinylidene chloride copolymer and a plasticizer, the product is reported to give a sprayable, webbable, strippable and moisture-impervious coating for metals, woods, plastics, rubbers, glass, etc.(531).

Fire-Retardant Coatings

Fire-retardant, intumescent, abrasion-resistant coating compositions have been described. They consist of a latex-like dispersion of an acrylonitrile-vinylidene chloride copolymer, a non-resinous carbon-containing compound, a foaming agent and a urea-formaldehyde resin (1030) or a non-resinous organic nitrogen compound (1408).

COPOLYMERS WITH MISCELLANEOUS MONOMERS

An interior, white, wall paint containing acrylonitrile-ethyl acrylate copolymer gives a film with superior scrub resistance, film hardness, resistance to blistering in water and resistance to solvents (1).

Copolymers of acrylonitrile and maleic anhydride, on reaction with oxazoline and thiazoline compounds, give resinous imido esters useful as coatings (938).

Coating and impregnating compositions prepared from acrylonitrile-trichloroethylene copolymers are suggested for application to wood, textiles, leather, metals, glass, etc. (50).

Coatings and films of acrylonitrile-isobutylene copolymers are said to be tough, resilient, impervious to acids and alkalis and resistant to weathering. These films are further claimed to be dimensionally stable, not shrinking appreciably even in boiling water (355, 709).

Waterproof coatings can be obtained by blending methylenedistearamide with polyamines prepared by reduction of butadiene-acrylonitrile copolymer (734).

Water-based surface coatings resistant to outdoor exposure have been reported. They are prepared from interpolymer latices of acrylonitrile, alkyl acrylates, styrene and acrylic or methacrylic acid (1413).

A three-component polymer of acrylonitrile, butyl acrylate and N-methyl-methacrylamide is useful as a protective coating for photographic prints (1404).

An aqueous wire-enamel composition having good abrasion-, heat- and solvent-resistance is obtained by blending an acrylonitrile-butyl acrylate-methacrylic acid interpolymer with a water-dilutable, heat-reactive synthetic resin (1395, 1396).

Cyanoethylated proteins are said to be useful as emulsion stabilizers for butadiene-styrene coating compositions (1335).

Textiles

Acrylonitrile and its polymers are useful in the treating of fabrics. Wool can be made shrink-resistant by polymerizing acrylonitrile within the fibers (704, 1110, 1434), or by treating with acrylonitrile-vinylaryl isocyanate

(838), acrylonitrile-glycidyl methacrylate (365), acrylonitrile-chloroprene (942, 943) or acrylonitrile-butadiene (944, 1373) copolymers. Although polychloroprene or polybutadiene alone will give this shrinkage control, the presence of up to 20% of copolymerized acrylonitrile improves the feel of the treated wool (942, 943).

Fabrics can be rendered crease-resistant by using a blend of urea-formaldehyde resin with butadiene-acrylonitrile latex (5, 1402) or a blend of melamine-formaldehyde resin with acrylonitrile-alkyl acrylate copolymer (398). Fabrics can be stiffened by polymerizing acrylonitrile on the fabric (227). A similar effect is obtained by impregnating the fabric with a copolymer of acrylonitrile and vinyl chloride or styrene (322, 323). Acrylonitrile-vinyl ester copolymers have also been used to give rigidity to fabrics (645).

Cellulose fabrics can be provided with increased abrasion resistance and a soft, pleasant hand by the application of nitrile latices (4, 517, 1402). Felting resistance is imparted to woolen fabrics by impregnating with a mixture of polybutadiene and acrylonitrile-butadiene copolymer (382). The latter copolymer can also be used to impart run resistance to hosiery (585). Improved adhesion of cloth to rubber (263, 793) and vinyl coatings (820) is imparted by pretreatment of the cloth with nitrile rubber. Sizing properties are claimed for copolymers of acrylonitrile with maleic and fumaric acids (565), for mixtures of polyacrylonitrile and hexamethylenediethylurea (590), for water-soluble cellulose derivatives prepared by cyanoethylation of cellulose xanthate (714) and cellulose esters (713), and for cyanoethylated starch and poly(vinyl alcohol) (714).

Cotton can be rendered mildewproof and, at the same time, more heat-resistant, dyeable and less hygroscopic by cyanoethylation (230, 231, 235, 262, 1019, 1236). The deposition of polyacrylonitrile on and within cotton fibers also renders cotton mildewproof (1229). The acrylonitrile is reported to polymerize and deposit preferentially at the carboxyl groups in the cotton.

Cellulosic fabrics can be made flameproof by treatment with a polymer of cyanoethylated diallyl phosphonate (1438). Alkali-soluble fabrics can be obtained by treating cyanoethylated cotton with chromic acid (1446). Non-woven fabrics are produced by rendering cyanoethylated cellulose fibers adhesive with a suitable solvent (715).

Compositions for printing of textiles include acrylonitrile-butadiene copolymer (115, 413, 419, 441), polyacrylonitrile (1173) and acrylonitrile-vinylidene chloride copolymer (48).

Water-insoluble, alkali-soluble cyanoethyl ethers of cellulose offer possibilities as "scaffolding" threads for cellulosic yarns such as cotton (714, 718). These ethers dissolved in dilute sodium hydroxide can be used for the fixation of pigments, as permanent finishing agents for textiles, as thickeners for printing pastes, for the production of novelty print effects and for the manufacture of non-woven fabrics (277, 714). Water-soluble cyanoethyl ethers of cellulose are useful as sizes for textile yarns since they are more easily removed than starch from woven fabrics in the scouring process.

The addition of copolymers of acrylonitrile and an acrylamide to anionic or nonionic detergents prevents redeposition of soil on textile fabrics during laundering (1428).

Viscosity Modifiers

As described in the Polymerization Section under "Modification of Acrylonitrile Polymers," polyacrylonitrile may be converted by aqueous alkaline hydrolysis into water-soluble polymers. Cyanamid's Cypan* drilling mud conditioner is one such polymer. The viscosity of these resulting polymer solutions is controlled by the molecular weight of the polyacrylonitrile chosen and the degree of hydrolysis obtained.

These water-soluble polymers have found use as additives to control water loss in oil-well drilling muds (392, 1128, 1366). The muds assist in lubricating the bit and in removing cuttings, but the unmodified mud may fail due to water loss and subsequent solidification. Small amounts (about one pound per barrel of mud) of hydrolyzed polyacrylonitrile are effective in retaining the water and in improving wall-building characteristics. A particular advantage of this polymer over some other common additives is its stability at high pH and temperature (1128). A related polymer which performs similarly is the sodium salt of a copolymer of acrylonitrile and acrylic acid (391).

Copolymers of dodecyl methacrylate and acrylonitrile can be added to lubricating oils to improve the temperature-viscosity characteristics (218, 1432). Copolymers of dodecyl fumarate or dodecyl maleate and acrylonitrile are useful as pour-point depressants in lubricating oils (1432).

Miscellaneous

Acrylonitrile has been added as a third component to *separate binary azeotropes*. For example it can be used to recover toluene (444) or benzene (445) from non-aromatics. Tetrachlorosilane (b.p. 57.6°C.) and trimethyl chlorosilane (b.p. 57.5°C.) form an azeotrope (b.p. 54.5°C.) and so cannot be separated by simple distillation. They can be separated, however, by azeotropic distillation with acrylonitrile (145, 950, 951). Acrylonitrile may also be used to dry propionitrile since the acrylonitrile-water azeotrope boils at a lower temperature than does propionitrile (1081).

Tubes knit from polyacrylonitrile fibers have been successfully used as *artery substitutes* in surgery on animals and humans (39, 635).

Asphalt additives which improve the bonding to gravel in roads may be made by reacting fatty amines with acrylonitrile (233). Asphalts reacted with acrylonitrile are claimed to have improved properties and softening-point relationships (720).

A mixture of acetylene black with an acrylonitrile-diolefin copolymer is useful either as a *lubricant* or a *hydraulic fluid* which is oil-insoluble (798). When branched-chain mercaptans are cyanoethylated the sodium salt obtained by hydrolysis of the nitrile is useful as a component of *high-temperature greases* (797). High-temperature greases can also be prepared by reaction of lithium hydroxide and acrylonitrile in a mixture of fatty acids and mineral oil (796).

Aqueous alkaline hydrolysis of polyacrylonitrile produces a water-soluble polymer which is useful in *froth flotation* (1193) and *cyanidation* (1216) of ores.

---

*Reg. U. S. Pat. Off.

Low-toxicity hardeners for epoxide-resin systems may be obtained by reacting aliphatic polyfunctional amines with acrylonitrile (1195).

Copolymers of acrylonitrile and vinyl acetate can be employed in *quenching baths* for steel (861). Trichloroethylene stabilized by acrylonitrile is suggested for the *degreasing of iron and aluminum* (637).

A copolymer of acrylonitrile and isobutylene can be converted into cellular microspheres by dropping the polymer particles while still wet with monomer into boiling water. The hollow spheres can be used in life belts or to inhibit surface evaporation in gasoline storage tanks (497).

A matrix for holding particles of cation-exchange resin in the form of a film can be made of acrylonitrile-butadiene copolymer (935). 1,3,5-Tri-acrylylhexahydro-s-triazine, prepared from acrylonitrile and formaldehyde, is useful as a cross-linking agent in the preparation of cation-exchange resins (375).

Pretreating Raney nickel catalyst with acrylonitrile is said to prevent nuclear hydrogenation in the catalytic reduction of anthraquinones (1433). Cyanoethylated ethanolamines are reported to be especially useful as activators in the preparation of acrylonitrile-butadiene copolymers (1264).

METHODS OF ANALYSIS

The qualitative detection of acrylonitrile in samples containing at least 1% acrylonitrile may be accomplished by conversion to 3-piperidinopropionitrile picrate (147). Methods have been devised for the quantitative determination of bound acrylonitrile in copolymers and polymerization systems (81, 373, 946, 1415), in air (138, 478, 864) and in aqueous industrial streams (1245, 1345). Polarographic reduction of acrylonitrile is a rapid, accurate method of assaying very dilute solutions of acrylonitrile (117, 1245). The purity of acrylonitrile can also be determined cryoscopically (1). Other procedures involve oxidative titration of the double bond (830), or addition of an amino- (1064, 1241) or sulfhydryl- (180) compound to the double bond. The latter method is based on the addition of standard dodecyl mercaptan followed by titration of the excess mercaptan with bromate-iodide solution to a yellow end point. In a variation of this method, useful in colored solutions, mercaptan is titrated potentiometrically with silver nitrate (605).

The following procedure presently is employed at the Stamford Laboratories of the American Cyanamid Company. It is a modification of the published mercaptan method (99).

PRINCIPLE OF THE METHOD

The acrylonitrile sample is added to a measured excess of dodecyl mercaptan in isopropyl alcohol. The cyanoethylation of the mercaptan is quantitative within two minutes in the presence of a basic catalyst, and the excess mercaptan is back-titrated with standard bromate-iodide reagent in acid solution.

Reagents

Mercaptan Reagent—Dissolve 35 g. (41 ml.) of crude *n*-dodecyl mercaptan in one liter of isopropyl alcohol (99%). Let stand for 1-2 days before using.

Basic Catalyst—Dissolve 28 g. of KOH in one liter of ethanol to make a 0.5 N solution.

Standard Bromate-Iodide Solution (0.125 N)—Dissolve 3.479 g. of reagent grade $KBrO_3$ and 30 g. of KI in water to make one liter. Standardize by acidifying a 25-ml. sample with 1-2 ml. of conc. HCl and immediately titrating with 0.1 N sodium thiosulfate which has been standardized by any of the familiar methods (660).

Acid Stop Solution—Add 16 ml. of conc. HCl to enough isopropyl alcohol to make one liter.

Procedure

Using a fast-flowing pipette, transfer accurately 25 ml. of mercaptan reagent into an iodine flask, and stopper the flask immediately. Prepare similar flasks for each sample and one for the blank. By means of a medicine dropper, transfer 9-12 drops (0.15-0.20 g.) of sample to a weighed vial, stopper quickly and weigh. Loosen the stopper and let the vial and then the stopper slide down the inside of the flask. Stopper the flask and swirl to effect thorough mixing.

Add 2 ml. of the basic catalyst, stopper again, and mix well by swirling. Start a stop-watch when the catalyst is added. At 20-30-second intervals, add catalyst solution to the other samples being run, last of all to the blank. At the end of two minutes stop the reaction in the first sample by adding 125 ml. of the acid stop-solution, then likewise with each flask at the end of its two-minute reaction period, the blank last of all. Immediately titrate the blank with standard bromate-iodide solution until one drop produces a faint yellow color which is permanent for 30 seconds of swirling. Titrate the samples in the order in which they were started.

Calculation

$$\% \text{ Acrylonitrile} = \frac{(\text{Blank Titer} - \text{Sample Titer}) \times \text{N Bromate-Iodide}}{\text{Grams of sample}} \times 5.306$$

Notes

1. In view of the volatility of acrylonitrile and of the reagent, speed is essential in all weighing and transfer operations.

2. One-dram vials with polythene (*not* cork) stoppers have been found to be the most satisfactory. Fragile ampules also may be used.

3. The blank loses titer slowly but steadily after adding the stop solution. It is therefore important to titrate the blank immediately after adding the stop solution. The blank may be run simultaneously with the sample, or before or after. If the mercaptan solution has been properly aged, the blank will change only very slowly with time and may be run only once a day if time is scarce.

4. In the original procedure (99) the use of ethyl or isopropyl alcohol was recommended. However, the end point in the titration of the blank has been found to be sharper in isopropyl or n-butyl alcohol than in ethyl alcohol.

5. The amount of sample specified above applies to relatively pure acrylonitrile. For the analysis of dilute solutions the quantity of sample taken should be increased accordingly. For aqueous solutions, sample size is limited by the fact that a maximum of 25% water may be tolerated in the reaction solution.

6. Compounds of similar structure will interfere, i.e., those containing the $-CH=CHCN$ structure. α, β-Unsaturated aldehydes react similarly but not appreciably within the two-minute period specified.

TOXICITY

Although acrylonitrile is a highly toxic substance by ingestion, by absorption through the intact skin and by inhalation of vapor, industrial experience and studies* in small animals indicate that it is not as hazardous as has been previously supposed. Several reports published prior to 1950 compared the hazard of acrylonitrile with that of HCN. It is now known that, while the toxic effects of the two substances are qualitatively similar, quantitatively they differ greatly.

Because the vapor pressure of this compound at room temperature is high, the hazard of intoxication by inhalation is greater than by other routes of exposure. The American Conference of Governmental Industrial Hygienists has established a level of 20 ppm as the maximum allowable concentration in the workroom atmosphere for 8-hour exposures. This hazard, together with others commonly encountered in the use of low-boiling organic compounds, requires that acrylonitrile be handled and processed in closed systems.

The manifestations of systemic intoxication in experimental animals resemble those of HCN. Blood cyanide and thiocyanate determinations, as well as other findings, suggest that the toxic action of acrylonitrile is due to the liberation of cyanide ion in vivo. However, the onset and development of symptoms are considerably slower than with HCN. This further suggests that the biological breakdown of acrylonitrile to cyanide ion is a rather slow, gradual process, thus permitting physiological detoxification to proceed apace. There is no evidence to indicate that repeated exposures produce a cumulative effect.

Acrylonitrile is readily absorbed through the intact skin and may with prolonged or repeated exposure produce systemic intoxication by this route. In addition, it is a low-grade primary irritant to the skin. Repeated or prolonged contact may produce a local cutaneous reaction with blistering, particularly if the exposure occurs inside shoes or under clothing that will retard its vaporization. The onset of dermatitis following such an exposure may be delayed for several hours.

*"Toxicology of Acrylonitrile," Petrochemicals Department Bulletin—American Cyanamid Company.

Industrial experience with acrylonitrile has been uniformly good. To date no case of human fatality or serious systemic poisoning through occupational exposure has come to our attention. Such a remarkable record may be attributed in large measure to the care with which the compound has been handled. Symptoms of poisoning that have been observed include headache, weakness, nausea, vomiting and abdominal cramps. Severe exposures might be expected to produce unconsciousness, convulsions and death through the action of the cyanide ion.

In mild cases of systemic poisoning, the victim should be kept under medical observation for 24 hours. No specific therapy is usually required and a prompt and complete spontaneous recovery may be anticipated. In more serious cases, especially when respiratory difficulty or unconsciousness has occurred, treatment with the nitrite-thiosulfate method* recommended by Chen for HCN poisoning may be expected to be effective. If the exposure has been by inhalation, irritation of the lower respiratory tract may warrant the institution of non-specific treatment usually employed in such cases.

First Aid Instructions (in order of importance)

Remove the patient from contact with the poison without delay and call a physician. If exposure has been:

BY INHALATION—Remove patient to fresh air. Rescuer entering contaminated area should wear an oxygen- or fresh-air-supplied gas mask.

BY SKIN CONTACT—Remove contaminated clothing and wash thoroughly with copious quantities of water and soap.

BY SWALLOWING—If conscious, induce vomiting by administration of strong solution of salt water. If unconscious, emptying of the stomach should be left to the physician.

BY EYE CONTACT—Hold eyelids apart and wash eye with continuous gentle stream of water for at least 15 minutes.

If breathing has stopped, give artificial respiration immediately and continuously until arrival of physician, preferably by the Holger-Nielsen method. The Eve rocking method is a satisfactory substitute.

If patient is unconscious, administer amyl nitrite by crushing a pearl (ampule) in a cloth and holding this under patient's nose for 15 seconds in every minute. Artificial respiration must not be interrupted during this procedure. The amyl nitrite pearl should be replaced when its strength is spent. Treatment should be continued until the patient's condition improves or the physician arrives.

By the Physician

The regimen of treatment recommended for acrylonitrile poisoning is that for cyanide poisoning. It is based upon the administration of nitrites to stimulate methemoglobin formation. Methemoglobin binds the cyanide group as cyanmethemoglobin. Thiosulfate is then administered to facilitate

*"Toxicology of Acrylonitrile," Petrochemicals Department Bulletin—American Cyanamid Company.

the conversion of cyanide to thiocyanate under the influence of the enzyme rhodanase. This ion is relatively far less toxic than cyanide and is readily excreted in the urine.

This method of treatment has been found to be highly effective in human experience with cyanide poisoning and experimentally in acrylonitrile poisoning. Instances of human intoxication with acrylonitrile of sufficient severity to warrant definitive treatment have been virtually unknown. However, if such cases were encountered, this form of treatment would be expected to be at least as effective as with cyanide poisoning of equal severity. The method, as described by Chen, Rose and Clowes (238A) is quoted as follows:

> "Instruct an assistant how to break, one at a time, pearls of amyl nitrite in a handkerchief and hold the latter over the victim's nose for 15-30 seconds per minute. At the same time the physician quickly loads his syringes, one with a 3 percent solution of sodium nitrite, and the other with a 25 percent solution of sodium thiosulphate.
>
> Stop administration of amyl nitrite and inject intravenously 0.3 g. (10 cc. of a 3 percent solution) of sodium nitrite at the rate of 2.5 to 5.0 cc. per minute.
>
> Inject by the same needle and vein, or by a larger needle and a new vein, 12.5 g. (50 cc. of a 25 percent solution) of sodium thiosulphate.
>
> The patient should be watched for at least 24 to 48 hours."

If signs of poisoning reappear, injection of both sodium nitrite and sodium thiosulphate should be repeated, but each in one-half of the dose. Even if the patient looks perfectly well, the medication may be given for prophylactic purposes two hours after the first injection.

TABLE I—Hydration, Hydrolysis and Alcoholysis

Reactants	Reaction Time (Hr.)	Reaction Temperature (°C.)	Products	% Yield	M.P. or B.P. (°C.)	References This Exam.	See Also:
H_2O *water*	1.5	100°	$CH_2=CHCONH_2$ *acrylamide*	95	M.P. 84-85°	29 30	622,857,859, 1250, 934, 1154, 149, 1298, 1139, 578, 579, 29, 1188, 1189, 216, 584, 580
$H_2O + HCl$ *water + hydrochloric acid*	—	0°	$ClCH_2CH_2CONH_2$ *3-chloropropionamide*	85	—	580	1138
$H_2O + HCl$ *water + hydrochloric acid*	6	reflux	$ClCH_2CH_2CO_2H$ *3-chloropropionic acid*	75	B.P. 115-117°/32 mm.	80	388, 387, 1356
CH_3OH *methanol*	—	—	$CH_2=CHCO_2CH_3$ *acrylic acid, methyl ester*	96	—	1341	1156, 1278
$CH_3OH + HCl$ *methanol + hydrochloric acid*	48	0°	$ClCH_2CH_2C(NH)OCH_3 \cdot HCl$ *3-chloropropionimidic acid, methyl ester, hydrochloride*	86	M.P. 93-94°	890	
C_2H_5OH *ethyl alcohol*	—	—	$CH_2=CHCO_2C_2H_5$ *acrylic acid, ethyl ester*	95	—	1341	1278
$C_2H_5OH + HBr$ *ethyl alcohol + hydrobromic acid*	O.N.	R.T.	$BrCH_2CH_2C(NH)OCH_2CH_3 \cdot HBr$ *3-bromopropionimidic acid, ethyl ester, hydrobromide*	54-56	B.P. 64-65°/5 mm.	20	
$C_2H_5OH + HCl$ *ethyl alcohol + hydrochloric acid*	24	R.T.	$CH_2=CHC(NH)OCH_2CH_3 \cdot HCl$ *acrylimidic acid, ethyl ester, hydrochloride*	~100	M.P. 104-104.5°	1051	
$C_2H_5OH + HCl$ *ethyl alcohol + hydrochloric acid*	2.5 2.0 then add water	10-15° 35-40°	$ClCH_2CH_2CO_2C_2H_5$ *3-chloropropionic acid, ethyl ester*	71.7	B.P. 70-75°/30 mm.	1312	
$CH_3CHOHCH_3$ *isopropyl alcohol*	1.0 0.5	100° reflux	$CH_2=CHCO_2CH(CH_3)_2$ *acrylic acid, isopropyl ester*	85	—	1278	

TABLE I—Continued

Hydration, Hydrolysis and Alcoholysis

Reactants	Reaction Time (Hr.)	Reaction Temperature (°C.)	Products	% Yield	M.P. or B.P. (°C.)	References	
						This Exam.	See Also:
$C_9H_{19}OH + HCl$ *nonyl alcohols + hydrochloric acid*	2.0 then add water	—	$ClCH_2CH_2CO_2C_9H_{19}$ *3-chloropropionic acid, nonyl ester*	81.9	B.P. 80-90°/0.3-0.4 mm.	1312	
$C_{13}H_{27}OH + HCl$ *tridecyl alcohols + hydrochloric acid*	2.5 then add water	10-15° then add water	$ClCH_2CH_2CO_2C_{13}H_{27}$ *3-chloropropionic acid, tridecyl ester*	85.0	B.P. 140-145°/0.7 mm.	1312	

TABLE IIA—Reactions with Alcohols

Reactants	Reaction Time (Hr.)	Reaction Temperature (°C.)	Products	% Yield	M.P. or B.P. (°C.)	This Exam.	See Also:
$HOCH(CH_3)_2$ *isopropyl alcohol*	1.0	<40°	$CH_2=CHCONHCH(CH_3)_2$ *N-isopropylacrylamide*	45	B.P. 110-115°/15 mm. M.P. 62°	879	
$HOCH(CH_3)CH_2CH_3$ *sec-butyl alcohol*	1.0	<40°	$CH_2=CHCONHCH(CH_3)CH_2CH_3$ *N-sec-butylacrylamide*	76	B.P. 125-130°/200 mm. M.P. 26°	879	
$HOC(CH_3)_3$ *tert-butyl alcohol*	1.0	<40°	$CH_2=CHCONHC(CH_3)_3$ *N-tert-butylacrylamide*	80	M.P. 126-128°	879	1250
$CH_3CH_2C(CH_3)_2OH$ *2-methyl-2-butanol*	0.17	49-51°	$CH_2=CHCONHC(CH_3)_2C_2H_5$ *N-(1,1-dimethylpropyl)acrylamide*	93.6	M.P. 92-93°	1	879
⬡—OH *cyclohexanol*	1.0	<40°	$CH_2=CHCONH$—⬡ *N-cyclohexylacrylamide*	72	M.P. 112-113°	879	
$HOC(CH_3)_2(CH_2)_2CH_3$ *2-methyl-2-pentanol*	1.0	<40°	$CH_2=CHCONHC(CH_3)_2CH_2CH_2CH_3$ *N-(1,1-dimethylbutyl)acrylamide*	71	M.P. 56-57°	879	
$HOC(CH_3)(C_2H_5)_2$ *3-methyl-3-pentanol*	1.0	<40°	$CH_2=CHCONHC(CH_3)(C_2H_5)_2$ *N-(1-ethyl-1-methylpropyl)acrylamide*	77	M.P. 63°	879	
$HOC(CH_3)_2CH(CH_3)_2$ *2,3-dimethyl-2-butanol*	1.0	<40°	$CH_2=CHCONHC(CH_3)_2CH(CH_3)_2$ *N-(1,1,2-trimethylpropyl)acrylamide*	71	M.P. 91-92°	879	
$HOC(CH_3)_2(CH_2)_3CH_3$ *2-methyl-2-hexanol*	1.0	<40°	$CH_2=CHCONHC(CH_3)_2(CH_2)_3CH_3$ *N-(1,1-dimethylpentyl)acrylamide*	90	M.P. 60°	879	

TABLE IIA—Continued

Reactions with Alcohols

Reactants	Reaction Time (Hr.)	Reaction Temperature (°C.)	Products	% Yield	M.P. or B.P. (°C.)	References This Exam.	References See Also:
HOC(CH₃)(C₂H₅)C₃H₇ *3-methyl-3-hexanol*	1.0	<40°	CH₂=CHCONHC(CH₃)(C₂H₅)C₃H₇ *N-(1-ethyl-1-methylbutyl)acrylamide*	82	M.P. 71-72°	879	
C₂H₅C(OH)(CH₃)CH₂CH(CH₃)₂ *3,5-dimethyl-3-hexanol*	1.0	60°	CH₂=CHCONHC(CH₃)(C₂H₅)CH₂CH(CH₃)₂ *N-(1-ethyl-1,3-dimethylbutyl)acrylamide*	57	M.P. 88-89°	879	

Additional examples of reactions involving complex alcohols are described in the following references: 878, 879, 1266.

TABLE IIB—Reactions with Olefins

Reactants	Reaction Time (Hr.)	Reaction Temperature (°C.)	Products	% Yield	M.P. or B.P. (°C.)	References This Exam.	References See Also:
CH₂=C(CH₃)CH₂Cl *1-chloro-2-methylpropene*	1.0	<40°	CH₂=CHCONHC(CH₃)₂CH₂Cl *N-(2-chloro-1,1-dimethylethyl)acrylamide*	92	M.P. 93-94°	879	
(CH₃)₂C=CHCH₃ *2-methyl-2-butene*	several hours	R.T.	CH₂=CHCONHC(CH₃)₂C₂H₅ *N-(1,1-dimethylpropyl)acrylamide*	75	M.P. 92-93°	923	924
 cyclohexene	1.0	<40°	CH₂=CHCONH— 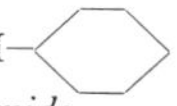 *N-cyclohexylacrylamide*	66	—	879	
(CH₃)₂C=CHC(CH₃)₃ *2,2,4-trimethyl-2-pentene* + CH₂=C(CH₃)CH₂C(CH₃)₃ *2,2,4-trimethyl-1-pentene*	1.0	<40°	CH₂=CHCONHC(CH₃)₂CH₂C(CH₃)₃ *N-(1,1,3,3-tetramethylbutyl)acrylamide*	71	M.P. 83° B.P. 140-142°/20 mm.	879	
CH₂=CH(CH₂)₈COOH *10-undecenoic acid*	2.0	20-40°	CH₂=CHCONHCH(CH₃)(CH₂)₈CO₂H *10-acrylamidoundecanoic acid*	—	M.P. 104-105°	878	1266

Additional examples of reactions involving complex olefins are described in the following references: 807, 878, 929.

TABLE III—Reactions with Aldehydes and Methylol Compounds

Reactants	Reaction Time (Hr.)	Reaction Temperature (°C.)	Products	% Yield	M.P. or B.P. (°C.)	References This Exam.	References See Also:
$CH_2O + H_2O$ *formaldehyde + water*	3.0	40-45°	$(CH_2=CHCONH)_2CH_2$ *N,N′-methylenebisacrylamide*	86	M.P. 185°	735	220
$-(CH_2O)-_x$ *paraformaldehyde*	—	40-80°	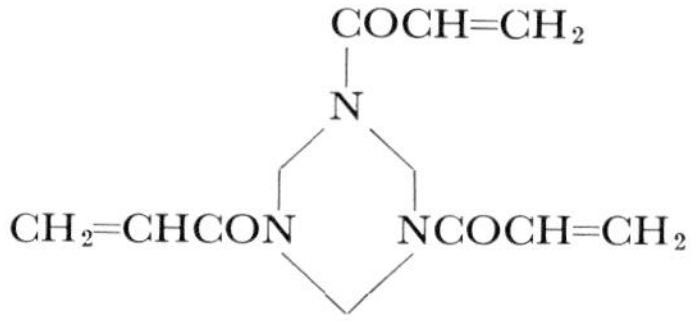 (structure) $CH_2=CHCON$ ... $NCOCH=CH_2$, with $COCH=CH_2$ on N *1,3,5-triacrylylhexahydro-s-triazine*	70-74	M.P. 155-156°	1137	70, 446, 447, 437, 1186, 1187
$CCl_3CHO + H_2O$ *chloral + water*	2.0	—	$(CH_2=CHCONH)_2CHCCl_3$ *N,N′-(2,2,2-trichloroethylidene)bisacrylamide*	18	—	735	
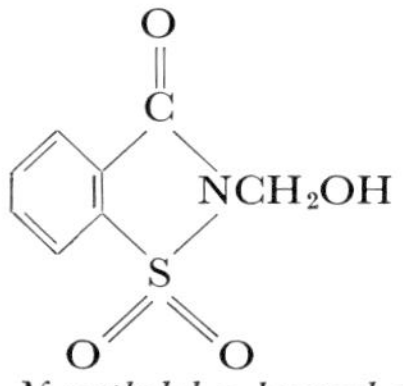 (structure) NCH_2OH ... *N-methylol-o-benzoyl-sulfimide*	during addn. O.N.	<5° R.T.	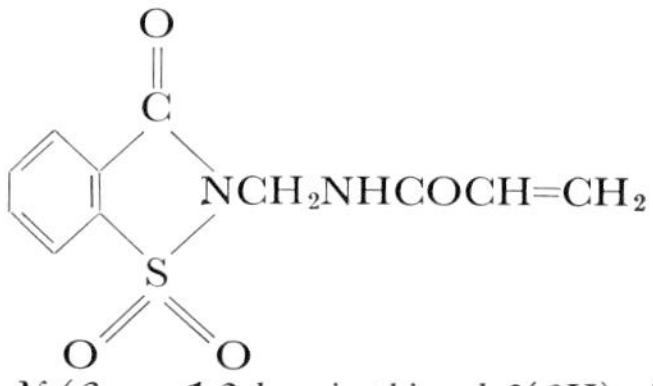 (structure) $NCH_2NHCOCH=CH_2$ *N-(3-oxo-1,2-benzisothiazol-2(3H)-ylmethyl)-acrylamide,1,1-dioxide*	—	M.P. 167-168°	804	
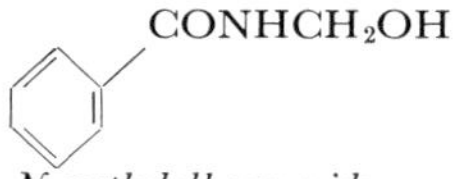 $CONHCH_2OH$ *N-methylolbenzamide*	during addn. 1.0	<5° 5-10°	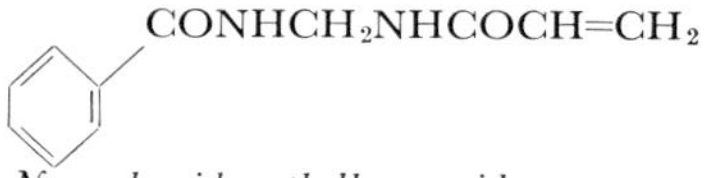 $CONHCH_2NHCOCH=CH_2$ *N-acrylamidomethylbenzamide*	83	—	804	

TABLE III—Continued

Reactions with Aldehydes and Methylol Compounds

Reactants	Reaction Temperature (°C.)	Reaction Time (Hr.)	Products	% Yield	M.P. or B.P. (°C.)	References — This Exam.	References — See Also:
(phthalimide) NCH₂OH *N-methylolphthalimide*	33-35° / 40°	during addn. / 1.0	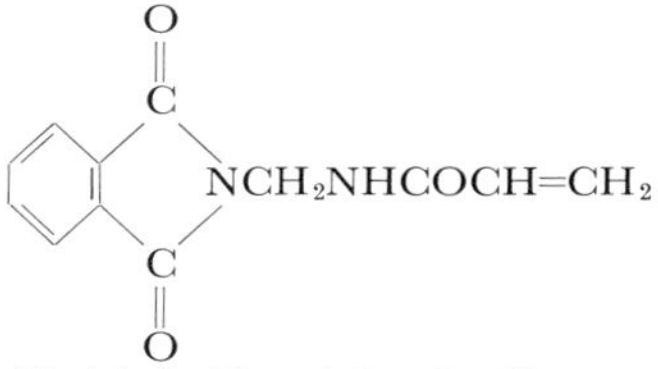 NCH₂NHCOCH=CH₂ *N-phthalimidomethylacrylamide*	95	M.P. 193°	804	

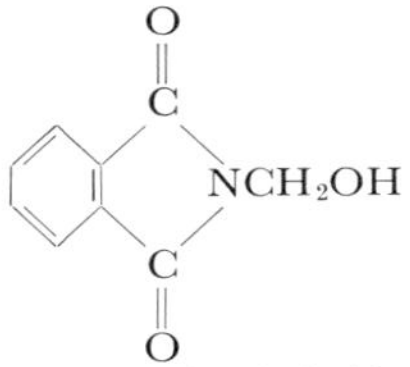

TABLE IV—Diels-Alder and Related Reactions

(A) Diels-Alder

Reactants	Reaction Temperature (°C.)	Reaction Time (Hr.)	Products	% Yield	M.P. or B.P. (°C.)	References — This Exam.	References — See Also:
CH₂=CBrCH=CH₂ *2-bromo-1,3-butadiene*	130-135°	18.0	 Br—CN *4-bromo-3-cyclohexene-1-carbonitrile*	31	M.P. 67°	867	
CH₂=CClCH=CH₂ *chloroprene*	145°	12.0	 Cl—CN *4-chloro-3-cyclohexene-1-carbonitrile*	34	B.P. 127-130°/20 mm. M.P. 54°	338	608
CH₂=CHCH=CH₂ *1,3-butadiene*	430°	4 sec.	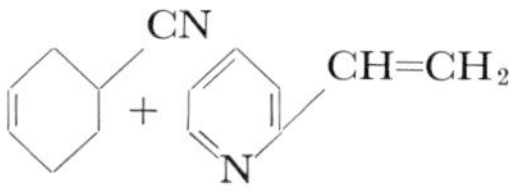 CN + CH=CH₂ (pyridine) *3-cyclohexene-1-carbonitrile + 2-vinylpyridine*	28 1.8	— —	607	3383 606
CH₂=CHCH=CH₂ *1,3-butadiene*	160-180°	cont.	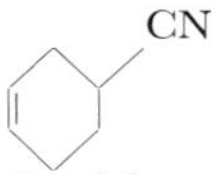 CN *3-cyclohexene-1-carbonitrile*	95	B.P. 190-195°/760 mm.	873	338, 867, 606, 607, 108, 1076, 1166, 598, 582, 592, 874

TABLE IV—Continued

(A) Diels-Alder

Reactants	Reaction Time (Hr.)	Reaction Temperature (°C.)	Products	% Yield	M.P. or B.P. (°C.)	References This Exam.	References See Also:
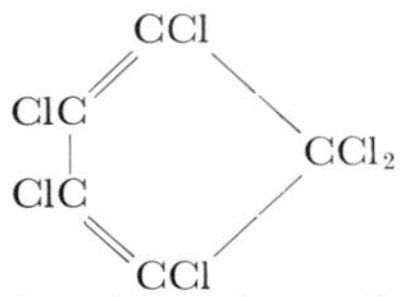 hexachlorocyclopentadiene	24.0	100°	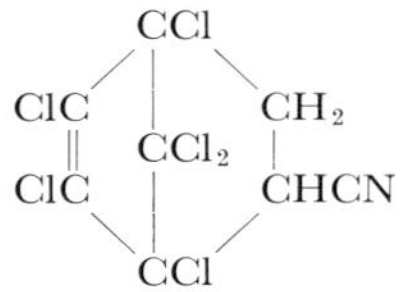 1,4,5,6,7,7-hexachlorobicyclo[2.2.1]hept-5-ene-2-carbonitrile	32.5	—	891	
 cyclopentadiene	—	—	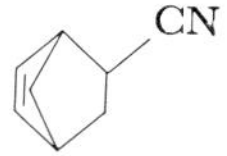 bicyclo[2.2.1]hept-5-ene-2-carbonitrile	95	B.P. 84-89°/13 mm.	17	921, 158
$CH_2=C(CH_3)CCl=CH_2$ 3-chloro-2-methyl-1,3-butadiene	12.0	150°	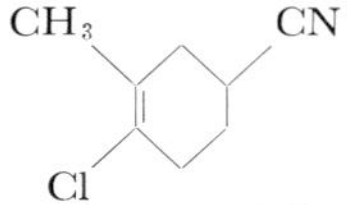 4-chloro-3-methyl-3-cyclohexene-1-carbonitrile	—	B.P. 122-123°/13 mm.	109	
$CH_3CH=CHCH=CH_2$ piperylene	20.0	100°	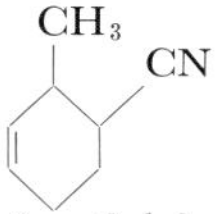 2-methyl-3-cyclohexene-1-carbonitrile	78	B.P. 202-203°/738 mm.	1076	45, 763, 404, 530, 866
$CH_2=C(CH_3)CH=CH_2$ isoprene	18.0	135°	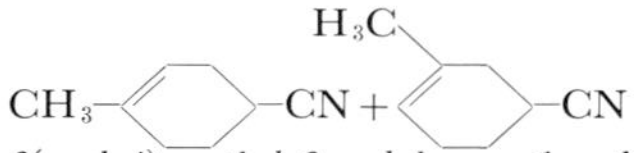 3(and 4)-methyl-3-cyclohexene-1-carbonitrile	92	B.P. 94-95°/20 mm.	866	20, 19, 108

TABLE IV—Continued

Reactants	Reaction Time (Hr.)	Reaction Temperature (°C.)	Products	% Yield	M.P. or B.P. (°C.)	This Exam.	See Also:
CH₂=C(OCH₃)CH=CH₂ $CH_2=C(OCH_3)CH=CH_2$ 2-methoxy-1,3-butadiene	12.0	145°	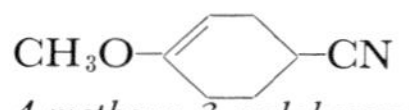 CH₃O—CN structure; 4-methoxy-3-cyclohexene-1-carbonitrile	60	B.P. 125.5°/20 mm.	868	
CH₃CH=CHCH=CHCH₃ $CH_3CH=CHCH=CHCH_3$ 2,4-hexadiene	12.0	120-130°	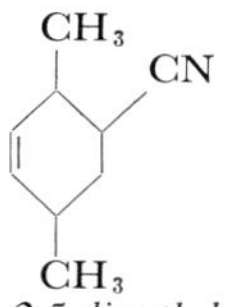 CH₃ CN structure; 2,5-dimethyl-3-cyclohexene-1-carbonitrile	40	B.P. 82-83°/8 mm.	46	1076
CH₂=C(CH₃)C(CH₃)=CH₂ $CH_2=C(CH_3)C(CH_3)=CH_2$ 2,3-dimethyl-1,3-butadiene	—	—	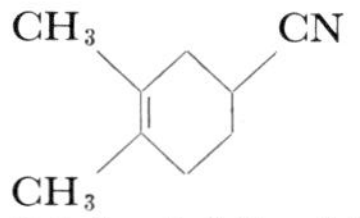 CH₃ CN structure; 3,4-dimethyl-3-cyclohexene-1-carbonitrile	63	B.P. 94°/7 mm. B.P. 102°/10 mm. B.P. 108-110°/15 mm. B.P. 222-224°/760 mm.	1076	774, 775
CH₂=C(OC₂H₅)CH=CH₂ $CH_2=C(OC_2H_5)CH=CH_2$ 2-ethoxy-1,3-butadiene	12.0	135-140°	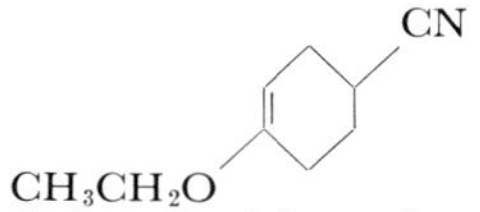 CH₃CH₂O—CN structure; 4-ethoxy-3-cyclohexene-1-carbonitrile	90	B.P. 125-126°/15 mm.	338	868
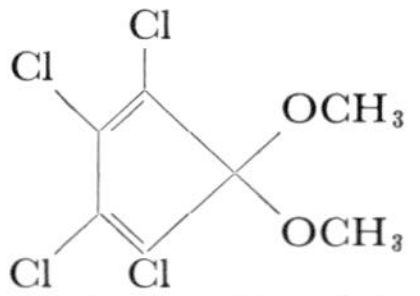 1,2,3,4-tetrachloro-5,5-dimethoxycyclopentadiene	48.0	reflux	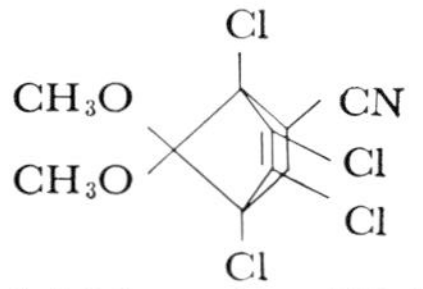 structure; 1,4,5,6-tetrachloro-7,7-dimethoxybicyclo[2.2.1]-hept-5-ene-2-carbonitrile	70	M.P. 88-89°	722	

TABLE IV—Continued

(A) Diels-Alder

Reactants	Reaction Time (Hr.)	Reaction Temperature (°C.)	Products	% Yield	M.P. or B.P. (°C.)	References This Exam.	See Also:
CH_2=CHCH=CHCH=CHCN *2,4,6-heptatrienenitrile*	—	125°	*Mixture of Diels-Alder adducts*	—	—	199	
CH_2=C(CH_3)CH=C(CH_3)$_2$ *2,4-dimethyl-1,3-pentadiene*	38.0	140-145°	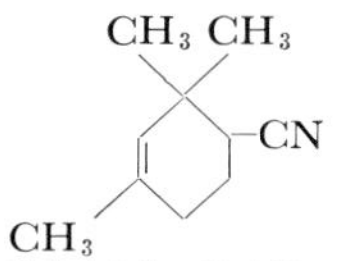 CH_3 CH_3 CN CH_3 *2,2,4-trimethyl-3-cyclohexene-1-carbonitrile*	71	B.P. 93-97°/10 mm. B.P. 50°/0.2 mm.	1025	
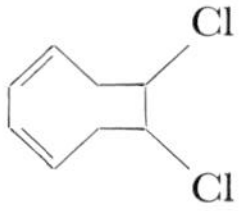 Cl Cl *cyclooctatetraene dichloride*	6.0	150°	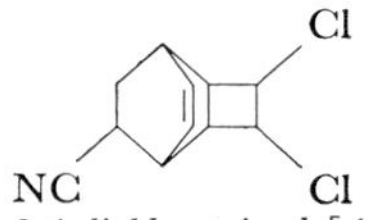 Cl Cl NC *3,4-dichlorotricyclo[4.2.2.0²·⁵]dec-9-ene-7-carbonitrile*	56	B.P. 177-184°/ 3.4-3.9 mm.	107	
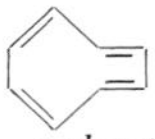 *cyclooctatetraene*	6.0	180°	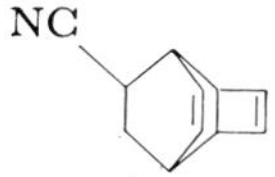 NC *tricyclo[4.2.2.0²·⁵]deca-3,9-diene-8-carbonitrile*	33	B.P. 68°/0.2 mm. B.P. 103-110°/ 2.0-2.5 mm.	107	
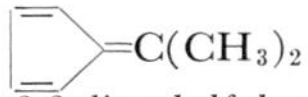 =C(CH_3)$_2$ *6,6-dimethylfulvene*	several hours	reflux	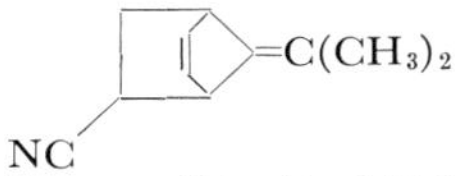 =C(CH_3)$_2$ NC *7-isopropylidenebicyclo[2.2.1]hept-5-ene-2-carbonitrile*	47	B.P. 95-100°/1 mm. M.P. 87°	158	18
(C$_2$H$_5$)$_2$NCH=CHCH=CH$_2$ *N,N-diethyl-1,3-butadienylamine*	48.0	20-30°	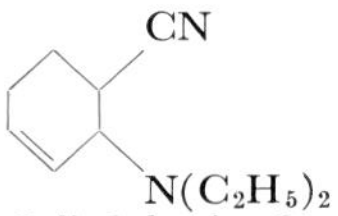 CN N(C$_2$H$_5$)$_2$ *2-diethylamino-3-cyclohexene-1-carbonitrile*	93	B.P. 125-126°/11 mm.	1288	

TABLE IV—Continued

Reactants	Reaction Time (Hr.)	Reaction Temperature (°C.)	Products	% Yield	M.P. or B.P. (°C.)	References — This Exam.	References — See Also:
$(CH_3)_2NCH=CHCH=CHN(CH_3)_2$ *N,N,N',N'-tetramethyl-1,3-butadiene- 1,4-diamine*	—	—	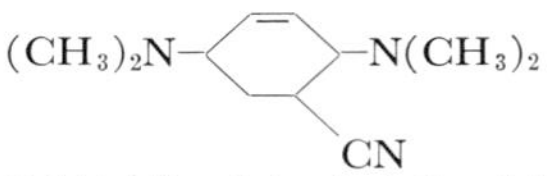 $(CH_3)_2N$—◯—$N(CH_3)_2$ with CN *2,5-bis(dimethylamino)-3-cyclohexene-1-carbonitrile*	30	B.P. 110-112°/0.5 mm.	1259	
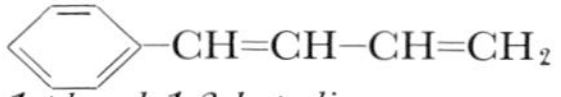 ◯—$CH=CH-CH=CH_2$ *1-phenyl-1,3-butadiene*	9.0	reflux	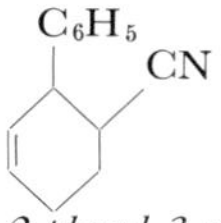 C_6H_5—◯—CN *2-phenyl-3-cyclohexene-1-carbonitrile*	71	B.P. 150-153°/5 mm. B.P. 119-121°/1 mm.	903	762
$C_2H_5O_2CCH=CHCH=CHCO_2C_2H_5$ *diethyl muconate*	—	150-160°	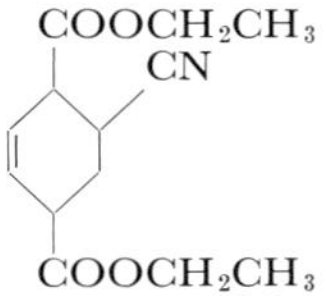 $COOCH_2CH_3$—◯—CN with $COOCH_2CH_3$ *5-cyano-2-cyclohexene-1,4-dicarboxylic acid, diethyl ester*	40-50	B.P. 175-180°	1175	
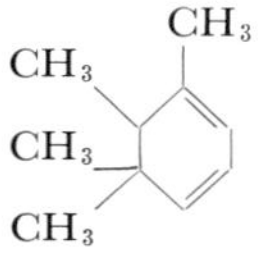 ◯ with CH₃, CH₃, CH₃, CH₃ *α-pyronene*	20.0	125-140°	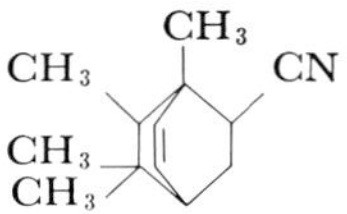 CH₃, CH₃, CH₃ CN *1,5,5,6-tetramethylbicyclo[2.2.2]oct-7-ene-2-carbonitrile* **or** 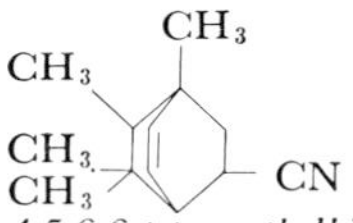 CH₃, CH₃, CH₃ CN *4,5,6,6-tetramethylbicyclo[2.2.2]oct-7-ene-2-carbonitrile*	36.2	B.P. 128-130°	47	

TABLE IV—Continued

(A) Diels-Alder

Reactants	Re-action Time (Hr.)	Reaction Tem-perature (°C.)	Products	% Yield	M.P. or B.P. (°C.)	References This Exam.	See Also:
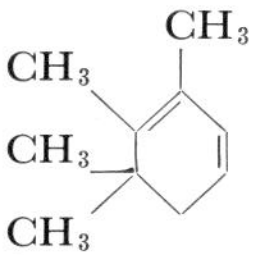 CH₃ ... β-pyronene	20.0	125-140°	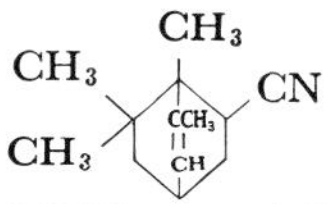 CH₃ ... CN *1,6,7-tetramethylbicyclo[2.2.2]oct-7-ene-2-carbonitrile* or 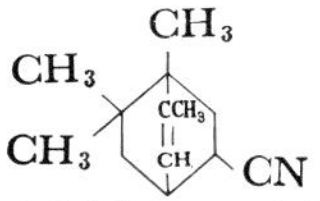 CH₃ ... CN *4,5,8-tetramethylbicyclo[2.2.2]oct-7-ene-2-carbonitrile*	77	M.P. 45-50° B.P. 125-127°/6 mm.	47	
$CH_2=CHC(=CH_2)(CH_2)_2CH=C(CH_3)_2$ myrcene	4.0	reflux	$CN-(CH_2)_2CH=C(CH_3)_2$ *4-(4-methyl-3-pentenyl)-3-cyclohexene-1-carbonitrile* 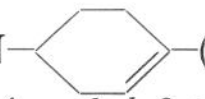	46	B.P. 115-120°/1 mm.	775	
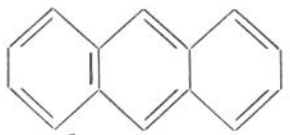 anthracene	—	—	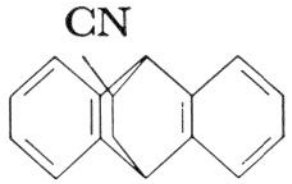 CN *9,10-dihydro-9,10-ethanoanthracene-11-carbonitrile*	—	—	818 822	581

TABLE IV—Continued

(A) Diels-Alder

Reactants	Re-action Time (Hr.)	Reaction Temperature (°C.)	Products	% Yield	M.P. or B.P. (°C.)	This Exam.	See Also:
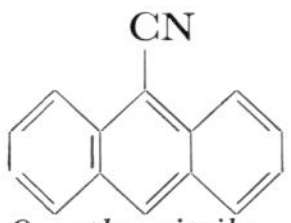 9-anthronitrile	18.0 22.0	135-145° 190-200°	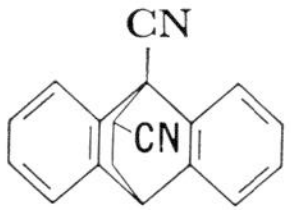 9,10-ethanoanthracene-9,12(10H)-dicarbonitrile	—	M.P. 167°	1337	
			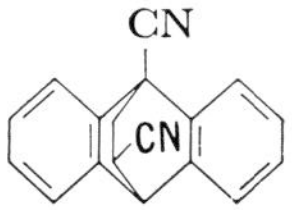 9,10-ethanoanthracene-9,11(10H)-dicarbonitrile	—	M.P. 205°		
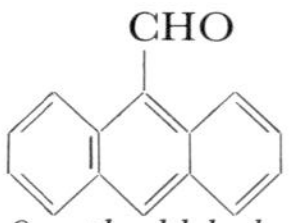 9-anthraldehyde	24.0	125-130°	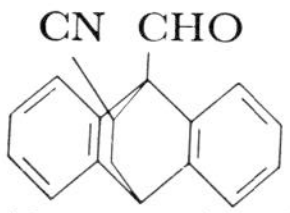 12-cyano-9,10-ethanoanthracene-9(10H)-carboxaldehyde	78	M.P. 172° M.P. 181.5-182°	761	
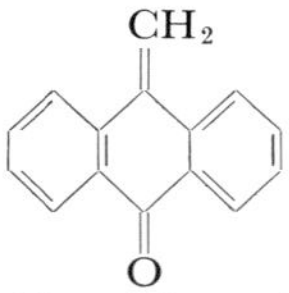 10-methyleneanthrone + oxygen	—	—	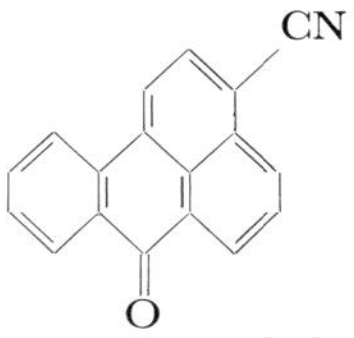 7-oxo-7H-benz[de]anthracene-3-carbonitrile	—	—	959	

TABLE IV—Continued

(A) Diels-Alder

Reactants	Reaction Time (Hr.)	Reaction Temperature (°C.)	Products	% Yield	M.P. or B.P. (°C.)	References This Exam.	References See Also:
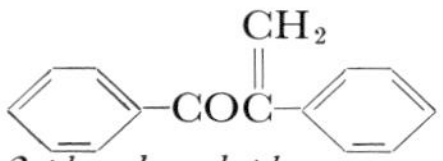 2-phenylacrylophenone	3.0	185-205°	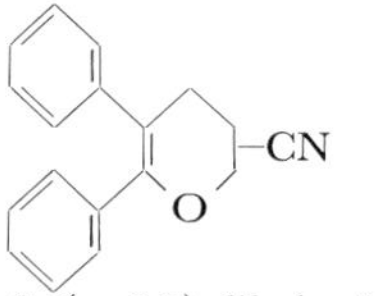 3,4(or 2,3)-dihydro-5,6-diphenyl-2H(or 4H)-pyran-2(or 3)-carbonitrile	3.1	M.P. 121-122°	1260	
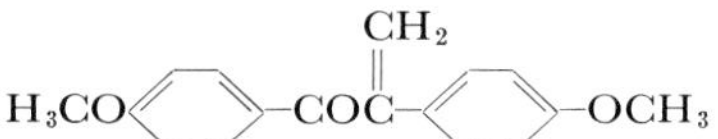 4-methoxy-2-(p-methoxyphenyl)-acrylophenone	6.0	190-220°	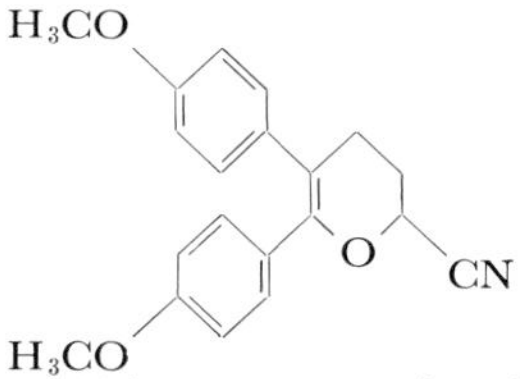 5,6-bis(p-methoxyphenyl)-3,4(or 2,3)-dihydro-2H(or 4H)-pyran-2-carbonitrile	16.7	B.P. 255-262°/0.3 mm. M.P. 147-148°	1260	
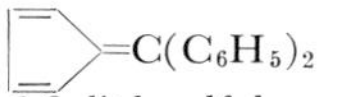 6,6-diphenylfulvene	2 mos.	R.T.	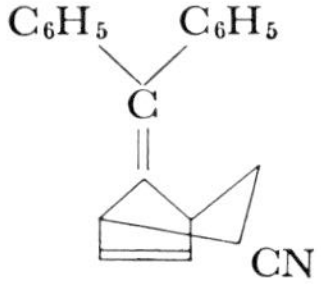 7-diphenylmethylenebicyclo[2.2.1]hept-5-ene-2-carbonitrile	80-90	M.P. 137°	16	
tung oil fatty acids (A)	48.0	reflux	Mixture of Diels-Alder adducts (4.61% N)	73	B.P. 240-255°/3 mm.	174	
octadienic acid (B)	4.0	180°	Mixture of Diels-Alder adducts	28.2	B.P. 250-260°/4 mm.	174	

TABLE IV—Continued

(A) Diels-Alder

Reactants	Reaction Time (Hr.)	Reaction Temperature (°C.)	Products	% Yield	M.P. or B.P. (°C.)	References This Exam.	References See Also:
CH₃(CH₂)₅(CH=CH)₂(CH₂)₇COOH *trans,trans-9,11-octadecadienoic acid*	24.0	200°	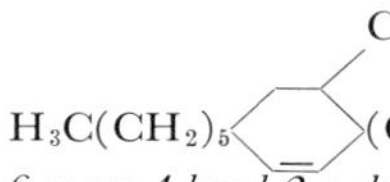 H₃C(CH₂)₅...(CH₂)₇-COOH *6-cyano-4-hexyl-2-cyclohexene-1-octanoic acid*	27	M.P. 67-77°	1416	
methyl octadecadienate	13.0	250°	*Mixture of Diels-Alder adducts (3.76% N)*	36.5	B.P. 235-245°/6 mm.	174	
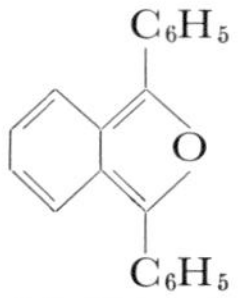 *1,3-diphenylisobenzofuran*	<1.00	in the shade	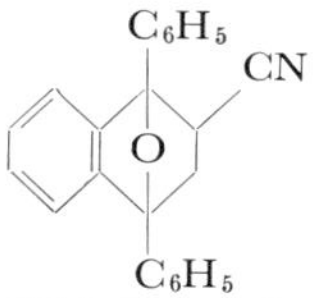 *1,2,3,4-tetrahydro-1,4-diphenyl-1,4-epoxynaphthalene-2-carbonitrile*	88	M.P. 153-154°	366	
"Conjulin" ©	48.0	reflux	*Mixture of Diels-Alder adducts (3.4% N)*	—	B.P. 245-260°/4 mm.	174	

Additional examples of Diels-Alder reactions are described in the following references: 174, 775.

(B) Related Reactions

Reactants	Reaction Time (Hr.)	Reaction Temperature (°C.)	Products	% Yield	M.P. or B.P. (°C.)	References This Exam.	References See Also:
CF₂=CFCl *chlorotrifluoroethylene*	8.0	150°	HO₂C(CH₂)₂CF₂CO₂H *2,2-difluoroglutaric acid*	54.1	M.P. 103-5°	1202	
CF₂=CF₂ *tetrafluoroethylene*	8.0	150°	CF₂—CH₂ CF₂—CH—CN *2,2,3,3-tetrafluorocyclobutanecarbonitrile*	84	B.P. 148°	258	85, 84
CH₂=CHCN *acrylonitrile*	24.0	195-200°	CH₂—CH—CN CH₂—CH—CN *1,2-cyclobutanedicarbonitrile*	3.5	cis M.P. <0°; B.P. 108-115°/3-4 mm. trans. M.P. 62°; B.P. 140-145°/3-4 mm.	284	

TABLE IV—Continued

(B) Related Reactions

Reactants	Reaction Temperature (°C.)	Reaction Time (Hr.)	Products	% Yield	M.P. or B.P. (°C.)	References This Exam.	References See Also:
⬡—C≡N→O *benzonitrile oxide*	reflux	1.0	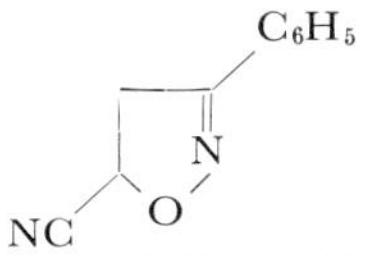 *3-phenyl-2-isoxazoline-5-carbonitrile* Ⓓ	73	M.P. 66–67°	301	
⬡—CH=NN=CH—⬡ *benzaldehyde azine*	135–142°	36.0	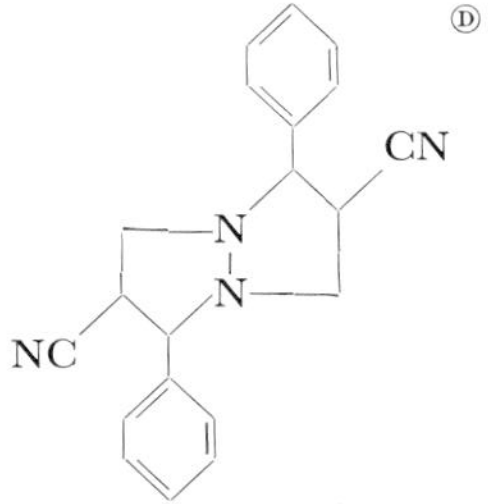 *1,2,3,5,6,7-hexahydro-1,5-diphenyl[pyrazolo[1,2]-pyrazole-2,6-dicarbonitrile*	2.0	M.P. 223–224°	1277	

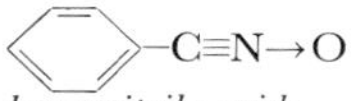

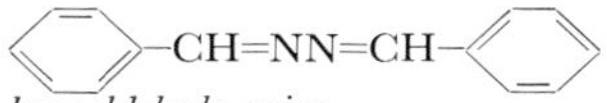

NOTES:
Ⓐ Tung Oil Fatty Acids; mixture of eleostearic acids and oleic acid.
Ⓑ Octadienic Acid; prepared by the dehydration of castor oil.
Ⓒ "Conjulin"; linseed oil fatty acid with conjugated double bonds prepared by heating linseed oil fatty acids with caustic soda.
Ⓓ Structure uncertain.

TABLE V—Reactions with Hydrogen

Reactants	Reaction Temperature (°C.)	Reaction Time (Hr.)	Products	% Yield	M.P. or B.P. (°C.)	References This Exam.	References See Also:
H_2 *hydrogen*	120°	—	CH_3CH_2CN *propionitrile* $CH_3CH_2CONH_2$ *propionamide*	91 2	— —	913	1159, 503
$Mg+CH_3OH$ *magnesium + methanol*	reflux	1.0 +O.N.	$NCCH_2CH_2CH_2CN$ *adiponitrile*	Ⓐ 29.3	B.P. 118–128°	687	589
$K(Hg)_x+HCl$ Ⓑ *potassium amalgam + hydrochloric acid*	—	—	$NCCH_2CH_2CH_2CN$ *adiponitrile*	62.2	B.P. 138–140°/3 mm.	1306	

NOTES: Ⓐ Isolated as adipic acid. Ⓑ Amalgam produced by electrolysis of 40% KOH in a pool of mercury.

TABLE VI—Reactions with Halogens

Reactants	Reaction Time (Hr.)	Reaction Temperature (°C.)	Products	% Yield	M.P. or B.P. (°C.)	References This Exam.	References See Also:
Cl_2 *chlorine*	—	—	$ClCH_2CCl_2CN$ *2,2,3-trichloropropionitrile*	95	B.P. 61°/13 mm.	140	1, 1039, 925
Cl_2 *chlorine*	—	R.T.	$ClCH_2CCl_2CN$ *2,2,3-trichloropropionitrile*	90	B.P. 70-75°/30 mm. 80-81°/63 mm.	695	247, 140
Cl_2 *chlorine*	—	—	$ClCH_2CCl_2CN$ *2,2,3-trichloropropionitrile* $Cl_2CHCHClCN$ *2,3,3-trichloropropionitrile* Cl_2CHCCl_2CN *2,2,3,3-tetrachloropropionitrile*	— — —	B.P. 53°/14 mm. B.P. 100°/15 mm. B.P. 92°/14 mm.	140	
Cl_2 *chlorine*	—	200-550°	$CH_2{=}CClCN$ *2-chloroacrylonitrile*	—	B.P. 44-45°/150 mm.	707	
$Cl_2 + H_2O$ *chlorine + water*	—	18°	$HOCH_2CHClCN$ *2-chlorohydracrylonitrile*	60	B.P. 92-93°/3 mm.	1100	324
$Cl_2 + H_2O$ *chlorine + water*	—	—	$ClCH_2C(CH_2CH_2CN)ClCN$ *2-chloro-2-chloromethylglutaronitrile*	28	B.P. 133°/115 mm.	1121	
$Cl_2 + H_2C{=}CH_2$ *chlorine + ethylene*	—	—	$ClCH_2CH_2N{=}CClCCl_2CH_2Cl$ *2-chloro-N-(1,2,2,3-tetrachloropropylidene)ethylamine*	34	B.P. 94-95°/4 mm.	200	
Br_2 *bromine*	—	R.T.	$BrCH_2CHBrCN$ *2,3-dibromopropionitrile*	65	B.P. 106-107°/22 mm.	803	
Br_2 *bromine*	—	R.T.	$BrCH_2CHBrCN$ *2,3-dibromopropionitrile* $CH_2{=}CBrCN$ *2-bromoacrylonitrile*	62 17	B.P. 120-130°/30 mm. B.P. 60°/30 mm.	697	

TABLE VI—Continued

Reactions with Halogens

Reactants	Reaction Time (Hr.)	Reaction Temperature (°C.)	Products	% Yield	M.P. or B.P. (°C.)	References This Exam.	See Also:
NO_2Cl *nitryl chloride*	—	0°	$O_2NCH_2CHClCN$ *2-chloro-3-nitropropionitrile* $ClCH_2CHClCN$ *2,3-dichloropropionitrile*	76 13.5	B.P. 83°/1 mm. B.P. 61-67°/14-15 mm.	991	139
NO_2Cl *nitryl chloride*	—	0°	$O_2NCH_2CHClCN$ *2-chloro-3-nitropropionitrile* $O_2NCH=CHCN$ *3-nitroacrylonitrile* $ClCH_2CHClCN$ *2,3-dichloropropionitrile*	25 48 16	B.P. 83°/1 mm. B.P. 53-59°/3 mm. B.P. 61-67°/14-15 mm.	991	139
dioxane dibromide	24	25°	$BrCH_2CHBrCN$ *2,3-dibromopropionitrile*	95	B.P. 173°	1253	

TABLE VII—Reactions with Diazo Compounds

Reactants	Reaction Time (Hr.)	Reaction Temperature (°C.)	Products	% Yield	M.P. or B.P. (°C.)	References This Exam.	See Also:
$H_2C \leftarrow N \equiv N$ *diazomethane*	—	"cooling"	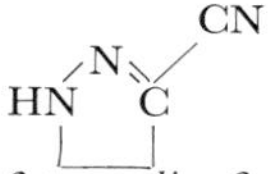 [structure] *2-pyrazoline-3-carbonitrile*	—	B.P. 93-94°/1 mm.	1418	
$CH_3CH_2OOCCH_2 \leftarrow N \equiv N$ *ethyl diazoacetate*	24	40° Ⓐ	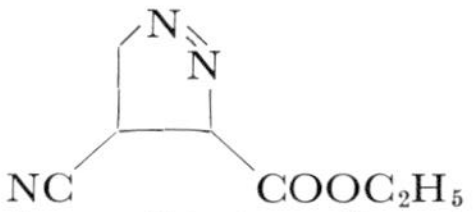 [structure] *4-cyano-3-isopyrazolinecarboxylic acid, ethyl ester*	65	M.P. 96°	1418	
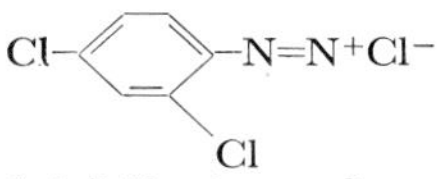 [structure] *2,4-dichlorobenzenediazonium chloride*	—	30-40°	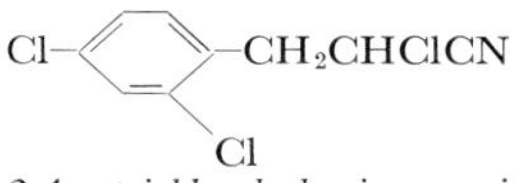 [structure] $CH_2CHClCN$ Ⓑ *2,4,α-trichlorohydrocinnamonitrile*	>71	B.P. 140°/5 mm. M.P. 45°	595 594	808

TABLE VII—Continued

Reactions with Diazo Compounds

Reactants	Reaction Time (Hr.)	Reaction Temperature (°C.)	Products	% Yield	M.P. or B.P. (°C.)	References This Exam.	References See Also:
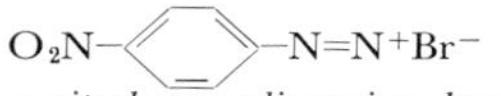 O₂N—⟨⟩—N=N⁺Br⁻ *p-nitrobenzenediazonium bromide*	1.5-2	5°	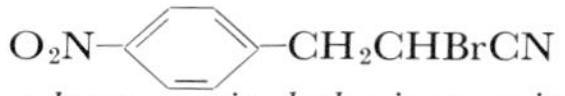 O₂N—⟨⟩—CH₂CHBrCN *α-bromo-p-nitrohydrocinnamonitrile*	54	B.P. 192-194°/2 mm. M.P. 98.5-99°	1254	595, 594
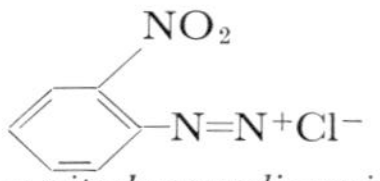 ⟨NO₂⟩—N=N⁺Cl⁻ *o-nitrobenzenediazonium chloride*	1.5-2	5°	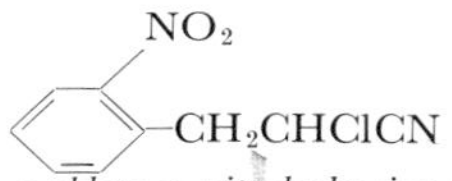 ⟨NO₂⟩—CH₂CHClCN *α-chloro-o-nitrohydrocinnamonitrile*	45	B.P. 166-168°/4 mm.	1254	736
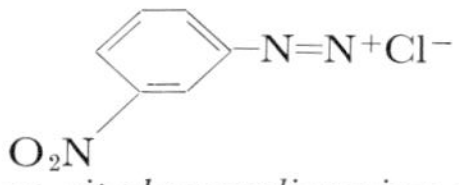 O₂N—⟨⟩—N=N⁺Cl⁻ *m-nitrobenzenediazonium chloride*	0.5	18°	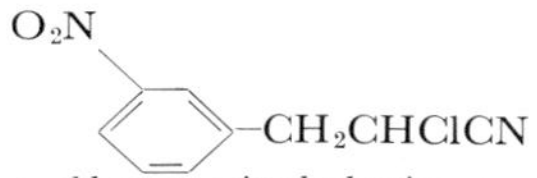 O₂N—⟨⟩—CH₂CHClCN *α-chloro-m-nitrohydrocinnamonitrile*	58.5	M.P. 74-76°	153	654, 808, 1254
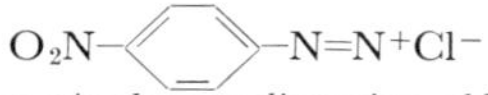 O₂N—⟨⟩—N=N⁺Cl⁻ *p-nitrobenzenediazonium chloride*	1.5-2	5°	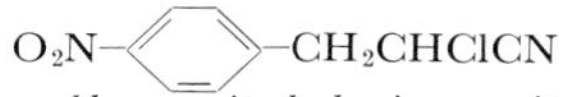 O₂N—⟨⟩—CH₂CHClCN *α-chloro-p-nitrohydrocinnamonitrile*	96.5	M.P. 110-111°	1254	595, 594, 808, 153, 654, 1308
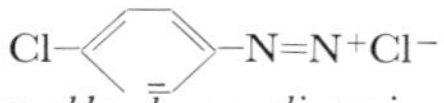 Cl—⟨⟩—N=N⁺Cl⁻ *p-chlorobenzenediazonium chloride*	0.5	18°	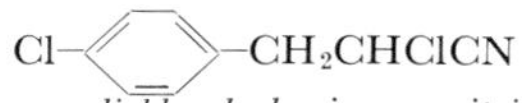 Cl—⟨⟩—CH₂CHClCN *p,α-dichlorohydrocinnamonitrile*	85.3	M.P. 56-59° B.P. 153-159°/15 mm.	153	1310, 1309
N=N⁺Cl⁻ + ⟨⟩—SO₂NH₂ *benzenesulfonamide* Cl—⟨⟩— *p-chlorobenzenediazonium chloride*	—	5°	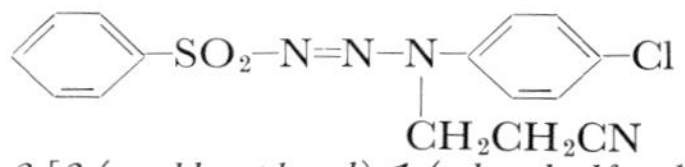 ⟨⟩—SO₂—N=N—N—⟨⟩—Cl CH₂CH₂CN *3-[3-(p-chlorophenyl)-1-(phenylsulfonyl)triazen-3-yl]-propionitrile*	—	M.P. 127-129°	1276	
 ⁻Cl⁺N=N—⟨⟩—N=N⁺Cl⁻ *p-phenylenebis[diazonium chloride]*	18	25°	 NCCHClCH₂—⟨⟩—CH₂CHClCN *α,α'-dichloro-p-benzenedipropionitrile*	40.1	M.P. 184°	1329	

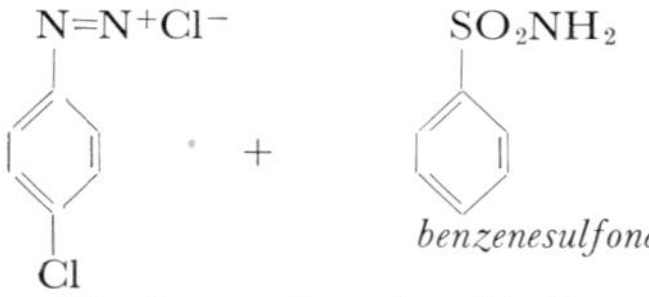

TABLE VII—Continued   Reactions with Diazo Compounds

Reactants	Reaction Time (Hr.)	Reaction Temperature (°C.)	Products	% Yield	M.P. or B.P. (°C.)	References This Exam.	References See Also:
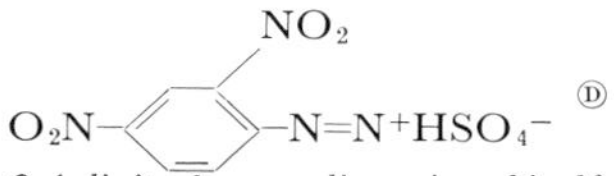 O₂N— benzene (NO₂) —N=N⁺HSO₄⁻ *2,4-dinitrobenzenediazonium bisulfate*	—	10°	©	—	M.P. 172°	595 594	
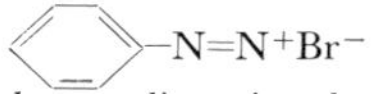 —N=N⁺Br⁻ *benzenediazonium bromide*	2.0	22°	 —CH₂CHBrCN *α-bromohydrocinnamonitrile*	42.3	—	153	1254
—N=N⁺Cl⁻ *benzenediazonium chloride*	1.5	10-11°	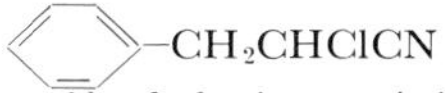 —CH₂CHClCN *α-chlorohydrocinnamonitrile*	39.5	—		
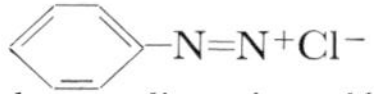 —N=N⁺Cl⁻ *benzenediazonium chloride*			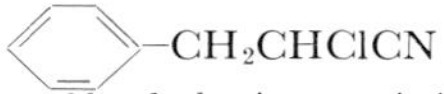 —CH₂CHClCN *α-chlorohydrocinnamonitrile*	81	B.P. 127-128°/12 mm. M.P. 21-22.5°	153	666, 654 1254
 N=N⁺Cl⁻ benzene + SO₂NH₂ benzene *benzenediazonium chloride* + *benzenesulfonamide*	—	5°	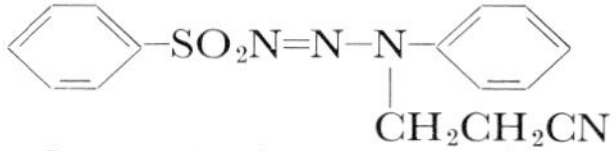 —SO₂N=N—N— CH₂CH₂CN *3-[3-phenyl-1-(phenylsulfonyl)triazen-3-yl]- propionitrile*	—	M.P. 109-111°	1276	
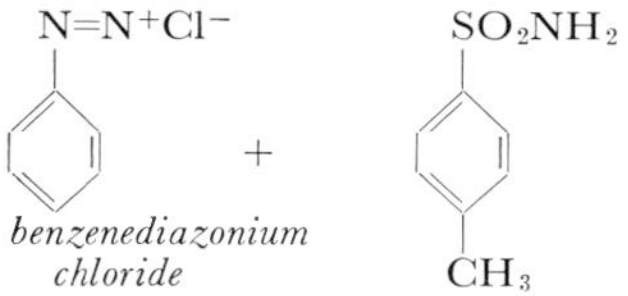 N=N⁺Cl⁻ benzene + CH₃ SO₂NH₂ benzene *benzenediazonium chloride* + *p-toluenesulfonamide*	5 25	—	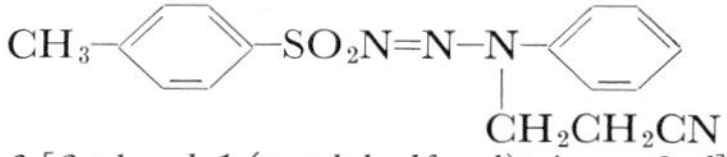 CH₃—SO₂N=N—N— CH₂CH₂CN *3-[3-phenyl-1-(p-tolylsulfonyl)triazen-3-yl]- propionitrile*	—	M.P. 110°	1276	

Reactions with Diazo Compounds

TABLE VII—Continued

Reactants	Reaction Time (Hr.)	Reaction Temperature (°C.)	Products	% Yield	M.P. or B.P. (°C.)	References This Exam.	See Also:
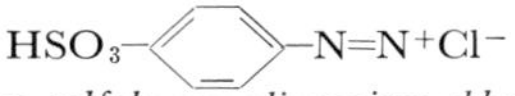 HSO₃-⬡-N=N⁺Cl⁻ *p-sulfobenzenediazonium chloride*	0.5	18°	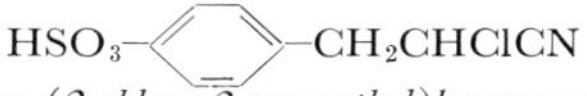 HSO₃-⬡-CH₂CHClCN *p-(2-chloro-2-cyanoethyl)benzenesulfonic acid*	92.7	M.P. 137-139°	153	
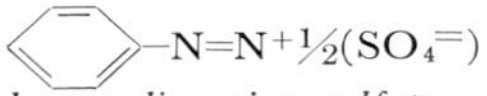 ⬡-N=N⁺½(SO₄⁼) *benzenediazonium sulfate*	0.5	18°	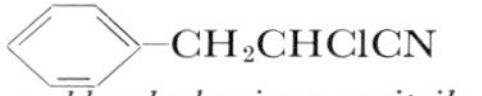 ⬡-CH₂CHClCN *α-chlorohydrocinnamonitrile*	6.0	B.P. 125-135°/14 mm.	153	
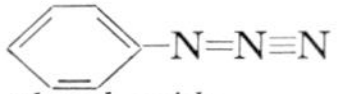 ⬡-N=N=N *phenyl azide*	4	steam bath	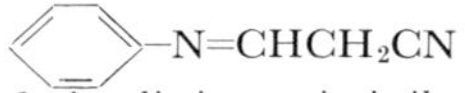 ⬡-N=CHCH₂CN *3-phenyliminopropionitrile*	75	B.P. 115°/4 mm.	1418	
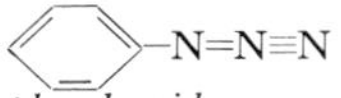 ⬡-N=N=N *phenyl azide*	288	R.T. (sealed tube)	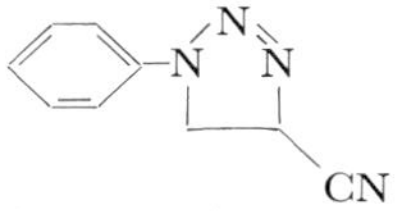 CN triazoline structure *1-phenyl-Δ²-1,2,3-triazoline-4-carbonitrile*	91	M.P. 98° (dec.)	1418	
 H₂N-SO₂-⬡-N=N⁺Cl⁻ *p-sulfamidobenzenediazonium chloride*	0.33	36-40°	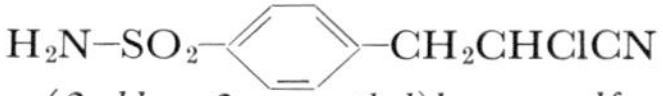 H₂N-SO₂-⬡-CH₂CHClCN *p-(2-chloro-2-cyanoethyl)benzenesulfonamide*	98	—	808	595
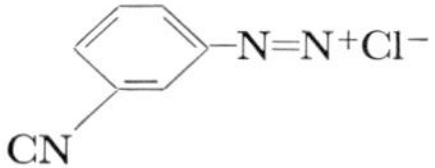 CN-⬡-N=N⁺Cl⁻ *m-cyanobenzenediazonium chloride*	—	—	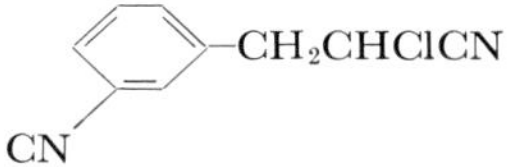 ⬡-CH₂CHClCN, CN *α-chloro-m-cyanohydrocinnamonitrile*	—	B.P. 159°/1 mm.	808	
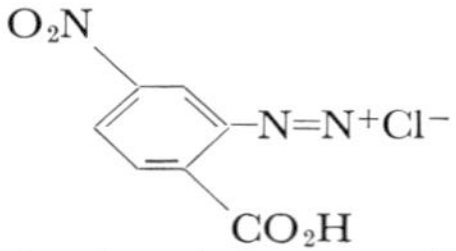 O₂N-⬡(CO₂H)-N=N⁺Cl⁻ *2-carboxy-4-nitrobenzenediazonium chloride*	8	20°	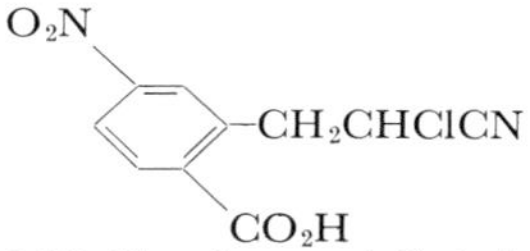 O₂N-⬡-CH₂CHClCN, CO₂H *2-(2-chloro-2-cyanoethyl)-4-nitrobenzoic acid*	47	M.P. 137°	736	

TABLE VII—Continued

Reactions with Diazo Compounds

Reactants	Reaction Temperature (°C.)	Reaction Time (Hr.)	Products	% Yield	M.P. or B.P. (°C.)	References — This Exam.	References — See Also:
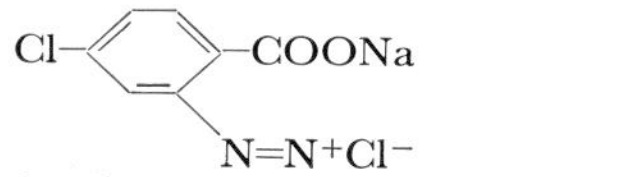 Cl—[C$_6$H$_3$]—COOH with —N=N$^+$Cl$^-$, 2-carboxy-5-chlorobenzenediazonium chloride, sodium salt	40-45°	—	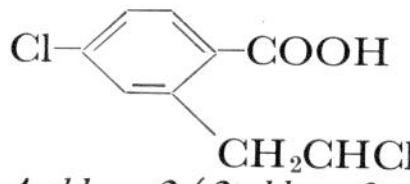 CH$_2$CHClCN; Cl—[C$_6$H$_3$]—COOH, 4-chloro-2-(2-chloro-2-cyanoethyl)benzoic acid	—	M.P. 139°	595 594	
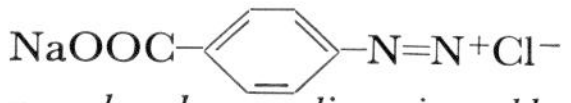 NaOOC—[C$_6$H$_4$]—N=N$^+$Cl$^-$, p-carboxybenzenediazonium chloride, sodium salt	18°	0.5	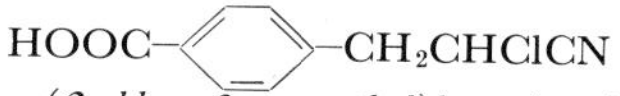 CH$_2$CHClCN; HOOC—[C$_6$H$_4$], p-(2-chloro-2-cyanoethyl)benzoic acid	88.1	M.P. 108-109°	153	
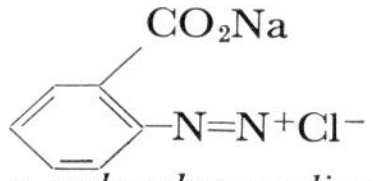 [C$_6$H$_4$—CO$_2$Na]—N=N$^+$Cl$^-$, o-carboxybenzenediazonium chloride, sodium salt	40°	0.5	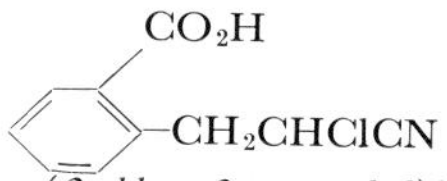 CO$_2$H; CH$_2$CHClCN, o-(2-chloro-2-cyanoethyl)benzoic acid	51	M.P. 121-122°	736	
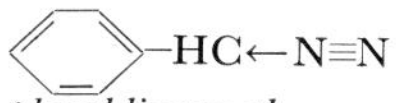 [C$_6$H$_5$]—HC←N≡N, phenyldiazomethane	5° 25°	0.58 18	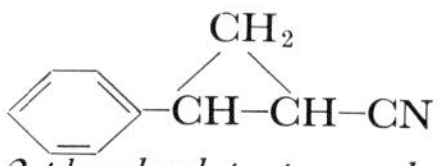 CH$_2$—CH—CH—CN, 2-phenylcyclopropanecarbonitrile	65	B.P. 114°/3.2 mm. M.P. 27-30°	1351	
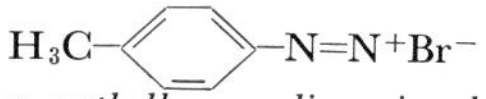 H$_3$C—[C$_6$H$_4$]—N=N$^+$Br$^-$, p-methylbenzenediazonium bromide	5°	1.5-2	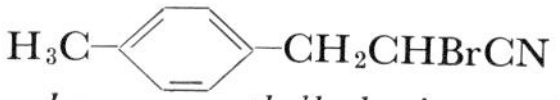 H$_3$C—[C$_6$H$_4$]—CH$_2$CHBrCN, α-bromo-p-methylhydrocinnamonitrile	30.2	B.P. 121-121.5°/2 mm.	1254	
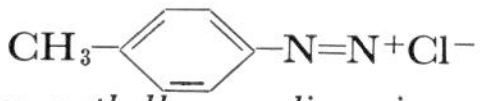 CH$_3$—[C$_6$H$_4$]—N=N$^+$Cl$^-$, p-methylbenzenediazonium chloride	35-40°	2.0	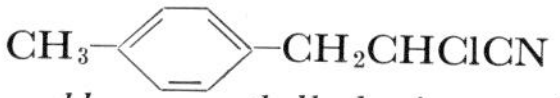 CH$_3$—[C$_6$H$_4$]—CH$_2$CHClCN, α-chloro-p-methylhydrocinnamonitrile	40	B.P. 140-145°/11 mm.	654	595, 594

TABLE VII—Continued

Reactions with Diazo Compounds

Reactants	Reaction Time (Hr.)	Reaction Temperature (°C.)	Products	% Yield	M.P. or B.P. (°C.)	References: This Exam.	See Also:
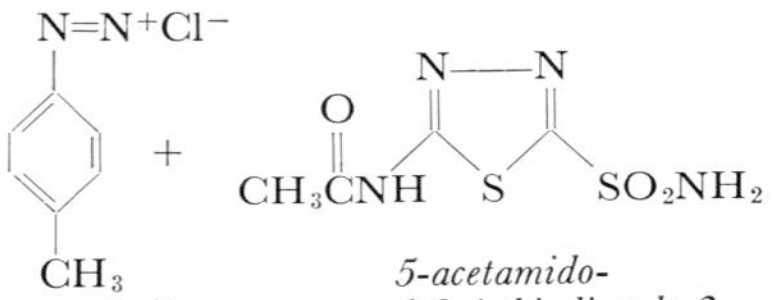 p-methylbenzenediazonium chloride + 5-acetamido-1,3,4-thiadiazole-2-sulfonamide	5	20-25°	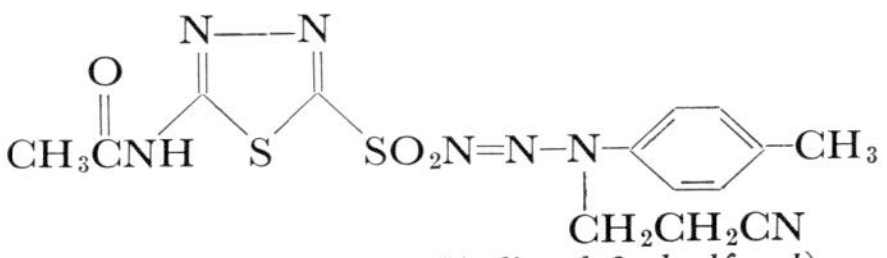 3-[1-(5-acetamido-1,3,4-thiadiazol-2-ylsulfonyl)-3-p-tolyl]propionitrile	—	—	1276	
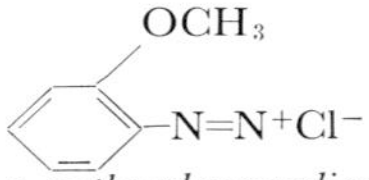 o-methoxybenzenediazonium chloride	4.0	12°	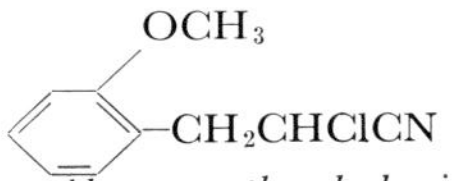 α-chloro-o-methoxyhydrocinnamonitrile	17.2	B.P. 135-140°/13 mm. M.P. 35-37°	153	
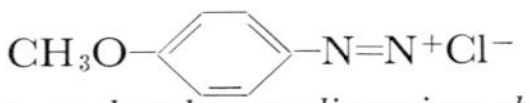 p-methoxybenzenediazonium chloride	4.0	12°	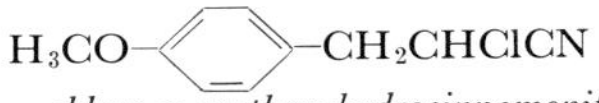 α-chloro-p-methoxyhydrocinnamonitrile	76.2	B.P. 174-179°/25 mm. M.P. 41-42°	153	
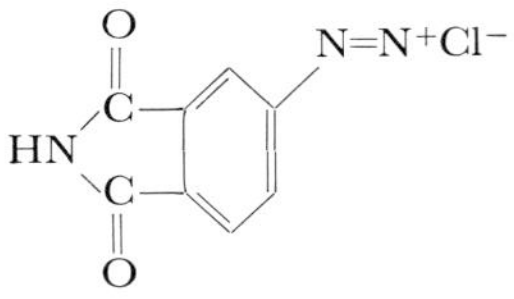 1,3-dioxo-5-isoindolinediazonium chloride	—	15-20° exothermic	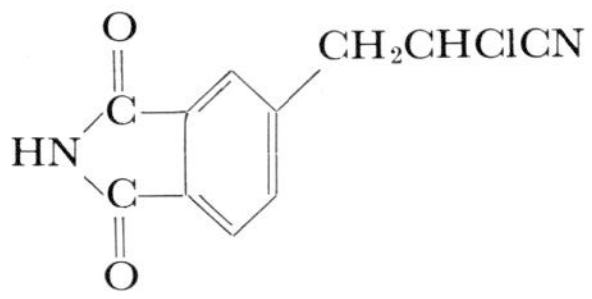 4-(2-chloro-2-cyanoethyl)phthalimide	—	M.P. 147°	1257	
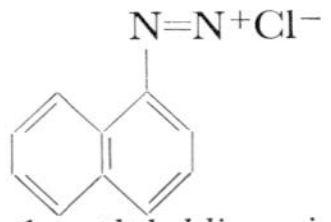 1-naphthyldiazonium chloride	2.0	110°	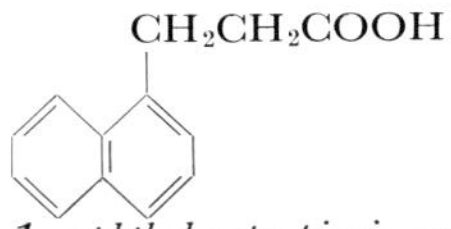 1-naphthalenepropionic acid	45	M.P. 154-155°	1255	

TABLE VII—Continued

Reactions with Diazo Compounds

Reactants	Reaction Time (Hr.)	Reaction Temperature (°C.)	Products	% Yield	M.P. or B.P. (°C.)	References This Exam.	See Also:
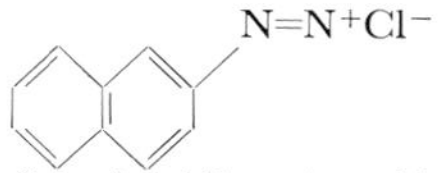 (structure) N=N+Cl− / 2-naphthyldiazonium chloride	2.0	110°	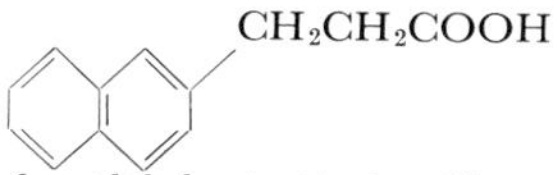 CH_2CH_2COOH / 2-naphthalenepropionic acid	50	M.P. 135°	1255	
 (structure) Cl−+N=N— ... —N=N+Cl− / 4,4'-biphenylbis(diazonium chloride)	—	30–40°	 $NCCHClCH_2$— ... —$CH_2CHClCN$ (D) / α,α'-dichloro-4,4'-biphenyldipropionitrile	—	M.P. 126°	595 594	808
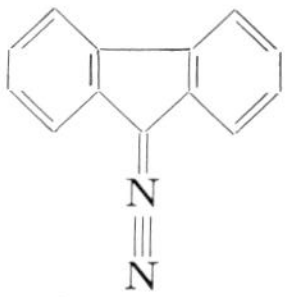 (structure) 9-diazofluorene	24.0	in the cold (E)	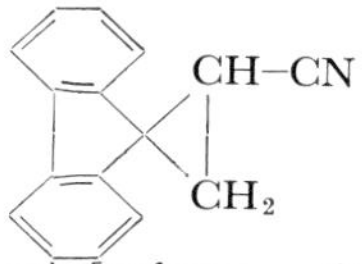 (structure) CH–CN CH₂ / spiro[cyclopropane-1,9'-fluorene]-2-carbonitrile	—	M.P. 102°	537	538
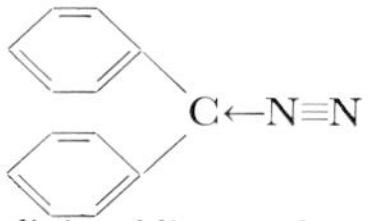 (structure) C←N=N / diphenyldiazomethane	—	25°	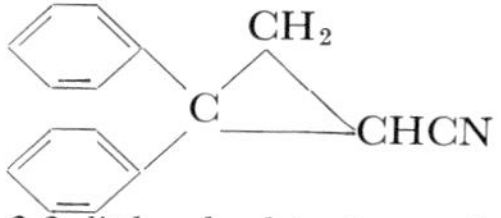 (structure) CH₂ C CHCN / 2,2-diphenylcyclopropanecarbonitrile	64	M.P. 106-107°	1439	

NOTES: (A) Cooling necessary, reaction explosive.
(B) This product is incorrectly identified in reference 808.
(C) Product not identified.
(D) Structure uncertain.
(E) The kinetics of this reaction were determined at 50°C.

TABLE VIII—Reactions with Alcohols and Carbon Monoxide

Reactants	Reaction Time (Hr.)	Reaction Temperature (°C.)	Products	% Yield	M.P. or B.P. (°C.)	References This Exam.	See Also:
$CO + H_2 + CH_3OH$ / carbon monoxide, hydrogen and methanol	—	250°	an amine mixture (avg. C_{15})	—	—	458	

TABLE VIII—Continued

Reactions with Alcohols and Carbon Monoxide

Reactants	Reaction Time (Hr.)	Reaction Temperature (°C.)	Products	% Yield	M.P. or B.P. (°C.)	References This Exam.	See Also:
CO + H₂ + CH₃OH *carbon monoxide, hydrogen and methanol*	1.0	150°	(CH₃O)₂CHCH₂CH₂CN *3-cyanopropionaldehyde, dimethyl acetal*	31.5	B.P. 90-91°/14 mm.	86	
CO + H₂ + HOCH₂CH₂OH *carbon monoxide, hydrogen and ethylene glycol*	1.0	175°	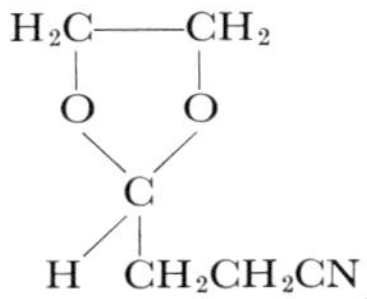 [structure: H₂C—CH₂ / O O / C / H CH₂CH₂CN] *1,3-dioxolane-2-propionitrile*	6.7	B.P. 71-75°/6 mm.	86	

TABLE IX—Miscellaneous Reactions

Reactants	Reaction Time (Hr.)	Reaction Temperature (°C.)	Products	% Yield	M.P. or B.P. (°C.)	References This Exam.	See Also:
CHCl₃ Ⓐ *chloroform*	6.0	190°	ClCH₂CH₂CN *3-chloropropionitrile* Cl₂CHCH₂CHClCN *2,4,4-trichlorobutyronitrile*	30.5 5.9	B.P. 88°/20 mm. B.P. 90.5°/20 mm.	1249	
CCl₄ Ⓐ *carbon tetrachloride*	6.0	160°	Cl₃CCH₂CHClCN *2,4,4,4-tetrachlorobutyronitrile* Cl₃CCH₂CH(CN)CH₂CHClCN *2-chloro-4-(2,2,2-trichloroethyl)glutaronitrile*	28.6 7.3 Ⓑ	B.P. 94°/15 mm. —	1249	
CF₃I *trifluoroiodomethane*	48	—	CF₃CH₂CHICN *3,3,3-trifluoro-2-iodobutyronitrile*	≥72	—	484	
O—O—O *ozone*	—	—	ozonized product Ⓒ	—	—	721	
NaOCOCH₃ + CH₃COOH *sodium acetate + acetic acid*	267	35°	polyacrylonitrile + C₈H₁₂N₂	1.0	B.P. 280°/766 mm.	454	
(CH₃)₂C(OH)CN *2-hydroxyisobutyronitrile*	3.0	70-75°	NCCH₂CH₂CN *succinonitrile*	88	B.P. 149-150°/16 mm. M.P. 53-54°	1361	

TABLE IX—Continued   **Miscellaneous Reactions**

Reactants	Reaction Time (Hr.)	Reaction Temperature (°C.)	Products	% Yield	M.P. or B.P. (°C.)	References This Exam.	See Also:
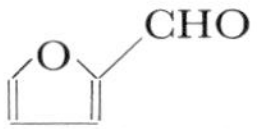 2-furaldehyde (CHO on furan)	5.0	25–30°	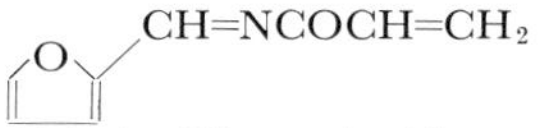 CH=NCOCH=CH₂ — *N-furfurylideneacrylamide*	12.3 cis 20.7 trans	B.P. 139–140°/0.45 mm. B.P. 127–128°/0.4 mm.	1430	
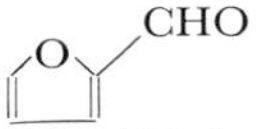 2-furaldehyde	4.0	120–140°	 CH=C(CN)CH₂OCH₂CH₂CN — *2-furfurylidene-3,3'-oxydipropionitrile*	—	B.P. 191–193°/2 mm.	1430	
			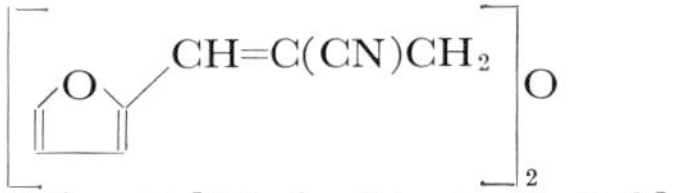 [CH=C(CN)CH₂]₂O — *3,3'-oxybis[2-furfurylidenepropionitrile]*	—	M.P. 85–87°		
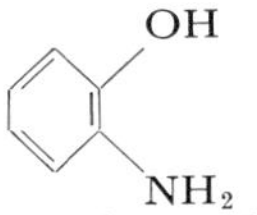 o-aminophenol	—	—	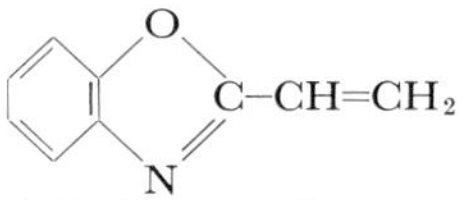 *2-vinylbenzoxazole*	—	—	1403	
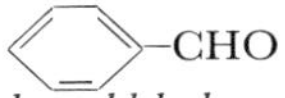 benzaldehyde	9.0	30°	 CH=C(CN)CH₂OCH₂CH₂CN — *2-benzylidene-3,3'-oxydipropionitrile*	18.8	B.P. 170°/0.3 mm.	1442	
			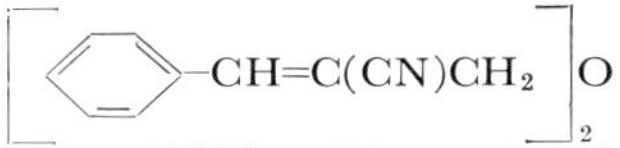 [CH=C(CN)CH₂]₂O — *3,3'-oxybis[2-benzylidenepropionitrile]*	18.1	M.P. 73°		

TABLE IX—Continued

Reactants	Reaction Time (Hr.)	Reaction Temperature (°C.)	Products	% Yield	M.P. or B.P. (°C.)	References: This Exam.	See Also:
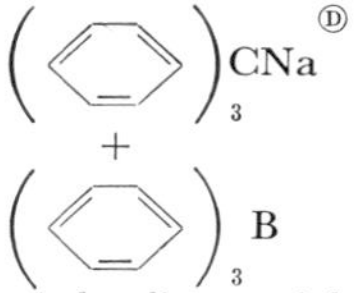 Ⓓ $(C_6H_5)_3CNa$ + B_3 (triphenylborine) trityl sodium + triphenylborine	—	—	 $(C_6H_5)_3CCH_2CH_2CN$ 4,4,4-triphenylbutyronitrile	70	M.P. 137.5-138°	1449	

NOTES: Ⓐ Hydroquinone employed as an inhibitor.
Ⓑ Mixture of isomers.
Ⓒ Structure not given.
Ⓓ Reaction does not occur with trityl sodium alone.

TABLE X—"C" Cyanoethylation: Aldehydes

Reactants	Reaction Time (Hr.)	Reaction Temperature (°C.)	Products	% Yield	M.P. or B.P. (°C.)	References: This Exam.	See Also:
CH_3CHO acetaldehyde	1.0	—	$CHOCH_2CH_2CH_2CN$ 4-cyanobutyraldehyde $CHOCH(CH_2CH_2CN)_2$ 4-cyano-2-(2-cyanoethyl)butyraldehyde	Ⓐ 40-50	B.P. 86-95°/3 mm.	1124	
$CH_3CH=N-$  (cyclohexyl) N-ethylidenecyclohexylamine	—	200°	 (cyclohexyl)$-N=CHC(CH_2CH_2CN)_3$ 4-cyclohexyliminomethylheptanedinitrile	Ⓑ 40	M.P. 109-110°	1315 1317	1258
CH_3CH_2CHO propionaldehyde	—	—	$CH_3CH(CH_2CH_2CN)CHO$ 4-cyano-2-methylbutyraldehyde $CH_3C(CH_2CH_2CN)_2CHO$ 4-cyano-2-(2-cyanoethyl)-2-methylbutyraldehyde	4.9 25.1	B.P. 92-94°/3 mm. B.P. 135.5-137°/3 mm.	1124	
$CH_3CH=CHCHO$ crotonaldehyde	8.0	25°	7.6% N dark red viscous balsam	—	—	182	
$CH_3CH_2CH_2CHO$ n-butyraldehyde	—	reflux	$CH_3CH_2CH_2COCH(CH_3)CN$ 2-methyl-3-oxohexanenitrile	—	B.P. 60°/15 mm.	1024	
$CH_3(CH_2)_2CH=N-(C_4H_9)$ N-butylidene-n-butylamine	—	160°	$CH_3CH_2CH_2CH[CH=N(C_4H_9)]CH_2CH_2CN$ 4-butyliminomethylhexanenitrile	69	B.P. 138-142°/10 mm.	1317	

TABLE X—Continued

"C" Cyanoethylation: Aldehydes

Reactants	Reaction Time (Hr.)	Reaction Temperature (°C.)	Products	% Yield	M.P. or B.P. (°C.)	References This Exam.	References See Also:
$CH_3(CH_2)_2CH=N-$[phenyl]  *N-butylideneaniline*	—	200°	$CH_3CH_2CH(CH_2CH_2CN)CH=N-$[phenyl]  *4-phenyliminomethylhexanenitrile*	76	B.P. 116-120°/0.4 mm.	1317	
$CH_3CH_2CH_2CH=N-$[cyclohexyl]  *N-butylidenecyclohexylamine*	—	150°	$CH_3CH_2CH(CH_2CH_2CN)CH=N-$[cyclohexyl] 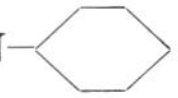 *4-cyclohexyliminomethylhexanenitrile*	80 [C]	B.P. 150-153°/10 mm.	1315 1317	1258
$CH_3CH_2CH_2CH=N-$[cyclohexyl]  *N-butylidenecyclohexylamine*	—	200°	$CH_3CH_2C(CH_2CH_2CN)_2CH=N-$[cyclohexyl]  *4-cyclohexyliminomethyl-4-ethylheptanedinitrile*	70 [D]	M.P. 63-64°	1315 1317	1258
$(CH_3)_2CHCHO$ *isobutyraldehyde*	—	95-105°	$NCCH_2CH_2C(CH_3)_2CHO$ *4-cyano-2,2-dimethylbutyraldehyde*	85	—	916	182, 587, 1084, 1124
$CH_3CHOHCH_2CHO$ *acetaldol*	3.0	25°	*syrup (10.4% N)*	—	—	182	
 [furan]CHO *2-furaldehyde*	—	—	—	—	—		Table IX
$(CH_3CH_2)_2CHCHO$ *2-ethylbutyraldehyde*	3.0	25°	$HCOC(CH_2CH_3)_2CH_2CH_2CN$ *4-cyano-2,2-diethylbutyraldehyde*	66	B.P. 124°/4 mm.	182	1334, 180
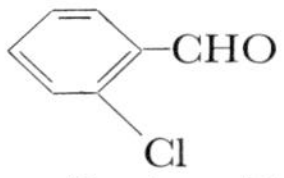 [benzene]CHO with Cl *o-chlorobenzaldehyde*	1.5	25°	*(monocyanoethylation product questionable)*	—	M.P. 125°	182	
C_6H_5CHO *benzaldehyde*	8.0	25°	*(dicyanoethylation product questionable)*	—	B.P. 225-230°/5 mm.	182	Table IX

TABLE X—Continued

"C" Cyanoethylation: Aldehydes

Reactants	Reaction Temperature (°C.)	Reaction Time (Hr.)	Products	% Yield	M.P. or B.P. (°C.)	References This Exam.	References See Also:
CH₃(CH₂)₅CH=N-⬡ *N-heptylidenecyclohexylamine*	150°	—	CH₃(CH₂)₄CH(CH₂CH₂CN)CH=N-⬡ *4-cyclohexyliminomethylnonanenitrile*	60	B.P. 190-194°/0.4 mm.	1315 1317	1258
CH₃CH₂CH₂CH=C(CH₂CH₃)CHO *2-ethylhexenal*	45-55°	4.5	CH₃CH₂CH=CHC(C₂H₅)(CH₂CH₂CN)CHO *2-(2-cyanoethyl)-2-ethylhydrosorbaldehyde*	49	B.P. 138-140°/6 mm.	180	183, 182
CH₃(CH₂)₃CH(C₂H₅)CHO *2-ethylhexanal*	55-58°	4.5	CH₃(CH₂)₃C(C₂H₅)(CH₂CH₂CN)CHO *2-(2-cyanoethyl)-2-ethylhexanal*	79.5	B.P. 140-142°/5 mm.	180	182, 1334
⬡-CH(CH₃)CHO *1-phenylpropionaldehyde*	25° 65°	0.5 1.5	⬡-C(CH₃)(CH₂CH₂CN)CHO *4-cyano-2-methyl-2-phenylbutyraldehyde*	74	B.P. 135-141°/0.6 mm.	411	182
C₆H₁₃CH(CH₃)CHO *2-methyloctanal*	35-38° 25°	0.67 3.5	HCOC(CH₃)(C₆H₁₃)CH₂CH₂CN *2-(2-cyanoethyl)-2-methyloctanal*	—	—	182	
⬡-CH=C(C₅H₁₁)CHO *2-pentylcinnamaldehyde*	25°	2.0	*yellow oil* *7.7% N red oil*	— —	B.P. 205-225°/5 mm. B.P. 260-265°/6 mm.	182	

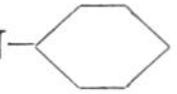

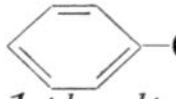

NOTES: Ⓐ One equivalent of acrylonitrile.   Ⓒ Combined yield.
　　　　Ⓑ Two equivalents of acrylonitrile.
　　　　Ⓑ Three equivalents of acrylonitrile.

TABLE XI—"C" Cyanoethylation: Ketones

(A) Aliphatic Ketones

Reactants	Reaction Temperature (°C.)	Reaction Time (Hr.)	Products	% Yield	M.P. or B.P. (°C.)	References This Exam.
CH₃COCH₃ *acetone*	reflux	1.0	CH₃COCH₂CH₂CH₂CN *5-oxohexanenitrile*	18	B.P. 108-112°/14 mm.	93
CH₃COCH₃ *acetone*	reflux	2.0	CH₃COCH₂CH₂CH₂CN *5-oxohexanenitrile* CH₃COCH(CH₂CH₂CN)₂ *4-acetylheptanedinitrile* CH₃COC(CH₂CH₂CN)₃ *4-acetyl-4-(2-cyanoethyl)heptanedinitrile*	8 15 24	B.P. 93-98°/6 mm. B.P. 196-199°/6 mm. M.P. 152°	1066 1067

TABLE XI—Continued

(A) Aliphatic Ketones

Reactants	Reaction Time (Hr.)	Reaction Temperature (°C.)	Products	% Yield	M.P. or B.P. (°C.)	References This Exam.	References See Also:
CH_3COCH_3 / acetone	2.0	0-5°	$CH_3COC(CH_2CH_2CN)_3$ / 4-acetyl-4-(2-cyanoethyl)heptanedinitrile	77	M.P. 154°	177 160	1077, 167, 169, 426, 989
$CH_3COCH_2CH_3$ / methyl ethyl ketone	0.1	10°	$CH_3COCH(CH_2CH_2CN)CH_3$ / 4-acetylvaleronitrile	29.4	B.P. 114-115°/15 mm.	93	1313
$CH_3COCH_2CH_3$ / methyl ethyl ketone	5.0	5-10°	$CH_3COC(CH_3)(CH_2CH_2CN)_2$ / 4-acetyl-4-methylheptanedinitrile	89	M.P. 67°	177	998, 1162, 1149, 167, 169, 692, 93, 962
$CH_3COCH_2CH_2CN$ / levulinonitrile	—	85-90°	$CH_3COC(CH_2CH_2CN)_2CH_2CN$ / 4-acetyl-4-cyanomethylheptanedinitrile	85	M.P. 85-86°	917	
$CH_3COCH_2CH_2CH_3$ / 2-pentanone	50	110°	$CH_3COCH(CH_2CH_3)CH_2CH_2CN$ / 4-acetylhexanenitrile	62	B.P. 85-92°/0.7 mm.	1318	1313
$CH_3COCH_2CH_2CH_3$ / 2-pentanone	1.0	15°	$CH_3COC(CH_2CH_3)(CH_2CH_2CN)_2$ / 4-acetyl-4-ethylheptanedinitrile / $NCCH_2CH_2COC(CH_2CH_2CN)_2CH_2CH_3$ / 4-(2-cyanoethyl)-4-ethyl-5-oxononanedinitrile	43 / 9	M.P. 109° / M.P. 90-91°	177	
$CH_3CH_2CH_2C(CH_3)=N(C_4H_9)$ / N-(1-methyl)butylidene-n-butylamine	—	160°	$CH_3CH_2CH_2CH(CH_2CH_2CN)C(CH_3)=N(C_4H_9)$ / 5-butylimino-4-ethylhexanenitrile	70	B.P. 98-101°/0.3 mm.	1316	1316
$CH_3CH_2CH_2C=N-\bigcirc$ 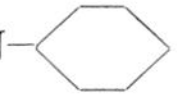 , CH_3 / 1-methylbutylidenecyclohexylamine	—	150°	$CH_3CH_2CH(CH_2CH_2CN)C(CH_3)=N-\bigcirc$ 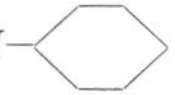 / 4-(1-cyclohexyliminoethyl)hexanenitrile	68	B.P. 111-114°/0.4 mm.	1315 1316	1258
$CH_3COCH(CH_3)_2$ / 3-methyl-2-butanone	—	—	$CH_3COC(CH_3)_2CH_2CH_2CN$ / 4,4-dimethyl-5-oxohexanenitrile	61	B.P. 134°/18 mm.	204	

TABLE XI—Continued

(A) Aliphatic Ketones

Reactants	Reaction Time (Hr.)	Reaction Temperature (°C.)	Products	% Yield	M.P. or B.P. (°C.)	References This Exam.	See Also:
$(CH_3)_2C=CHCOCH_3$ *mesityl oxide*	—	5-10°	$(CH_3)_2C=C(CH_2CH_2CN)COCH_3$ *4-acetyl-5-methyl-4-hexenenitrile* $CH_2=C(CH_3)C(CH_2CH_2CN)_2COCH_3$ *4-acetyl-4-isopropenylheptanedinitrile*	10-15 73.5	B.P. 110-115°/2 mm. M.P. 116-117°	178	167, 169, 998, 405
$CH_3COCH_2(CH_2)_2CH_3$ *2-hexanone*	3.0 2.0	<5° 5-10°	$CH_3COC(CH_2CH_2CN)_2CH_2CH_2CH_3$ *4-acetyl-4-propylheptanedinitrile*	—	B.P. 205-210°/2 mm. M.P. 63°	177	
$CH_3COCH_2CH(CH_3)_2$ *4-methyl-2-pentanone*	3.0 2.0	<5° 5-10°	$CH_3COC(CH_2CH_2CN)_2CH(CH_3)_2$ *4-acetyl-4-isopropylheptanedinitrile*	20	B.P. 200-205°/1 mm. M.P. 101°	177	178
$CH_3COCH_2CH_2CH_2CH_2CH_3$ *2-heptanone*	3.0 2.0	<5° 5-10°	$CH_3COC(C_4H_9)(CH_2CH_2CN)_2$ *4-acetyl-4-butylheptanedinitrile*	50	B.P. 195-200°/1 mm. M.P. 47° M.P. 63°	177	167, 169
$(CH_3)_2CHCOCH(CH_3)_2$ *2,4-dimethyl-3-pentanone*	4.0	100°	$(CH_3)_2CHCOC(CH_2CH_2CN)(CH_3)_2$ *4,4,6-trimethyl-5-oxoheptanenitrile* $[(CH_3)_2C(CH_2CH_2CN)]_2C=O$ *4,4,6,6-tetramethyl-5-oxononanedinitrile*	46	B.P. 116-118°/7 mm. B.P. 165-170°/1 mm.	1422 169	167, 1419
$CH_3CH_2CH_2COCH_2CH_2CH_3$ *4-heptanone*	5.5 O.N.	50-60° 25°	$CH_3(CH_2)_2COCH(C_2H_5)CH_2CH_2CN$ *4-ethyl-5-oxooctanenitrile*	31	B.P. 101.5-102°/4 mm.	1423	
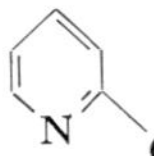 (2-pyridyl)—CH_2COCH_3 *(2-pyridyl)-2-propanone*	— 5 min.	60° reflux	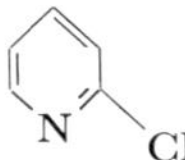 (2-pyridyl)—$CH(COCH_3)CH_2CH_2CN$ *γ-acetyl-2-pyridinebutyronitrile*	44.5	M.P. 34°	1211	
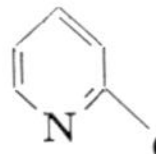 (2-pyridyl)—CH_2COCH_3 *(2-pyridyl)-2-propanone*	— 5 min.	60° reflux	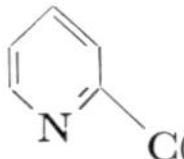 (2-pyridyl)—$C(CH_2CH_2CN)_2COCH_3$ *4-acetyl-4-(2-pyridyl)heptanedinitrile*	82	M.P. 111.5°	1211	

TABLE XI—Continued

(A) Aliphatic Ketones

Reactants	Reaction Temperature (°C.)	Reaction Time (Hr.)	Products	% Yield	M.P. or B.P. (°C.)	References — This Exam.	References — See Also:
$(CH_3)_2CHCOCH_2CH_2CH_2CH_3$ *2-methyl-3-heptanone*	—	—	$CH_3(CH_2)_3COC(CH_3)_2CH_2CH_2CN$ *4,4-dimethyl-5-oxononanenitrile* $(CH_3)_2CHCOCH(C_3H_7)CH_2CH_2CN$ *6-methyl-5-oxo-4-propylheptanenitrile*	— —	B.P. 132°/5 mm. B.P. 127°/5 mm.	1224	
$CH_3CO(CH_2)_5CH_3$ *2-octanone*	<5° 5-10°	3.0 2.0	$CH_3COC(C_5H_{11})(CH_2CH_2CN)_2$ *4-acetyl-4-pentylheptanedinitrile*	50	—	177	167, 169
[C6H5]—CH₂COCH₃ *phenyl-2-propanone*	20-25°	1.0	[C6H5]—C(COCH₃)(CH₂CH₂CN)₂ *4-acetyl-4-phenylheptanedinitrile*	86 (A)	M.P. 109-110°	177	1222
$(CH_3)_2C{=}CH{-}CO{-}CH{=}C(CH_3)_2$ *phorone*	25°	20.0	$(CH_3)_2C{=}CHCOC(CH_2CH_2CN){=}C(CH_3)_2$ *4-isopropylidene-7-methyl-5-oxo-6-octenenitrile* $O{=}C[C(CH_2CH_2CN){=}C(CH_3)_2]_2$ *4,6-diisopropylidene-5-oxononanedinitrile*		B.P. 120°/1 mm. B.P. 190-200°/1 mm.	167 169	
$C_5H_{11}COCH(CH_3)_2$ *2-methyl-3-octanone*	—	—	$C_5H_{11}COC(CH_3)_2CH_2CH_2CN$ *4,4-dimethyl-5-oxodecanenitrile*	—	B.P. 156-159°/11 mm.	204	
$CH_3COCH(C_2H_5)PO(OC_2H_5)_2$ *3-diethylphosphono-2-pentanone*	reflux	4.0	$(C_2H_5O)_2POC{-}COCH_3$ with C_2H_5 and CH_2CH_2CN *(1-acetyl-3-cyano-1-ethylpropyl)phosphonic acid, diethyl ester*	70.5	B.P. 185°/5 mm.	1386	
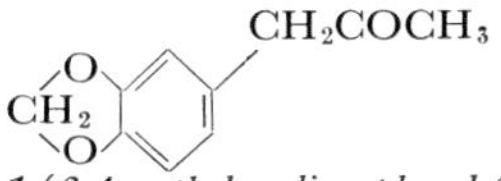 [3,4-methylenedioxyphenyl]—CH₂COCH₃ *1-(3,4-methylenedioxyphenyl)-2-propanone*	50°	3.0	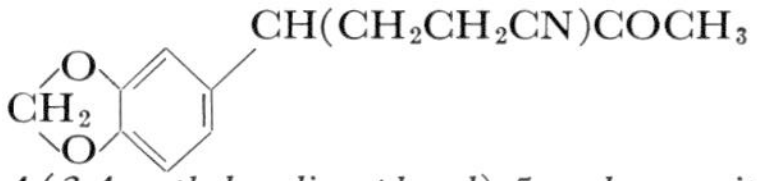 [3,4-methylenedioxyphenyl]—CH(CH₂CH₂CN)COCH₃ *4-(3,4-methylenedioxyphenyl)-5-oxohexanenitrile*	22.9	B.P. 220-225°/20 mm.	1222	
$CH_3COC(CH_3)(CH_2CH_2CN)_2$ *4-acetyl-4-methylheptanedinitrile*	25°	48.0	$(NCCH_2CH_2)_2CHCOC(CH_3)(CH_2CH_2CN)_2$ *4-methyl-4,4'-carbonyldiheptanedinitrile*	13	B.P. 345-355°/2 mm. M.P. 84-85°	177	

TABLE XI—Continued

(A) Aliphatic Ketones

Reactants	Reaction Time (Hr.)	Reaction Temperature (°C.)	Products	% Yield	M.P. or B.P. (°C.)	References This Exam.	References See Also:
 $COCH(CH_3)_2$ (cyclohexane ring) *cyclohexyl isopropyl ketone*	—	—	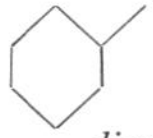 $COC(CH_3)_2CH_2CH_2CN$ (cyclohexane ring) *γ,γ-dimethyl-δ-oxocyclohexanevaleronitrile*	22	M.P. 63°	1423	
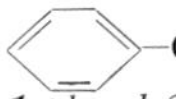 (phenyl)$-CH_2COCH(CH_3)_2$ *1-phenyl-3-methyl-2-butanone*	3.0	—	 (phenyl)$-CH(CH_2CH_2CN)COCH(CH_3)_2$ *6-methyl-5-oxo-4-phenylheptanenitrile*	75	B.P. 218-222°/71 mm.	204	
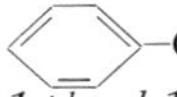 (phenyl)$-CH(C_2H_5)COCH_3$ *1-phenyl-1-ethyl-2-propanone*	—	—	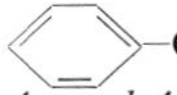 (phenyl)$-C(CH_2CH_3)(CH_2CH_2CN)COCH_3$ *4-acetyl-4-phenylhexanenitrile*	59	B.P. 205-215°/20 mm.	204	
$CH_3COC(CH_2CH_2CN)_3$ *4-acetyl-4-(2-cyanoethyl)heptanedinitrile*	2.0	40°	$NC(CH_2)_3COC(CH_2CH_2CN)_3$ *4,4-bis(2-cyanoethyl)-5-oxononanedinitrile*	13	B.P. 320-340°/1-3 mm. M.P. 121-122°	177	
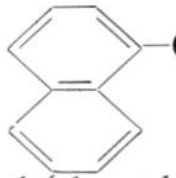 (naphthyl)$-CH_2COCH_3$ *1-(1-naphthyl)-2-propanone*	3.0	50°	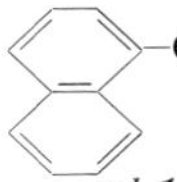 (naphthyl)$-CH(CH_2CH_2CN)COCH_3$ *γ-acetyl-1-naphthalenebutyronitrile*	62.5	B.P. 195-200°/6 mm.	1222	
$C_9H_{19}COCH(CH_3)_2$ *2-methyl-3-dodecanone*	—	—	$C_9H_{19}COC(CH_3)_2CH_2CH_2CN$ *4,4-dimethyl-5-oxotetradecanenitrile*	64	B.P. 210-220°/10 mm.	204	
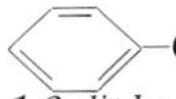 (phenyl)$-CH_2COCH_2-$(phenyl)  *1,3-diphenyl-2-propanone*	18.0	25°	 $\left[-C(CH_2CH_2CN)_2\right]_2CO$ (phenyl) *4,4'-carbonylbis[4-phenylheptanedinitrile]*	—	—	159	167, 169, 177
 (diphenyl)$-CHCOCH_3$ *1,1-diphenyl-2-propanone*	—	—	 $NCCH_2CH_2CCOCH_3$  (diphenyl) *5-oxo-4,4-diphenylhexanenitrile*	—	—	765	

TABLE XI—Continued

(A) Aliphatic Ketones

Reactants	Reaction Time (Hr.)	Reaction Temperature (°C.)	Products	% Yield	M.P. or B.P. (°C.)	References This Exam.	See Also:
 C6H5—CH(C8H17)COCH3 — 3-phenyl-2-undecanone	—	—	 C6H5—C(CH2CH2CN)(C8H17)COCH3 — 4-acetyl-4-phenyldodecanenitrile	44	B.P. 217°/2-3 mm.	204	

(B) Alkylaryl Ketones

Reactants	Reaction Time (Hr.)	Reaction Temperature (°C.)	Products	% Yield	M.P. or B.P. (°C.)	References This Exam.	See Also:
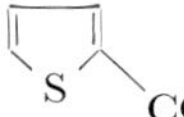 S-COCH3 — 2-thienyl methyl ketone	2.0	30°	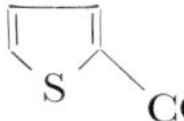 S-COC(CH2CH2CN)3 — 4-(2-cyanoethyl)-4-(2-thenoyl)heptanedinitrile	89	M.P. 145-146°	1185	184
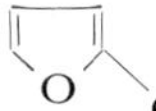 O-COCH3 — 2-furyl methyl ketone	18.0	30°	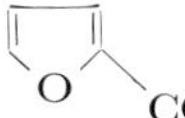 O-COC(CH2CH2CN)3 — 4-(2-cyanoethyl)-4-(2-furoyl)heptanedinitrile	90	M.P. 121-122°	184	1185
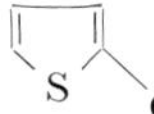 S-COC2H5 — 2-thienyl ethyl ketone	24.0	30°	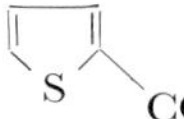 S-COC(CH2CH2CN)2CH3 — 4-methyl-4-(2-thenoyl)heptanedinitrile	98	M.P. 81-82°	184	
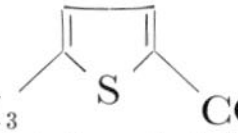 CH3-S-COCH3 — methyl 5-methyl-2-thienyl ketone	2.0	25°	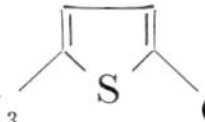 CH3-S-COC(CH2CH2CN)3 — 4-(2-cyanoethyl)-4-(5-methyl-2-thenoyl)heptanedinitrile	79.6	M.P. 130.5-131.5°	6	
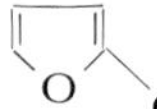 O-COCH2CH3 — 2-furyl ethyl ketone	24.0	30°	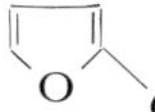 O-COC(CH2CH2CN)2CH3 — 4-(2-furoyl)-4-methylheptanedinitrile	98	M.P. 49°	184	
 CH3-O-COCH3 — methyl 5-methyl-2-furyl ketone	2.0	25°	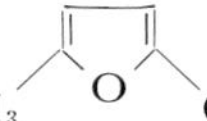 CH3-O-COC(CH2CH2CN)3 — 4-(2-cyanoethyl)-4-(5-methyl-2-furoyl)heptanedinitrile	70.9	M.P. 177-177.7°	6	

TABLE XI—Continued

(B) Alkylaryl Ketones

Reactants	Reaction Time (Hr.)	Reaction Temperature (°C.)	Products	% Yield	M.P. or B.P. (°C.)	References	
						This Exam.	See Also:
Br—⟨ring⟩—COCH₃ $\ p$-bromoacetophenone	2–4.0	25–30°	Br—⟨ring⟩—COC(CH₂CH₂CN)₃ $\ 4$-(p-bromobenzoyl)-4-(2-cyanoethyl)heptanedinitrile	85	M.P. 151-152°	159 177	167, 169
Cl—⟨ring⟩—COCH₃ $\ p$-chloroacetophenone	2–4.0	25–30°	Cl—⟨ring⟩—COC(CH₂CH₂CN)₃ $\ 4$-(p-chlorobenzoyl)-4-(2-cyanoethyl)heptanedinitrile	90	M.P. 141-142°	177 159	167, 169
C₆H₅COCH₃ $\ $acetophenone	26	180°	C₆H₅CO(CH₂)₃CN $\ 4$-benzoylbutyronitrile	75.5	B.P. 128-135°/0.7 mm.	1318	1222
C₆H₅COCH₃ $\ $acetophenone	—	—	C₆H₅COC(CH₂CH₂CN)₃ $\ 4$-benzoyl-4-(2-cyanoethyl)heptanedinitrile	—	M.P. 126°	1334	
C₆H₅COCH₃ $\ $acetophenone	0.2	<95°	C₆H₅COCH(CH₂CH₂CN)₂ $\ 4$-benzoylheptanedinitrile	90 [B]	B.P. 190-240°/2 mm.	407	1077, 159, 11, 1085, 177, 1185, 167, 169
⟨S-thienyl⟩—COCH₂CH₂CH₃ $\ $2-thienyl propyl ketone	2.0	25°	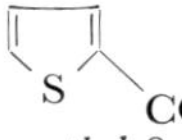 ⟨S-thienyl⟩—COCH(CH₂CH₂CN)CH₂CH₃ $\ \gamma$-ethyl-8-oxo-2-thiophenevaleronitrile	36	B.P. 154-156°/2.5 mm.	6	
			⟨S-thienyl⟩—COC(CH₂CH₂CN)₂CH₂CH₃ $\ 4$-ethyl-4-(2-thenoyl)heptanedinitrile	48.3	M.P. 95.5-96°		
CH₃⟨S-thienyl⟩—COCH₂CH₃ $\ $ethyl 5-methyl-2-thienyl ketone	2.0	25°	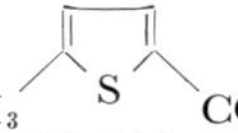 CH₃⟨S-thienyl⟩—COC(CH₂CH₂CN)₂CH₂CH₃ $\ 4$-methyl-4-(5-methyl-2-thenoyl)heptanedinitrile	70.4	M.P. 79-80°	6	
⟨O-furyl⟩—COCH₂CH₂CH₃ $\ $2-furyl propyl ketone	24.0	R.T.	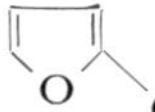 ⟨O-furyl⟩—COC(CH₂CH₂CN)₂CH₂CH₃ $\ 4$-ethyl-4-(2-furoyl)heptanedinitrile	68	M.P. 102°	184	

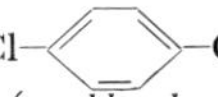

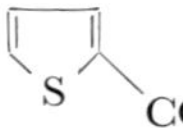

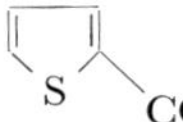

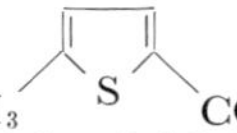

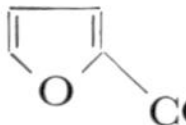

TABLE XI—Continued

(B) Alkylaryl Ketones

Reactants	Reaction Time (Hr.)	Reaction Temperature (°C.)	Products	% Yield	M.P. or B.P. (°C.)	References: This Exam.	References: See Also:
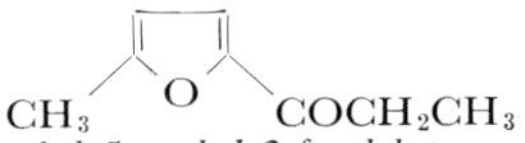 CH3 O COCH2CH3 *ethyl 5-methyl-2-furyl ketone*	2.0	25°	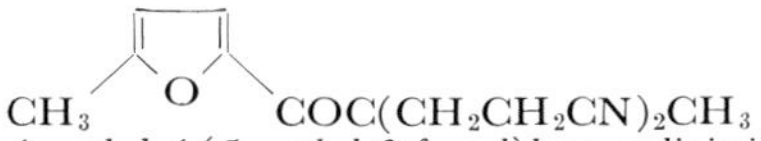 CH3 O COC(CH2CH2CN)2CH3 *4-methyl-4-(5-methyl-2-furoyl)heptanedinitrile*	61.5	M.P. 58-59° B.P. 215-218°/3 mm.	6	
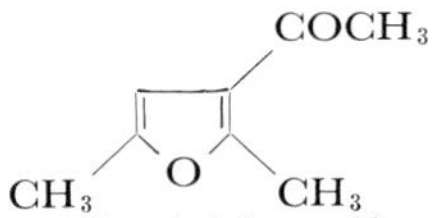 COCH3 CH3 O CH3 *2,5-dimethyl-3-acetylfuran*	168.0	25°	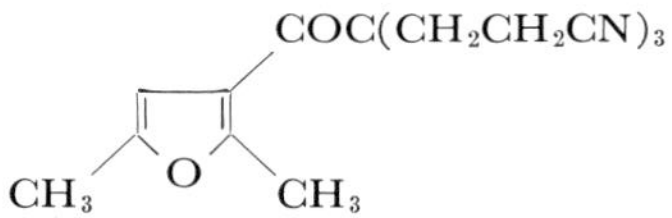 COC(CH2CH2CN)3 CH3 O CH3 *4-(2-cyanoethyl)-4-(2,5-dimethyl-3-furoyl)heptanedinitrile*	15.7	M.P. 169-170°	6	
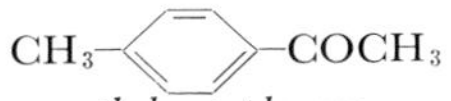 CH3 COCH3 p-*methylacetophenone*	2-4.0	25-30°	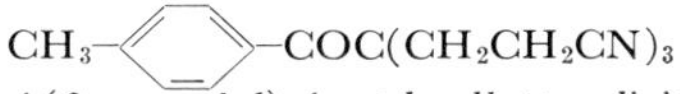 CH3 COC(CH2CH2CN)3 *4-(2-cyanoethyl)-4-*p-*toluoylheptanedinitrile*	90	M.P. 161-162°	177 159	167 169
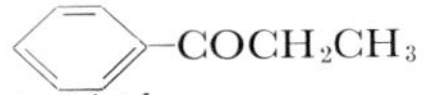 COCH2CH3 *propiophenone*	3.0	50-60°	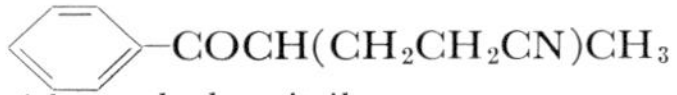 COCH(CH2CH2CN)CH3 *4-benzoylvaleronitrile*	72	B.P. 121-123°/17 mm.	1423	
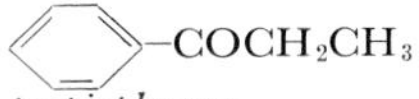 COCH2CH3 *propiophenone*	5.0	25-30°	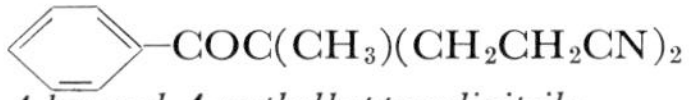 COC(CH3)(CH2CH2CN)2 *4-benzoyl-4-methylheptanedinitrile*	95	M.P. 66°	159 177 167 169	411
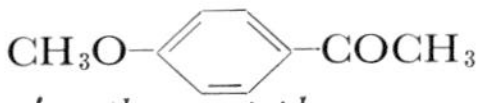 CH3O COCH3 p′-*methoxyacetophenone*	5.0	25°	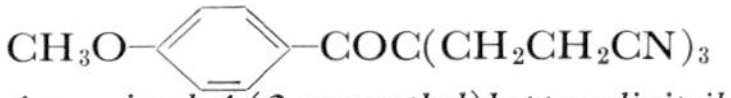 CH3O COC(CH2CH2CN)3 *4-*p-*anisoyl-4-(2-cyanoethyl)heptanedinitrile*	—	M.P. 133°	167 169	159 177
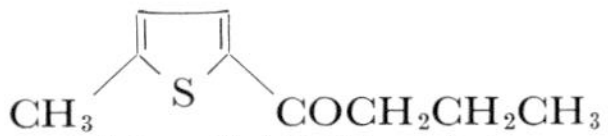 CH3 S COCH2CH2CH3 *propyl 5-methyl-2-thienyl ketone*	3.0	reflux	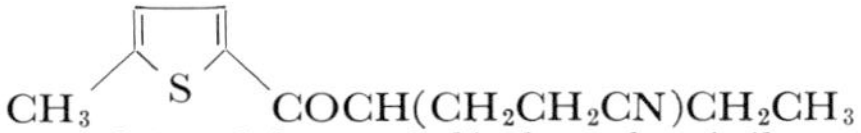 CH3 S COCH(CH2CH2CN)CH2CH3 *γ-ethyl-5-methyl-δ-oxo-2-thiophenevaleronitrile*	43.2	B.P. 159-160°/2 mm.	6	

89359

TABLE XI—Continued

(B) Alkylaryl Ketones

Reactants	Reaction Temperature (°C.)	Reaction Time (Hr.)	Products	% Yield	M.P. or B.P. (°C.)	References This Exam.	References See Also:
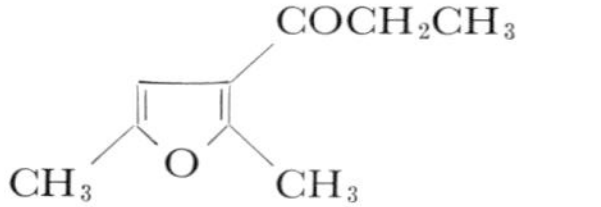 COCH₂CH₃ structure with CH₃, O, CH₃ — *2,5-dimethylfuryl ethyl ketone*	reflux	3.0	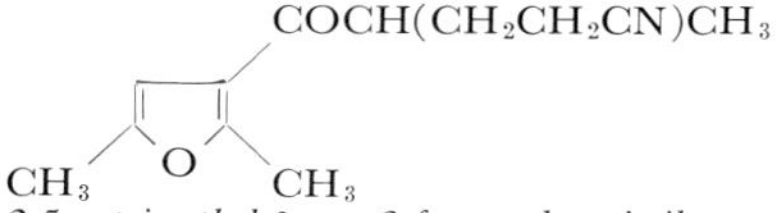 COCH(CH₂CH₂CN)CH₃ on furan with CH₃, O, CH₃ — *2,5,γ-trimethyl-δ-oxo-3-furanvaleronitrile*	56	B.P. 157-158°/8 mm.	6	
 COCH₂CH₂CH₃ on furan with CH₃, O — *propyl 5-methyl-2-furyl ketone*	25°	120.0	 COCH(CH₂CH₂CN)CH₂CH₃ on furan with CH₃, O — *γ-ethyl-5-methyl-δ-oxo-2-furanvaleronitrile*	22.9	B.P. 153-154.5°/5 mm.	6	
			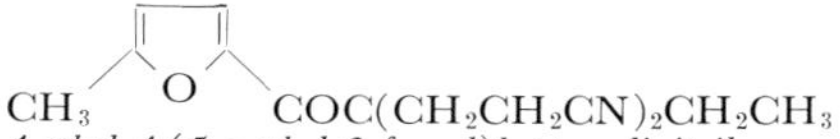 COC(CH₂CH₂CN)₂CH₂CH₃ on furan with CH₃, O — *4-ethyl-4-(5-methyl-2-furoyl)heptanedinitrile*	47.2	M.P. 93-94°	177 167 168 169	
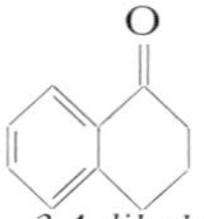 *3,4-dihydro-1[2H]-naphthalenone* (structure)	30°	24.0	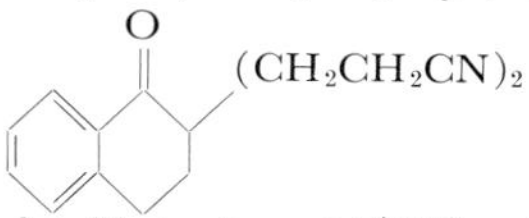 (CH₂CH₂CN)₂ (structure) — *3,4-dihydro-1-oxo-2,2(1H)-naphthalenedipropionitrile*	—	B.P. 250-260°/1 mm. M.P. 80°		
—COCH₂CH₂CH₃ *butyrophenone*	25°	O.N.	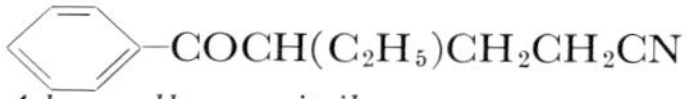 —COCH(C₂H₅)CH₂CN *4-benzoylhexanenitrile*	62	B.P. 153-154°/4 mm.	1314	
—COCH(CH₃)₂ *isobutyrophenone*	25°	1.5	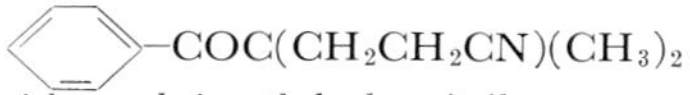 —COC(CH₂CH₂CN)(CH₃)₂ *4-benzoyl-4-methylvaleronitrile*	62	B.P. 159-162°/4 mm.	1419	1422
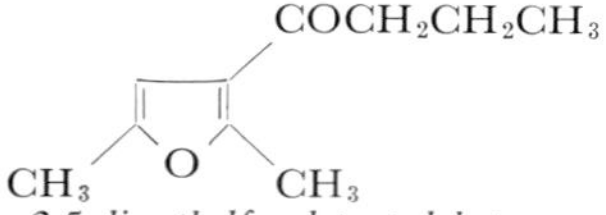 COCH₂CH₂CH₃ on furan with CH₃, O, CH₃ — *2,5-dimethylfuryl propyl ketone*	25°	168.0	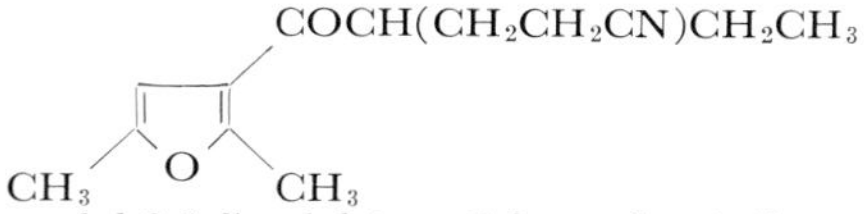 COCH(CH₂CH₂CN)CH₂CH₃ on furan with CH₃, O, CH₃ — *γ-ethyl-2,5-dimethyl-δ-oxo-3-furanvaleronitrile*	54.3	B.P. 137.5-138°/2 mm. M.P. 51-52°	6	

TABLE XI—Continued

(B) Alkylaryl Ketones

Reactants	Reaction Temperature (°C.)	Reaction Time (Hr.)	Products	% Yield	M.P. or B.P. (°C.)	References This Exam.	References See Also:
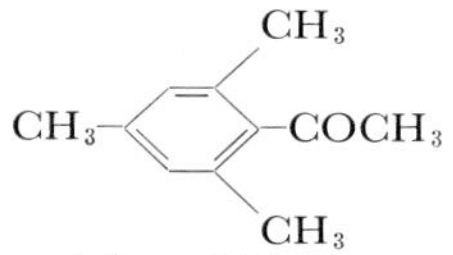 methyl mesityl ketone (CH₃)₃C₆H₂COCH₃	25-30°	2-4.0	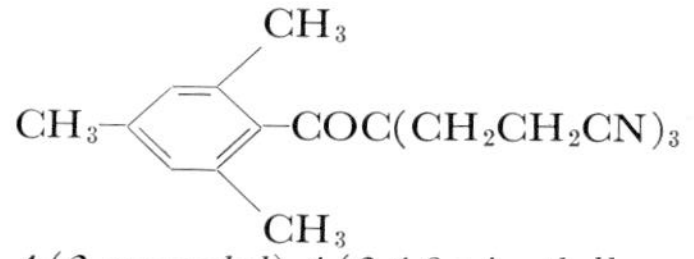 4-(2-cyanoethyl)-4-(2,4,6-trimethylbenzoyl)heptane-dinitrile $CH_3C_6H_2(CH_3)_2COC(CH_2CH_2CN)_3$	30	M.P. 126°	177	
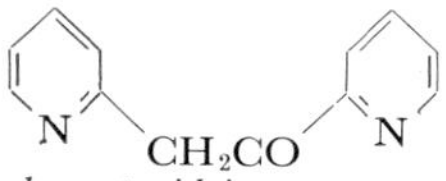 desoxypyridoin	<60° reflux	— 5 min.	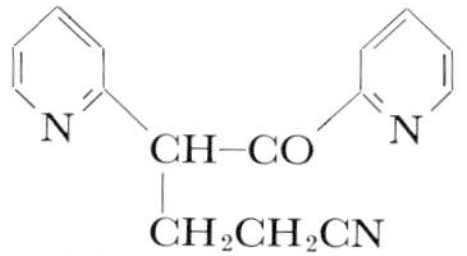 4,5-di-2-pyridyl-5-oxovaleronitrile	51	M.P. 72°	1211	
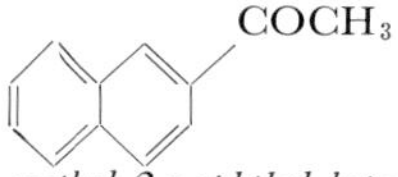 methyl 2-naphthyl ketone	25-30°	2-4.0	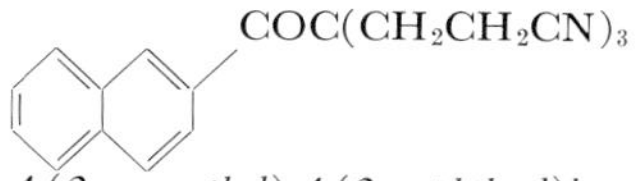 4-(2-cyanoethyl)-4-(2-naphthoyl)heptanedinitrile	90	M.P. 122°	159 177 167 169	
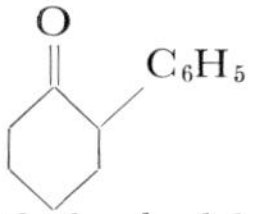 2-phenylcyclohexanone	25-45°	2.0	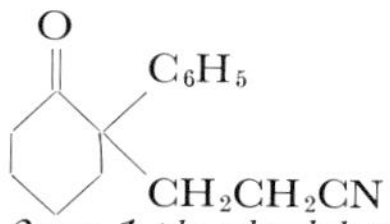 2-oxo-1-phenylcyclohexanepropionitrile	70	B.P. 150-160°/0.4 mm.	60	
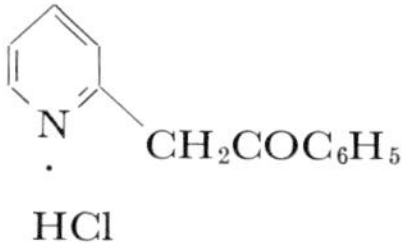 2-pyridylacetophenone hydrochloride (HCl)	<60° reflux	— 5 min.	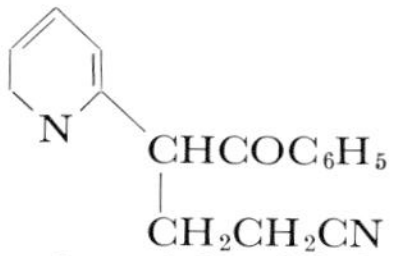 γ-benzoyl-2-pyridinebutyronitrile	48	M.P. 75°	1211	

TABLE XI—Continued

(B) Alkylaryl Ketones

Reactants	Re-action Time (Hr.)	Reaction Tem-perature (°C.)	Products	% Yield	M.P. or B.P. (°C.)	References This Exam.	See Also:
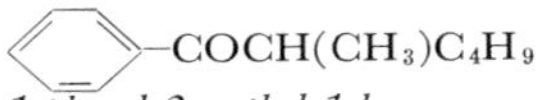 —COCH(CH₃)C₄H₉ *1-phenyl-2-methyl-1-hexanone*	—	—	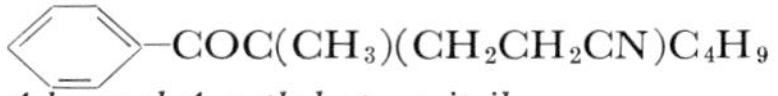 —COC(CH₃)(CH₂CH₂CN)C₄H₉ *4-benzoyl-4-methyloctanenitrile*	47	—	204	
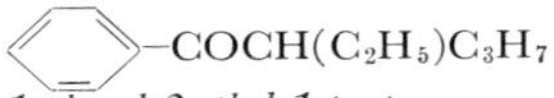 —COCH(C₂H₅)C₃H₇ *1-phenyl-2-ethyl-1-pentanone*	—	—	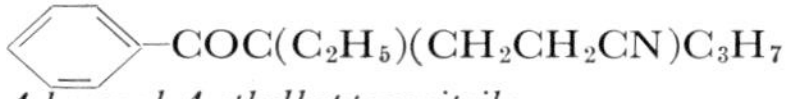 —COC(C₂H₅)(CH₂CH₂CN)C₃H₇ *4-benzoyl-4-ethylheptanenitrile*	—	—	204	
 —COCH₃ *p-phenylacetophenone*	2-4.0	25-30°	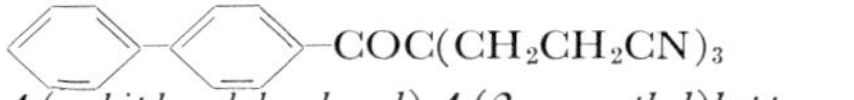 —COC(CH₂CH₂CN)₃ *4-(p-biphenylylcarbonyl)-4-(2-cyanoethyl)heptane-dinitrile*	90	M.P. 178°	159 177 167 169	
 —COCH₂— *desoxybenzoin*	3.0	50°	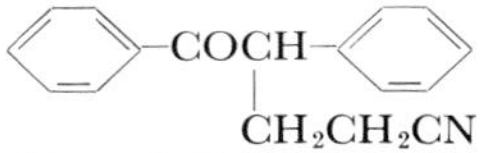 —COCH CH₂CH₂CN *4-benzoyl-4-phenylbutyronitrile*	93.9	M.P. 86.7-87°	1222	
 —COCH₂— *desoxybenzoin*	3.0	45°	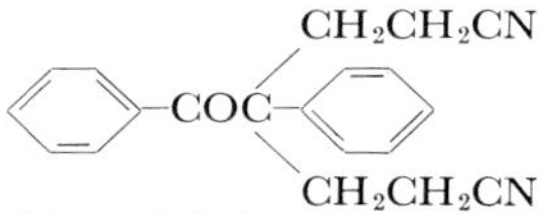 CH₂CH₂CN —COC— CH₂CH₂CN *4-benzoyl-4-phenylheptanedinitrile*	95	M.P. 149-150°	159 177	
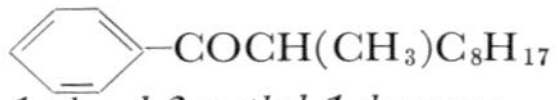 —COCH(CH₃)C₈H₁₇ *1-phenyl-2-methyl-1-decanone*	—	—	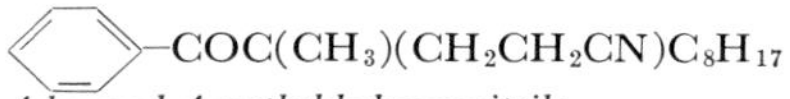 —COC(CH₃)(CH₂CH₂CN)C₈H₁₇ *4-benzoyl-4-methyldodecanenitrile*	82	B.P. 190-197°/1 mm.	204	
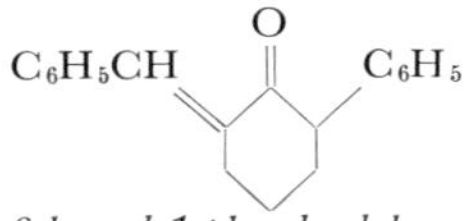 C₆H₅CH O C₆H₅ *6-benzal-1-phenylcyclohexanone*	12.0	25°	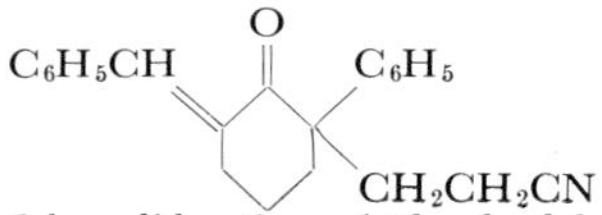 C₆H₅CH C₆H₅ O CH₂CH₂CN *3-benzylidene-2-oxo-1-phenylcyclohexanepropionitrile*	83	M.P. 82-83.5°	60	

TABLE XI—Continued

(B) Alkylaryl Ketones

Reactants	Reaction Time (Hr.)	Reaction Temperature (°C.)	Products	% Yield	M.P. or B.P. (°C.)	References This Exam.	References See Also:
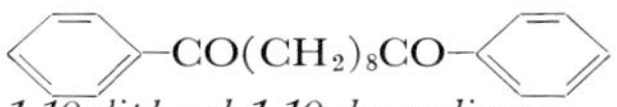 $\langle\text{phenyl}\rangle$—CO(CH₂)₈CO—$\langle\text{phenyl}\rangle$ *1,10-diphenyl-1,10-decanedione*	4.0	25-30°	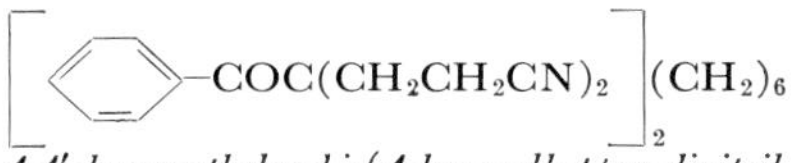 $\left[\langle\text{phenyl}\rangle\text{—COC(CH}_2\text{CH}_2\text{CN)}_2\right]_2$ (CH₂)₆ *4,4'-hexamethylenebis(4-benzoylheptanedinitrile)*	—	—	159 169 167	

(C) Cyclic Ketones

Reactants	Reaction Time (Hr.)	Reaction Temperature (°C.)	Products	% Yield	M.P. or B.P. (°C.)	References This Exam.	References See Also:
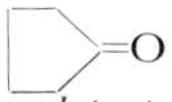 *cyclopentanone*	18.0	25°	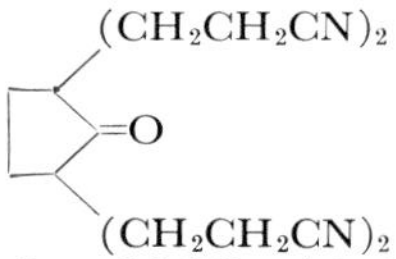 (CH₂CH₂CN)₂ ... (CH₂CH₂CN)₂ *2-oxo-1,1,3,3-cyclopentanetetrapropionitrile*	97.3	M.P. 175.5°	167 169	1077 168 177
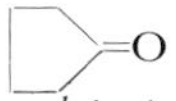 *cyclopentanone*	2.0	129°	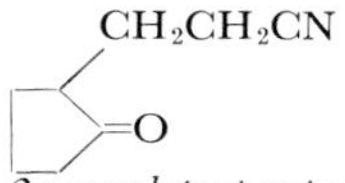 CH₂CH₂CN *2-oxocyclopentanepropionitrile*	73	B.P. 98-105°/0.9 mm.	1318	1230
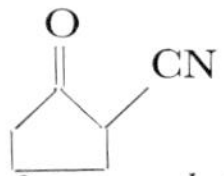 *2-cyanocyclopentanone*	—	—	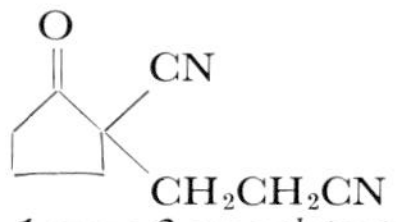 CN CH₂CH₂CN *1-cyano-2-oxocyclopentanepropionitrile*	90	B.P. 217-218°/21 mm.	1322	1323
 *cyclohexanone*	2.0	180°	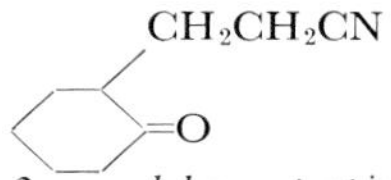 CH₂CH₂CN *2-oxocyclohexanepropionitrile*	95	B.P. 109-110°/0.8 mm.	1318	1419, 1423, 1359, 1222

TABLE XI—Continued

(C) Cyclic Ketones

Reactants	Reaction Time (Hr.)	Reaction Temperature (°C.)	Products	% Yield	M.P. or B.P. (°C.)	This Exam.	See Also:
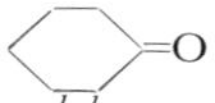 cyclohexanone	0.5 1.0	60° 40°	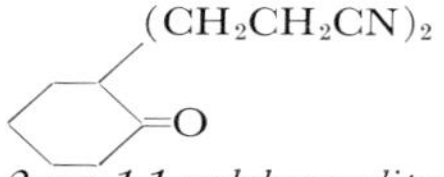 (CH₂CH₂CN)₂ *2-oxo-1,1-cyclohexanedipropionitrile*	35	M.P. 68°	1423	1359, 1222
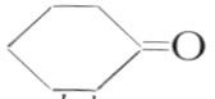 cyclohexanone	15.0	25°	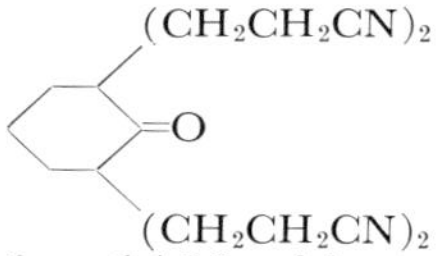 (CH₂CH₂CN)₂ (CH₂CH₂CN)₂ *2-oxo-1,1,3,3-cyclohexanetetrapropionitrile*	88	M.P. 165°	177 168	1362, 167, 426, 169, 691, 1149, 196, 93, 406, 1334, 1423
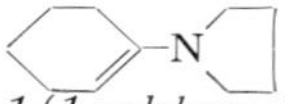 *1-(1-cyclohexenyl)pyrrolidine*	—	—	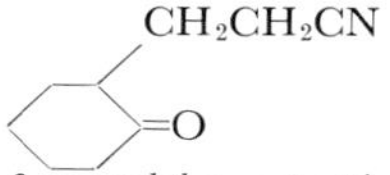 CH₂CH₂CN *2-oxocyclohexanepropionitrile*	80	—	1033	1234
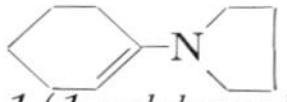 *1-(1-cyclohexenyl)pyrrolidine*	1.5	105°	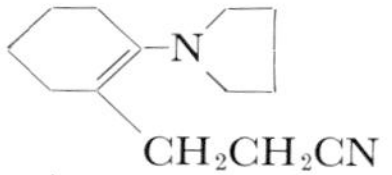 CH₂CH₂CN-N *2-(1-pyrrolidinyl)-1-cyclohexene-1-propionitrile*	87	B.P. 150-172°/10 mm. (pure) 170-172°/10 mm.	1234	
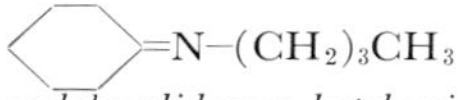 =N—(CH₂)₃CH₃ *cyclohexylidene-n-butylamine*	—	160°	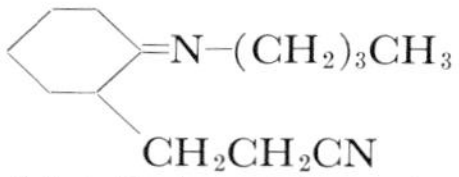 CH₂CH₂CN =N—(CH₂)₃CH₃ *2-butyliminocyclohexanepropionitrile*	74	B.P. 116-118°/0.9 mm.	1315 1316	1258
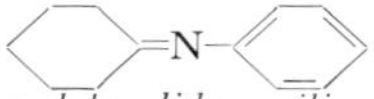 =N— *cyclohexylideneaniline*	2 3 —	100° 130° 150°	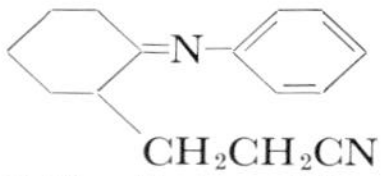 =N— CH₂CH₂CN *2-phenyliminocyclohexanepropionitrile*	63	B.P. 166-168°/0.3 mm.	1315 1316	1258

References

TABLE XI—Continued

(C) Cyclic Ketones

Reactants	Products	Reaction Time (Hr.)	Reaction Temperature (°C.)	% Yield	M.P. or B.P. (°C.)	This Exam.	See Also:
						References	
cyclohexylidenecyclohexylamine	CH₂CH₂CN 2-cyclohexyliminocyclohexanepropionitrile	1.5 —	100° 150°	78	B.P. 120-122°/0.2 mm.	1315 1316	1258
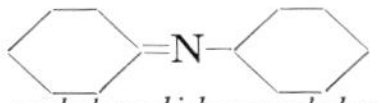 cyclohexylidenecyclohexylamine	CH₂CH₂CN / CH₂CH₂CN 2-cyclohexylimino-1,3-cyclohexanedipropionitrile	2.0 2.0	130° 150°	79	B.P. 200-205°/0.2 mm.	1315 1316	1258
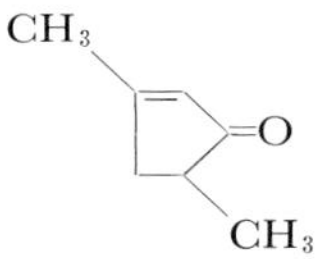 3,5-dimethyl-2-cyclopenten-1-one	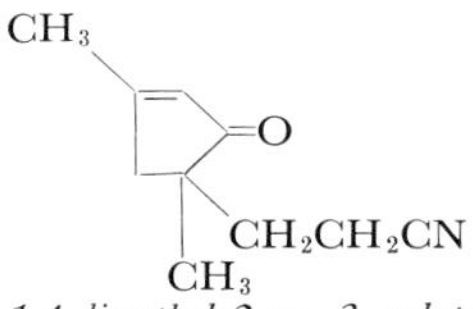 CH₂CH₂CN / CH₃ 1,4-dimethyl-2-oxo-3-cyclopentene-1-propionitrile	1.0	70-75°	24.2	B.P. 118-122°/5.5 mm.	1359	
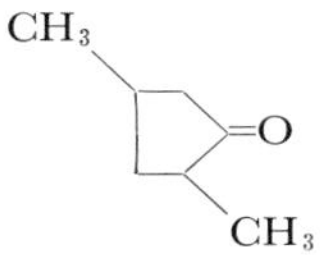 2,4-dimethylcyclopentanone	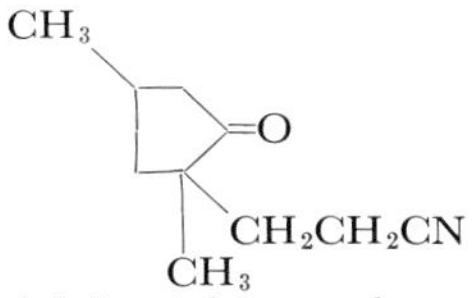 CH₂CH₂CN / CH₃ 1,4-dimethyl-2-oxocyclopentanepropionitrile	1.0	70-75°	70.6	B.P. 109.5-110°/3 mm.	1359	

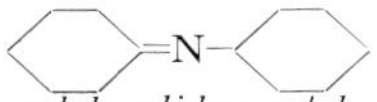

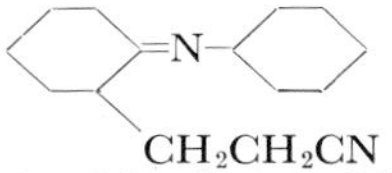

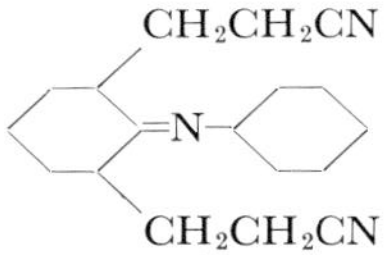

TABLE XI—Continued

(C) Cyclic Ketones

Reactants	Reaction Time (Hr.)	Reaction Temperature (°C.)	Products	% Yield	M.P. or B.P. (°C.)	This Exam.	See Also:
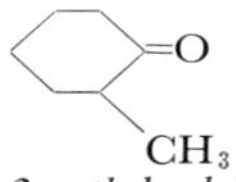 2-methylcyclohexanone	18.0	35-40°	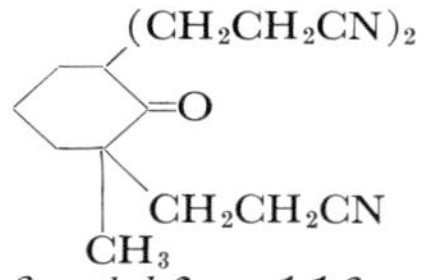 $(CH_2CH_2CN)_2$ / CH_2CH_2CN / CH_3 — 3-methyl-2-oxo-1,1,3-cyclohexanetripropionitrile	88	B.P. 275-285°/1 mm.	168 177	167 169
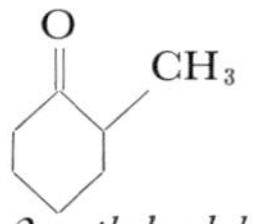 2-methylcyclohexanone	5-16	25°	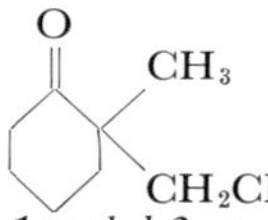 CH_2CH_2CN / CH_3 — 1-methyl-2-oxocyclohexanepropionitrile	80	B.P. 131°/1 mm.	406	
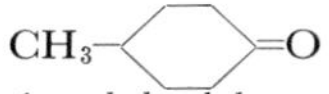 4-methylcyclohexanone	4.0	25°	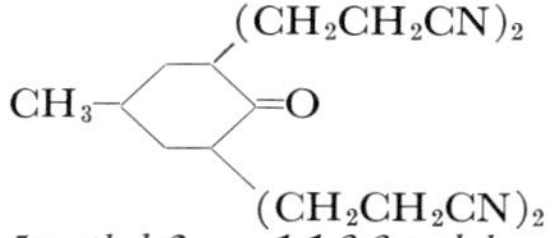 $(CH_2CH_2CN)_2$ / CH_2CH_2CN — 5-methyl-2-oxo-1,1,3,3-cyclohexanetetrapropionitrile	91	M.P. 138.5°	168	177, 406
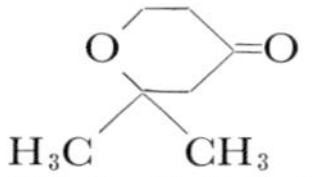 2,2-dimethyltetrahydro-4-pyrone	—	—	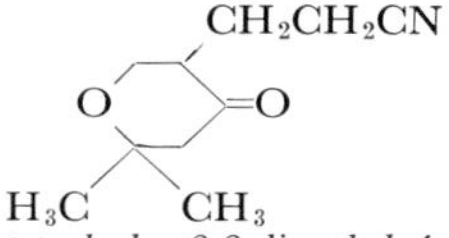 CH_2CH_2CN / H_3C CH_3 — tetrahydro-6,6-dimethyl-4-oxopyran-3-propionitrile	26	B.P. 132-136°/5 mm.	1359	
			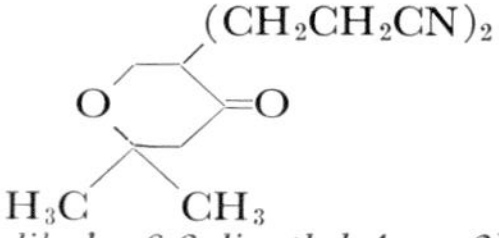 $(CH_2CH_2CN)_2$ / H_3C CH_3 — dihydro-6,6-dimethyl-4-oxo-2H-pyran-3,3(4H)-dipropionitrile	100	M.P. 105.5-106.5°		

References

TABLE XI—Continued   **(C) Cyclic Ketones**

Reactants	Re-action Time (Hr.)	Reaction Temperature (°C.)	Products	% Yield	M.P. or B.P. (°C.)	References — This Exam.	References — See Also:
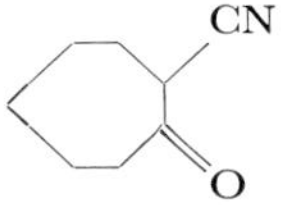 2-cyanocycloheptanone	1.0	60-70°	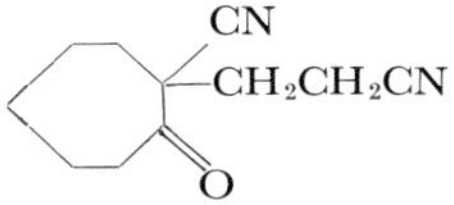 *1-cyano-2-oxocycloheptanepropionitrile*	65	M.P. 51-52.5°	601	
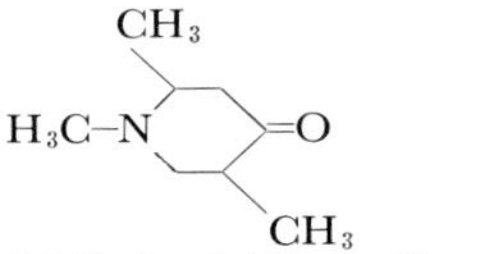 1,2,5-trimethyl-4-piperidone	54.0	25°	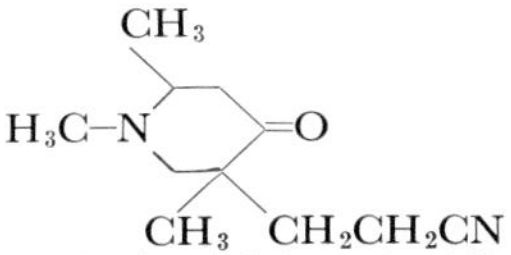 *1,3,6-trimethyl-4-oxopiperidinepropionitrile*	90.5	M.P. 66.5-67.5°	1359	
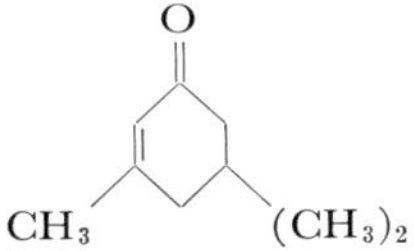 isophorone	4.0	30°	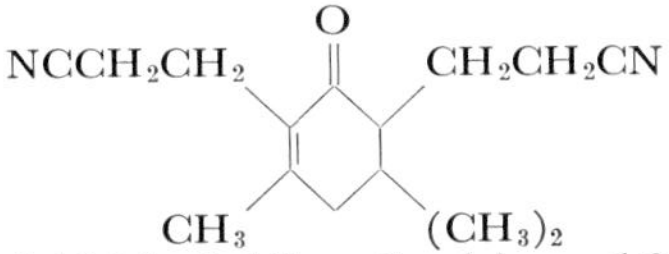 *4,4,6-trimethyl-2-oxo-6-cyclohexene-1,3-dipropionitrile*	22	B.P. 210-220°/1 mm. M.P. 83	186	
			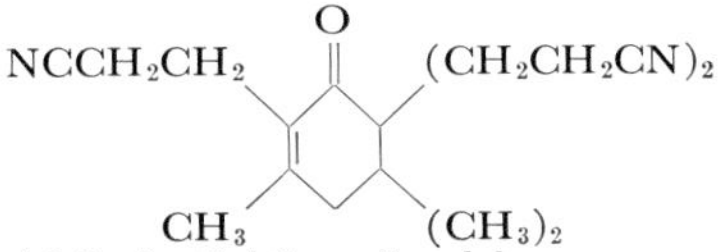 *4,6,6-trimethyl-2-oxo-3-cyclohexene-1,1,3-tripropionitrile*	2.5	M.P. 120-121°		

TABLE XI—Continued   **(C) Cyclic Ketones**

Reactants	Re-action Time (Hr.)	Reaction Temperature (°C.)	Products	% Yield	M.P. or B.P. (°C.)	References This Exam.	See Also:
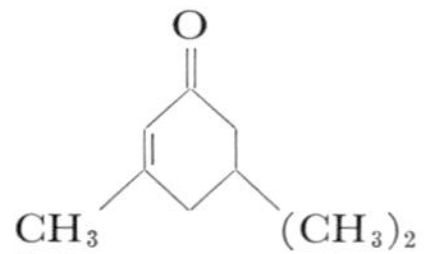 isophorone (structure: O= ring with CH₃, (CH₃)₂)	4.0	26–30°	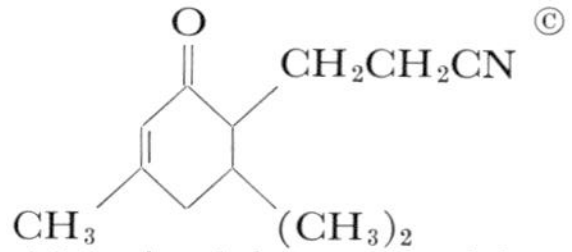 CH₂CH₂CN structure; 4,6,6-trimethyl-2-oxo-3-cyclohexene-1-propionitrile	9.2	B.P. 109–111°/0.3 mm. M.P. 23–24°	186	
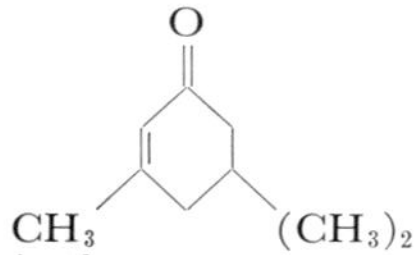 isophorone (structure: O= ring with CH₃, (CH₃)₂)	—	—	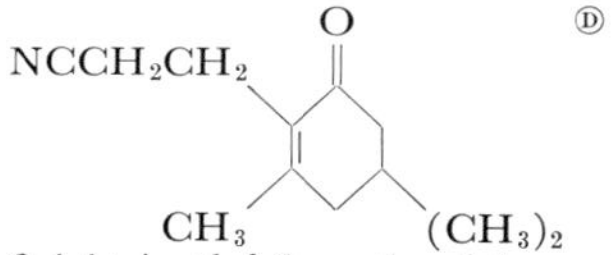 NCCH₂CH₂ structure; 2,4,4-trimethyl-6-oxo-1-cyclohexene-1-propionitrile	—	B.P. 125°/5 mm.	617	
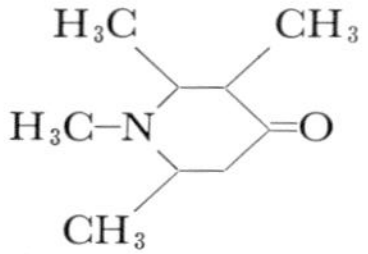 1,2,3,6-tetramethyl-4-piperidone (structure with H₃C, CH₃, H₃C–N, CH₃)	1.0	70–75°	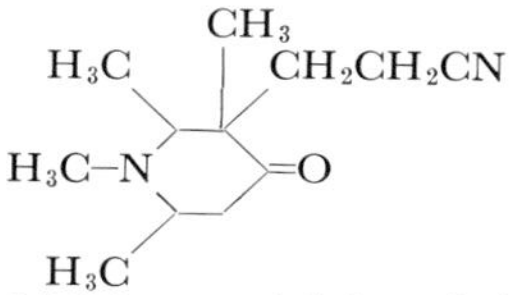 1,2,3,6-tetramethyl-4-oxo-3-piperidinepropionitrile (structure with CH₃, CH₂CH₂CN, H₃C–N, H₃C)	71.4	B.P. 142–145°/1 mm.	1359	
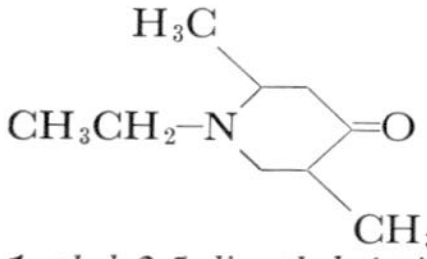 1-ethyl-2,5-dimethyl-4-piperidone (structure with H₃C, O=, CH₃CH₂–N, CH₃)			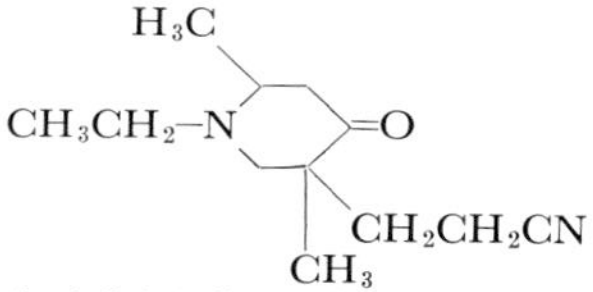 1-ethyl-3,6-dimethyl-4-oxo-3-piperidinepropionitrile (structure with H₃C, CH₂CH₂CN, CH₃CH₂–N, CH₃)	91.3	B.P. 155–158°/7 mm.	1359	

TABLE XI—Continued

(C) Cyclic Ketones

Reactants	Reaction Time (Hr.)	Reaction Temperature (°C.)	Products	% Yield	M.P. or B.P. (°C.)	References This Exam.	References See Also:
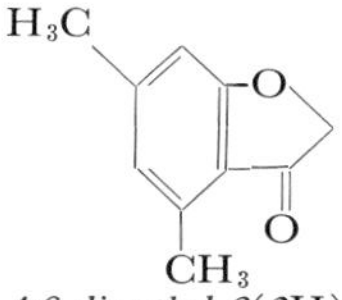 H₃C— ... CH₃ *4,6-dimethyl-3(2H)-benzofuranone*	4.0	<45°	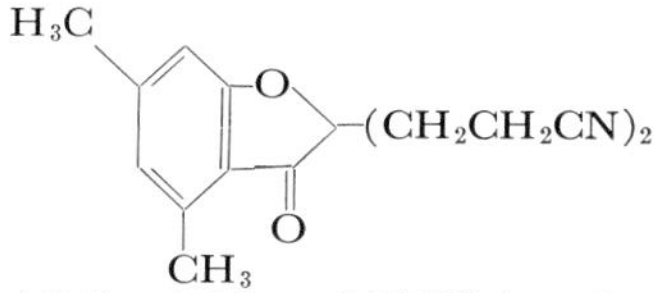 H₃C— ...(CH₂CH₂CN)₂ CH₃ *4,6-dimethyl-3-oxo-2,2(3H)-benzofurandipropionitrile*	80.2	M.P. 96-97°	1246	
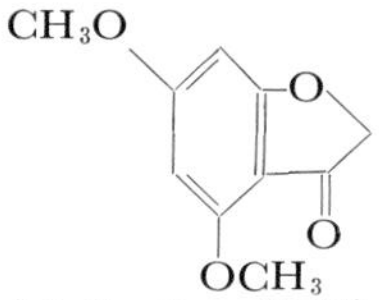 CH₃O— ... OCH₃ *4,6-dimethoxy-3(2H)-benzofuranone*	4.0	<45°	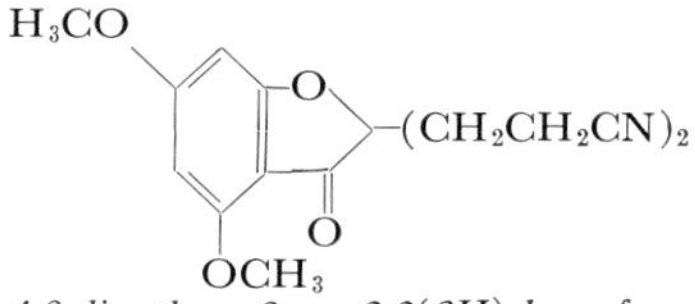 H₃CO— ...(CH₂CH₂CN)₂ OCH₃ *4,6-dimethoxy-3-oxo-2,2(3H)-benzofurandipropionitrile*	80.7	M.P. 154-155°	1246	
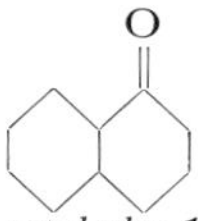 *octahydro-1(2H)-naphthalenone*	30	190°	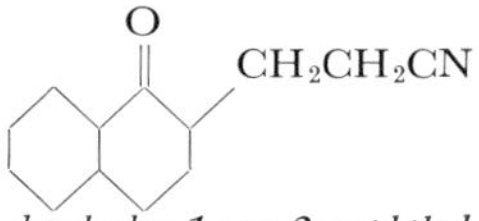 CH₂CH₂CN *decahydro-1-oxo-2-naphthalenepropionitrile*	65	B.P. 143-147°/0.9 mm.	1318	
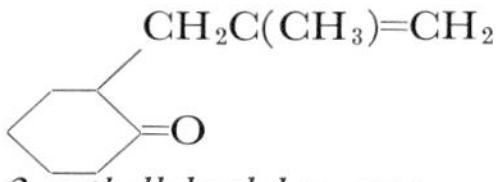 CH₂C(CH₃)=CH₂ *2-methallylcyclohexanone*	4.5	25-50°	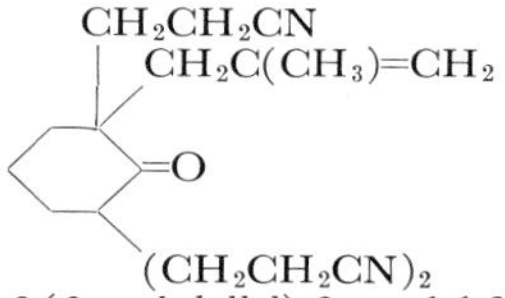 CH₂CH₂CN CH₂C(CH₃)=CH₂ (CH₂CH₂CN)₂ *3-(2-methylallyl)-2-oxo-1,1,3-cyclohexanetripropionitrile*	—	B.P. 230-270°/1-3 mm.	168	

TABLE XI—Continued

(C) Cyclic Ketones

Reactants	Reaction Time (Hr.)	Reaction Temperature (°C.)	Products	% Yield	M.P. or B.P. (°C.)	References This Exam.	References See Also:
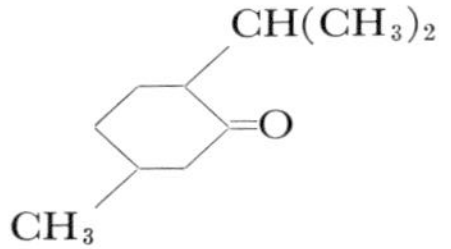 menthone	24.0	25°	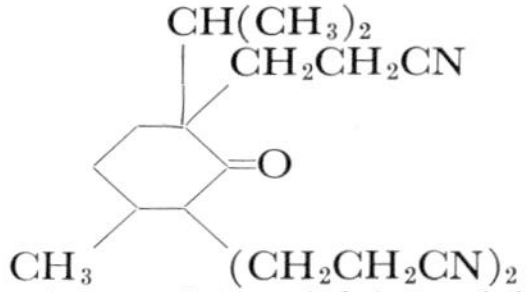 $CH(CH_3)_2$ / CH_2CH_2CN (on cyclohexanone with CH_3) 3-isopropyl-6-methyl-2-oxo-1,1,3-cyclohexanetripropionitrile	—	B.P. 295-300°/1 mm.	168	
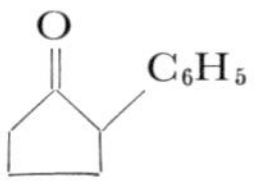 2-phenylcyclopentanone	0.5	25-30°	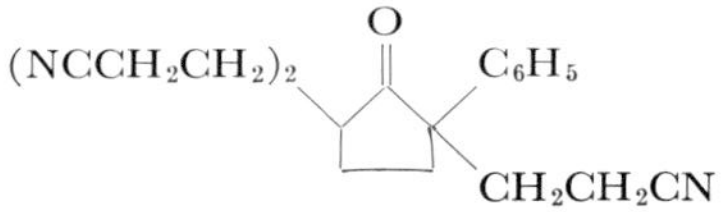 $(NCCH_2CH_2)_2$ $(CH_2CH_2CN)_2$ C_6H_5 CH_2CH_2CN 2-oxo-3-phenyl-1,1,3-cyclopentanetripropionitrile	75	M.P. 81.5-83°	52	
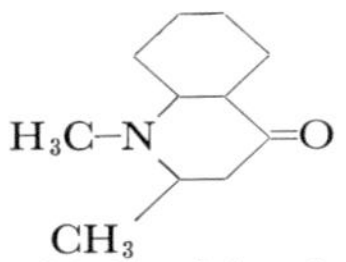 1,2-dimethyloctahydro-4(1H)-quinolone	—	—	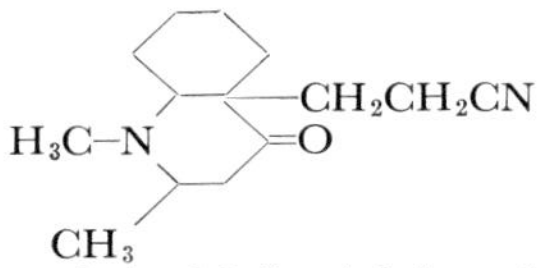 H_3C-N CH_2CH_2CN CH_3 octahydro-1,2-dimethyl-4-oxo-4a(1H)-quinoline-propionitrile	90.6	B.P. 166-170°/2 mm.	1359	
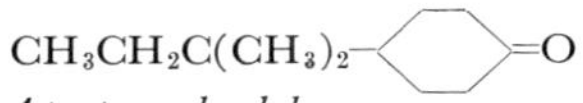 $CH_3CH_2C(CH_3)_2$ 4-tert-amylcyclohexanone	18.0	35-40°	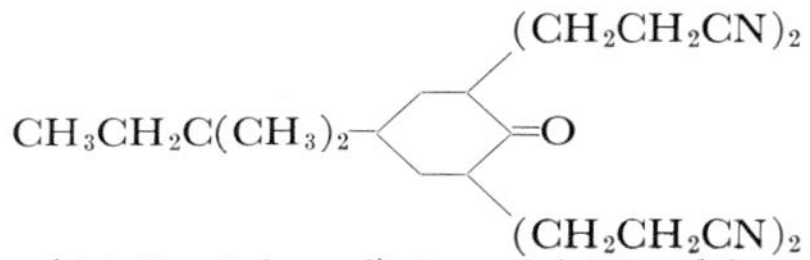 $CH_3CH_2C(CH_3)_2$ $(CH_2CH_2CN)_2$ $(CH_2CH_2CN)_2$ 5-(1,1-dimethylpropyl)-2-oxo-1,1,3,3-cyclohexane-tetrapropionitrile	80	M.P. 148°	177	168

TABLE XI—Continued   **(C) Cyclic Ketones**

Reactants	Reaction Time (Hr.)	Reaction Temperature (°C.)	Products	% Yield	M.P. or B.P. (°C.)	References This Exam.	See Also:
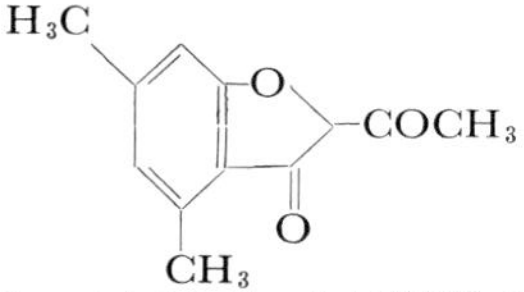 2-acetyl-4,6-dimethyl-3(2H)-benzofuranone	4.0	<45°	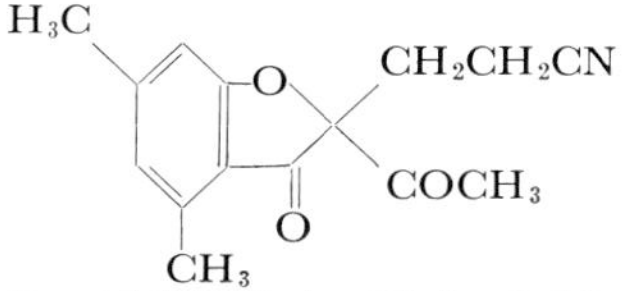 2-acetyl-2,3-dihydro-4,6-dimethyl-3-oxo-2-benzofuranpropionitrile	39.9	M.P. 108°	1246	
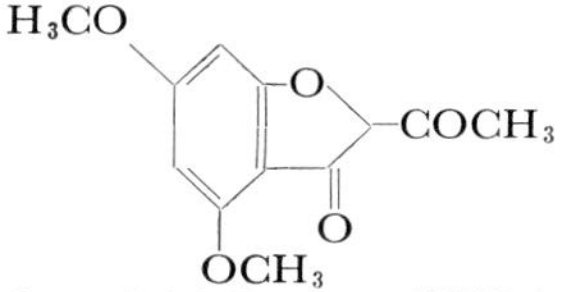 2-acetyl-4,6-dimethoxy-3(2H)-benzofuranone	3.0	—	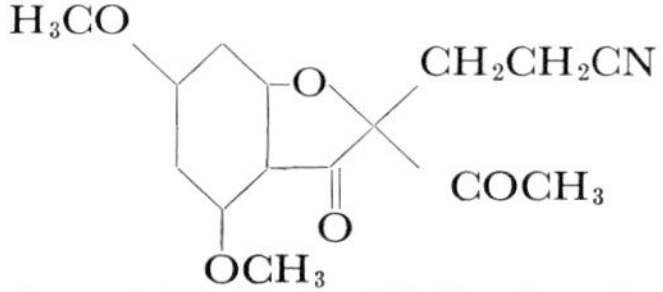 2-acetyl-2,3-dihydro-4,6-dimethoxy-3-oxo-2-benzofuranpropionitrile	74.9	M.P. 140°	1246	
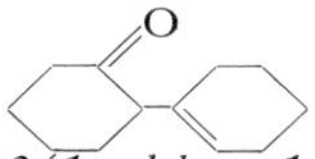 2-(1-cyclohexen-1-yl)cyclohexanone	2.0	30°	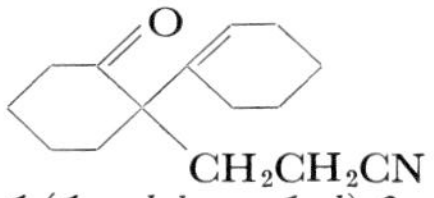 1-(1-cyclohexen-1-yl)-2-oxocyclohexanepropionitrile	47.6	M.P. 61-62°	184	172
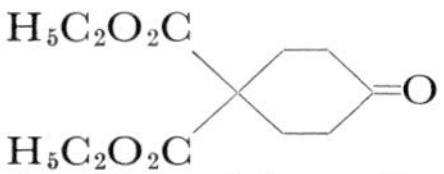 4-oxo-1,1-cyclohexanedicarboxylic acid, diethyl ester	—	—	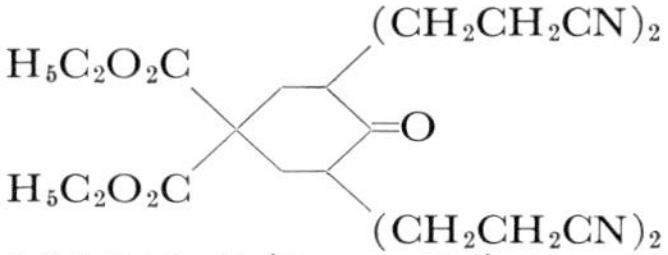 3,3,5,5-tetrakis(2-cyanoethyl)-4-oxo-1,1-cyclohexanedicarboxylic acid, diethyl ester	19	M.P. 205°	1331	

TABLE XI—Continued

(C) Cyclic Ketones

Reactants	Reaction Time (Hr.)	Reaction Temperature (°C.)	Products	% Yield	M.P. or B.P. (°C.)	References This Exam.	References See Also:
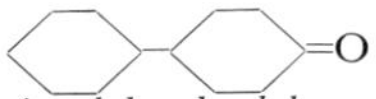 4-cyclohexylcyclohexanone	18.0	35–40°	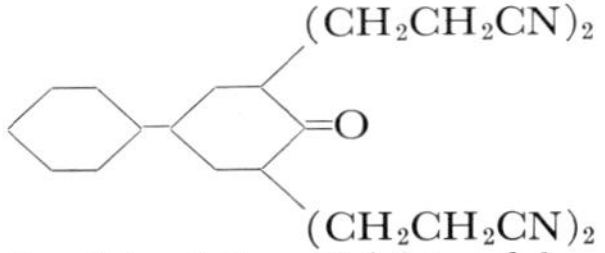 $(CH_2CH_2CN)_2$ / 5-cyclohexyl-2-oxo-1,3,3-cyclohexanetetrapropionitrile	80	M.P. 223–224°	177	168
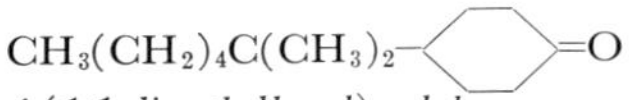 $CH_3(CH_2)_4C(CH_3)_2$ / 4-(1,1-dimethylhexyl)cyclohexanone	18.0	35–40°	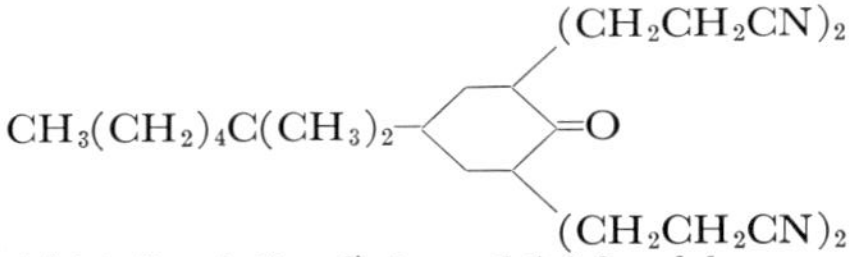 $(CH_2CH_2CN)_2$ $CH_3(CH_2)_4C(CH_3)_2$ $(CH_2CH_2CN)_2$ / 5-(1,1-dimethylhexyl)-2-oxo-1,3,3-cyclohexane-tetrapropionitrile	80	M.P. 155–156°	177	
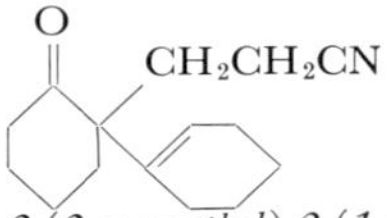 CH_2CH_2CN / 2-(2-cyanoethyl)-2-(1-cyclohexen-1-yl)-cyclohexanone	10.0	30°	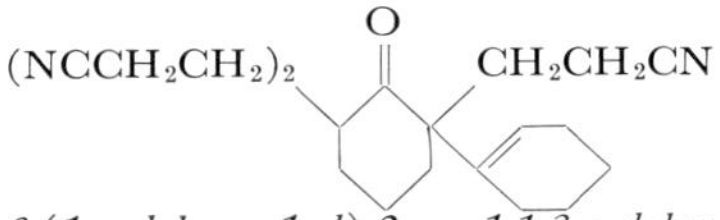 $(NCCH_2CH_2)_2$ CH_2CH_2CN / 3-(1-cyclohexen-1-yl)-2-oxo-1,3-cyclohexane-tripropionitrile	54	M.P. 111°	184	
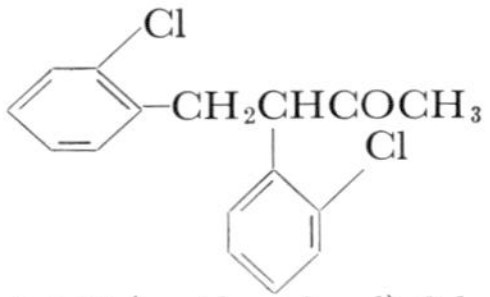 $CH_2CHCOCH_3$ / 3,4-bis(o-chlorophenyl)-2-butanone	2.0 / 1.0	25° / 45°	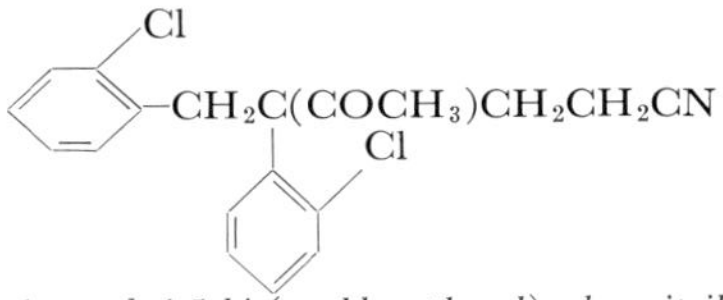 $CH_2C(COCH_3)CH_2CH_2CN$ / 4-acetyl-4,5-bis(o-chlorophenyl)valeronitrile	16	B.P. 195–200°/0.1 mm.	1240	

TABLE XI—Continued

(C) Cyclic Ketones

Reactants	Reaction Time (Hr.)	Reaction Temperature (°C.)	Products	% Yield	M.P. or B.P. (°C.)	References This Exam.	References See Also:
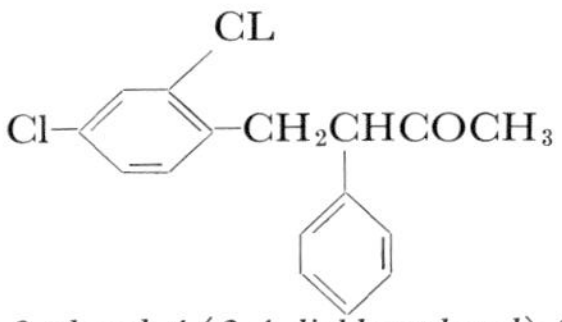 CH₂CHCOCH₃ (2,4-dichlorophenyl) 3-phenyl-4-(2,4-dichlorophenyl)-2-butanone	3.0	25°	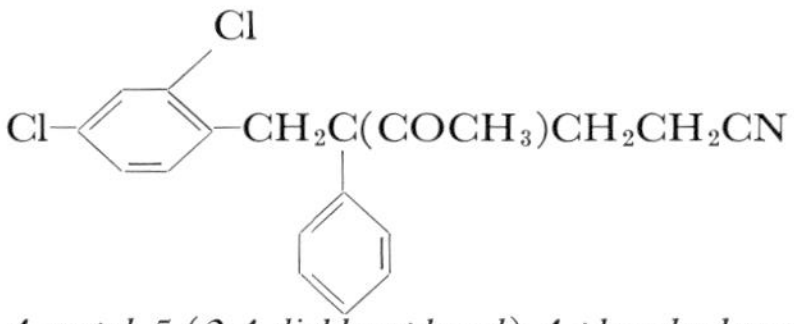 —CH₂C(COCH₃)CH₂CH₂CN 4-acetyl-5-(2,4-dichlorophenyl)-4-phenylvaleronitrile	79	M.P. 89-91°	1240	
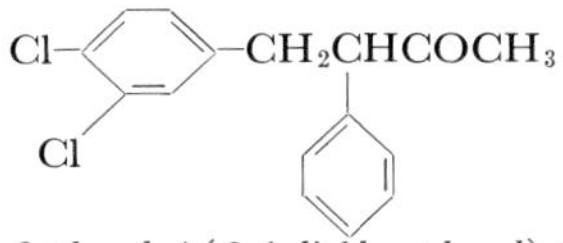 CH₂CHCOCH₃ (3,4-dichlorophenyl) 3-phenyl-4-(3,4-dichlorophenyl)-2-butanone	2.0 1.0	25° 40°	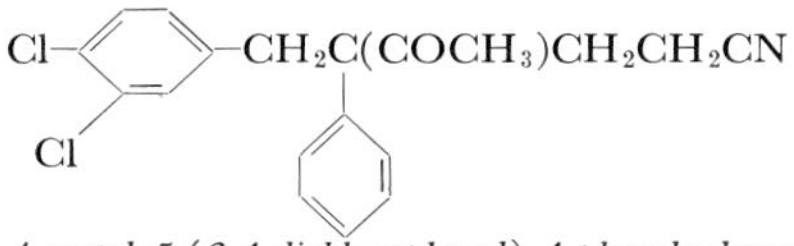 —CH₂C(COCH₃)CH₂CH₂CN 4-acetyl-5-(3,4-dichlorophenyl)-4-phenylvaleronitrile	87	M.P. 105-107°	1240	
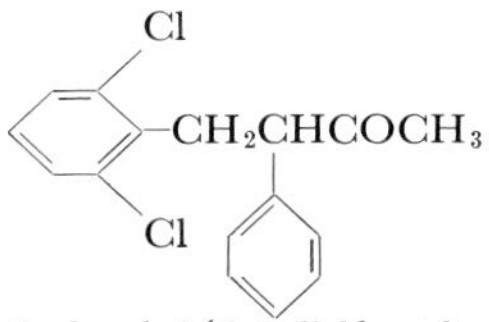 CH₂CHCOCH₃ (2,6-dichlorophenyl) 3-phenyl-4-(2,6-dichlorophenyl)-2-butanone	2.0 1.0	25° 82°	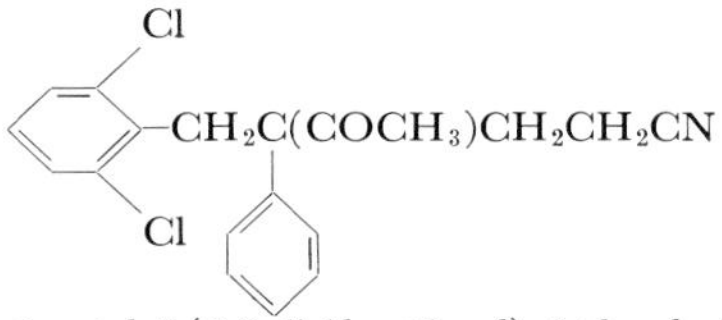 —CH₂C(COCH₃)CH₂CH₂CN 4-acetyl-5-(2,6-dichlorophenyl)-4-phenylvaleronitrile	31	M.P. 97.5-99.5°	1240	
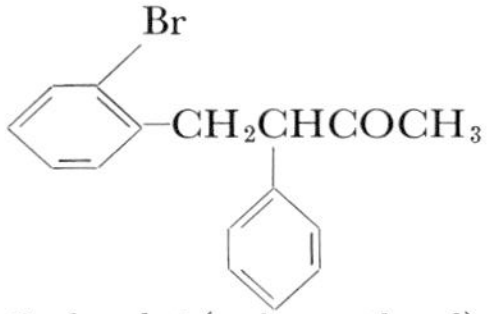 CH₂CHCOCH₃ (o-bromophenyl) 3-phenyl-4-(o-bromophenyl)-2-butanone	2.0 1.0	25° 45°	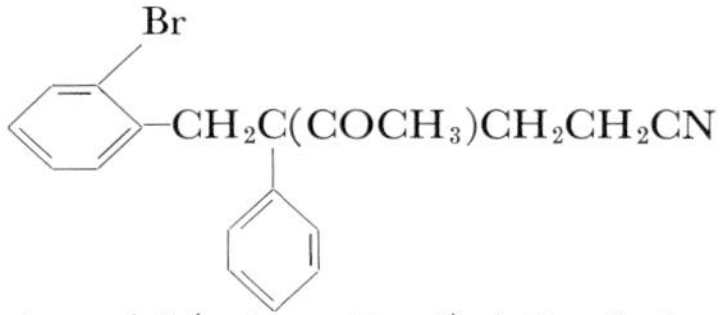 —CH₂C(COCH₃)CH₂CH₂CN 4-acetyl-5-(o-bromophenyl)-4-phenylvaleronitrile	85	M.P. 114-115°	1240	

TABLE XI—Continued

(C) Cyclic Ketones

Reactants	Reaction Time (Hr.)	Reaction Temperature (°C.)	Products	% Yield	M.P. or B.P. (°C.)	References This Exam.	See Also:
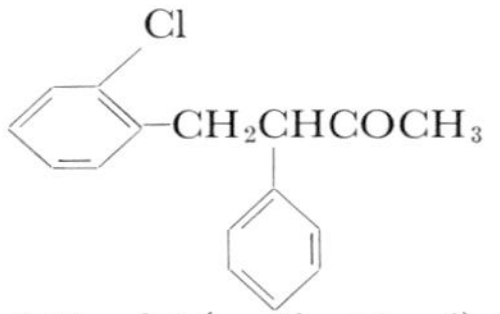 Cl—(phenyl)—CH₂CHCOCH₃ 3-phenyl-4-(o-chlorophenyl)-2-butanone	3.0	25°	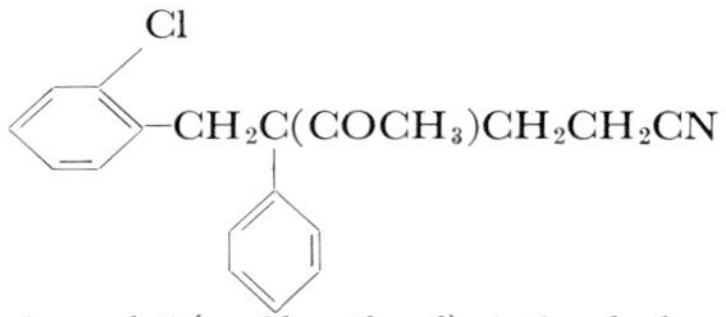 Cl—(phenyl)—CH₂C(COCH₃)CH₂CH₂CN 4-acetyl-5-(o-chlorophenyl)-4-phenylvaleronitrile	92	M.P. 106–108°	1240	
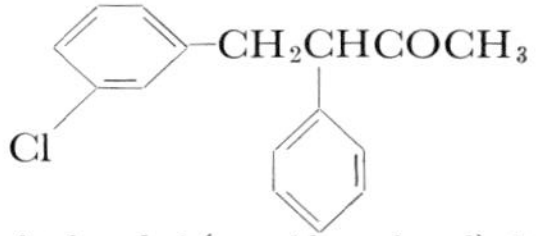 (Cl-phenyl)—CH₂CHCOCH₃ 3-phenyl-4-(m-chlorophenyl)-2-butanone	2.0 1.0	25° 40°	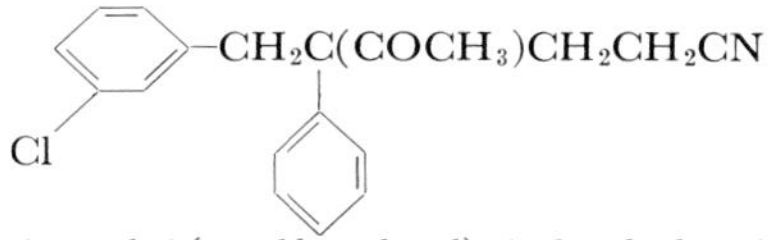 (Cl-phenyl)—CH₂C(COCH₃)CH₂CH₂CN 4-acetyl-5-(m-chlorophenyl)-4-phenylvaleronitrile	81	M.P. 53.5–55.5°	1240	
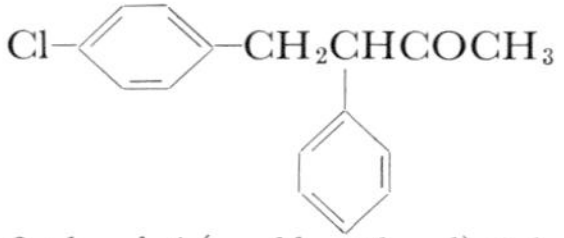 Cl—(phenyl)—CH₂CHCOCH₃ 3-phenyl-4-(p-chlorophenyl)-2-butanone	2.0 1.0	25° 40°	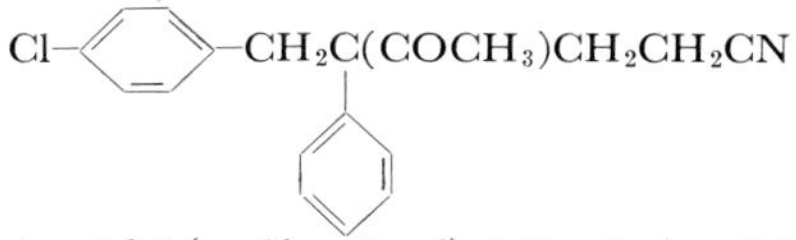 Cl—(phenyl)—CH₂C(COCH₃)CH₂CH₂CN 4-acetyl-5-(p-chlorophenyl)-4-phenylvaleronitrile	80	M.P. 86–88°	1240	
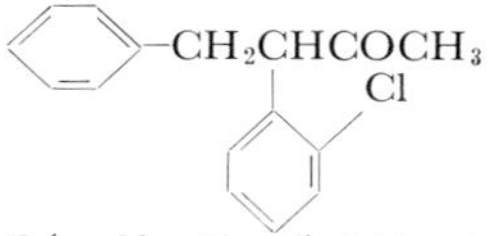 (phenyl)—CH₂CHCOCH₃ (Cl) 3-(o-chlorophenyl)-4-phenyl-2-butanone	2.0 1.0	25° 45°	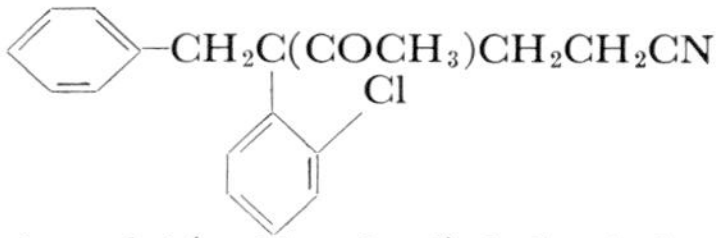 (phenyl)—CH₂C(COCH₃)CH₂CH₂CN (Cl) 4-acetyl-4-(o-chlorophenyl)-5-phenylvaleronitrile	30	M.P. 124–126°	1240	

TABLE XI—Continued

(C) Cyclic Ketones

Reactants	Reaction Time (Hr.)	Reaction Temperature (°C.)	Products	% Yield	M.P. or B.P. (°C.)	References This Exam.	See Also:
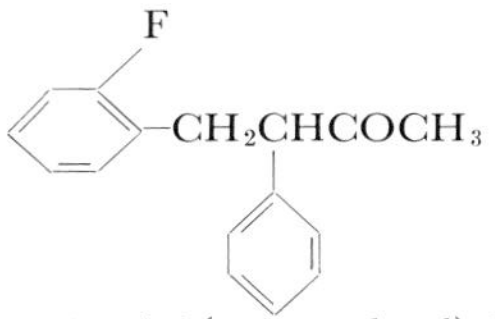 F ...CH₂CHCOCH₃ (phenyl) $3\text{-phenyl-4-(o-fluorophenyl)-2-butanone}$	2.0 1.0	25° 40°	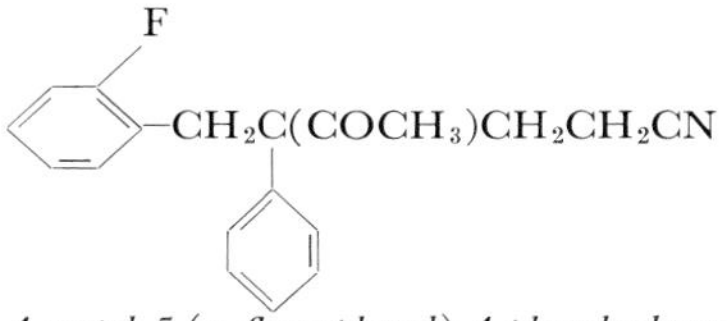 F ...CH₂C(COCH₃)CH₂CH₂CN (phenyl) $4\text{-acetyl-5-(o-fluorophenyl)-4-phenylvaleronitrile}$	95	M.P. 123.5-125.5°	1240	
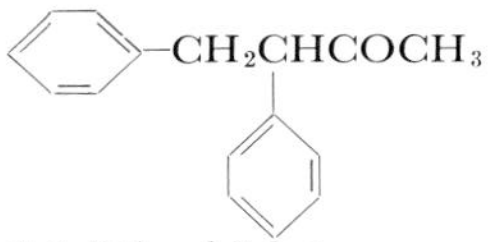 CH₂CHCOCH₃ (phenyl) $3,4\text{-diphenyl-2-butanone}$	3.0	25°	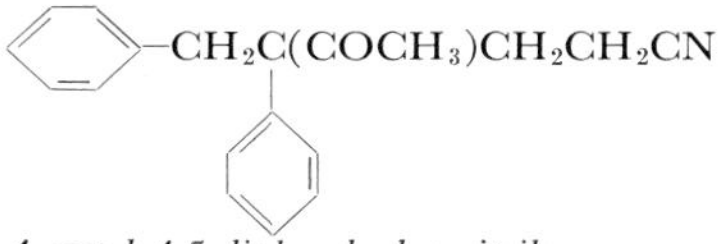 CH₂C(COCH₃)CH₂CH₂CN (phenyl) $4\text{-acetyl-4,5-diphenylvaleronitrile}$	95	M.P. 127.5-129°	1240	
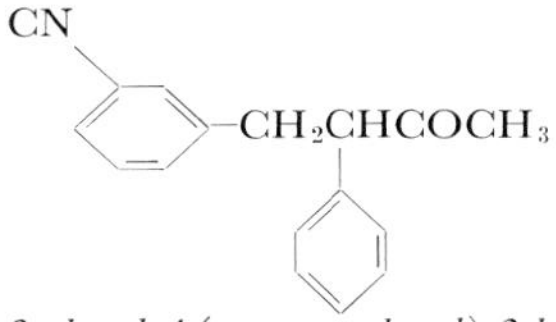 CN ...CH₂CHCOCH₃ (phenyl) $3\text{-phenyl-4-(m-cyanophenyl)-2-butanone}$	2.0 1.0	25° 40°	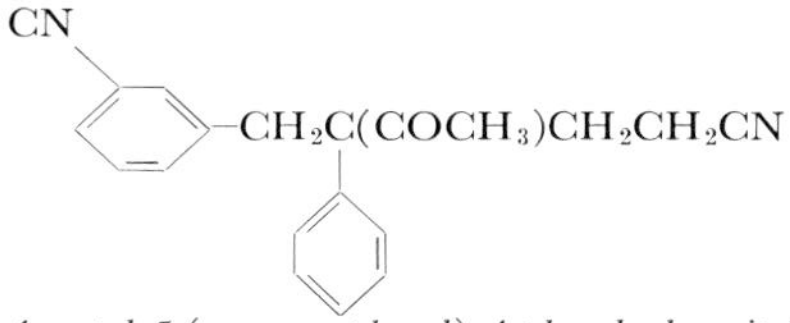 CN ...CH₂C(COCH₃)CH₂CH₂CN (phenyl) $4\text{-acetyl-5-(m-cyanophenyl)-4-phenylvaleronitrile}$	83	M.P. 86-88°	1240	
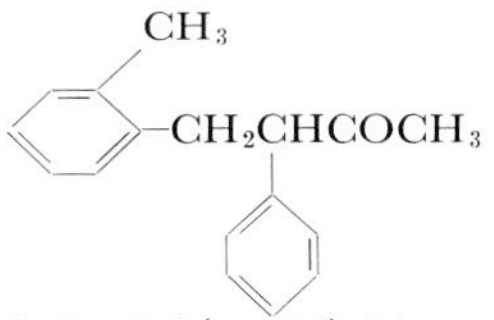 CH₃ / CH₂CHCOCH₃ (phenyl) $3\text{-phenyl-4-(o-tolyl)-2-butanone}$	2.0 1.0	25° 40°	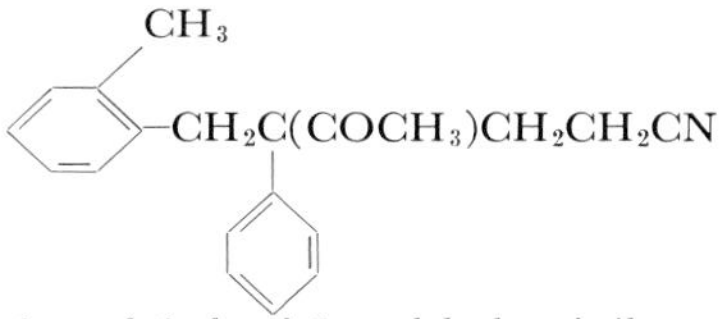 CH₃ / CH₂C(COCH₃)CH₂CH₂CN (phenyl) $4\text{-acetyl-4-phenyl-5-o-tolylvaleronitrile}$	89	M.P. 89-90°	1240	

TABLE XI—Continued   (C) Cyclic Ketones

Reactants	Reaction Time (Hr.)	Reaction Temperature (°C.)	Products	% Yield	M.P. or B.P. (°C.)	References This Exam.	References See Also:
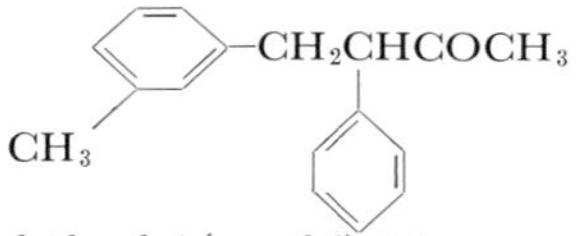 $-CH_2CHCOCH_3$ (ring with CH_3) *3-phenyl-4-(m-tolyl)-2-butanone*	2.0 1.0	25° 40°	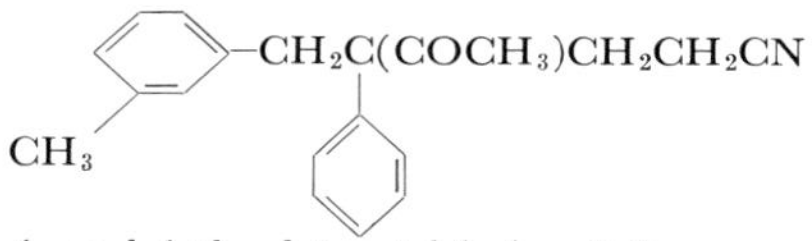 $-CH_2C(COCH_3)CH_2CH_2CN$ (ring with CH_3) *4-acetyl-4-phenyl-5-m-tolylvaleronitrile*	87	M.P. 94.5-96°	1240	
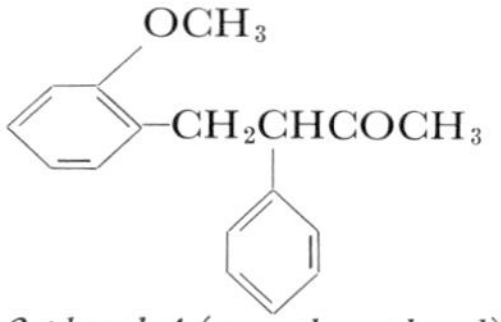 OCH_3 $-CH_2CHCOCH_3$ *3-phenyl-4-(o-methoxyphenyl)-2-butanone*	2.0 1.0	25° 42°	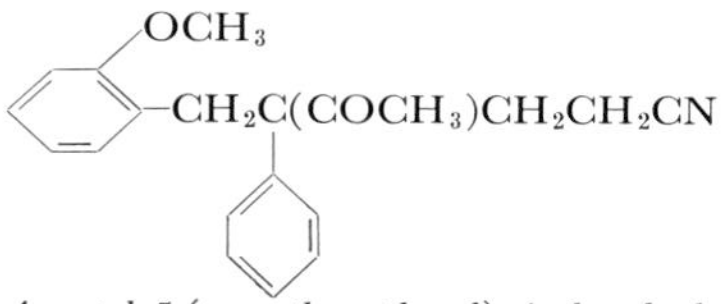 OCH_3 $-CH_2C(COCH_3)CH_2CH_2CN$ *4-acetyl-5-(o-methoxyphenyl)-4-phenylvaleronitrile*	83	M.P. 110-111°	1240	
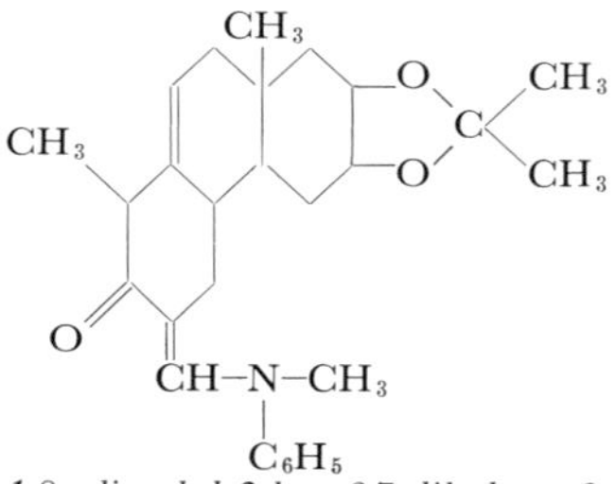 (steroid structure) *1,8a-dimethyl-2-keto-6,7-dihydroxy-3-(N-methylanilinomethylene)-Δ^{10a}-dodecahydrophenanthrene acetonide*	45.0	50°	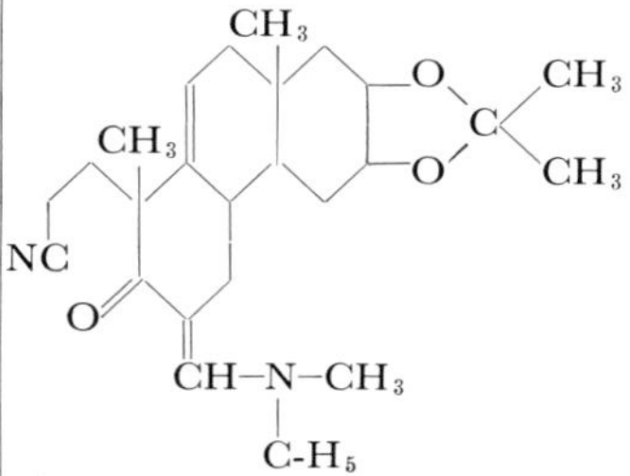 (steroid structure) *1,2,3,4,6,6a,7,7a,10a,11,11a,11b-dodecahydro-4,6a,9-tetramethyl-2-(N-methylanilinomethylene)-3-oxophenanthro[2,3][1,3]dioxole-4-propionitrile*	—	—	1172 1171	

Additional examples of reactions involving complex cyclic ketones are described in the following references: 167, 168, 169, 353.
Several cyclic ketimines have been included in the table since monocyanoethylation proceeds more readily than with the corresponding cyclic ketones.

TABLE XI—Continued

(D) Diketones

Reactants	Re-action Time (Hr.)	Reaction Temperature (°C.)	Products	% Yield	M.P. or B.P. (°C.)	References This Exam.	References See Also:
CH₃COCH₂COCH₃ $CH_3COCH_2COCH_3$ 2,4-pentandione	12.0	25°	$CH_3COC(CH_2CH_2CN)_2COCH_3$ 4,4-diacetylheptanedinitrile	99	M.P. 181-182°	1349	1185, 130, 1364
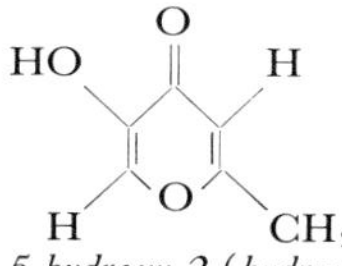 5-hydroxy-2-(hydroxymethyl)-4H-pyran-4-one (kojic acid)	19.0	reflux	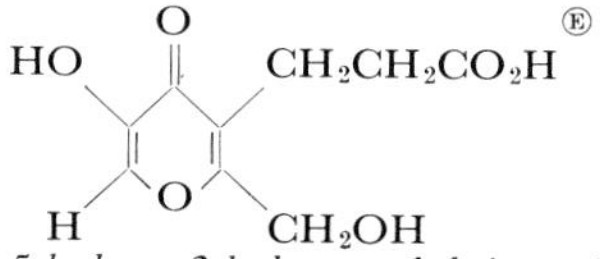 5-hydroxy-2-hydroxymethyl-4-oxo-4H-pyran-3-propionic acid	—	M.P. 155°	1170	
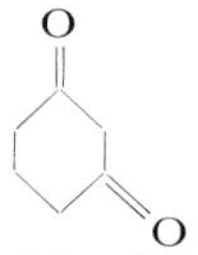 1,3-cyclohexanedione	7.0	reflux	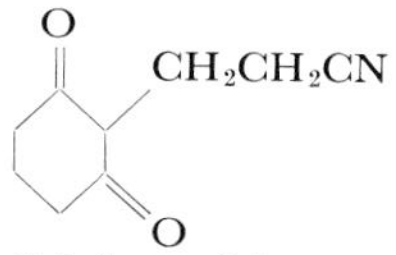 2,6-dioxocyclohexanepropionitrile	60.5	—	1026	87
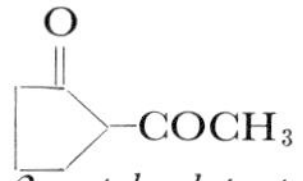 2-acetylcyclopentanone	24.0	25°	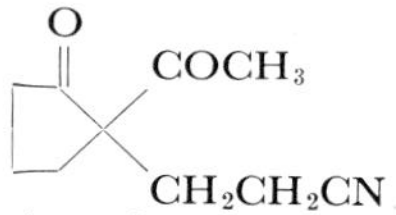 1-acetyl-2-oxocyclopentanepropionitrile	71	—	898	176
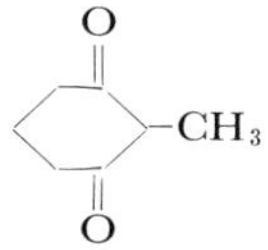 2-methyl-1,3-cyclohexanedione	3.0	reflux	$HO_2C(CH_2)_3COCH(CH_3)CH_2CH_2CN$ 9-cyano-6-methyl-5-oxononanoic acid	74	B.P. 200-203°/2 mm.	817	

TABLE XI—Continued

(D) Diketones

Reactants	Reaction Time (Hr.)	Reaction Temperature (°C.)	Products	% Yield	M.P. or B.P. (°C.)	References	
						This Exam.	See Also:
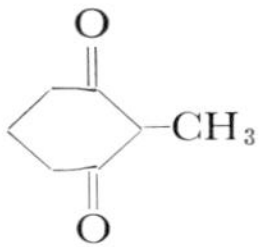 2-methyl-1,3-cyclohexanedione	3.0	reflux	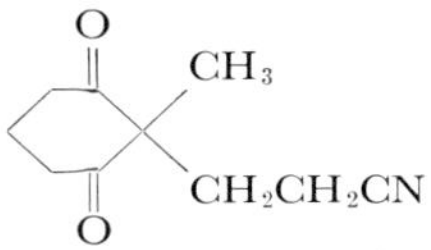 1-methyl-2,6-dioxocyclohexanepropionitrile	82	B.P. 142.4°/1 mm.	817	
$CH_3COCH(C_2H_5)COCH_3$ 3-ethyl-2,4-pentanedione	2.0	reflux	$CH_3COC(CH_2CH_2CN)(C_2H_5)COCH_3$ 4,4-diacetylhexanenitrile	78	B.P. 134-136°/4 mm. M.P. 54-56°	129	
CH_3COCH_2CO—[S]  1-(2-thienyl)-1,3-butanedione	2.0	reflux	$CH_3COC(CH_2CH_2CN)_2CO$—[S]  4-acetyl-4-(2-thenoyl)heptanedinitrile	40	M.P. 127-127.5°	1185	
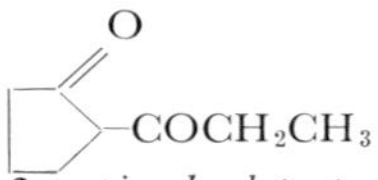 $COCH_2CH_3$ 2-propionylcyclopentanone	24.0	25°	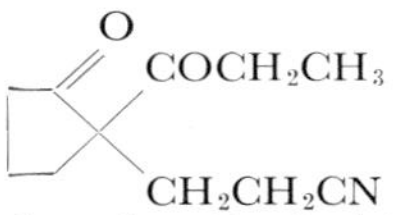 $COCH_2CH_3$ CH_2CH_2CN 2-oxo-1-propionylcyclopentanepropionitrile	86	B.P. 140-150°/1 mm.	898	
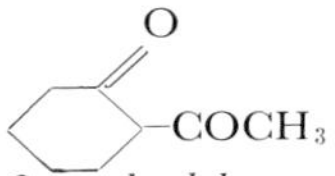 $COCH_3$ 2-acetylcyclohexanone	24.0	25°	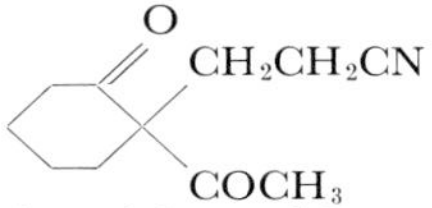 CH_2CH_2CN $COCH_3$ 1-acetyl-2-oxocyclohexanepropionitrile	75	—	898	176
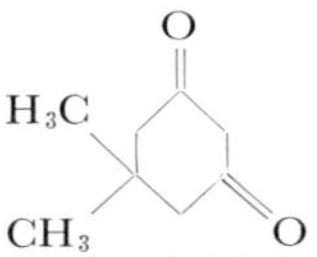 H_3C CH_3 5,5-dimethyl-1,3-cyclohexanedione	3.5	reflux	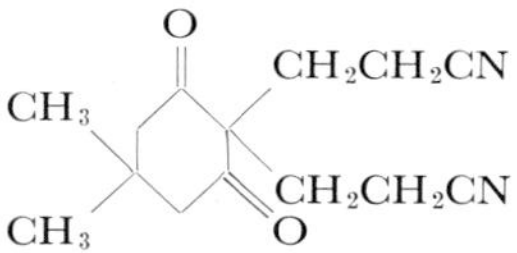 CH_2CH_2CN CH_2CH_2CN CH_3 CH_3 4,4-dimethyl-2,6-dioxo-1,1-cyclohexanedipropionitrile	81	M.P. 146-147°	817	

TABLE XI—Continued

(D) Diketones

Reactants	Reaction Time (Hr.)	Reaction Temperature (°C.)	Products	% Yield	M.P. or B.P. (°C.)	References This Exam.	References See Also:
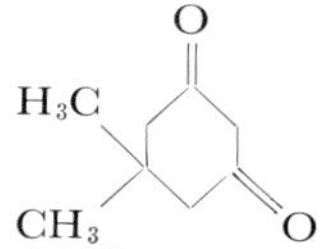 H_3C , CH_3 structure — 5,5-dimethyl-1,3-cyclohexanedione	5.0	60–70°	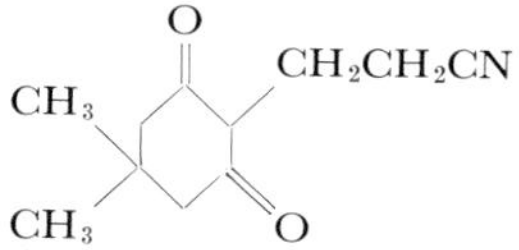 CH_2CH_2CN structure — 4,4-dimethyl-2,6-dioxocyclohexanepropionitrile	56	M.P. 151–152°	817	
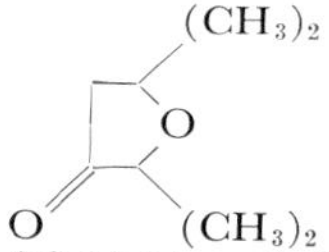 $(CH_3)_2$, $(CH_3)_2$ structure — 2,2,5-tetramethyltetrahydro-3-furanone	3.0	25°	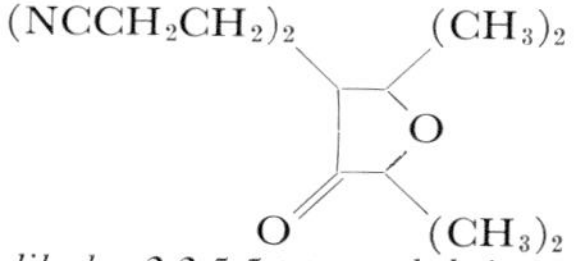 $(NCCH_2CH_2)_2$, $(CH_3)_2$, $(CH_3)_2$ structure — dihydro-2,2,5,5-tetramethyl-4-oxo-3,3(2H)-furandipropionitrile	71	M.P. 153°	168 177	
 $COCH_2CH_2CH_3$ structure — 2-butyrylcyclopentanone	—	—	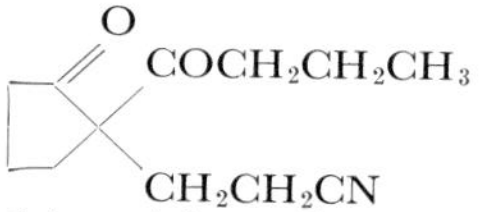 $COCH_2CH_2CH_3$, CH_2CH_2CN structure — 1-butyryl-2-oxocyclopentanepropionitrile	84	B.P. 148–152°/0.6 mm.	898	
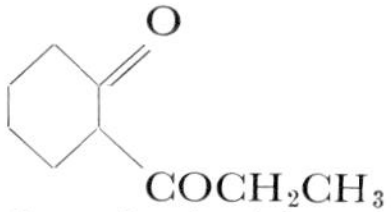 $COCH_2CH_3$ structure — 2-propionylcyclohexanone	24.0	25°	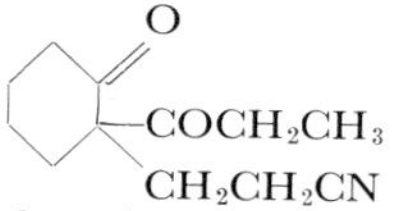 $COCH_2CH_3$, CH_2CH_2CN structure — 2-oxo-1-propionylcyclohexanepropionitrile	70	M.P. 58°	898	
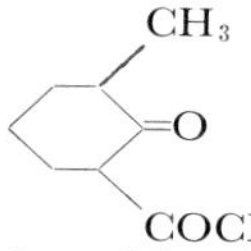 CH_3 , $COCH_3$ structure — 2-acetyl-6-methylcyclohexanone	24.0	25°	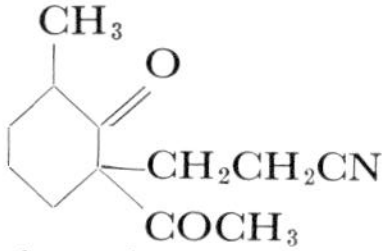 CH_3 , CH_2CH_2CN , $COCH_3$ structure — 1-acetyl-3-methyl-2-oxocyclohexanepropionitrile	—	—	898	

TABLE XI—Continued

(D) Diketones

Reactants	Reaction Time (Hr.)	Reaction Temperature (°C.)	Products	% Yield	M.P. or B.P. (°C.)	References This Exam.	References See Also:
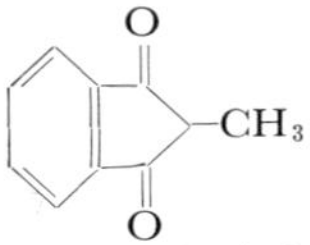 2-methyl-1,3-indanedione	5.0	25°	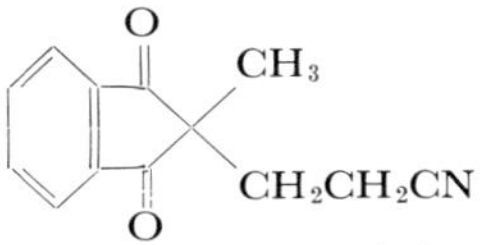 2-methyl-1,3-dioxo-2-indanpropionitrile	55	M.P. 84-85°	1363	
$C_6H_5COCH_2COCH_3$ 1-phenyl-1,3-butanedione	2.0	reflux	$CH_3COC(CH_2CH_2CN)_2COC_6H_5$ 4-acetyl-4-benzoylheptanedinitrile	65	B.P. 175-178°/2.5 mm.	130	1185
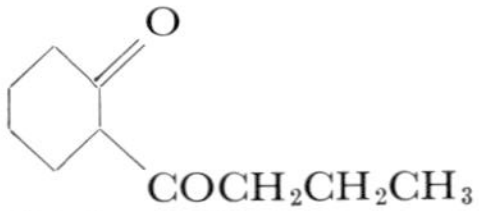 2-butyrylcyclohexanone	1.0 48.0	85° 25°	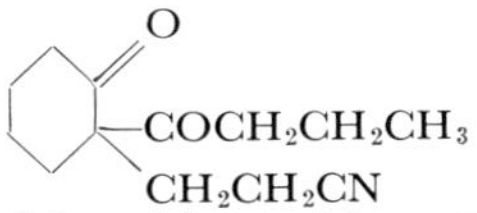 1-butyryl-2-oxocyclohexanepropionitrile	55	B.P. 159-162°/1 mm. M.P. 54°	898	
$CH_3COCH(CH_2C_6H_5)COCH_3$ 3-benzyl-2,4-pentanedione	—	—	$CH_3COC(CH_2CH_2CN)(CH_2C_6H_5)COCH_3$ 4,4-diacetyl-5-phenylvaleronitrile	62	—	129	
 4,4'-diketodicyclohexane	15.0	25°	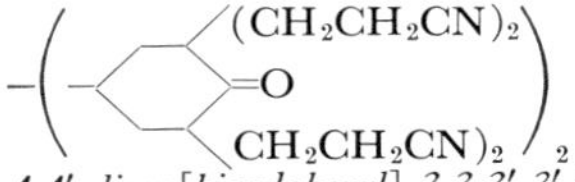 4,4'-dioxo[bicyclohexyl]-3,3,3',3',5,5,5',5'-octa-propionitrile	66	M.P. 280-287°	395 957	
 dibenzoylmethane	48.0	25°	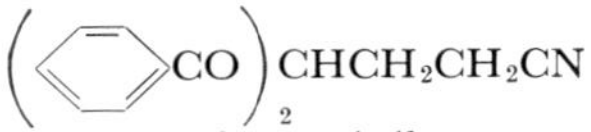 4,4-dibenzoylbutyronitrile	50	M.P. 117-118°	1349	

Additional examples of reactions involving diketones are described in the following references: 167, 169, 1027, 1185.

NOTES: (A) Based on unrecovered phorone. (C) Reaction failed if isophorone was not free from acidic impurities. (E) After hydrolysis with HCl.
(B) Based on unrecovered acetophenone. (D) Structure uncertain.

TABLE XII—"C" Cyanoethylation: Esters and Amides

(A) Malonic Esters

Reactants	Reaction Temperature (°C.)	Reaction Time (Hr.)	Products	% Yield	M.P. or B.P. (°C.)	References This Exam.	References See Also:
$BrCH(CO_2C_2H_5)_2$ / bromomalonic acid, diethyl ester	—	—	[structure] CN … $CO_2C_2H_5$ / $CO_2C_2H_5$ / 2-cyano-1,1-cyclopentanedicarboxylic acid, diethyl ester	35	—	1265	
$CH_2(CO_2C_2H_5)_2$ / malonic acid, diethyl ester	reflux	2.0	$HC(CH_2CH_2CN)(CO_2C_2H_5)_2$ / (2-cyanoethyl)malonic acid, diethyl ester	57	B.P. 163-173°/15 mm.	507	426, 656 1148, 772
$CH_2(CO_2C_2H_5)_2$ / malonic acid, diethyl ester	100-130°	—	$(NCCH_2CH_2)_2C(COOC_2H_5)_2$ / bis(2-cyanoethyl)malonic acid, diethyl ester	83	B.P. 175-180°/.02 mm. M.P. 65°	426	179, 1334, 1148, 772
$(C_2H_5OCO)_2CHNH_2$ / aminomalonic acid, diethyl ester	25° / reflux	4.0 / 1.25	$(C_2H_5OCO)_2C(NH_2)CH_2CH_2CN$ / amino(2-cyanoethyl)malonic acid, diethyl ester	47	B.P. 150-154°	254	
$C_2H_5OCOCH(CH_3)CO_2C_2H_5$ / methylmalonic acid, diethyl ester	25-35°	3.0	$C_2H_5OCOC(CH_3)(CH_2CH_2CN)CO_2C_2H_5$ / (2-cyanoethyl)methylmalonic acid, diethyl ester	97	B.P. 110°/0.04 mm.	42	
$CH_3CONHCH(COOC_2H_5)_2$ / acetaminomalonic acid, diethyl ester	25°	1.0	$CH_3CONHC(CH_2CH_2CN)(COOC_2H_5)_2$ / acetamido(2-cyanoethyl)malonic acid, diethyl ester	95	M.P. 92-94°	13 / 14	
$C_2H_5CH(COOC_2H_5)_2$ / ethylmalonic acid, diethyl ester	25°	5.0	$C_2H_5C(CH_2CH_2CN)(COOC_2H_5)_2$ / (2-cyanoethyl)ethylmalonic acid, diethyl ester	96	M.P. 47°	179	42
$(C_2H_5OCO)_2CHCH_2CH_2CH_3$ / n-propylmalonic acid, diethyl ester	—	—	$(C_2H_5OCO)_2C(CH_2CH_2CN)CH_2CH_2CH_3$ / (2-cyanoethyl)propylmalonic acid, diethyl ester	—	M.P. 31-32°	42	
$(C_2H_5OCO)_2CHCH(CH_3)_2$ / isopropylmalonic acid, diethyl ester	—	—	$(C_2H_5OCO)_2C(CH_2CH_2CN)CH(CH_3)_2$ / (2-cyanoethyl)isopropylmalonic acid, diethyl ester	—	B.P. 125°/0.035 mm.	42	
$n\text{-}C_4H_9CH(CO_2C_2H_5)_2$ / n-butylmalonic acid, diethyl ester	70°	—	$n\text{-}C_4H_9C(CH_2CH_2CN)(CO_2C_2H_5)_2$ / butyl(2-cyanoethyl)malonic acid, diethyl ester	87	B.P. 133-134°/1 mm.	396	179, 772, 42

TABLE XII—Continued

(A) Malonic Esters

Reactants	Reaction Time (Hr.)	Reaction Temperature (°C.)	Products	% Yield	M.P. or B.P. (°C.)	References This Exam.	References See Also:
[cyclopentyl]—CH(CO$_2$C$_2$H$_5$)$_2$ cyclopentylmalonic acid, diethyl ester	1.0 2.0	35-40° 50°	[cyclopentyl]—C(CH$_2$CH$_2$CN)(CO$_2$C$_2$H$_5$)$_2$ α-(2-cyanoethyl)cyclopentanemalonic acid, diethyl ester	61	B.P. 162°/2 mm.	705	
(C$_2$H$_5$OCO)$_2$CHC$_6$H$_5$ phenylmalonic acid, diethyl ester	3.0	25-35°	(C$_2$H$_5$OCO)$_2$C(CH$_2$CH$_2$CN)C$_6$H$_5$ (2-cyanoethyl)phenylmalonic acid, diethyl ester	93	M.P. 37°	42	1146
(C$_2$H$_5$OCO)$_2$CH(OC$_6$H$_5$) phenoxymalonic acid, diethyl ester	1.0	reflux	(C$_2$H$_5$OCO)$_2$C(OC$_6$H$_5$)CH$_2$CH$_2$CN (2-cyanoethyl)phenoxymalonic acid, diethyl ester	87	B.P. 158°/0.1 mm.	69	
n-C$_6$H$_{13}$CH(CO$_2$C$_2$H$_5$)$_2$ n-hexylmalonic acid, diethyl ester	—	70°	n-C$_6$H$_{13}$C(CH$_2$CH$_2$CN)(CO$_2$C$_2$H$_5$)$_2$ (2-cyanoethyl)hexylmalonic acid, diethyl ester	82	B.P. 149-150°/1 mm.	396	
C$_6$H$_5$CH$_2$CH(COOC$_2$H$_5$)$_2$ benzylmalonic acid, diethyl ester	3.0	25°	C$_6$H$_5$CH$_2$C(CH$_2$CH$_2$CN)(COOC$_2$H$_5$)$_2$ benzyl(2-cyanoethyl)malonic acid, diethyl ester	79	B.P. 175-180°/1 mm. M.P. 47°	179	42
[CH(CO$_2$C$_2$H$_5$)$_2$]$_2$ ethanetetracarboxylic acid, tetraethyl ester	5.0	55-60°	(C$_2$H$_5$OCO)$_2$CHC(CH$_2$CH$_2$CN)(CO$_2$C$_2$H$_5$)$_2$ 4-cyano-1,1,2,2-butanetetracarboxylic acid, tetraethyl ester	77	B.P. 165-170°/0.01 mm.	122	
(C$_2$H$_5$OCO)$_2$CHCH$_2$CH$_2$C$_6$H$_5$ 2-phenylethylmalonic acid, diethyl ester	3.0	25-35°	(C$_2$H$_5$OCO)$_2$C(CH$_2$CH$_2$CN)CH$_2$CH$_2$C$_6$H$_5$ (2-cyanoethyl)(2-phenethyl)malonic acid, diethyl ester	97	B.P. 168-170°/0.03 mm.	42	
n-C$_8$H$_{17}$CH(CO$_2$C$_2$H$_5$)$_2$ n-octylmalonic acid, diethyl ester	—	30-40°	n-C$_8$H$_{17}$C(CH$_2$CH$_2$CN)(CO$_2$C$_2$H$_5$)$_2$ (2-cyanoethyl)octylmalonic acid, diethyl ester	90	B.P. 163-165°/1 mm.	396	
[1-naphthyl](C$_2$H$_5$OCO)$_2$CH— 1-naphthylmalonic acid, diethyl ester	3.0	25-35°	(C$_2$H$_5$OCO)$_2$C(CH$_2$CH$_2$CN)[1-naphthyl] α-(2-cyanoethyl)-1-naphthalenemalonic acid, diethyl ester	90	M.P. 82.5-83.5°	42	

TABLE XII—Continued (A) Malonic Esters

Reactants	Reaction Time (Hr.)	Reaction Temperature (°C.)	Products	% Yield	M.P. or B.P. (°C.)	References This Exam.	See Also:
$(C_2H_5OCO)_2CH$—[2-naphthyl] 2-naphthylmalonic acid, diethyl ester 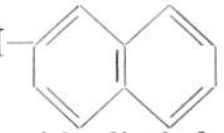	3.0	25-40°	$(C_2H_5OCO)_2C(CH_2CH_2CN)$—[2-naphthyl] α-(2-cyanoethyl)-2-naphthalenemalonic acid, diethyl ester 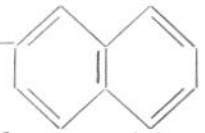	93	B.P. 170-175°/0.03 mm.	42	
$(C_2H_5OCO)_2CHC_{10}H_{21}$ n-decylmalonic acid, diethyl ester	1.0	—	$(C_2H_5OCO)_2C(CH_2CH_2CN)C_{10}H_{21}$ (2-cyanoethyl)decylmalonic acid, diethyl ester	90	B.P. 145-147°/0.1 mm.	397	396
$(C_2H_5OCO)_2CHCH_2$—[1-naphthyl] 1-naphthylmethylmalonic acid, diethyl ester 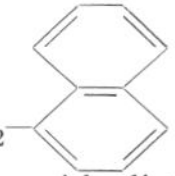	3.0	25-35°	$(C_2H_5OCO)_2C(CH_2CH_2CN)CH_2$—[1-naphthyl] (2-cyanoethyl)(1-naphthylmethyl)malonic acid, diethyl ester 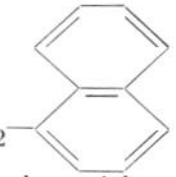	95	B.P. 156-158°/0.003 mm.	42	
$(C_2H_5OCO)_2CHCH_2$—[2-naphthyl] 2-naphthylmethylmalonic acid, diethyl ester 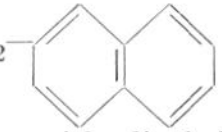	3.0	25-40°	$(C_2H_5OCO)_2C(CH_2CH_2CN)CH_2$—[2-naphthyl] (2-cyanoethyl)(2-naphthylmethyl)malonic acid, diethyl ester 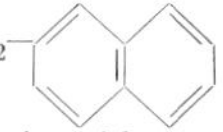	94	—	42	
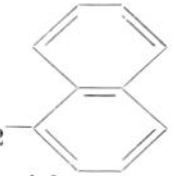 $(C_2H_5OCO)_2CHCH_2$—[naphthyl] 2-(1'-naphthyl)ethylmalonic acid, diethyl ester	3.0	25-35°	$(C_2H_5OCO)_2C(CH_2CH_2CN)CH_2CH_2$—[naphthyl] (2-cyanoethyl)[2-(1'-naphthyl)ethyl]malonic acid, diethyl ester 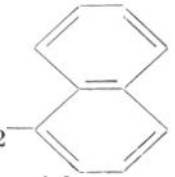	95	—	42	
$n\text{-}C_{12}H_{25}CH(CO_2C_2H_5)_2$ n-dodecylmalonic acid, diethyl ester	—	30-40°	$n\text{-}C_{12}H_{25}C(CH_2CH_2CN)(CO_2C_2H_5)_2$ (2-cyanoethyl)dodecylmalonic acid, diethyl ester	92	B.P. 182-183°/1 mm.	396 397	
$n\text{-}C_{14}H_{29}CH(CO_2C_2H_5)_2$ n-tetradecylmalonic acid, diethyl ester	—	60-70°	$n\text{-}C_{14}H_{29}C(CH_2CH_2CN)(CO_2C_2H_5)_2$ (2-cyanoethyl)tetradecylmalonic acid, diethyl ester	86	B.P. 189-190°/1 mm.	396	
$n\text{-}C_{16}H_{33}CH(CO_2C_2H_5)_2$ n-hexadecylmalonic acid, ethyl ester	—	70°	$n\text{-}C_{16}H_{33}C(CH_2CH_2CN)(CO_2C_2H_5)_2$ (2-cyanoethyl)hexadecylmalonic acid, diethyl ester	89	M.P. 45°	396	

TABLE XII—Continued

(B) **Acylacetic Esters**

Reactants	Reaction Temperature (°C.)	Reaction Time (Hr.)	Products	% Yield	M.P. or B.P. (°C.)	References This Exam.	References See Also:
$CH_3OCOCH_2COCH_3$ *acetoacetic acid, methyl ester*	25°	0.5	$CH_3OCOC(CH_2CH_2CN)_2COCH_3$ *2,2-bis(2-cyanoethyl)acetoacetic acid, methyl ester*	>69	M.P. 154°	166	177, 167, 169
$CH_3OCOCH_2COCH_3$ *acetoacetic acid, methyl ester*	25–40°	20.0	$CH_3COCH(\dot{C}H_2CH_2CN)COOCH_3$ *2-(2-cyanoethyl)acetoacetic acid, methyl ester*	—	B.P. 141–145°/7 mm.	167 169	
$C_2H_5OCOCH_2COCH_3$ *acetoacetic acid, ethyl ester*	—	—	$C_2H_5OCOCH(CH_2CH_2CN)COCH_3$ *2-(2-cyanoethyl)acetoacetic acid, ethyl ester*	63	B.P. 121°/2 mm.	11	1180, 1313
$C_2H_5OCOCH_2COCH_3$ *acetoacetic acid, ethyl ester*	20°	—	$C_2H_5OCOC(CH_2CH_2CN)_2COCH_3$ *2,2-bis(2-cyanoethyl)acetoacetic acid, ethyl ester*	83	M.P. 82°	1077	170, 168, 169, 1185, 583, 962, 177, 1148
$C_2H_5OCOCH(CH_3)COCH_3$ *2-methylacetoacetic acid, ethyl ester*	—	—	$C_2H_5OCOC(CH_3)(CH_2CH_2CN)COCH_3$ *2-(2-cyanoethyl)-2-methylacetoacetic acid, ethyl ester*	59	B.P. 118–118.5°/4 mm.	657	778
$C_2H_5OCOCOCH_2CO_2C_2H_5$ *oxalacetic acid, diethyl ester*	30–35°	48.0	$C_2H_5OCOCOCH(CO_2C_2H_5)CH_2CH_2CN$ *2-(2-cyanoethyl)oxalacetic acid, diethyl ester*	15	B.P. 215–220°/5 mm.	1349	
$C_2H_5OCOCH_2COCH_2CH_2CH_3$ *3-oxohexanoic acid, ethyl ester*	30–35° reflux	0.5 0.3	$C_2H_5OCOCH(CH_2CH_2CN)COCH_2CH_2CH_3$ *2-(2-cyanoethyl)-3-oxohexanoic acid, ethyl ester*	63.1	B.P. 152–158°/9 mm.	812	1185, 1180
$C_2H_5OCOCH_2COCH(CH_3)_2$ *4-methyl-3-oxopentanoic acid, ethyl ester*	25–45°	1.0	$C_2H_5OCOCH(CH_2CH_2CN)COCH(CH_3)_2$ *2-(2-cyanoethyl)-4-methyl-3-oxovaleric acid, ethyl ester*	53.0	B.P. 134–137°/3 mm.	1180	
$C_2H_5OCOCH(CH_2CH_3)COCH_3$ *2-ethylacetoacetic acid, ethyl ester*	25°	4.0	$C_2H_5OCOC(CH_2CH_2CN)(CH_2CH_3)COCH_3$ *2-(2-cyanoethyl)-2-ethylacetoacetic acid, ethyl ester*	71	B.P. 164–164.5°/11 mm.	1313	778
$C_2H_5OCOCH_2CO$ —[2-thienyl] *3-(2-thienyl)-3-oxopropanoic acid, ethyl ester*	25–45°	1.0	$C_2H_5OCOCH(CH_2CH_2CN)CO$ —[2-thienyl] *α-(2-cyanoethyl)-β-oxo-2-thiophenepropionic acid, ethyl ester*	64.0	B.P. 175–176°/1 mm.	1180	1185

TABLE XII—Continued

(B) Acylacetic Esters

Reactants	Reaction Time (Hr.)	Reaction Temperature (°C.)	Products	% Yield	M.P. or B.P. (°C.)	This Exam.	See Also:
C₂H₅OCOCH₂CO [2-furyl] 3(2-furyl)-3-oxopropanoic acid, ethyl ester	1.0	25–45°	C₂H₅OCOCH(CH₂CH₂CN)CO [2-furyl] α-(2-cyanoethyl)-3-oxo-2-furanpropionic acid, ethyl ester	37.1	B.P. 180–185°/2.5 mm.	1180	
C₂H₅OCOCH₂CO [2-furyl] 3-(2-furyl)-3-oxopropanoic acid, ethyl ester	2.0	R.T.	C₂H₅OCOC(CH₂CH₂CN)₂CO [2-furyl] α,α-bis(2-cyanoethyl)-β-oxo-2-furanpropionic acid, ethyl ester	25	M.P. 91–91.5°	1185	
C₂H₅OCOCH(CH₂CH=CH₂)COCH₃ 2-allylacetoacetic acid, ethyl ester	3.0	30–35°	C₂H₅OCOC(CH₂CH₂CN)(CH₂CH=CH₂)COCH₃ 2-acetyl-2-(2-cyanoethyl)-4-pentenoic acid, ethyl ester	76	B.P. 180–181°/10 mm.	778	
C₂H₅OCOCH₂COCH(CH₃)₂ 5-methyl-3-oxohexanoic acid, ethyl ester	2.0	R.T.	C₂H₅OCOC(CH₂CH₂CN)₂COCH(CH₃)₂ 2,2-bis(2-cyanoethyl)-5-methyl-3-oxohexanoic acid, ethyl ester	68	M.P. 53.5–54.4°	1185	1180
C₂H₅OCOCH(CH₂CH₂CH₃)COCH₃ 2-propylacetoacetic acid, ethyl ester	5.0	30–35°	C₂H₅OCOC(CH₂CH₂CN)(CH₂CH₂CH₃)COCH₃ 2-acetyl-2-(2-cyanoethyl)valeric acid, ethyl ester	88	B.P. 192°/6 mm.	778	
C₂H₅OCOCH[CH(CH₃)₂]COCH₃ 2-isopropylacetoacetic acid, ethyl ester	5.0	30–35°	C₂H₅OCOC(CH₂CH₂CN)[CH(CH₃)₂]COCH₃ 2-(2-cyanoethyl)-2-isopropylacetoacetic acid, ethyl ester	43	B.P. 183–185°/4 mm.	778	11
C₂H₅OCOCH(CH₂CO₂C₂H₅)COCH₃ acetosuccinic acid, diethyl ester	—	—	C₂H₅OCOC(CH₂CH₂CN)(CH₂CO₂C₂H₅)COCH₃ (A) 2-acetyl-2-(2-cyanoethyl)succinic acid, diethyl ester	12	B.P. 165–166°/1.7 mm.	12	1057
C₂H₅OCOCH₂COC₅H₁₁ 3-oxooctanoic acid, ethyl ester	0.5 0.3	30–35° reflux	C₂H₅OCOCH(CH₂CH₂CN)COC₅H₁₁ 2-(2-cyanoethyl)-3-oxooctanoic acid, ethyl ester	66.9	B.P. 170–177°/9 mm.	813	1180
C₂H₅OCOCH(i-C₄H₉)COCH₃ 2-isobutylacetoacetic acid, ethyl ester	—	—	C₂H₅OCOC(i-C₄H₉)(CH₂CH₂CN)COCH₃ 2-acetyl-2-(2-cyanoethyl)-4-methylvaleric acid, ethyl ester	60	B.P. 125°/0.1 mm.	11	

TABLE XII—Continued

(B) Acylacetic Esters

Reactants	Reaction Time (Hr.)	Reaction Temperature (°C.)	Products	% Yield	M.P. or B.P. (°C.)	References This Exam.	References See Also:
$C_2H_5OCOCH_2COC_6H_5$, *3-phenyl-3-oxopropanoic acid, ethyl ester*	—	—	$C_2H_5OCOCH(CH_2CH_2CN)COC_6H_5$ *2-benzoyl-4-cyanobutyric acid, ethyl ester*	86	B.P. 176°/0.7 mm.	11	1180, 167, 169
$C_2H_5OCOCH_2COC_6H_5$, *3-phenyl-3-oxopropanoic acid, ethyl ester*	2.0	R.T.	$C_2H_5OCOC(CH_2CH_2CN)_2COC_6H_5$ *2-benzoyl-4-cyano-2-(2-cyanoethyl)butyric acid, ethyl ester*	53	M.P. 61.5-62°	1185	
$C_2H_5OCOCH_2CO(n\text{-}C_6H_{13})$, *3-oxononanoic acid, ethyl ester*	1.0	25-45°	$C_2H_5OCOCH(CH_2CH_2CN)CO(n\text{-}C_6H_{13})$ *2-(2-cyanoethyl)-3-oxononanoic acid, ethyl ester*	34.6	B.P. 154-156°/1.3 mm.	1180	
$C_2H_5OCOCH(n\text{-}C_5H_{11})COCH_3$, *2-amylacetoacetic acid, ethyl ester*	5.0	30-35°	$C_2H_5OCOC(CH_2CH_2CN)(n\text{-}C_5H_{11})COCH_3$ *2-acetyl-2-(2-cyanoethyl)heptanoic acid, ethyl ester*	71	B.P. 182°/4 mm.	778	772
$C_2H_5OCOCH(i\text{-}C_5H_{11})COCH_3$, *2-isoamylacetoacetic acid, ethyl ester*	3.0	30-35°	$C_2H_5OCOC(CH_2CH_2CN)(i\text{-}C_5H_{11})COCH_3$ *2-acetyl-2-(2-cyanoethyl)-5-methylhexanoic acid, ethyl ester*	72	B.P. 187-189°/4-6 mm.	778	
$CH_3OCOCH(CH_2C_6H_5)COCH_3$, *2-benzylacetoacetic acid, methyl ester*	—	—	$CH_3OCOC(CH_2C_6H_5)(CH_2CH_2CN)COCH_3$ *α-acetyl-α-(2-cyanoethyl)hydrocinnamic acid, methyl ester*	56	B.P. 163°/0.2 mm.	11	
$C_2H_5OCOCH(C_6H_5)COCH_3$, *2-phenylacetoacetic acid, ethyl ester*	—	—	$C_2H_5OCOC(C_6H_5)(CH_2CH_2CN)COCH_3$ *2-(2-cyanoethyl)-2-phenylacetoacetic acid, ethyl ester*	27	B.P. 180-220° / 0.003 mm.	657	
$C_2H_5OCOCH(n\text{-}C_6H_{13})COCH_3$, *2-n-hexylacetoacetic acid, ethyl ester*	3.0	30-35°	$C_2H_5OCOC(CH_2CH_2CN)(n\text{-}C_6H_{13})COCH_3$ *2-acetyl-2-(2-cyanoethyl)octanoic acid, ethyl ester*	84	B.P. 168°/4 mm.	778	11
$C_2H_5OCOCH(CH_2C_6H_5)COCH_3$, *2-benzylacetoacetic acid, ethyl ester*	0.5	25-35°	$C_2H_5OCOC(CH_2C_6H_5)(CH_2CH_2CN)COCH_3$ *α-acetyl-α-(2-cyanoethyl)hydrocinnamic acid, ethyl ester*	85[B]	B.P. 172°/1.5 mm.	11	12, 778
$C_2H_5OCOCH(n\text{-}C_7H_{15})COCH_3$, *2-n-heptylacetoacetic acid, ethyl ester*	—	—	$C_2H_5OCOC(n\text{-}C_7H_{15})(CH_2CH_2CN)COCH_3$ *2-acetyl-2-(2-cyanoethyl)nonanoic acid, ethyl ester*	81	B.P. 145°/0.9 mm.	11	

TABLE XII—Continued

(C) Cyclic Ketoesters

Reactants	Reaction Time (Hr.)	Reaction Temperature (°C.)	Products	% Yield	M.P. or B.P. (°C.)	References — This Exam.	References — See Also:
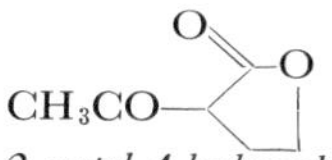 CH_3CO 2-acetyl-4-hydroxybutyric acid, γ-lactone	1.0	—	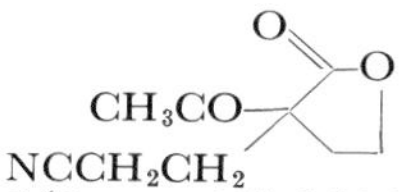 CH_3CO $NCCH_2CH_2$ 2-(2-cyanoethyl)-2-(2-hydroxyethyl)acetoacetic acid, γ-lactone	86–92	B.P. 162°/1.5 mm.	11 12	
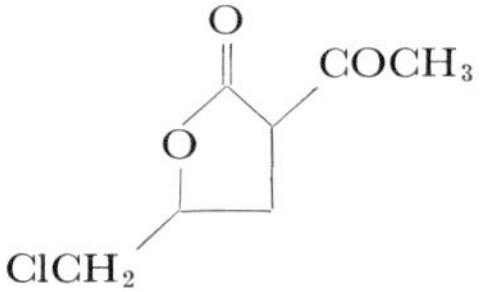 $COCH_3$ $ClCH_2$ 2-acetyl-4-hydroxy-4-chloromethylbutyric acid, γ-lactone	—	—	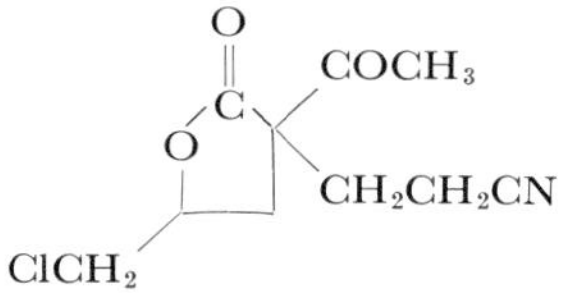 $COCH_3$ CH_2CH_2CN $ClCH_2$ 2-acetyl-5-chloro-2-(2-cyanoethyl)-4-hydroxyvaleric acid, γ-lactone	61	B.P. 199°/1.6 mm.	11	
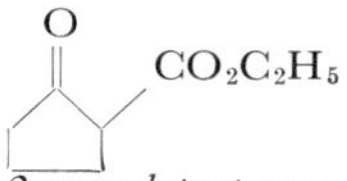 $CO_2C_2H_5$ 2-oxocyclopentanecarboxylic acid, ethyl ester	—	—	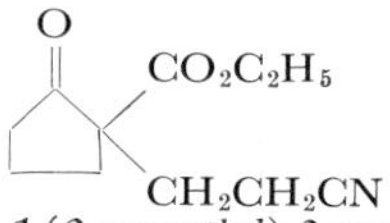 $CO_2C_2H_5$ CH_2CH_2CN 1-(2-cyanoethyl)-2-oxocyclopentanecarboxylic acid, ethyl ester	82	B.P. 145°/1.5 mm.	11	1363
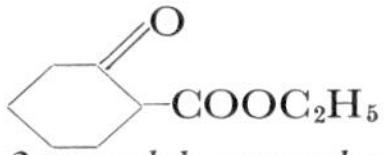 $COOC_2H_5$ 2-oxocyclohexanecarboxylic acid, ethyl ester	—	120–125°	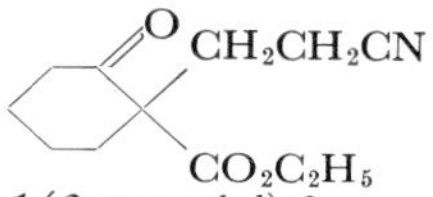 CH_2CH_2CN $CO_2C_2H_5$ 1-(2-cyanoethyl)-2-oxocyclohexanecarboxylic acid, ethyl ester	85	B.P. 142°/0.3 mm.	500	1363

TABLE XII—Continued

(C) Cyclic Ketoesters

Reactants	Reaction Time (Hr.)	Reaction Temperature (°C.)	Products	% Yield	M.P. or B.P. (°C.)	References This Exam.	See Also:
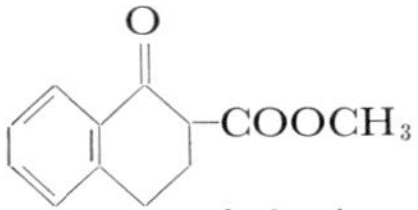 [structure] COOCH₃ 1,2,3,4-tetrahydro-1-oxo-2-naphthoic acid, methyl ester	2.0	25°	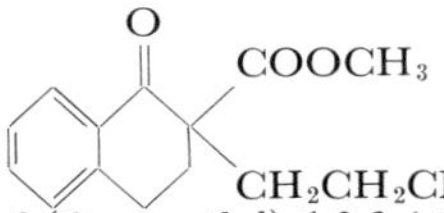 [structure] COOCH₃ CH₂CH₂CN 2-(2-cyanoethyl)-1,2,3,4-tetrahydro-1-oxo-2-naphthoic acid, methyl ester	92	M.P. 75-76°	56	
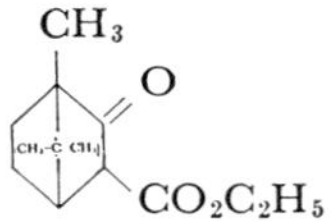 [structure] CH_3 $CO_2C_2H_5$ camphocarboxylic acid, ethyl ester	—	110-117°	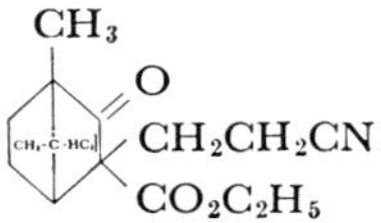 [structure] CH_3 CH_2CH_2CN $CO_2C_2H_5$ 2-(2-cyanoethyl)-4,7,7-trimethyl-3-oxo-2-nor-camphanecarboxylic acid, ethyl ester	78.3	B.P. 160-162°/0.5 mm.	500	
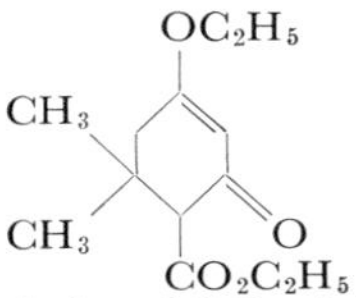 [structure] OC_2H_5 CH_3 CH_3 $CO_2C_2H_5$ 4-ethoxy-6,6-dimethyl-2-oxo-3-cyclohexene-1-carboxylic acid, ethyl ester	—	110°	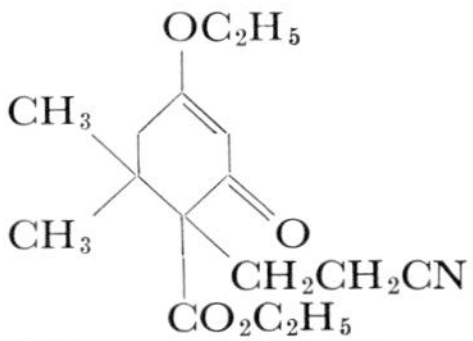 [structure] OC_2H_5 CH_3 CH_3 CH_2CH_2CN $CO_2C_2H_5$ 1-(2-cyanoethyl)-4-ethoxy-6,6-dimethyl-2-oxo-3-cyclohexene-1-carboxylic acid, ethyl ester	60	B.P. 160°/0.05 mm.	500	

(D) Miscellaneous Esters

Reactants	Reaction Time (Hr.)	Reaction Temperature (°C.)	Products	% Yield	M.P. or B.P. (°C.)	References This Exam.	See Also:
CH_3OCOCH_2CN cyanoacetic acid, methyl ester	—	80-90°	$CH_3OCOC(CH_2CH_2CN)_2CN$ 2-(2-cyanoethyl)-2,4-dicyanobutyric acid, methyl ester	68	B.P. 218-225°/3 mm.	426	

TABLE XII—Continued

(D) Miscellaneous Esters

Reactants	Reaction Time (Hr.)	Reaction Temperature (°C.)	Products	% Yield	M.P. or B.P. (°C.)	References This Exam.	References See Also:
$O_2NCH_2CO_2C_2H_5$ *nitroacetic acid, ethyl ester*	4	80-90°	$O_2NCH(CH_2CH_2CN)CO_2C_2H_5$ *4-cyano-2-(2-cyanoethyl)-2-nitrobutyric acid, ethyl ester*	52	B.P. 147-151°/4 mm.	1392	
$O_2NCH_2CO_2C_2H_5$ *nitroacetic acid, ethyl ester*	4	80-90°	$O_2NC(CH_2CH_2CN)_2CO_2C_2H_5$ *4-cyano-2-(2-cyanoethyl)-2-nitrobutyric acid, ethyl ester*	80	M.P. 51.9-52.7°	1392	
$C_2H_5OCOCH_2CN$ *cyanoacetic acid, ethyl ester*	—	150-165°	$C_2H_5OCOCH(CN)CH_2CH_2CN$ *2,4-dicyanobutyric acid, ethyl ester* $C_2H_5OCOC(CN)(CH_2CH_2CN)_2$ *2,4-dicyano-2-(2-cyanoethyl)butyric acid, ethyl ester*	39 26	— —	931	
$C_2H_5OCOCH_2CN$ *cyanoacetic acid, ethyl ester*	1.0	25°	$C_2H_5OCOC(CH_2CH_2CN)_2CN$ *2,4-dicyano-2-(2-cyanoethyl)butyric acid, ethyl ester*	98	M.P. 37°	179	931, 1148
$C_2H_5OCOCH(NHCOCH_3)CN$ *N-acetyl-2-cyanoglycine, ethyl ester*	1.0	<20°	$C_2H_5OCOC(CH_2CH_2CN)(NHCOCH_3)CN$ *2-acetamido-2,4-dicyanobutyric acid, ethyl ester*	86-90	M.P. 101-102°	464	
$(C_2H_5O)_2\overset{O}{\underset{\|}{P}}CH_2CO_2C_2H_5$ *phosphonoacetic acid, triethyl ester*	3.0	25°	$(C_2H_5O)_2\overset{O}{\underset{\|}{P}}C(CH_2CH_2CN)_2CO_2C_2H_5$ *4-cyano-2-(2-cyanoethyl)-2-diethylphosphonobutyric acid, ethyl ester*	88	—	679 680	
$C_2H_5OOCCH_2\overset{O}{\underset{\|}{P}}(OCH_2CH_3)_2$ *phosphonoacetic acid, triethyl ester*	—	—	$C_2H_5OOCCH(CH_2CH_2CN)\overset{O}{\underset{\|}{P}}(OCH_2CH_3)_2$ *4-cyano-2-diethylphosphonobutyric acid, ethyl ester* $C_2H_5OOCC(CH_2CH_2CN)_2\overset{O}{\underset{\|}{P}}(OCH_2CH_3)_2$ *4-cyano-2-(2-cyanoethyl)-2-diethylphosphono-butyric acid, ethyl ester*	27 27	B.P. 185-186°/4 mm.	894	

TABLE XII—Continued

(D) Miscellaneous Esters

Reactants	Reaction Time (Hr.)	Reaction Temperature (°C.)	Products	% Yield	M.P. or B.P. (°C.)	References This Exam.	References See Also:
$C_2H_5OOCCH(CH_3)P(OCH_2CH_3)_2$ 2-phosphonopropionic acid, triethyl ester	0.5	R.T.	$C_2H_5OOCC(CH_2CH_2CN)(CH_3)P(OC_2H_5)_2$ 4-cyano-2-diethylphosphono-2-methylbutyric acid, ethyl ester	59	B.P. 176-178°/5 mm.	894	
$NCCH(C_6H_5)CO_2C_2H_5$ 2-phenyl-2-cyanoacetic acid, ethyl ester	1.0 18.0	40-45° 25°	$NCC(CH_2CH_2CN)(C_6H_5)CO_2C_2H_5$ 2,4-dicyano-2-phenylbutyric acid, ethyl ester	83	B.P. 157-167°/ 0.5-1.0 mm.	542	543
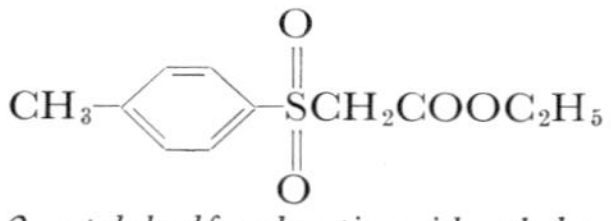 CH_3—⬡—$SCH_2COOC_2H_5$ 2-p-tolylsulfonylacetic acid, ethyl ester	2.0	25°	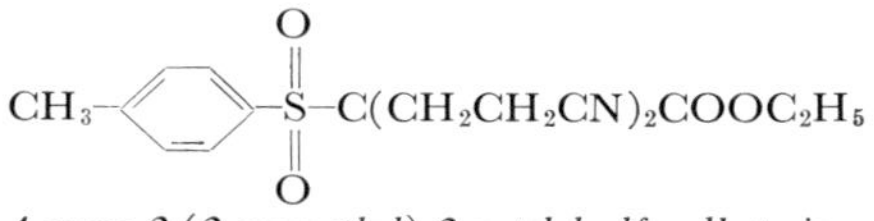 CH_3—⬡—$S-C(CH_2CH_2CN)_2COOC_2H_5$ 4-cyano-2-(2-cyanoethyl)-2-p-tolylsulfonylbutyric acid, ethyl ester	—	M.P. 100-106°	171	
$C_2H_5OOCCH(C_4H_9)P(OC_2H_5)_2$ 2-phosphonohexanoic acid, triethyl ester	0.5	R.T.	$C_2H_5OCOC(CH_2CH_2CN)(C_4H_9)P(OC_2H_5)_2$ 2-(2-cyanoethyl)-2-diethylphosphonohexanoic acid, ethyl ester	74	B.P. 186-187°/2 mm.	894	
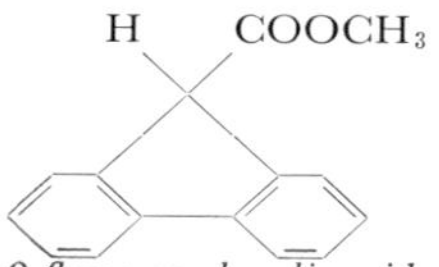 H—COOCH₃ (fluorene structure) 9-fluorenecarboxylic acid, methyl ester	0.25	—	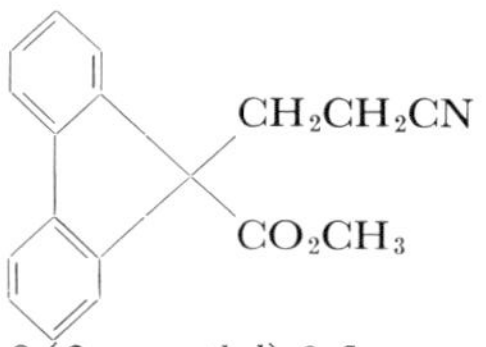 CH_2CH_2CN / CO_2CH_3 (fluorene structure) 9-(2-cyanoethyl)-9-fluorenecarboxylic acid, methyl ester	94	M.P. 84-86°	206	1099

TABLE XII—Continued

(D) Miscellaneous Esters

Reactants	Re-action Time (Hr.)	Reaction Tem-perature (°C.)	Products	% Yield	M.P. or B.P. (°C.)	References	
						This Exam.	See Also:
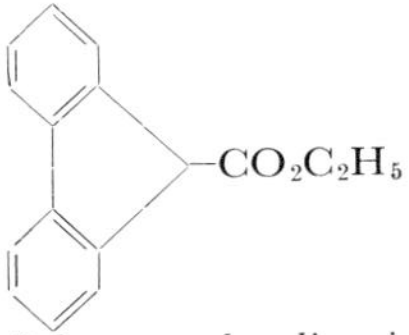 9-fluorenecarboxylic acid, ethyl ester	0.5	25°	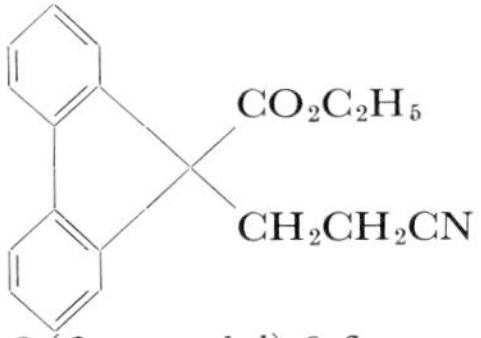 9-(2-cyanoethyl)-9-fluorenecarboxylic acid, ethyl ester	94	B.P. 210-220°/1-2 mm.	642	206
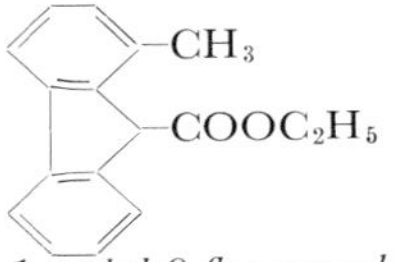 1-methyl-9-fluorenecarboxylic acid, ethyl ester	0.5	R.T.	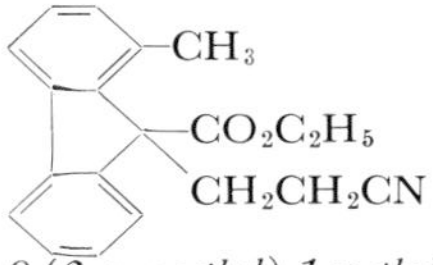 9-(2-cyanoethyl)-1-methyl-9-fluorenecarboxylic acid, ethyl ester	78	B.P. 190-196°/1 mm. M.P. 92-93°	643	

(E) Amides

Reactants	Re-action Time (Hr.)	Reaction Tem-perature (°C.)	Products	% Yield	M.P. or B.P. (°C.)	References	
						This Exam.	See Also:
$NCCH_2CONH_2$ cyanoacetamide	1.0	25°	$NCCH(CH_2CH_2CN)_2CONH_2$ 2,4-dicyano-2-(2-cyanoethyl)butyramide	74	M.P. 118°	179	
$CH_2(CONH_2)_2$ malonamide	1.0	35-38°	$(NCCH_2CH_2)_2C(CONH_2)_2$ bis(2-cyanoethyl)malonamide	13	M.P. 210°	179	
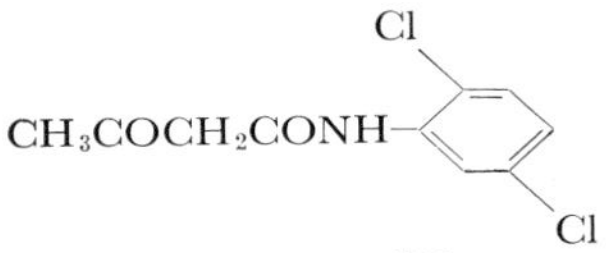 CH_3COCH_2CONH— 2,5-dichloroacetoacetanilide	2.5	40-45°	 $CH_3COC(CH_2CH_2CN)_2CONH$— 2,2-bis(2-cyanoethyl)-2',5'-dichloroacetanilide	84	M.P. 121°	166 167 169	

TABLE XII—Continued

Reactants	Products	Reaction Temperature (°C.)	Reaction Time (Hr.)	M.P. or B.P. (°C.)	% Yield	References: This Exam.	See Also:
CH_3COCH_2CONH— 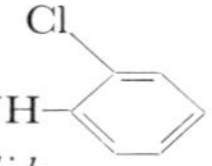 (o-chlorophenyl ring, Cl) *o-chloroacetoacetanilide*	$CH_3COC(CH_2CH_2CN)_2CONH$— 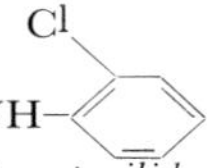 (o-chlorophenyl ring, Cl) *2,2-bis(2-cyanoethyl)-2'-chloroacetoacetanilide*	40-50°	3.0	M.P. 105°	96	166 167 167	
$CH_3COCH_2CONHC_6H_5$ *acetoacetanilide*	$CH_3COC(CH_2CH_2CN)_2CONHC_6H_5$ *2,2-bis(2-cyanoethyl)acetoacetanilide*	45-50°	2.5	M.P. 82°	—	166 167 169	

NOTES   Ⓐ Deacetylation occurs when absolute alcohol is used.   Ⓑ Based on unrecovered starting material.

TABLE XIII—"C" Cyanoethylation: Nitriles (Including HCN)

Reactants	Products	Reaction Temperature (°C.)	Reaction Time (Hr.)	M.P. or B.P. (°C.)	% Yield	References: This Exam.	See Also:
HCN *hydrocyanic acid*	$NCCH_2CH_2CN$ *succinonitrile*	55-60°	5.0	—	97.2	211	962, 787, 678, 677, 342, 1074, 1071, 148
$NaCN + CH_3CO_2H$ *sodium cyanide + acetic acid*	$NCCH_2CH_2CN$ + (succinimide ring structure) *succinonitrile + succinimide*	70°	~2.0	—	—	244 768 767 766	1168
$NaCN + H_2SO_4$ *sodium cyanide + sulfuric acid*	$HO_2CCH_2CH_2CO_2H$ *succinic acid*	70°	—	M.P. 182-183°	90	244 769 768 766	
$NCCH_2CO_2Na$ *cyanoacetic acid, sodium salt*	$NaO_2CCH(CN)CH_2CH_2CN$ *2,4-dicyanobutyric acid, sodium salt*	—	21.0	decomposes	96	1331	
$NCCH_2CN$ *malononitrile*	$(NC)_2C(CH_2CH_2CN)_2$ *1,3,3,5-pentanetetracarbonitrile*	—	—	M.P. 92°	95	1331	

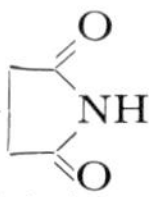

"C" Cyanoethylation: Nitriles (Including HCN)

TABLE XIII—Continued

Reactants	Products	Reaction Temperature (°C.)	Reaction Time (Hr.)	% Yield	M.P. or B.P. (°C.)	References This Exam.	See Also:
$CH_2=CHCH_2CN$ *3-butenenitrile*	$CH_3CH=C(CN)CH_2CH_2CN$ *2-ethylideneglutaronitrile* $CH_2=CHC(CH_2CH_2CN)_2CN$ *3-vinyl-1,3,5-pentanetricarbonitrile*	10° 25°	1.0 2.0	9 55	B.P. 134-137°/10 mm. B.P. 210-245°/1 mm. M.P. 60-61°	162 178	15
$CH_3CH=CHCN$ *cis-and trans-crotononitrile (mixture)*	$CH_3CH=C(CH_2CH_2CN)CN$ *2-ethylideneglutaronitrile* $CH_2=CHC(CH_2CH_2CN)_2CN$ *3-vinyl-1,3,5-pentanetricarbonitrile*	25°	24.0	14 14	B.P. 134-137°/10 mm. M.P. 60-61°	162 178	
$CH_3CH=CHCH_2CN +$ $CH_2=CHCH(CH_3)CN$ *3-pentenenitrile + 2-methyl-3-butenenitrile*	$C_8H_{10}N_2 + C_{11}H_{13}N_3$	25°	18.0	—	B.P. 140-150°/10 mm. B.P. 200-210°/1 mm.	162	
$(CH_3)_2C=CHCN$ *3-methyl-3-butenenitrile*	$(CH_3)_2C=C(CH_2CH_2CN)CN$ Ⓐ *2-isopropylideneglutaronitrile* $CH_2=C(CH_3)C(CH_2CH_2CN)_2CN$ *3-isopropenyl-1,3,5-pentanetricarbonitrile*	25°	2.0	4.5 13	B.P. 150°/10 mm. M.P. 67-68°	162 178	
$(C_2H_5O)_2\overset{O}{\overset{\|}{P}}-CH_2CN$ *cyanomethylphosphonic acid, diethyl ester*	$(C_2H_5O)_2\overset{O}{\overset{\|}{P}}C(CH_2CH_2CN)_2CN$ *[1,3-dicyano-1-(2-cyanoethyl)propyl]phosphonic acid, diethyl ester*	25-50°	—	92	M.P. 75-76°	679 680	1387
$CH_3CH=C(CH_2CH_2CN)CN$ *2-(2-cyanoethyl)-2-butenenitrile*	$CH_2=CHC(CH_2CH_2CN)_2CN$ *3-vinyl-1,3,5-pentanetricarbonitrile*	25°	24.0	79Ⓑ	M.P. 60-61°	162 178	
$CH_2=C(CH_3)CH_2CH_2CH_2CN$ *5-methyl-5-hexenitrile*	$CH_2=C(CH_2CH_2CN)_2$ *5-methylenenonanedinitrile*	235° (pressure)	4.0	71Ⓒ	B.P. 132-137°/0.5 mm.	15	
Br–⟨phenyl⟩–CH₂CN *m-bromophenylacetonitrile*	Br–⟨phenyl⟩–C(CH₂CH₂CN)₂CN *3-(m-bromophenyl)-1,3,5-pentanetricarbonitrile*	25°	2.0	89	M.P. 83°	778	

TABLE XIII—Continued

"C" Cyanoethylation: Nitriles (Including HCN)

Reactants	Reaction Time (Hr.)	Reaction Temperature (°C.)	Products	% Yield	M.P. or B.P. (°C.)	References This Exam.	References See Also:
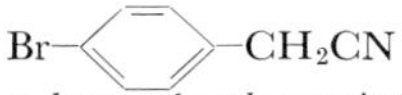 Br—⬡—CH₂CN p-bromophenylacetonitrile	2.0	25°	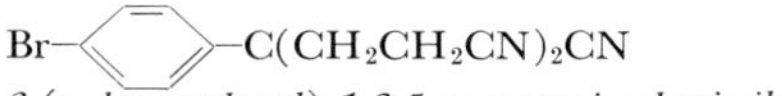 Br—⬡—C(CH₂CH₂CN)₂CN 3-(p-bromophenyl)-1,3,5-pentanetricarbonitrile	84	M.P. 132°	778	
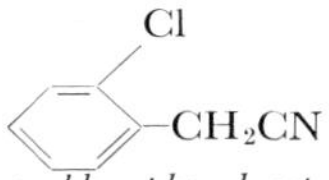 (Cl) ⬡—CH₂CN o-chlorophenylacetonitrile	2.0	25°	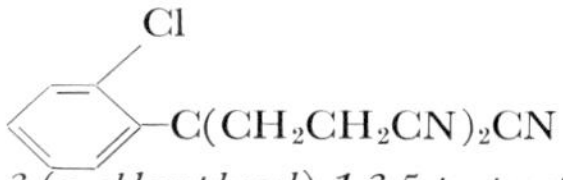 (Cl) C(CH₂CH₂CN)₂CN 3-(o-chlorophenyl)-1,3,5-pentanetricarbonitrile	47	M.P. 73°	778	
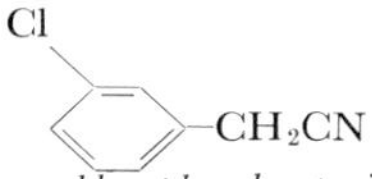 (Cl) ⬡—CH₂CN m-chlorophenylacetonitrile	2.0	25°	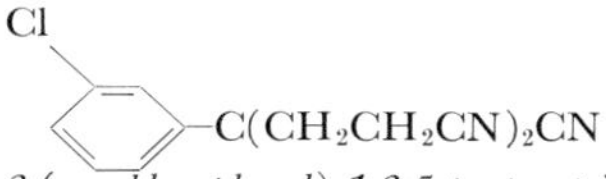 ⬡—C(CH₂CH₂CN)₂CN 3-(m-chlorophenyl)-1,3,5-pentanetricarbonitrile	64	M.P. 80°	778	
p-ClC₆H₄CH₂CN p-chlorophenylacetonitrile	—	—	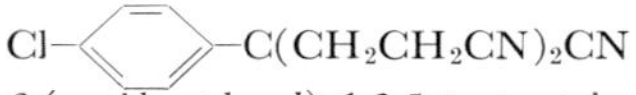 Cl—⬡—C(CH₂CH₂CN)₂CN 3-(p-chlorophenyl)-1,3,5-pentanetricarbonitrile	80	M.P. 124-125°	940	
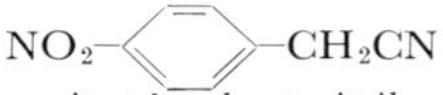 NO₂—⬡—CH₂CN p-nitrophenylacetonitrile	2.0	25°	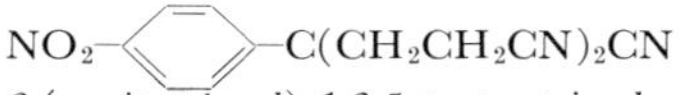 NO₂—⬡—C(CH₂CH₂CN)₂CN 3-(p-nitrophenyl)-1,3,5-pentanetricarbonitrile	92	M.P. 147-148°	179 508	
C₆H₅CH₂CN phenylacetonitrile	0.5	225°	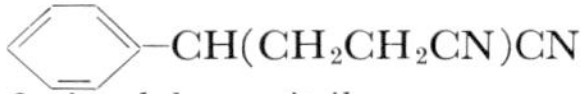 ⬡—CH(CH₂CH₂CN)CN 2-phenylglutaronitrile	80	B.P. 163°/1 mm.	931	203, 666, 1222
C₆H₅CH₂CN phenylacetonitrile	—	50-60°	C₆H₅C(CN)(CH₂CH₂CN)₂ 3-phenyl-1,3,5-pentanetricarbonitrile	100	—	1148	179, 1077, 931, 508
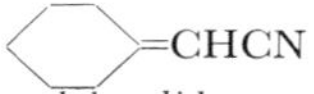 ⬡=CHCN cyclohexylideneacetonitrile	2.0	25°	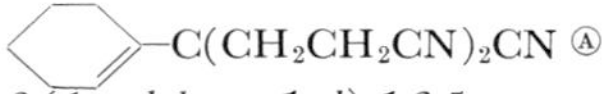 C(CH₂CH₂CN)₂CN Ⓐ 3-(1-cyclohexen-1-yl)-1,3,5-pentanetricarbonitrile	38	M.P. 81-82°	178	162

TABLE XIII—Continued

"C" Cyanoethylation: Nitriles (Including HCN)

Reactants	Products	Reaction Temperature (°C.)	Reaction Time (Hr.)	% Yield	M.P. or B.P. (°C.)	References This Exam.	References See Also:
CH_3 —◯— CH_2CN m-methylphenylacetonitrile	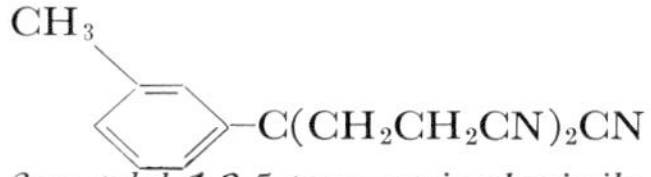 CH_3 —◯— $C(CH_2CH_2CN)_2CN$ 3-m-tolyl-1,3,5-pentanetricarbonitrile	25°	2.0	88	M.P. 67-68°	778	
CH_3 —◯— CH_2CN p-methylphenylacetonitrile	 CH_3 —◯— $C(CH_2CH_2CN)_2CN$ 3-p-tolyl-1,3,5-pentanetricarbonitrile	25°	2.0	95	M.P. 104°	778	
◯— $CH(CH_3)CN$ hydratroponitrile	$CH_3C(CH_2CH_2CN)(C_6H_5)CN$ 2-methyl-2-phenylglutaronitrile	20°	2.0	55	B.P. 151°/0.3 mm. B.P. 165°/2 mm.	411	
CH_3O —◯— CH_2CN m-methoxyphenylacetonitrile	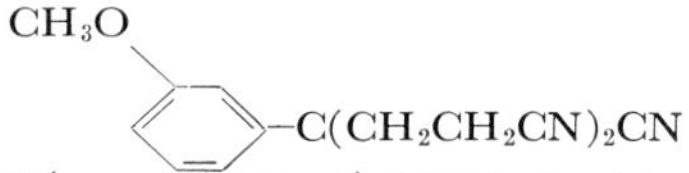 CH_3O —◯— $C(CH_2CH_2CN)_2CN$ 3-(m-methoxyphenyl)-1,3,5-pentanetricarbonitrile	25°	24.0	77	M.P. 73-74°	512	
CH_3O —◯— CH_2CN p-methoxyphenylacetonitrile	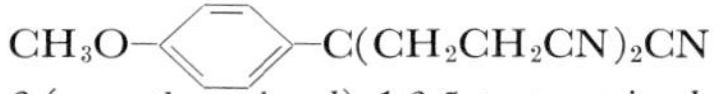 CH_3O —◯— $C(CH_2CH_2CN)_2CN$ 3-(p-methoxyphenyl)-1,3,5-pentanetricarbonitrile	25°	24.0	68	M.P. 83-83.5°	512	
$(C_2H_5O)_2PCH(CN)CH_2CH=CH_2$ (with O) 1-cyano-3-butenylphosphonic acid, diethyl ester	$(C_2H_5O)_2PC(CN)(CH_2CH_2CN)CH_2CH=CH_2$ (with O) [1-cyano-1-(2-cyanoethyl)-3-butenyl]phosphonic acid, diethyl ester	90-100°	—	42.6	B.P. 175°/3 mm.	1387	
$CH_3CH=CCN$ —◯— 2-phenylcrotononitrile	 $CH_2=CHC(CN)CH_2CH_2CN$ —◯— 2-phenyl-2-vinylglutaronitrile	0-5° 10°	1.5 1.0	30	B.P. 132-135°/0.15 mm.	1287	

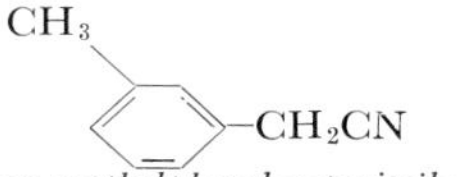

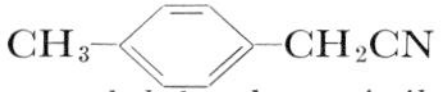

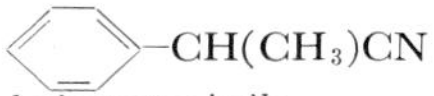

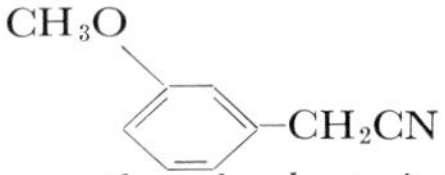

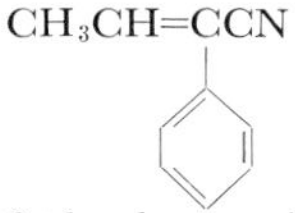

TABLE XIII—Continued

"C" Cyanoethylation: Nitriles (Including HCN)

Reactants	Reaction Time (Hr.)	Reaction Temperature (°C.)	Products	% Yield	M.P. or B.P. (°C.)	References This Exam.	See Also:
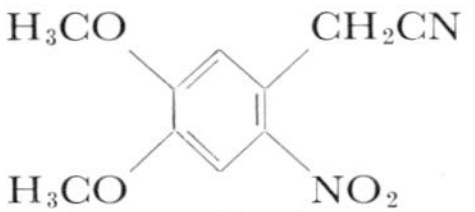 H₃CO ... CH₂CN / 2-nitro-4,5-dimethoxyphenylacetonitrile	1.0	reflux	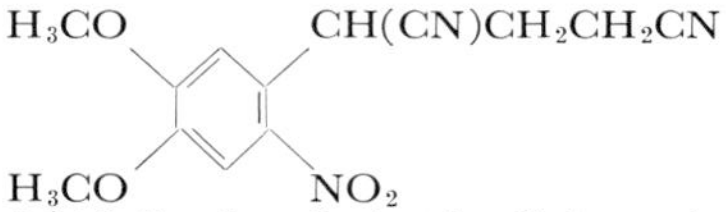 H₃CO ... CH(CN)CH₂CH₂CN / NO₂ / 2-(4,5-dimethoxy-2-nitrophenyl)glutaronitrile	41	M.P. 140-142°	1440	
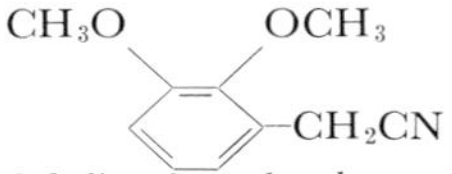 CH₃O OCH₃ ... CH₂CN / 2,3-dimethoxyphenylacetonitrile	2.0	25°	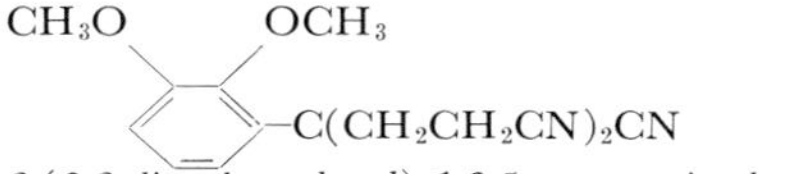 CH₃O OCH₃ ... C(CH₂CH₂CN)₂CN / 3-(2,3-dimethoxyphenyl)-1,3,5-pentanetricarbonitrile	96	M.P. 65-66°	545	
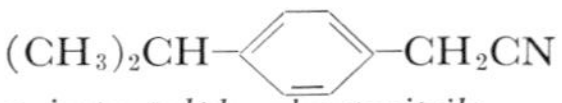 (CH₃)₂CH ... CH₂CN / p-isopropylphenylacetonitrile	—	—	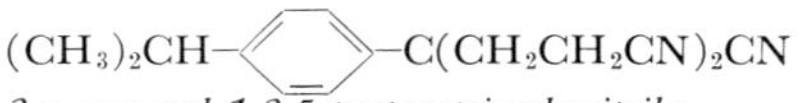 (CH₃)₂CH ... C(CH₂CH₂CN)₂CN / 3-p-cumenyl-1,3,5-pentanetricarbonitrile	—	M.P. 58-59°	940	
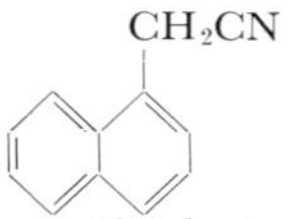 CH₂CN (naphthyl) / α-naphthylacetonitrile	—	—	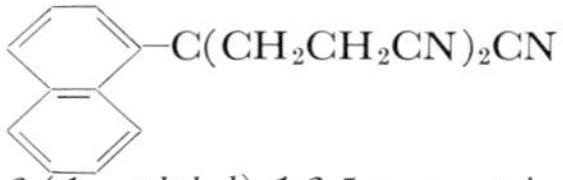 C(CH₂CH₂CN)₂CN (naphthyl) / 3-(1-naphthyl)-1,3,5-pentanetricarbonitrile	—	M.P. 103-104.5°	940	
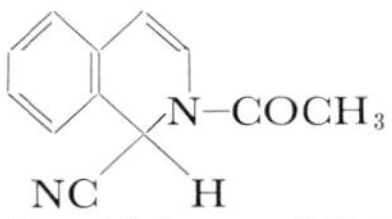 N—COCH₃ / NC H / 2-acetyl-1-cyano-1,2-dihydroisoquinoline	18.0	25°	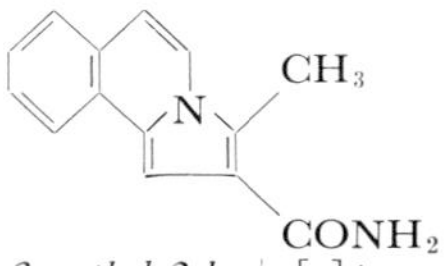 CH₃ / CONH₂ / 3-methyl-2-benzo[g]pyrrocolinecarboxamide	60	M.P. 189-190°	128	
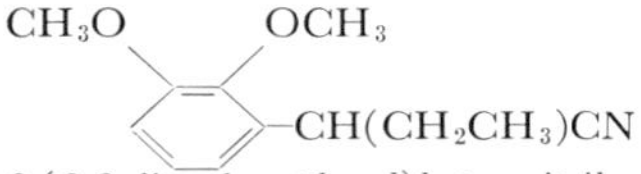 CH₃O OCH₃ ... CH(CH₂CH₃)CN / 2-(2,3-dimethoxyphenyl)butyronitrile	1.0 / 18.0	40-45° / 25°	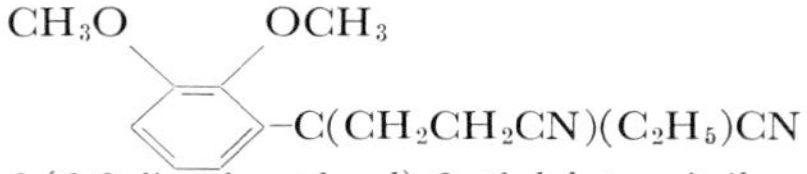 CH₃O OCH₃ ... C(CH₂CH₂CN)(C₂H₅)CN / 2-(2,3-dimethoxyphenyl)-2-ethylglutaronitrile	87©	B.P. 190-191°/2 mm.	544	

TABLE XIII—Continued

"C" Cyanoethylation: Nitriles (Including HCN)

Reactants	Reaction Time (Hr.)	Reaction Temperature (°C.)	Products	% Yield	M.P. or B.P. (°C.)	References — This Exam.	References — See Also:
(C$_6$H$_5$)$_2$CHCN *diphenylacetonitrile*	3.0	50°	(C$_6$H$_5$)$_2$C(CN)CH$_2$CH$_2$CN *2,2-diphenylglutaronitrile*	82	M.P. 71.5-72.5°	228	
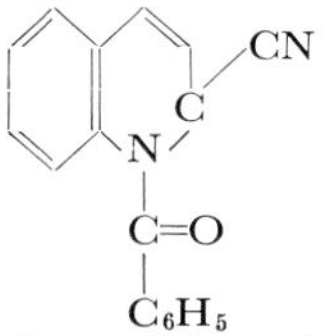 2-cyano-1-benzoyl-1,2-dihydroquinoline	18.0	25°	*unidentified red gum*	—	—	128	
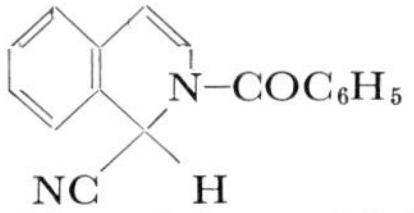 2-benzoyl-1-cyano-1,2-dihydroisoquinoline	18.0	25°	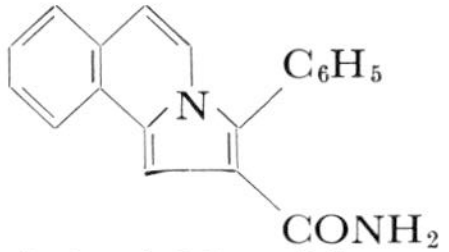 3-phenyl-2-benzo[g]pyrrocolinecarboxamide	76	M.P. 168-169°	128	

Additional examples involving complex nitriles may be found in the following references: 162 and 546.

NOTES: Ⓐ *Structure uncertain.*   Ⓑ *Based on unrecovered starting material.*   Ⓒ *Based on unrecovered hexenenitrile.*

TABLE XIV—"C" Cyanoethylation: Nitro Compounds

Reactants	Reaction Time (Hr.)	Reaction Temperature (°C.)	Products	% Yield	M.P. or B.P. (°C.)	References — This Exam.	References — See Also:
KCH(NO$_2$)$_2$ *dinitromethane, potassium derivative*	3.0	35-45°	(NO$_2$)$_2$C(CH$_2$CH$_2$CN)$_2$ *4,4-dinitroheptanedinitrile* NO$_2$C(CH$_2$CH$_2$CN)$_3$ *4-(2-cyanoethyl)-4-nitroheptanedinitrile*	35 12	M.P. 79° M.P. 114.5-116°	506	
NO$_2$CH$_3$ *nitromethane*	25-30	reflux	NO$_2$CH$_2$CH$_2$CH$_2$CN *4-nitrobutyronitrile*	29	B.P. 123-132°/15 mm.	1089	192

TABLE XIV—Continued

"C" Cyanoethylation: Nitro Compounds

Reactants	Reaction Time (Hr.)	Reaction Temperature (°C.)	Products	% Yield	M.P. or B.P. (°C.)	References This Exam.	References See Also:
NO_2CH_3 nitromethane	—	—	$NO_2CH(CH_2CH_2CN)_2$ 4-nitroheptanedinitrile	44	M.P. 65-66°	1089	
NO_2CH_3 nitromethane	3.0	50°	$NO_2C(CH_2CH_2CN)_3$ 4-(2-cyanoethyl)-4-nitroheptanedinitrile	63	M.P. 114°	962	1176, 179, 23, 163, 1334
$NO_2CH_2CH_3$ nitroethane	—	R.T.	$CH_3CH(NO_2)CH_2CH_2CN$ 4-nitrovaleronitrile	31	B.P. 96-101°/1 mm.	1089	163, 192, 194
$NO_2CH_2CH_3$ nitroethane	1.0	40°	$CH_3C(NO_2)(CH_2CH_2CN)_2$ 4-methyl-4-nitroheptanedinitrile	67	—	173	1089
$HOCH_2C(NO_2)_2CH_2OH$ 2,2-dinitro-1,3-propanediol	9.0	30°	$NCCH_2CH_2C(NO_2)_2CH_2CH_2CN$ 4,4-dinitroheptanedinitrile	37	M.P. 78°	760	
$CH_3CH_2CH_2NO_2$ 1-nitropropane	18.0	50°	$CH_3CH_2CH(NO_2)CH_2CH_2CN$ 4-nitrohexanenitrile	80	B.P. 76°/0.1 mm.	192	163
$CH_3CH(NO_2)CH_3$ 2-nitropropane	1.0	reflux	$CH_3C(NO_2)(CH_3)CH_2CH_2CN$ 4-methyl-4-nitrovaleronitrile	79	B.P. 70°/0.09 mm.	192	1089, 163, 193
 (nitrocyclohexane)	1.0	reflux	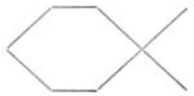 (structure) NO_2 / CH_2CH_2CN 1-nitrocyclohexanepropionitrile	40	B.P. 98-108°/0.15 mm. M.P. 42°	192 193	
$Br{-}C_6H_4{-}CH_2NO_2$ p-bromophenylnitromethane 	24.0	25°	$Br{-}C_6H_4{-}C(NO_2)(CH_2CH_2CN)_2$ 4-(p-bromophenyl)-4-nitroheptanedinitrile 	32	M.P. 138-139°	192	
 $C_6H_5{-}CH_2NO_2$ phenylnitromethane	48.0	25°	 $C_6H_5{-}C(CH_2CH_2CN)_2NO_2$ 4-nitro-4-phenylheptanedinitrile	42	M.P. 206-207°	1349	

TABLE XIV—Continued

"C" Cyanoethylation: Nitro Compounds

Reactants	Reaction Time (Hr.)	Reaction Temperature (°C.)	Products	% Yield	M.P. or B.P. (°C.)	References This Exam.	References See Also:
n-C$_4$H$_9$–S(O)$_2$–CH$_2$CH$_2$CHNO$_2$CH$_3$ *butyl 3-nitrobutyl sulfone*	3.0	reflux	n-C$_4$H$_9$–S(O)$_2$–CH$_2$CH$_2$C(CH$_2$CH$_2$CN)(NO$_2$)CH$_3$ *6-butylsulfonyl-4-methyl-4-nitrohexanenitrile*	—	—	192 193	
CH$_3$OCH(C$_6$H$_5$)CH(NO$_2$)CH$_3$ *methyl 2-nitro-1-phenylpropyl ether*	18.0	20–25°	CH$_3$OCH(C$_6$H$_5$)C(CH$_2$CH$_2$CN)(NO$_2$)CH$_3$ *5-methoxy-4-methyl-4-nitro-5-phenylvaleronitrile*	82	B.P. 163-167°/0.5 mm.	192 193	
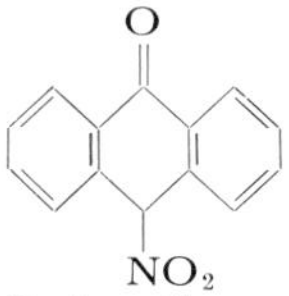 *9-nitroanthrone*	48.0	25°	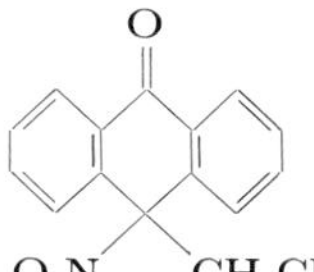 *9,10-dihydro-9-nitro-10-oxo-9-anthracenepropionitrile*	77	M.P. > 270°	163	
11-nitro-9,10-dihydro-9,10-ethanoanthracene	6.0	60°	*9,10-dihydro-11-nitro-9,10-ethanoanthracene-11-propionitrile*	49	M.P. 114-115° M.P. (Pure) 121-122°	638	

TABLE XV—"C" Cyanoethylation: Sulfones

Reactants	Reaction Time (Hr.)	Reaction Temperature (°C.)	Products	% Yield	M.P. or B.P. (°C.)	References This Exam.	References See Also:
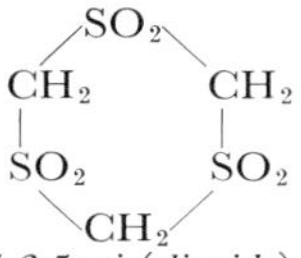 *1,3,5-tris(dioxide)-s-trithiane*	2.0	0°	*monocyanoethyl derivative*	—	—	532	370

TABLE XV—Continued

"C" Cyanoethylation: Sulfones

Reactants	Re-action Time (Hr.)	Reaction Tem-perature (°C.)	Products	% Yield	M.P. or B.P. (°C.)	References	
						This Exam.	See Also:
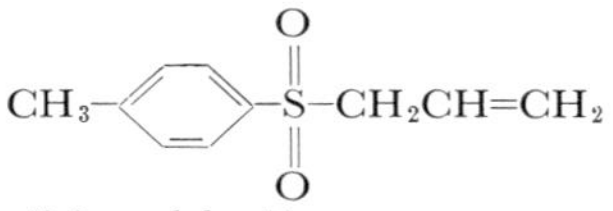 CH₃—⟨⟩—S(O)(O)—CH₂CH=CH₂ *allyl p-tolyl sulfone*	2.0	25°	 CH₃—⟨⟩—S(O)(O)—CH(CH₂CH₂CN)CH=CH₂ *4-p-tolylsulfonyl-5-hexenenitrile*	—	—	171	
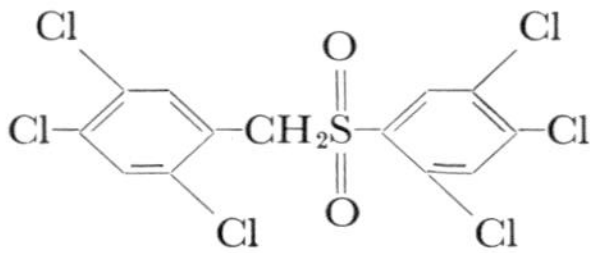 Cl—⟨⟩—CH₂—S(O₂)— (2,4,5-trichlorobenzyl 2,4,5-trichlorophenyl sulfone)	20.0	R.T.	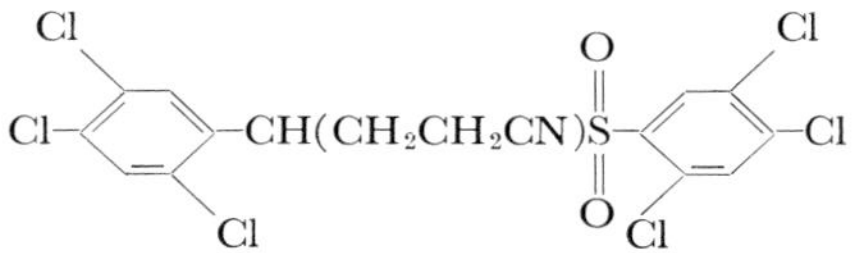 Cl—⟨⟩—CH(CH₂CH₂CN)S(O)(O)—⟨⟩ (4-(2,4,5-trichlorophenyl)-4-(2,4,5-trichlorophenyl-sulfonyl)butyronitrile)	65	M.P. 210–211°	1300	
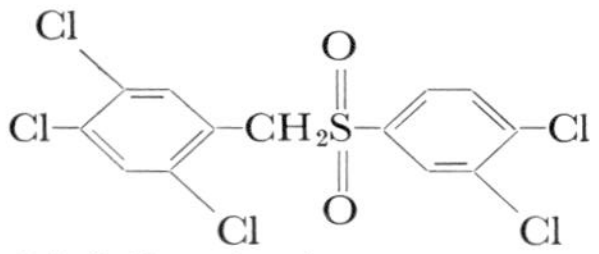 Cl—⟨⟩—CH₂S(O)(O)— (3,4-dichlorophenyl 2,4,5-trichlorobenzyl sulfone)	20.0	R.T.	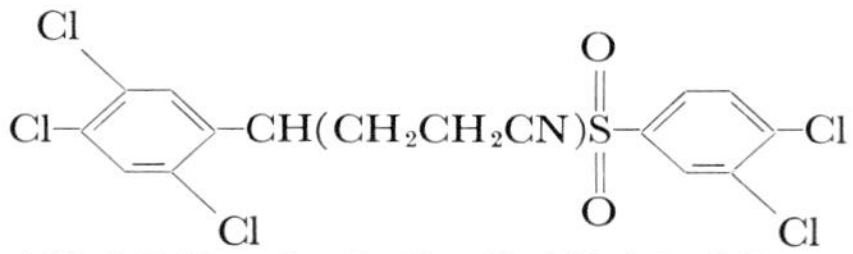 Cl—⟨⟩—CH(CH₂CH₂CN)S(O)(O)—⟨⟩ (4-(3,4-dichlorophenylsulfonyl)-4-(2,4,5-trichloro-phenyl)butyronitrile)	73	M.P. 159–160.5°	1300	

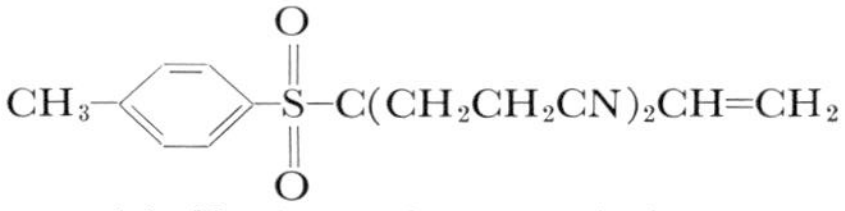

TABLE XV—Continued

"C" Cyanoethylation: Sulfones

Reactants	Reaction Time (Hr.)	Reaction Temperature (°C.)	Products	% Yield	M.P. or B.P. (°C.)	References This Exam.	See Also:
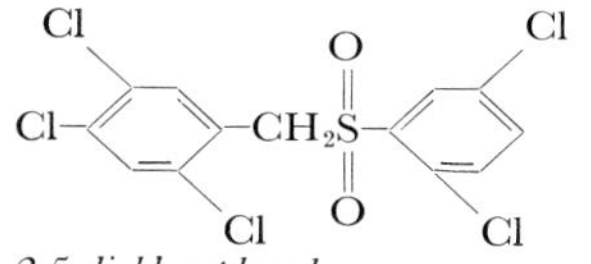 *2,5-dichlorophenyl 2,4,5-trichlorobenzyl sulfone*	20.0	R.T.	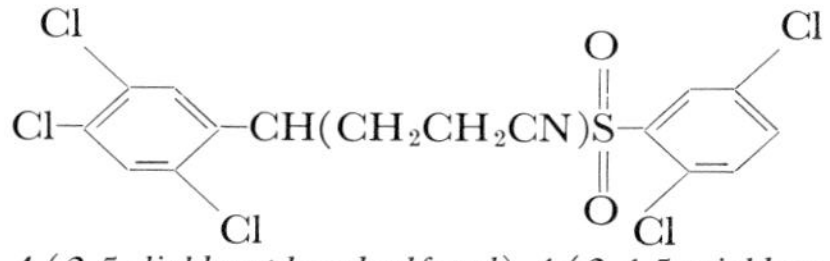 *4-(2,5-dichlorophenylsulfonyl)-4-(2,4,5-trichlorophenyl)butyronitrile*	58	M.P. 118.5-120°	1300	
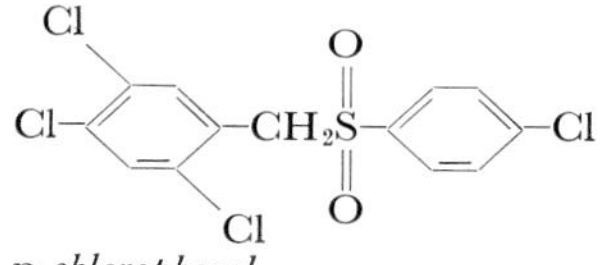 *p-chlorophenyl 2,4,5-trichlorobenzyl sulfone*	20.0	R.T.	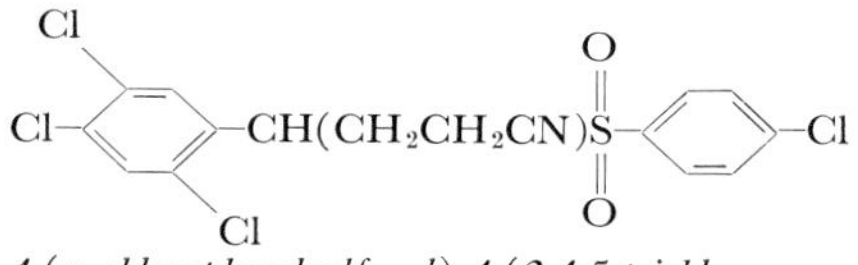 *4-(p-chlorophenylsulfonyl)-4-(2,4,5-trichlorophenyl)butyronitrile*	76	M.P. 130-131.5°	1300	
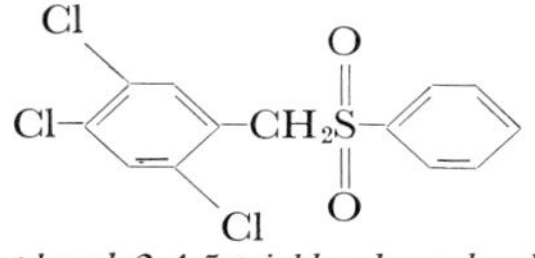 *phenyl 2,4,5-trichlorobenzyl sulfone*	20.0	R.T.	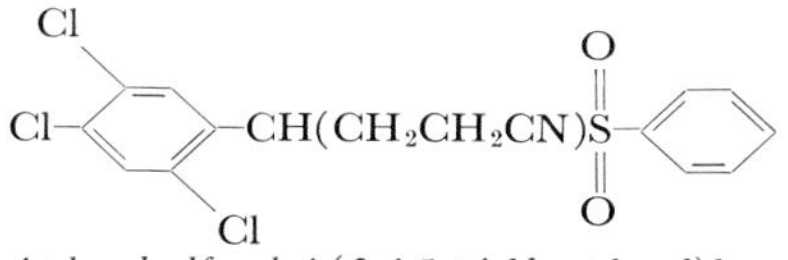 *4-phenylsulfonyl-4-(2,4,5-trichlorophenyl)butyronitrile*	70	M.P. 130-130.5°	1300	
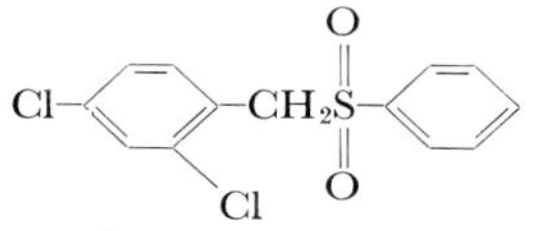 *2,4-dichlorobenzyl phenyl sulfone*	20.0	R.T.	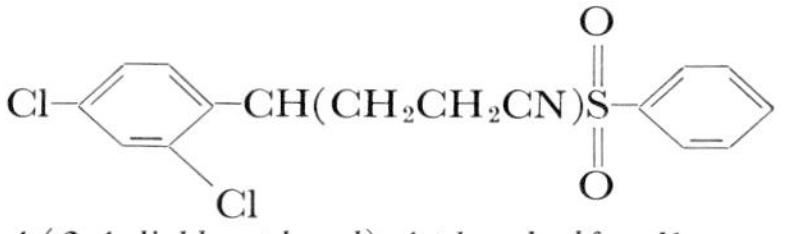 *4-(2,4-dichlorobenzyl)-4-phenylsulfonylbutyronitrile*	76	M.P. 105-105.5°	1300	

TABLE XV—Continued

"C" Cyanoethylation: Sulfones

Reactants	Reaction Time (Hr.)	Reaction Temperature (°C.)	Products	% Yield	M.P. or B.P. (°C.)	This Exam.	See Also:
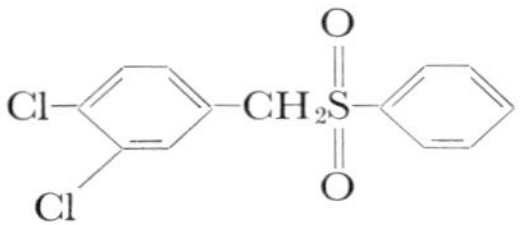 3,4-dichlorobenzyl phenyl sulfone	20.0	R.T.	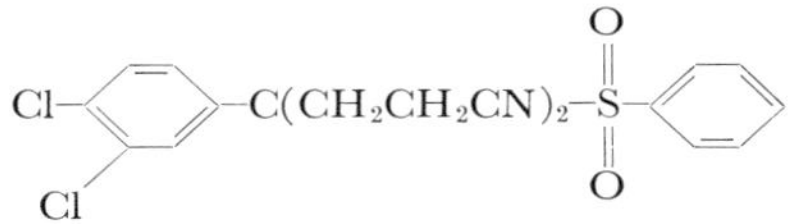 4-(3,4-dichlorophenyl)-4-phenylsulfonylheptane-dinitrile	59	M.P. 199.5-201°	1300	
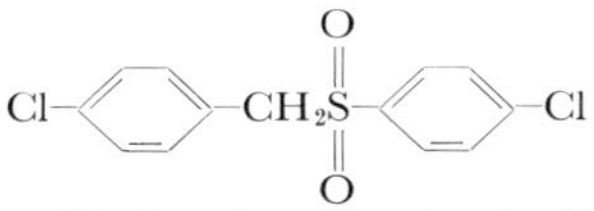 p-chlorobenzyl p-chlorophenyl sulfone	48.0	R.T.	 4-(p-chlorophenyl)-4-(p-chlorophenylsulfonyl)-heptanedinitrile	80	M.P. 184-185°	1348	
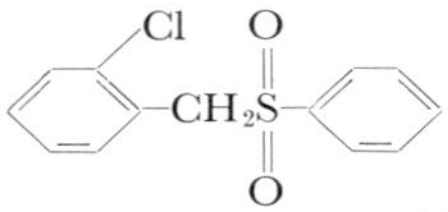 o-chlorobenzyl phenyl sulfone	20.0	R.T.	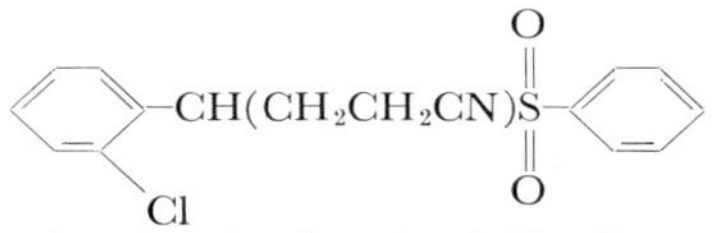 4-(o-chlorophenyl)-4-phenylsulfonylbutyronitrile	63	M.P. 85-86°	1300	
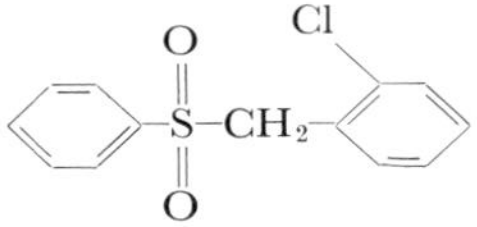 o-chlorobenzyl phenyl sulfone	48.0	30-35°	 4-(o-chlorophenyl)-4-phenylsulfonylheptanedinitrile	83.5	M.P. 87-88°	54	
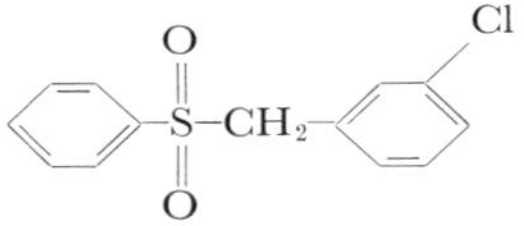 m-chlorobenzyl phenyl sulfone	48.0	30-35°	 4-(m-chlorophenyl)-4-phenylsulfonylheptanedinitrile	24	M.P. 162-163°	54	

TABLE XV—Continued

"C" Cyanoethylation: Sulfones

Reactants	Reaction Time (Hr.)	Reaction Temperature (°C.)	Products	% Yield	M.P. or B.P. (°C.)	References This Exam.	References See Also:
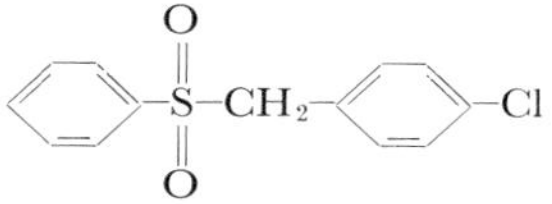 p-chlorobenzyl phenyl sulfone	55.0	30-35°	 C(CH₂CH₂CN)₂ — 4-(p-chlorophenyl)-4-phenylsulfonylheptanedinitrile	60	M.P. 194-195°	54	
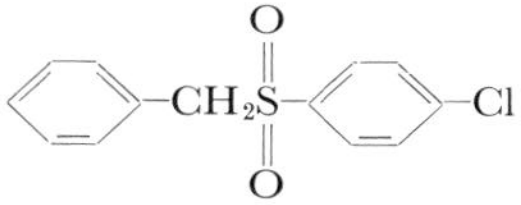 benzyl p-chlorophenyl sulfone	48.0	25°	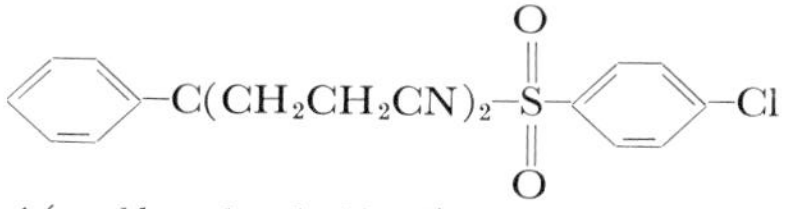 C(CH₂CH₂CN)₂ — 4-(p-chlorophenylsulfonyl)-4-phenylheptanedinitrile	78	M.P. 179-180°	1348	
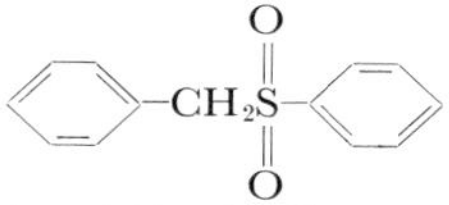 benzyl phenyl sulfone	18.0	2.5°	 C(CH₂CH₂CN)₂ — 4-phenyl-4-phenylsulfonylheptanedinitrile	59	M.P. 180°	184, 171	
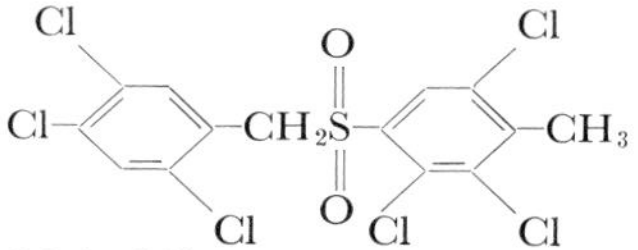 2,3,5-trichloro-4-methylphenyl 2,4,5-trichlorobenzyl sulfone	20	R.T.	 CH(CH₂CH₂CN) — 4-(2,4,5-trichlorophenyl)-4-(2,3,5-p-tolylsulfonyl)-butyronitrile	20	M.P. 196-200°	1300	
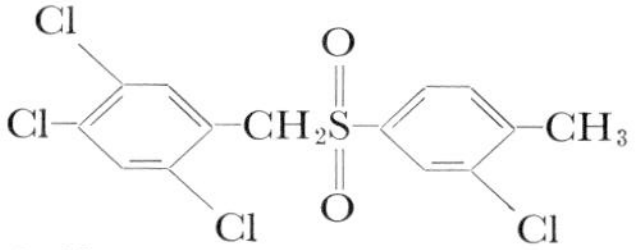 3-chloro-4-methylphenyl 2,4,5-trichlorobenzyl sulfone	20	R.T.	 CH(CH₂CH₂CN) — 4-(3-chloro-p-tolylsulfonyl)-4-(2,4,5-trichlorophenyl)-butyronitrile	88	M.P. 200-202.5°	1300	

TABLE XV—Continued

"C" Cyanoethylation: Sulfones

Reactants	Reaction Time (Hr.)	Reaction Temperature (°C.)	Products	% Yield	M.P. or B.P. (°C.)	References	
						This Exam.	See Also:
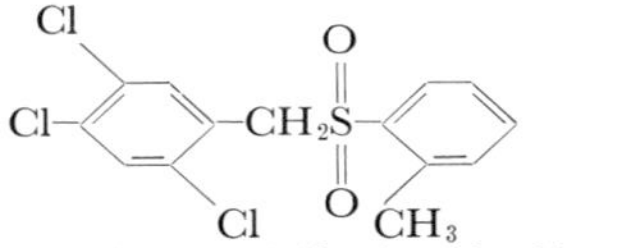 o-tolyl 2,4,5-trichlorobenzyl sulfone	20	R.T.	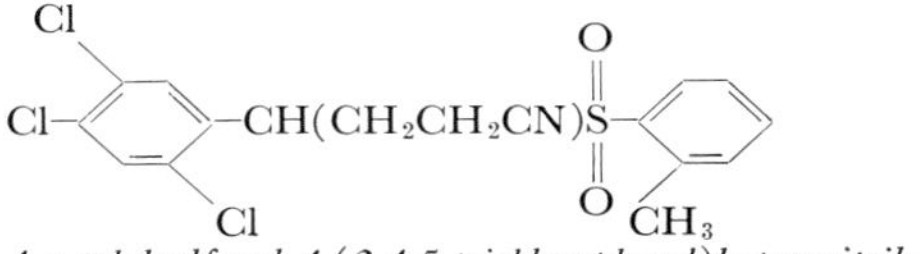 4-o-tolylsulfonyl-4-(2,4,5-trichlorophenyl)butyronitrile	94	M.P. 155-156.5°	1300	
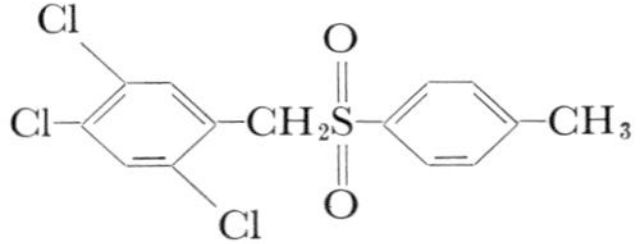 p-tolyl 2,4,5-trichlorobenzyl sulfone	20	R.T.	 4-p-tolylsulfonyl-4-(2,4,5-trichlorophenyl)butyronitrile	96	M.P. 143-144.5°	1300	
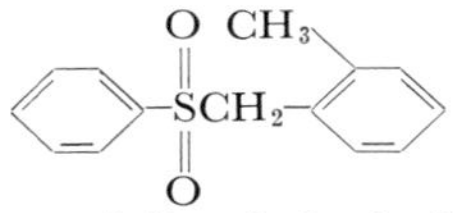 o-methylbenzyl phenyl sulfone	48.0	30-35°	oil	—	—	54	
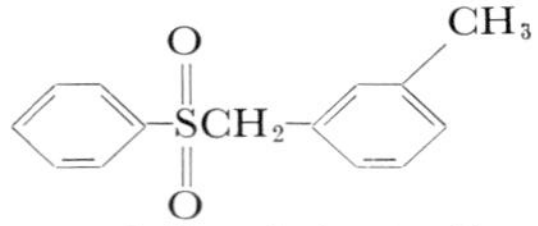 m-methylbenzyl phenyl sulfone	48.0	30-35°	oil	—	—	54	

TABLE XVI—"C" Cyanoethylation: Aromatic Hydrocarbons

Reactants	Re-action Time (Hr.)	Reaction Temperature (°C.)	Products	% Yield	M.P. or B.P. (°C.)	References This Exam.	References See Also:
 cyclopentadiene	3.0	20°	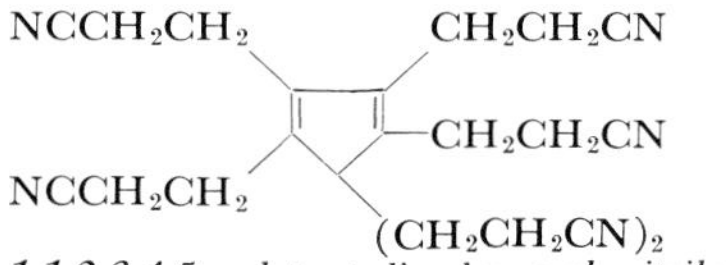 NCCH₂CH₂ / CH₂CH₂CN / CH₂CH₂CN / NCCH₂CH₂ / (CH₂CH₂CN)₂ *1,1,2,3,4,5-cyclopentadienehexacarbonitrile*	27	M.P. 203°	154 158	
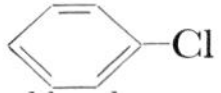 Cl / chlorobenzene	30.0	140-165°	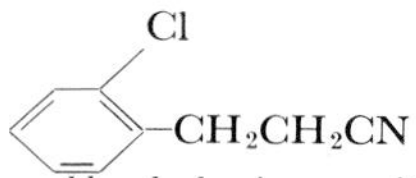 Cl / CH₂CH₂CN *o-chlorohydrocinnamonitrile*	12	B.P. 147-152°/15 mm.	442	
benzene + HCl + hydrogen chloride	12-15 30.0	R.T. Ⓐ 84-98°	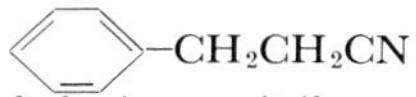 CH₂CH₂CN *hydrocinnamonitrile*	66	B.P. 125-126°/15 mm.	442	575
 benzene	10.0	150-160°	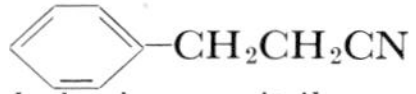 CH₂CH₂CN *hydrocinnamonitrile*	27	B.P. 128-130°/16 mm.	442	1296
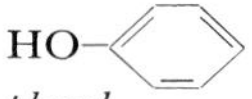 HO / phenol	1.5 1.5	15° 80°	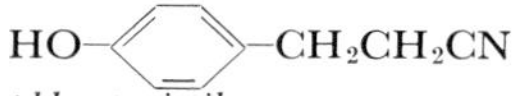 HO / CH₂CH₂CN *phloretonitrile*	72	M.P. 58-59°	1297	
			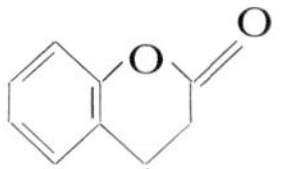 O / O *hydrocoumarin*	3	B.P. 111-112°/2.5 mm.		
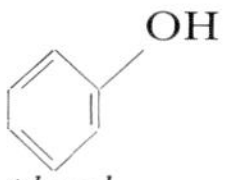 OH / phenol	1 O.N.	18° 25°	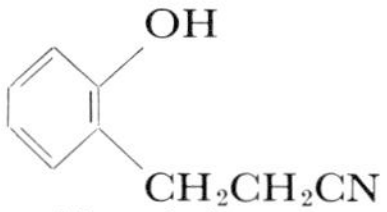 OH / CH₂CH₂CN *melilotonitrile*	12	B.P. 153-155°/1 mm.	1296	

TABLE XVI—Continued

"C" Cyanoethylation: Aromatic Hydrocarbons

Reactants	Reaction Time (Hr.)	Reaction Temperature (°C.)	Products	% Yield	M.P. or B.P. (°C.)	References This Exam.	References See Also:
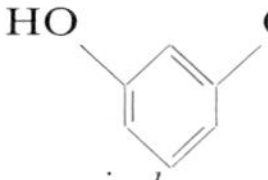 resorcinol (HO—⬡—OH + H₂O ®)	12.0	25°	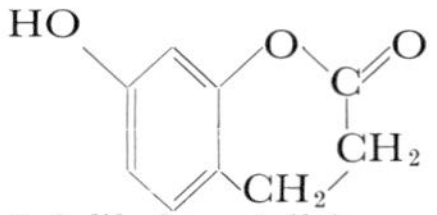 3,4-dihydroumbelliferone	—	M.P. 133-134°	681	
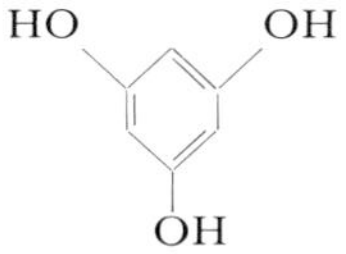 phloroglucinol	8.0	reflux	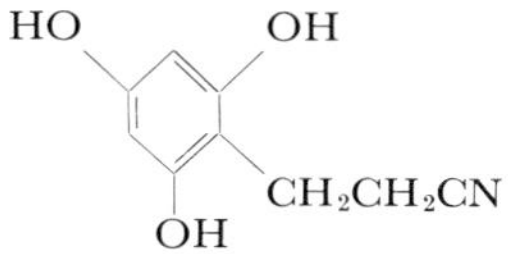 2,4,6-trihydroxyhydrocinnamonitrile	78	M.P. 179-180°	1349	681
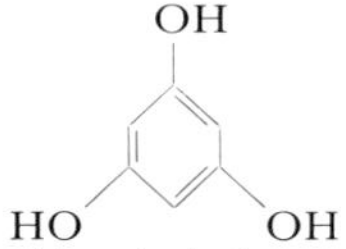 phloroglucinol	8.0	reflux	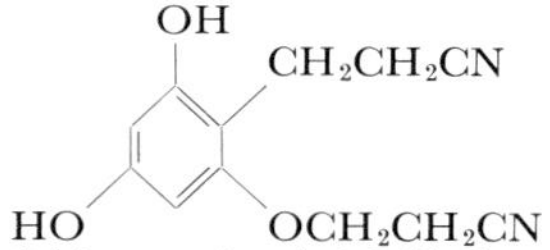 2-(2-cyanoethoxy)-4,6-dihydroxyhydrocinnamonitrile	56	M.P. 160-161°	1349	
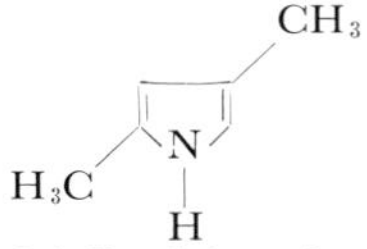 2,4-dimethylpyrrole	—	—	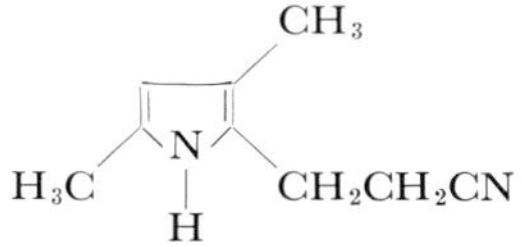 3,5-dimethyl-2-pyrrolepropionitrile	—	B.P. 128°/1 mm.	1429	
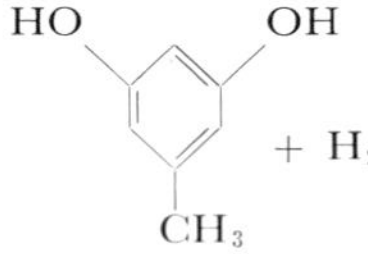 orcinol (+ H₂O ®)	—	—	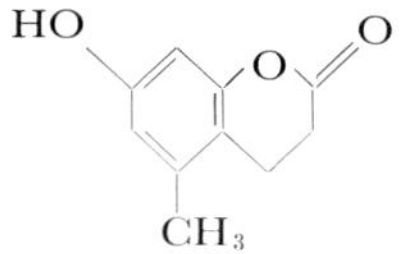 3,4-dihydro-5-methylumbelliferone	51	M.P. 140-141.5°	681	

TABLE XVI—Continued

"C" Cyanoethylation: Aromatic Hydrocarbons

Reactants	Reaction Time (Hr.)	Reaction Temperature (°C.)	Products	% Yield	M.P. or B.P. (°C.)	References This Exam.	See Also:
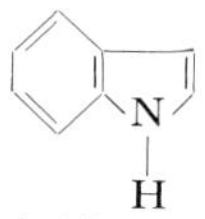 indole	6.0	180-190°	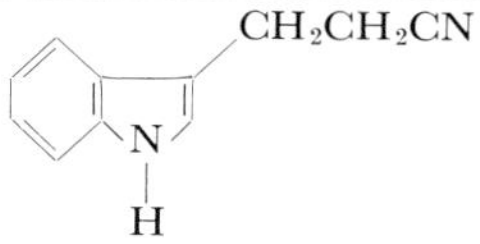 [structure] CH₂CH₂CN — *3-indolepropionitrile*	81.3	M.P. 67-68°	1425	
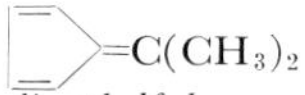 dimethylfulvene	—	—	*higher cyanoethylation products in impure form*	—	—	158	
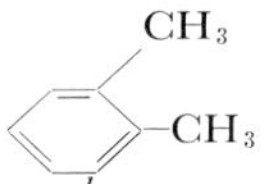 o-xylene	9.0	130°	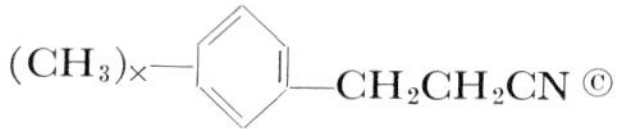 $(CH_3) \times$ [structure] —CH₂CH₂CN	55.4	B.P. 124-160°/15 mm.	442	
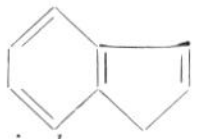 indene	1.0	25°	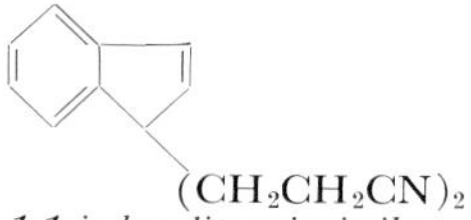 [structure] (CH₂CH₂CN)₂ *1,1-indenedipropionitrile*	14	B.P. 210-220°/2 mm.	154 158	
			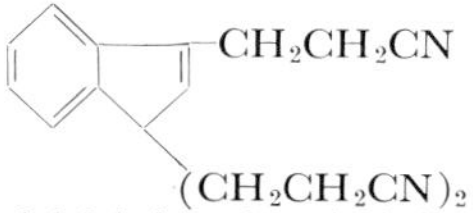 [structure] (CH₂CH₂CN)₂ CH₂CH₂CN *1,1,3-indenetripropionitrile*	35	B.P. 280-290°/1 mm. M.P. 65°		
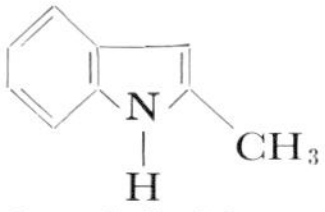 2-methylindole	6.0	180-190°	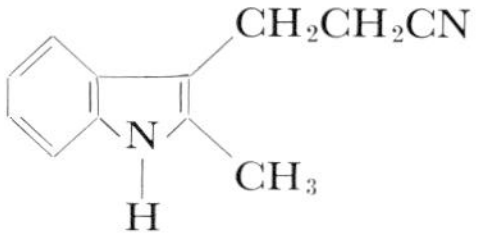 [structure] CH₂CH₂CN CH₃ *2-methyl-3-indolepropionitrile*	81	M.P. 79.5°	1425	572

TABLE XVI—Continued

"C" Cyanoethylation: Aromatic Hydrocarbons

Reactants	Reaction Temperature (°C.)	Reaction Time (Hr.)	Products	% Yield	M.P. or B.P. (°C.)	This Exam.	See Also:
CH₃—⟨⟩—CH₃ CH₃ *mesitylene*	130-135°	9.5	$(CH_3)_3 \times$ —CH₂CH₂CN ©	47	B.P. 128-138°/12 mm.	442	
OH *2-naphthol*	reflux	2.0	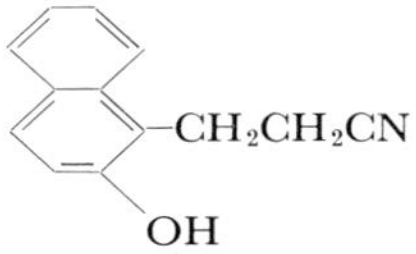 CH₂CH₂CN OH *2-hydroxy-1-naphthalenepropionitrile*	93	M.P. 142°	467 485	1311
OH *2-naphthol*	0° 25° 100°	— 16.0 1.0	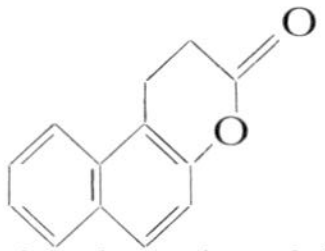 *2-hydroxy-1-naphthalenepropionic acid, δ-lactone*	40.1	M.P. 73-74.5°	1311	
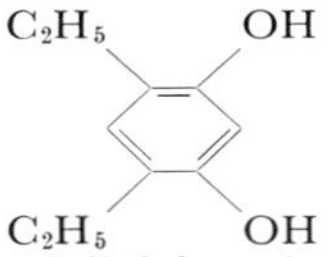 C₂H₅ OH C₂H₅ OH *4,6-diethylresorcinol*	—	—	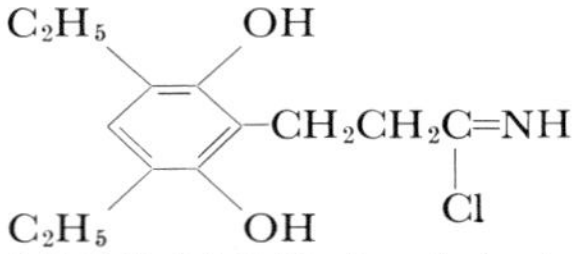 C₂H₅ OH —CH₂CH₂C=NH Cl C₂H₅ OH *3,5-diethyl-2,6-dihydroxyhydrocinnamimidyl chloride*	—	M.P. 156°	360	

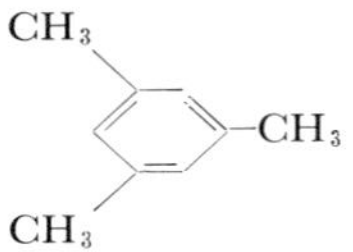

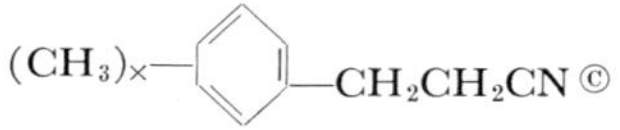

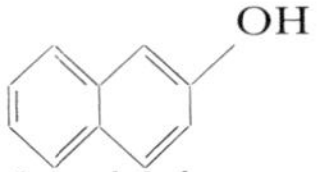

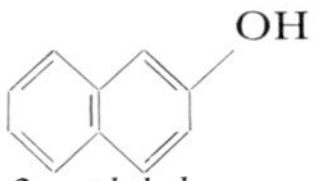

TABLE XVI—Continued

"C" Cyanoethylation: Aromatic Hydrocarbons

Reactants	Reaction Time (Hr.)	Reaction Temperature (°C.)	Products	% Yield	M.P. or B.P. (°C.)	References This Exam.	See Also:
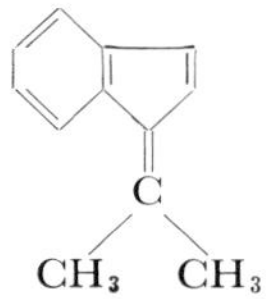 1-isopropylidenindene	4.0	25°	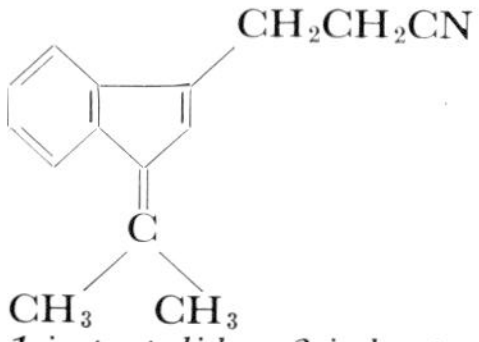 1-isopropylidene-3-indenepropionitrile	22	M.P. 121°	158	
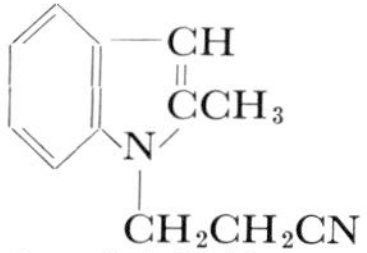 2-methyl-N-(2-cyanoethyl)indole	—	—	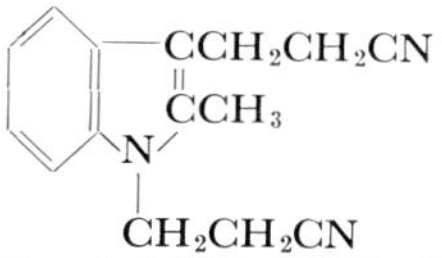 1-isopropenyl-2-indenepropionitrile; 2-methyl-1,3-indenedipropionitrile	—	M.P. 138°	572	
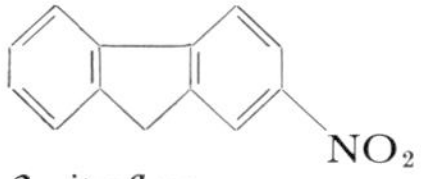 2-nitrofluorene	2.0	25°	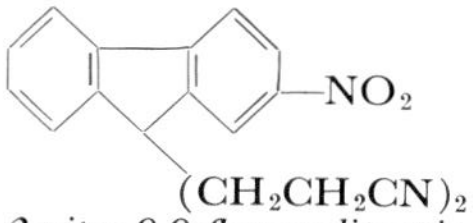 2-nitro-9,9-fluorenedipropionitrile	70	M.P. 236-237°	154	

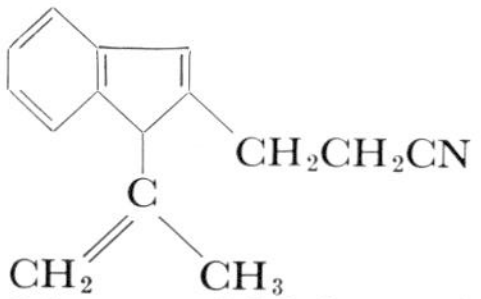

TABLE XVI—Continued

"C" Cyanoethylation: Aromatic Hydrocarbons

Reactants	Reaction Time (Hr.)	Reaction Temperature (°C.)	Products	% Yield	M.P. or B.P. (°C.)	References This Exam.	References See Also:
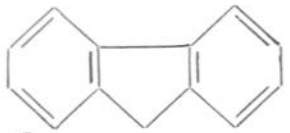 fluorene	3.0	25°	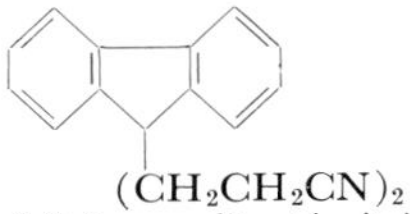 $(CH_2CH_2CN)_2$ 9,9-fluorenedipropionitrile	74	M.P. 121°	158	154, 998
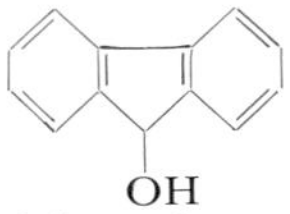 9-fluorenol	3.0	25°	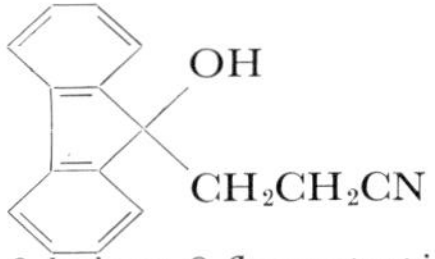 OH CH_2CH_2CN 9-hydroxy-9-fluorenepropionitrile	14	M.P. 105-107°	205	
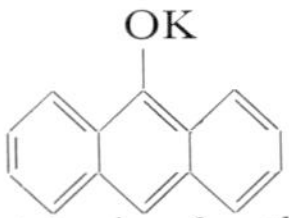 potassium 9-anthrolate	2.0	reflux	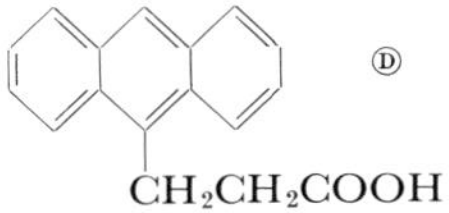 CH_2CH_2COOH 9-anthracenepropionic acid	90	M.P. 190-193°	309	
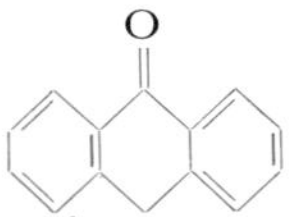 anthrone	19.0	35°	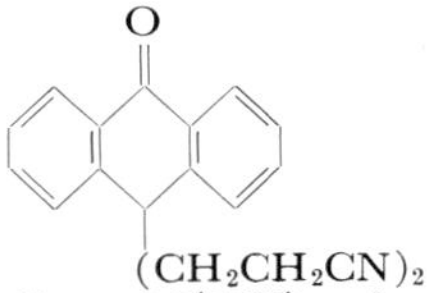 $(CH_2CH_2CN)_2$ 10-oxo-9,9(10H)-anthracenedipropionitrile	89	M.P. 215°	154 158	

TABLE XVI—Continued

"C" Cyanoethylation: Aromatic Hydrocarbons

Reactants	Reaction Time (Hr.)	Reaction Temperature (°C.)	Products	% Yield	M.P. or B.P. (°C.)	References This Exam.	See Also:
2-phenylindole (C₆H₅, N–H)	1-2.0	75°	2-phenyl-1-indolepropionitrile (C₆H₅, CH₂CH₂CN); 2-phenyl-1,3-indoledipropionitrile (C₆H₅, CH₂CH₂CN)	~100	M.P. 90°; M.P. 159°	572	
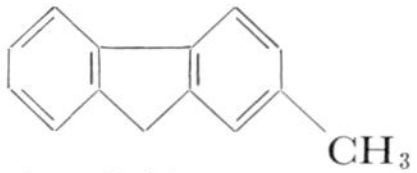 1-methylfluorene (CH₃)	—	—	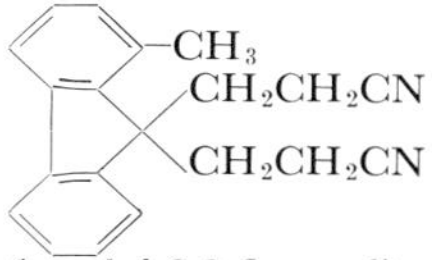 1-methyl-9,9-fluorenedipropionitrile (CH₃, CH₂CH₂CN, CH₂CH₂CN)	70	M.P. 105-106°	643	
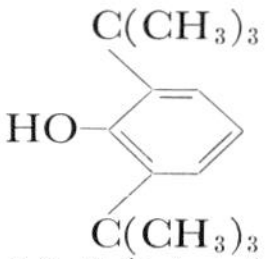 2,6-di-(t-butyl)phenol (C(CH₃)₃, HO, C(CH₃)₃)	1.0; 7.0	55°; 85°	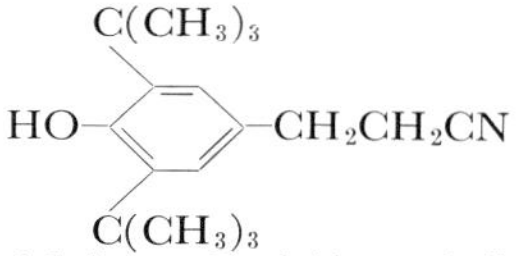 3,5-di-tert-butylphloretonitrile (C(CH₃)₃, CH₂CH₂CN, HO, C(CH₃)₃)	13	M.P. 111-113°	1233	255
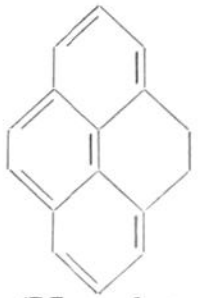 4H-cyclopenta[def]phenanthrene	—	—	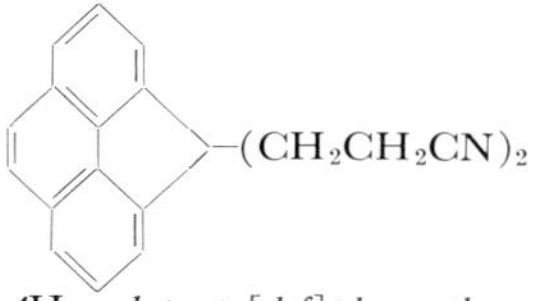 4H-cyclopenta[def]phenanthrene-4,4-dipropionitrile (CH₂CH₂CN)₂	—	—	522	

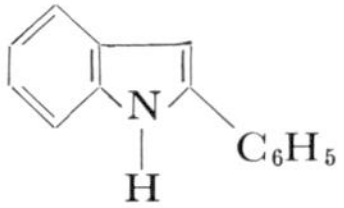

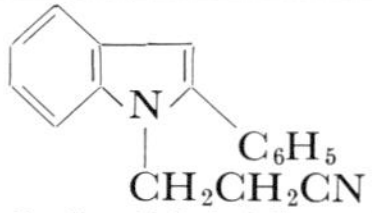

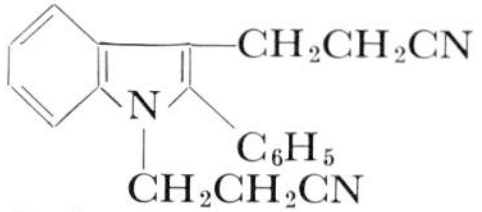

TABLE XVI—Continued

"C" Cyanoethylation: Aromatic Hydrocarbons

Reactants	Re-action Time (Hr.)	Reaction Tem-perature (°C.)	Products	% Yield	M.P. or B.P. (°C.)	References	
						This Exam.	See Also:
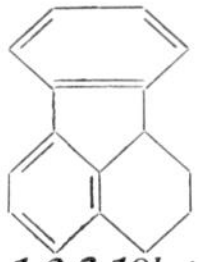 1,2,3,10b-tetrahydrofluoranthene	—	50°	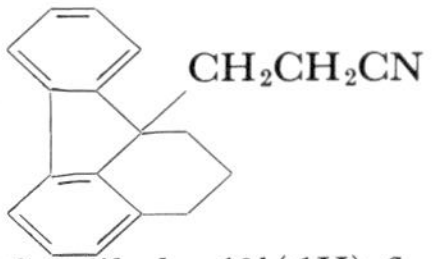 CH₂CH₂CN / 2,3-dihydro-10b(1H)-fluoranthrenepropionitrile	—	M.P. 110°	522	243
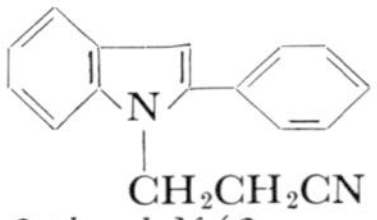 CH₂CH₂CN / 2-phenyl-N-(2-cyanoethyl)indole	—	—	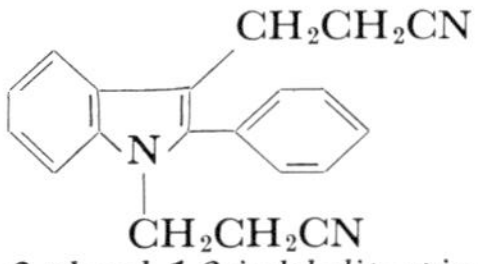 CH₂CH₂CN / 2-phenyl-1,3-indoledipropionitrile	—	M.P. 159°	572	
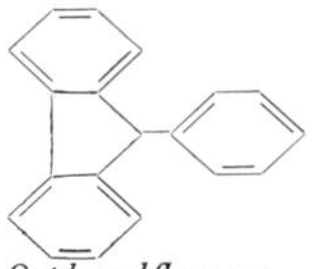 9-phenylfluorene	2.0	25°	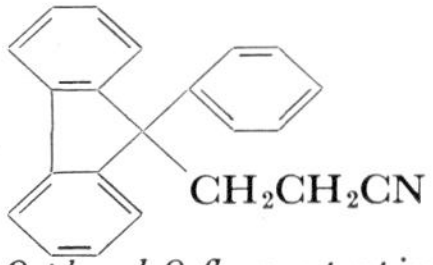 CH₂CH₂CN / 9-phenyl-9-fluorenepropionitrile	74	M.P. 148-149°	205	
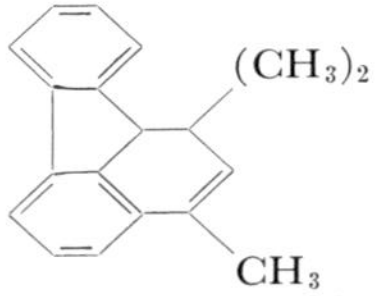 (CH₃)₂ / CH₃ / 1,10b-dihydro-1,1,3-trimethyl-fluoranthrene	1.0	60°	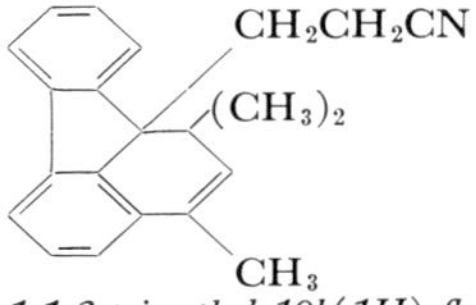 CH₂CH₂CN / (CH₃)₂ / CH₃ / 1,1,3-trimethyl-10b(1H)-fluoranthrenepropionitrile	—	B.P. 185-194°/0.1 mm.	522	

NOTES: (A) Before AlCl₃ addition. (B) Added after the condensation reaction. (C) 4-Methyl and 2,4-dimethyl isomers were identified in the mixture. (D) After acid hydrolysis and reduction with zinc dust.

TABLE XVII—"C" Cyanoethylation: Aliphatic Hydrocarbons

Reactants	Reaction Time (Hr.)	Reaction Temperature (°C.)	Products	% Yield	M.P. or B.P. (°C.)	References — This Exam.	References — See Also:
HC≡CH *acetylene*	—	65-71° 155-200 p.s.i.	$CH_2=CHCH=CHCH=CHCN$ *2,4,6-heptatrienenitrile*	89Ⓐ	B.P. 58-59°/1 mm.	620	199
$CH_3CH=CH_2$ *propylene*	4.0	240° (pressure)	$CH_2=CHCH_2CH_2CH_2CN$ *5-hexenenitrile*	18	B.P. 162°	1194	
$CH_3CH=CHCH_3$ *2-butene*	5.0	245° (pressure)	$CH_2=CHCH(CH_3)CH_2CH_2CN$ *4-methyl-5-hexenenitrile*	4	B.P. 174°	1194	
$CH_2=C(CH_3)_2$ *2-methylpropene*	4.0	235° (585-1020 atm.)	$CH_2=C(CH_3)CH_2CH_2CH_2CN$ *5-methyl-5-hexenenitrile*	56		15	970, 971
$CH_3CH(CH_3)CH_3$ *2-methylpropane*	17 min.	450°F. (4500 p.s.i.)	$CH_3C(CH_3)_2CH_2CH_2CN$Ⓑ *4,4-dimethylvaleronitrile*	38	B.P. 165-178°	1034	
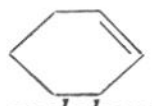 *cyclohexene*	5.0	250° (pressure)	 CH₂CH₂CN *2-cyclohexene-1-propionitrile*	5	B.P. 230°	1194	15
$(CH_3)_2C=C(CH_3)_2$ *2,3-dimethyl-2-butene*	8.0	235° (190 atm.)	$CH_2=C(CH_3)C(CH_3)_2CH_2CH_2CN$ *4,4,5-trimethyl-5-hexenenitrile*	16Ⓒ	B.P. 205-209°	15	1194
$CH_2=C(CH_3)CH_2CH_2CH_2CN$ *5-methyl-5-hexenenitrile*	0.25	300° (pressure)	$NCCH_2CH_2C(=CH_2)CH_2CH_2CH_2CN$ *5-methylenenonanedinitrile*	61	B.P. 152-154°/2.5 mm.	1194	
 CH=CH₂ *4-vinylcyclohexene*	4.0	240° (pressure)	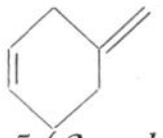 CHCH₂CH₂CN *5-(3-cyclohexen-1-ylidene)valeronitrile*	3	B.P. 117°/7 mm.	1194	

TABLE XVII—Continued

"C" Cyanoethylation: Aliphatic Hydrocarbons

Reactants	Reaction Time (Hr.)	Reaction Temperature (°C.)	Products	% Yield	M.P. or B.P. (°C.)	References This Exam.	References See Also:
CH₃OCOCH₂CH₂CH₂C(CH₃)=CH₂ *methyl 5-methyl-5-hexenoate*	5.0	230° (pressure)	CH₃OCO(CH₂)₃C(=CH₂)(CH₂)₃CN *8-cyano-5-methyleneoctanoic acid, methyl ester*	19			
CH₂=C(CH₃)CH₂C(CH₃)₃ *2,4,4-trimethyl-1-pentene*	4.0	225° (pressure)	(CH₃)₃CCH₂C(=CH₂)CH₂CH₂CH₂CN *7,7-dimethyl-5-methyleneoctanenitrile*	—	—	971	
CH₂=C(CH₃)CH₂C(CH₃)₃ *2,4,4-trimethyl-1-pentene* CH₃C(CH₃)=CHC(CH₃)₃ *2,4,4-trimethyl-2-pentene*	4.0 2.0 (23.8 28.6 atm.)	245° 255°	C(CH₃)₃C(=CH₂)CH₂CH₂CH₂CN *6,6-dimethyl-5-methyleneheptanenitrile* CH₂=C(CH₃)CH[C(CH₃)₃]CH₂CH₂CN *4-tert-butyl-5-methyl-5-hexenenitrile*	17 combined	B.P. 126-134°/30 mm.	15	
CH₂C(CH₃)=CH₂ (2-methylallyl)benzene	6.0	240° (pressure)	CH=C(CH₃)CH₂CH₂CH₂CN *5-methyl-6-phenyl-5-hexenenitrile* CH₂C(=CH₂)CH₂CH₂CH₂CH₂CN *5-benzyl-5-hexenenitrile*	23(D)	B.P. 142°/4 mm.(E) B.P. 151°/4 mm.	1194	

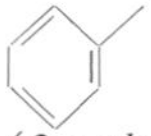

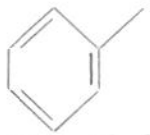

NOTES: (A) Based on unrecovered acrylonitrile.
(B) Possible structure of main component.
(C) Based on unrecovered olefin.
(D) Yield of mixed isomers.
(E) Boiling points not assigned to specific isomers.

TABLE XVIII—"C" Cyanoethylation: Haloforms

Reactants	Reaction Time (Hr.)	Reaction Temperature (°C.)	Products	% Yield	M.P. or B.P. (°C.)	References This Exam.	References See Also:
Br₃CH *bromoform*	3.0 3.0	5-10° 25°	Br₃CCH₂CH₂CN *4,4,4-tribromobutyronitrile*	11	B.P. 126-128°/6 mm. M.P. 98°	827	175
Cl₃CH *cloroform*	— —	—	Cl₃CCH₂CH₂CN *4,4,4-trichlorobutyronitrile*	18		1372	175, 485

TABLE XIX—"N" Cyanoethylation

(A) Amino and Primary Aliphatic Amines

Reactants	Reaction Time (Hr.)	Reaction Temperature (°C.)	Products	% Yield	M.P. or B.P. (°C.)	References	
						This Exam.	See Also:
NH₃ (A) *ammonia*	2 min.	112°	NH₂CH₂CH₂CN *3-aminopropionitrile* NH(CH₂CH₂CN)₂ *3,3'iminodipropionitrile*	82.2 17.8	— —	188	189, 664, 207, 963, 187, 34, 399, 566, 1145, 579
NH₃ (B) *ammonia*	— (T)	30°	NH₂CH₂CH₂CN *3-aminopropionitrile* NH(CH₂CH₂CN)₂ *3,3'-iminodipropionitrile* N(CH₂CH₂CN)₃ *3,3',3''-nitrilotripropionitrile*	1.7 88.5 6.0	— — —	1147	1135, 1065, 568, 665, 520, 1145
NH₃ + HCHO *ammonia + formaldehyde*	8-10	350-400°	CH₂(N(CH₂CH₂CN)₂)₂ *3,3'-(methylenediimino)dipropionitrile*	—	B.P. 140°/10 mm.	1437	
CH₃NH₂ *methylamine*	—	—	CH₃NHCH₂CH₂CN *3-methylaminopropionitrile* CH₃N(CH₂CH₂CN)₂ *3,3'(methylimino)dipropionitrile*	85 12	—	963	815, 702, 267, 1053
CH₃NH₂ *methylamine*	16	80-90°	CH₃N(CH₂CH₂CN)₂ *3,3'-(methylimino)dipropionitrile*	51	B.P. 195-197°/22 mm.	1409	
CH₃CH₂NH₂ *ethylamine*	5.0 1.0 16.0	R.T. steam bath R.T.	CH₃CH₂NHCH₂CH₂CN *3-ethylaminopropionitrile*	90.4	B.P. 92-95°/30 mm.	1145	1055, 1120
CH₃CH₂NH₂ + CS₂ (C) *ethylamine + carbon disulfide*	—	R.T.	CH₃CH₂N⁺H₂CH₂CH₂CN ⁻SCNCH₂CH₂CN (S, CH₂CH₃) *3-ethylaminopropionitrile, compound with (2-cyanoethyl)ethyldithiocarbamic acid*	~100	—	471	
HOCH₂CH₂NH₂ *2-aminoethanol*	—	—	HOCH₂CH₂NHCH₂CH₂CN *3-(3-hydroxyethylamino)propionitrile*	100		567 569	521, 1041, 1040, 1364

TABLE XIX—Continued

(A) Amino and Primary Aliphatic Amines

Reactants	Reaction Time (Hr.)	Reaction Temperature (°C.)	Products	% Yield	M.P. or B.P. (°C.)	References This Exam.	References See Also:
HOCH$_2$CH$_2$NH$_2$ 2-aminoethanol	—	—	HOCH$_2$CH$_2$N(CH$_2$CH$_2$CN)$_2$ 3,3''-(2-hydroxyethylimino)dipropionitrile	—	—	1145	
CH$_3$COONH$_4$ ammonium acetate	20	68°	N(CH$_2$CH$_2$CN)$_3$ 3,3',3''-nitrilotrispropionitrile	30	M.P. 55-57°	1352	
H$_2$NCH$_2$CH$_2$NH$_2$ ethylenediamine	19.5	25°	H$_2$NCH$_2$CH$_2$NHCH$_2$CH$_2$CN 3-(2-aminoethylamino)propionitrile	59	B.P. 124-127°/10 mm.	1252	
H$_2$NCH$_2$CH$_2$NH$_2$ ethylenediamine	2.0 0.25	R.T. 100°	NCCH$_2$CH$_2$HNCH$_2$CH$_2$NHCH$_2$CH$_2$CN 3,3'-(ethylenediimino)dipropionitrile	93	B.P. 186-192°/0.2 mm.	699	1073, 665, 664, 786
NH$_2$CH$_2$CH$_2$NH$_2$ + CS$_2$© ethylenediamine + carbon disulfide	—	<60°	+ NC(CH$_2$)$_2$—N—CH$_2$CH$_2$NH$_2$CH$_2$CH$_2$CN | S=C—S— ® (2-cyanoethyl)[2-(2-cyanoethylamino)ethyl] dithiocarbamic acid	—	—	471	
CH$_2$=CHCH$_2$NH$_2$ allylamine	5.0	reflux	CH$_2$=CHCH$_2$NHCH$_2$CH$_2$CN 3-allylaminopropionitrile	79	B.P. 75°/5 mm.	731	
CH$_3$CH$_2$CH$_2$NH$_2$ n-propylamine	—	—	CH$_3$CH$_2$CH$_2$NHCH$_2$CH$_2$CN 3-propylaminopropionitrile	92	B.P. 119-121°/30 mm.	1055	885, 1120
(CH$_3$)$_2$CHNH$_2$ isopropylamine	O.N.	R.T.	(CH$_3$)$_2$CHNHCH$_2$CH$_2$CN 3-isopropylaminopropionitrile	95	B.P. 86-87°/17 mm.	860	
HOCH(CH$_3$)CH$_2$NH$_2$ 1-amino-2-propanol	5.0 0.5 18.0	25° steam bath 25°	CH$_3$CH(OH)CH$_2$NHCH$_2$CH$_2$CN 3-(2-hydroxypropylamino)propionitrile	25	B.P. 111-113°/0.6 mm.	1042	
NH$_2$CH$_2$CH$_2$CH$_2$NH$_2$ 1,3-propanediamine	— 2.0	40-45° water bath	NH$_2$CH$_2$CH$_2$CH$_2$NHCH$_2$CH$_2$CN 3-(3-aminopropylamino)propionitrile NCCH$_2$CH$_2$NHCH$_2$CH$_2$CH$_2$NHCH$_2$CH$_2$CN 3,3'-(trimethylenediimino)dipropionitrile	80	B.P. 200-210°/3 mm. B.P. 230-270°/3 mm.	1075	

TABLE XIX—Continued

(A) Amino and Primary Aliphatic Amines

Reactants	Reaction Temperature (°C.)	Reaction Time (Hr.)	Products	% Yield	M.P. or B.P. (°C.)	This Exam.	References See Also:
NCC(CH₃)₂NH₂ / *2-aminoisobutyronitrile*	R.T. / 75°	15 / 1	NCC(CH₃)₂NHCH₂CH₂CN / *2-methyl-2,3'-iminodipropionitrile*	40	B.P. 115-116°/15 mm.	1417	
CH₂=C(CH₃)CH₂NH₂ / *2-methylallylamine*	30°	—	CH₂=C(CH₃)CH₂NHCH₂CH₂CN / *3-(2-methylallylamino)propionitrile* — CH₂=C(CH₃)CH₂N(CH₂CH₂CN)₂ / *3,3'-(2-methylallylimino)dipropionitrile*	— / —	— / —	731	
CH₃(CH₂)₃NH₂ / *n-butylamine*	10° / —	— / 1.0	CH₃CH₂CH₂CH₂NHCH₂CH₂CN / *3-butylaminopropionitrile*	~100	B.P. 114-116°/20 mm.	520 566 568 519	1055, 963, 408, 1120
CH₃CH₂CH(CH₃)NH₂ / *sec-butylamine*	—	—	CH₃CH₂CH(CH₃)NHCH₂CH₂CN / *3-sec-butylaminopropionitrile*	83	B.P. 92-96°/10 mm.	1055	
(CH₃)₂CHCH₂NH₂ / *isobutylamine*	R.T. / reflux / R.T.	4.0 / 1.0 / O.N.	(CH₃)₂CHCH₂NHCH₂CH₂CN / *3-isobutylaminopropionitrile*	91	B.P. 82-88°/7 mm. / B.P. 107°/11 mm.	1053	1023
(CH₃)₃CNH₂ / *tert-butylamine*	reflux	20	(CH₃)₃CNHCH₂CH₂CN / *3-tert-butylaminopropionitrile* — (CH₃)₃CN(CH₂CH₂CN)₂ / *3,3'-(tert-butylimino)dipropionitrile*	78 / 8	B.P. 69-71°/1.5 mm. / B.P. 121-130°/0.4 mm.	1327	1055
CH₃CH(OH)CH₂CH₂NH₂ / *1-amino-3-butanol*	—	—	CH₃CH(OH)CH₂CH₂NHCH₂CH₂CN / *3-(3-hydroxybutylamino)propionitrile*	74	B.P. 132-135°/0.8 mm.	1042	
HOCH₂CH(CH₂CH₃)NH₂ / *2-amino-1-butanol*	—	—	HOCH₂CH(CH₂CH₃)NHCH₂CH₂CN / *3-(1-hydroxymethylpropylamino)propionitrile*	75	B.P. 120-122°/3 mm.	59	
HOCH₂C(CH₃)₂NH₂ / *2-amino-2-methyl-1-propanol*	40-60°	—	HOCH₂C(CH₃)₂NHCH₂CH₂CN / *3-(2-hydroxy-1,1-dimethylethylamino)propionitrile*	88.5	M.P. 55-56°	59	
(CH₃)₂C(OH)CH₂NH₂ / *1-amino-2-methyl-2-propanol*	R.T.	O.N.	(CH₃)₂C(OH)CH₂NHCH₂CH₂CN / *3-(2-hydroxy-2-methylpropylamino)propionitrile*	86.5	B.P. 94-96°/1 mm.	1023	1054

TABLE XIX—Continued

(A) Amino and Primary Aliphatic Amines

Reactants	Reaction Time (Hr.)	Reaction Temperature (°C.)	Products	% Yield	M.P. or B.P. (°C.)	This Exam.	See Also:
$H_2N(CH_2)_4NH_2$ *putrescine*	23.0 1.0 1.0	R.T. steam bath R.T.	$NCCH_2CH_2HN(CH_2)_4NHCH_2CH_2CN$ *3,3'(tetramethylenediimino)dipropionitrile*	—	(E)	974	
$CH_3(CH_2)_4NH_2$ *n-amylamine*	O.N.	50° R.T.	$CH_3CH_2CH_2CH_2CH_2NHCH_2CH_2CN$ *3-pentylaminopropionitrile*	88	B.P. 112-113°/10 mm.	195	1120
$HOCH_2C(CH_3)(CH_2CH_3)NH_2$ *2-amino-2-methyl-1-butanol*	—	—	$HOCH_2C(CH_3)(CH_2CH_3)NHCH_2CH_2CN$ *3-(1-hydroxymethyl-1-methylpropylamino)propionitrile*	73	B.P. 125-127°/3 mm. M.P. 35-36°	59	
$(CH_3)_2C(OCH_3)CH_2NH_2$ *2-methoxy-2-methylpropylamine*	2.0 18.0	50° 25°	$(CH_3)_2C(OCH_3)CH_2NHCH_2CH_2CN$ *3-(2-methoxy-2-methylpropylamino)propionitrile*	71	B.P. 85°/1 mm.	1054	
$CH_3OCH_2CH(CH_3)CH_2NH_2$ *3-methoxy-2-methylpropylamine*	— 18.0	50° 25°	$CH_3OCH_2CH(CH_3)CH_2NHCH_2CH_2CN$ *3-(3-methoxy-2-methylpropylamino)propionitrile*	91	B.P. 90-91°/2 mm.	1054	
⬡—NH_2 *cyclohexylamine*	1.0	reflux	⬡—$NHCH_2CH_2CN$ *3-cyclohexylaminopropionitrile*	~100	B.P. 149-151°/11 mm.	568 520 566 519	1055, 408
O⬡$NCH_2CH_2NH_2$ *N-(2-aminoethyl)morpholine*	—	—	O⬡$NCH_2CH_2NHCH_2CH_2CN$ *3-(2-morpholinoethylamino)propionitrile*	81.5	B.P. 183°/20 mm.	1145	
$CH_3COHN(CH_2)_4NH_2 \cdot HCl$ *monoacetylputrescine hydrochloride*	16 1 2	R.T. reflux R.T.	$CH_3COHN(CH_2)_4NHCH_2CH_2CN \cdot HCl$ *3-(4-acetamidobutylamino)propionitrile, hydrochloride*	70	M.P. 143-144°	1293	
$CH_3(CH_2)_4CH_2NH_2$ *n-hexylamine*	1-2.0	100°	$CH_3(CH_2)_4CH_2NHCH_2CH_2CN$ *3-(hexylamino)propionitrile*	77	B.P. 126°/9 mm.	1120	
$H_2N(CH_2)_6NH_2$ *1,6-hexanediamine*	—	—	$NCCH_2CH_2HN(CH_2)_6NHCH_2CH_2CN$ *3,3'(hexamethylenediimino)dipropionitrile*	85	B.P. 230-238°/2 mm.	699	472

TABLE XIX—Continued

(A) Amino and Primary Aliphatic Amines

Reactants	Reaction Time (Hr.)	Reaction Temperature (°C.)	Products	% Yield	M.P. or B.P. (°C.)	References This Exam.	References See Also:
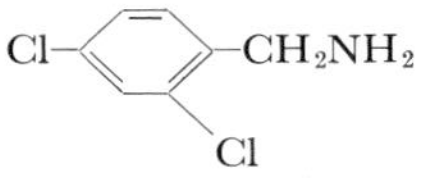 Cl—⬡—CH₂NH₂ (Cl) / 2,4-dichlorobenzylamine	—	R.T.	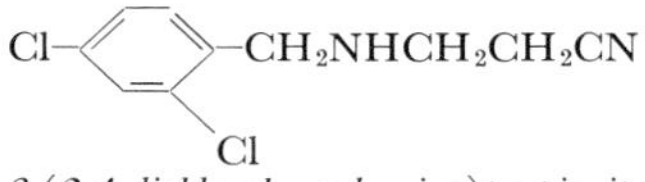 Cl—⬡—CH₂NHCH₂CH₂CN (Cl) / 3-(2,4-dichlorobenzylamino)propionitrile	77	B.P. 158°/1 mm.	1412	
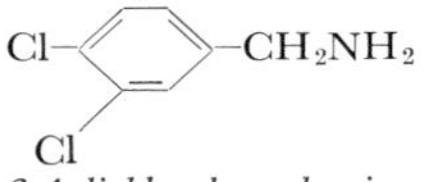 Cl—⬡—CH₂NH₂ (Cl) / 3,4-dichlorobenzylamine	—	R.T.	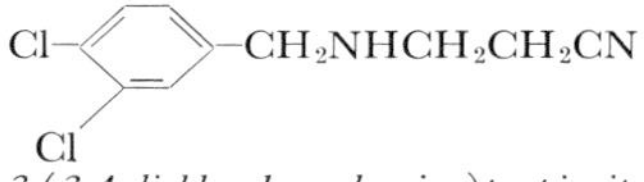 Cl—⬡—CH₂NHCH₂CH₂CN (Cl) / 3-(3,4-dichlorobenzylamino)propionitrile	97	B.P. 165°/0.8 mm.	1412	
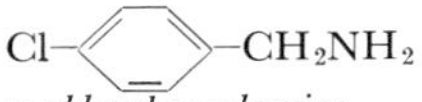 Cl—⬡—CH₂NH₂ / p-chlorobenzylamine	—	R.T.	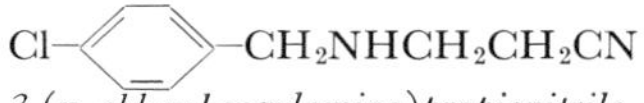 Cl—⬡—CH₂NHCH₂CH₂CN / 3-(p-chlorobenzylamino)propionitrile	83	B.P. 120°/0.07 mm.	1412	
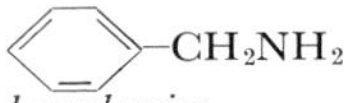 ⬡—CH₂NH₂ / benzylamine	—	R.T.	C₆H₅CH₂NHCH₂CH₂CN / 3-benzylaminopropionitrile	100	B.P. 124°/0.9 mm.	1412	633, 408, 1383
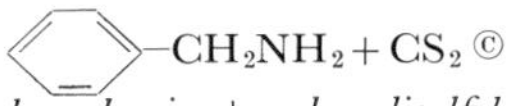 ⬡—CH₂NH₂ + CS₂ / benzylamine + carbon disulfide	1.0	100–110°	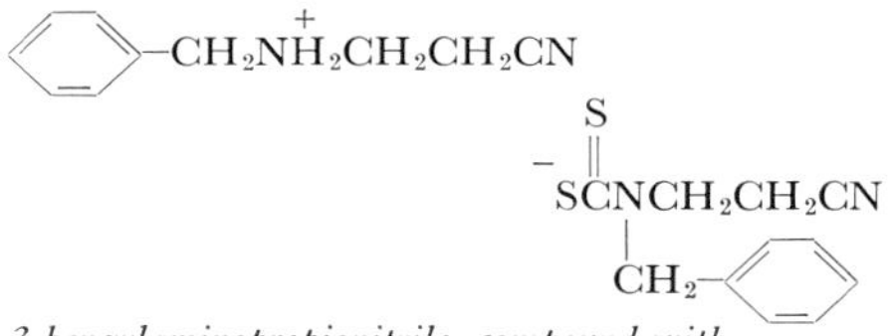 ⬡—CH₂NH₂CH₂CH₂CN / S=SCNCH₂CH₂CN–CH₂–⬡ / 3-benzylaminopropionitrile, compound with benzyl(2-cyanoethyl)dithiocarbamic acid	~100	—	471	
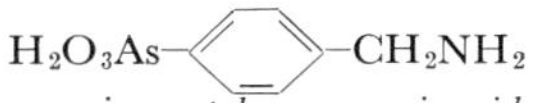 H₂O₃As—⬡—CH₂NH₂ / α-amino-p-toluene arsonic acid	1.25	—	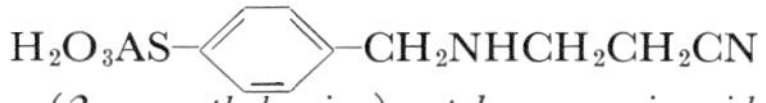 H₂O₃As—⬡—CH₂NHCH₂CH₂CN / α-(2-cyanoethylamino)-p-toluenearsonic acid	—	M.P. > 300°	402	
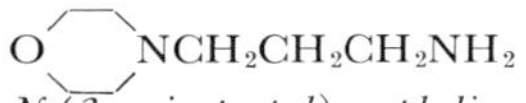 O⬡NCH₂CH₂CH₂NH₂ / N-(3-aminopropyl)morpholine	—	—	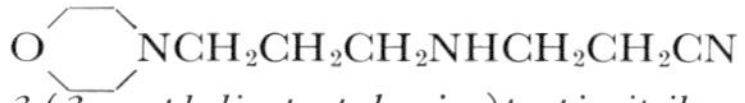 O⬡NCH₂CH₂CH₂NHCH₂CH₂CN / 3-(3-morpholinopropylamino)propionitrile	76	B.P. 178–180°/9 mm.	1145	

TABLE XIX—Continued

(A) Amino and Primary Aliphatic Amines

Reactants	Re-action Time (Hr.)	Reaction Temperature (°C.)	Products	% Yield	M.P. or B.P. (°C.)	References — This Exam.	References — See Also:
$(CH_3)_2CHNHCH_2C(CH_3)_2NH_2$ *N'-isopropyl-2-methyl-1,2-propanediamine*	—	—	$(CH_3)_2CHNHCH_2C(CH_3)_2NHCH_2CH_2CN$ *3-(2-isopropylamino-1,1-dimethylethylamino)-propionitrile*	56.7	B.P. 104-105°/3 mm.	59	
$(CH_3CH_2)_2NCH_2CH_2CH_2NH_2$ *N,N-diethyl-1,3-propanediamine*	—	—	$(CH_3CH_2)_2NCH_2CH_2CH_2NHCH_2CH_2CN$ *3-(3-diethylaminopropylamino)propionitrile*	79.4	B.P. 163-165°/25 mm.	1145	
$(CH_3CH_2)_2NCH_2CH_2CH_2NH_2$ *N,N-diethyl-1,3-propanediamine*	—	—	$(C_2H_5)_2NCH_2CH_2CH_2N(CH_2CH_2CN)_2$ *3,3'-(3-diethylaminopropylimino)dipropionitrile*	8.8	B.P. 233-235°/25 mm.	1145	
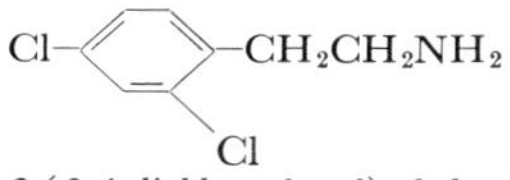 *2-(2,4-dichlorophenyl)ethylamine*	—	R.T.	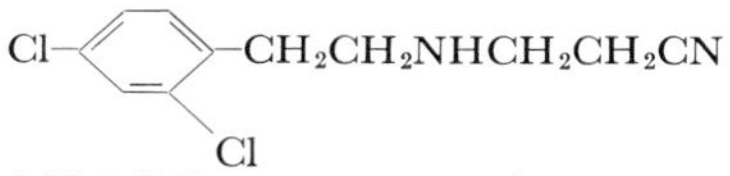 *3-(2,4-dichlorophenethylamino)propionitrile*	65	B.P. 130°/0.3 mm.	1412	
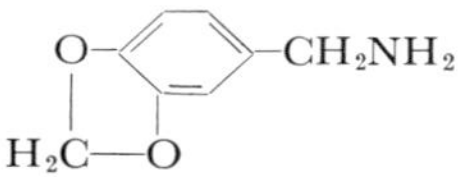 *3,4-dioxymethylenebenzylamine*	—	R.T.	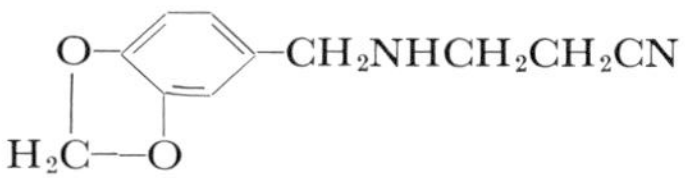 *3-(3,4-methylenedioxybenzylamino)propionitrile*	79	B.P. 127°/0.03 mm.	1412	
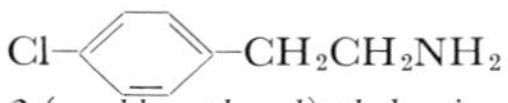 *2-(p-chlorophenyl)ethylamine*	—	R.T.	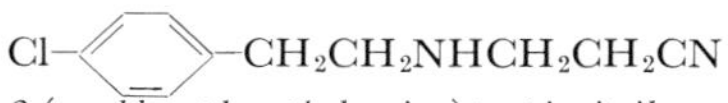 *3-(p-chlorophenethylamino)propionitrile*	87	B.P. 110°/0.03 mm.	1412	
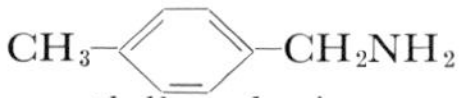 *p-methylbenzylamine*	—	R.T.	 *3-(p-methylbenzylamino)propionitrile*	74	B.P. 123°/0.7 mm.	1412	
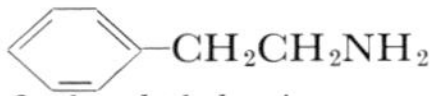 *2-phenylethylamine*	—	R.T.	 *3-phenethylaminopropionitrile*	96	B.P. 133°/0.08 mm.	1412	
$(CH_3)_3CCH_2C(CH_3)_2NH_2$ *t-octylamine*	20	reflux	$(CH_3)_3CCH_2C(CH_3)_2NHCH_2CH_2CN$ *3-(1,1,3,3-tetramethylbutylamino)propionitrile*	83	B.P. 100-105°/1.5-2.0 mm.	1327	

TABLE XIX—Continued

(A) Amino and Primary Aliphatic Amines

Reactants	Reaction Temperature (°C.)	Reaction Time (Hr.)	Products	% Yield	M.P. or B.P. (°C.)	This Exam.	See Also:
$(NH_2CH_2CH_2OCH_2)_2$ *3,3'-(ethylenedioxy)bispropylamine*	R.T.	18.0	$(NCCH_2CH_2NHCH_2CH_2OCH_2)_2$ *3,3'-[ethylenebis(oxytrimethyleneimino)]dipropionitrile*	100	—		
$NH(CH_2CH_2NHCH_2CH_2NH_2)_2$ *tetraethylenepentamine*	steam bath —	1.0 0.50	(F)	—	—	487	
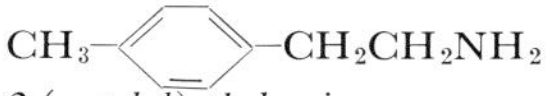 CH_3—⬡—$CH_2CH_2NH_2$ *2-(p-tolyl)ethylamine*	R.T.	—	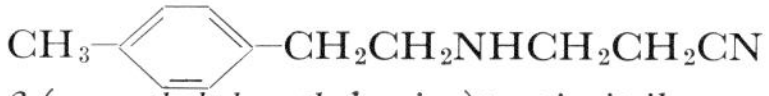 CH_3—⬡—$CH_2CH_2NHCH_2CH_2CN$ *3-(p-methylphenethylamino)propionitrile*	92	B.P. 130°/0.5 mm.	1412	
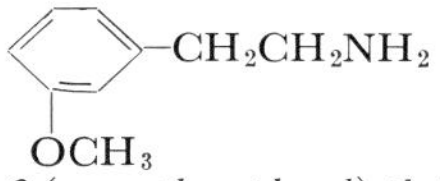 ⬡(OCH_3)—$CH_2CH_2NH_2$ *2-(m-methoxyphenyl)ethylamine*	R.T.	—	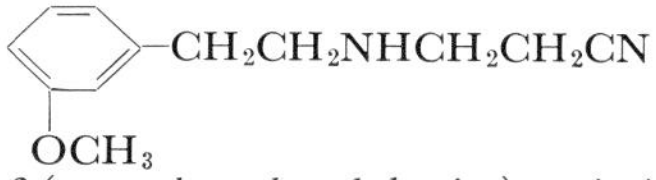 ⬡(OCH_3)—$CH_2CH_2NHCH_2CH_2CN$ *3-(m-methoxyphenethylamino)propionitrile*	86	B.P. 128°/0.05 mm.	1412	
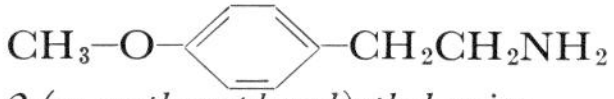 CH_3—O—⬡—$CH_2CH_2NH_2$ *2-(p-methoxyphenyl)ethylamine*	R.T.	—	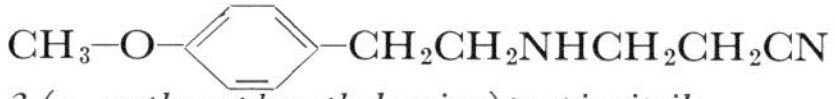 CH_3—O—⬡—$CH_2CH_2NHCH_2CH_2CN$ *3-(p-methoxyphenethylamino)propionitrile*	88	B.P. 118°/0.07 mm.	1412	
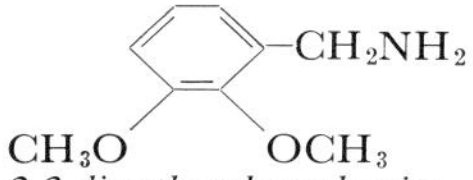 CH_3O, OCH_3 ⬡—CH_2NH_2 *2,3-dimethoxybenzylamine*	R.T.	—	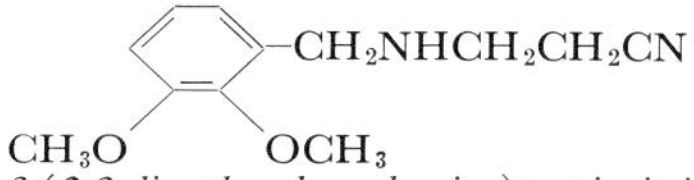 CH_3O, OCH_3 ⬡—$CH_2NHCH_2CH_2CN$ *3-(2,3-dimethoxybenzylamino)propionitrile*	73	B.P. 125°/0.06 mm.	1412	
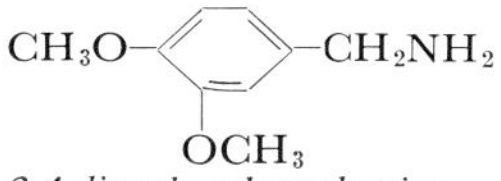 CH_3O—⬡(OCH_3)—CH_2NH_2 *3,4-dimethoxybenzylamine*	R.T.	—	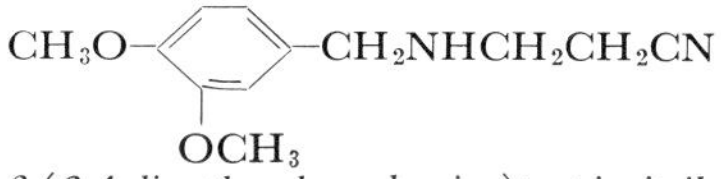 CH_3O—⬡(OCH_3)—$CH_2NHCH_2CH_2CN$ *3-(3,4-dimethoxybenzylamino)propionitrile*	79	B.P. 158°/0.05 mm.	1412	1383
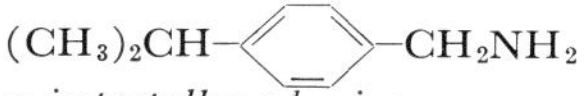 $(CH_3)_2CH$—⬡—CH_2NH_2 *p-isopropylbenzylamine*	R.T.	—	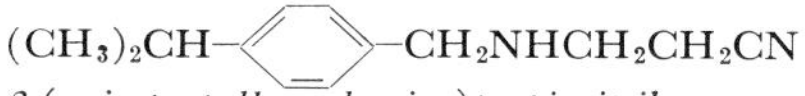 $(CH_3)_2CH$—⬡—$CH_2NHCH_2CH_2CN$ *3-(p-isopropylbenzylamino)propionitrile*	91	B.P. 102°/0.07 mm.	1412	

TABLE XIX—Continued

(A) Amino and Primary Aliphatic Amines

Reactants	Reaction Temperature (°C.)	Reaction Time (Hr.)	Products	% Yield	M.P. or B.P. (°C.)	References This Exam.	References See Also:
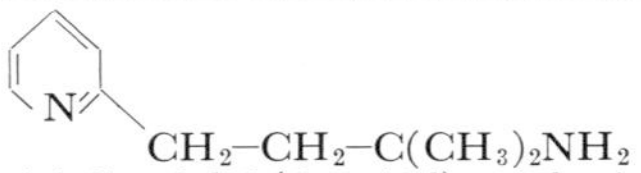 [2-pyridyl] CH₂-CH₂-C(CH₃)₂NH₂ — 1,1-dimethyl-3-(2-pyridyl)propylamine	reflux	1	 [2-pyridyl] CH₂CH₂C(CH₃)₂NHCH₂CH₂CN — 3-[1,1-dimethyl-3-(2-pyridyl)propylamino]propionitrile	59	B.P. 154-157°/1.2 mm.	1385	
 C₄H₉O—[benzene]—CH₂NH₂ — p-butoxybenzylamine	R.T.	—	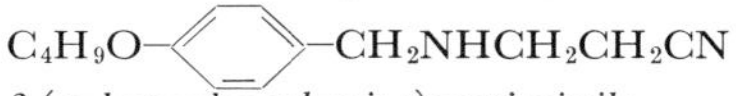 C₄H₉O—[benzene]—CH₂NHCH₂CH₂CN — 3-(p-butoxybenzylamino)propionitrile	94	B.P. 138°/0.05 mm.	1412	
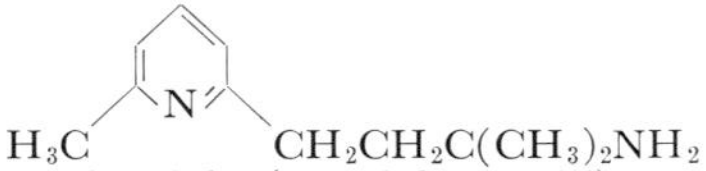 H₃C—[2-pyridyl] CH₂CH₂C(CH₃)₂NH₂ — 1,1-dimethyl-3-(6-methyl-2-pyridyl)propylamine	reflux	3	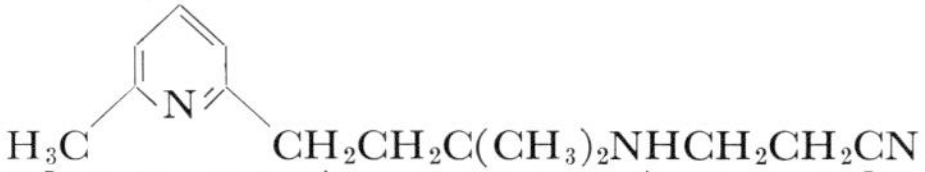 H₃C—[2-pyridyl] CH₂CH₂C(CH₃)₂NHCH₂CH₂CN — 3-[1,1-dimethyl-3-(6-methyl-2-pyridyl)propylamino]propionitrile	64	B.P. 147-150°/0.6 mm.	1385	
$CH_3(CH_2)_{10}CH_2NH_2$ — n-dodecylamine	35° reflux	0.5 1.0	$CH_3(CH_2)_{10}CH_2NHCH_2CH_2CN$ — 3-dodecylaminopropionitrile	95	B.P. 140°/0.5 mm.	344	408, 519, 963
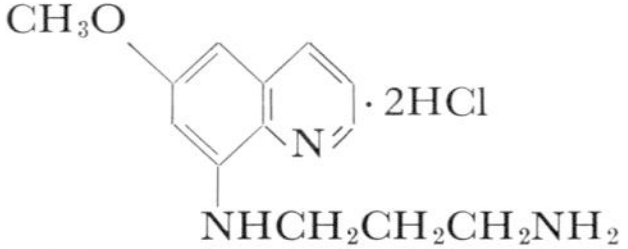 CH₃O—[quinoline]—NHCH₂CH₂CH₂NH₂ · 2HCl — 8-(3-aminopropylamino)-6-methoxy-quinoline dihydrochloride	R.T. R.T.	2.0 4.0	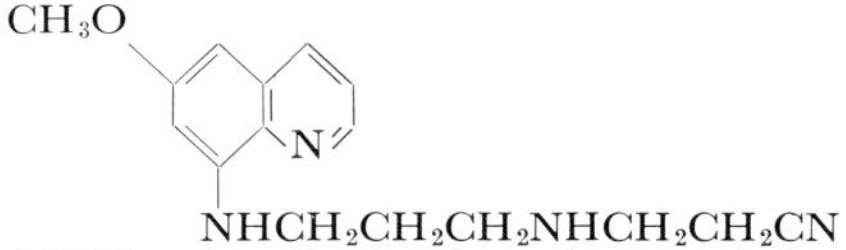 CH₃O—[quinoline]—NHCH₂CH₂CH₂NHCH₂CH₂CN — 3-[3-(6-methoxy-8-quinolylamino)propylamino]-propionitrile	31.2	M.P. 217-218°	636	
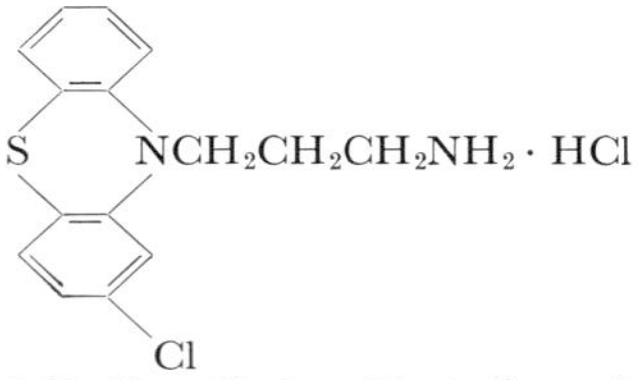 [phenothiazine, S, Cl] NCH₂CH₂CH₂NH₂ · HCl — 3-(2-chloro-10-phenothiazinyl)propylamine hydrochloride	R.T. 70°	3 0.3	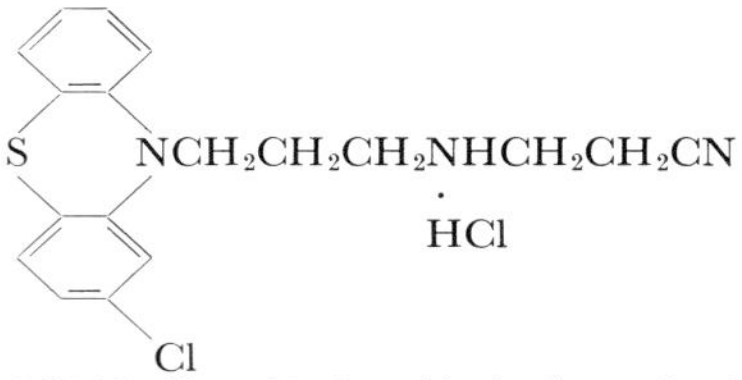 [phenothiazine, S, Cl] NCH₂CH₂NHCH₂CH₂CN · HCl — 3-[3-(2-chloro-10-phenothiazinyl)propylamino]-propionitrile, hydrochloride	—	M.P. 194-197° (dec.)	1270	

TABLE XIX—Continued

(A) Amino and Primary Aliphatic Amines

Reactants	Reaction Temperature (°C.)	Reaction Time (Hr.)	Products	% Yield	M.P. or B.P. (°C.)	References — This Exam.	References — See Also:
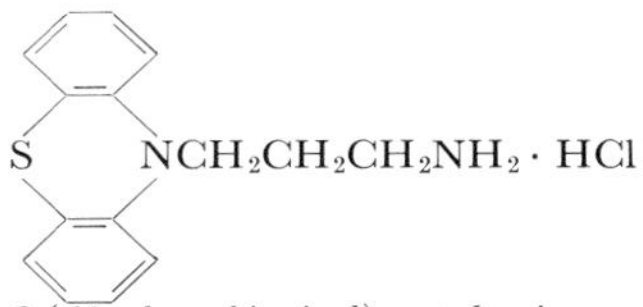 S NCH₂CH₂CH₂NH₂·HCl, *3-(10-phenothiazinyl)propylamine hydrochloride*	R.T. 70°	3 0.3	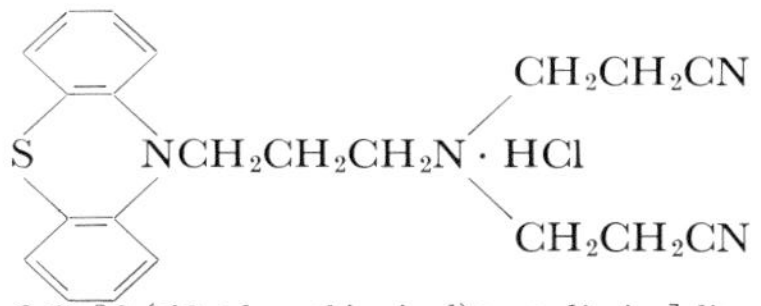 S NCH₂CH₂CH₂N(CH₂CH₂CN)₂·HCl, *3,3'-[3-(10-phenothiazinyl)propylimino]dipropionitrile, hydrochloride*	62	M.P. 158-160°	1270	
CH₃(CH₂)₁₇NH₂ *octadecylamine*	steam bath		CH₃(CH₂)₁₇NHCH₂CH₂CN *3-octadecylaminopropionitrile*	~100	—	963	
CH₃ CH₂NH₂ (dehydroabietylamine structure, CH(CH₃)₂) *dehydroabietylamine*	90° pressure	16.0	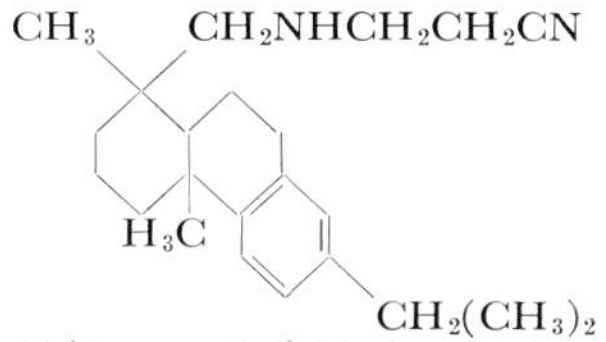 CH₃ CH₂NHCH₂CH₂CN (structure, CH(CH₃)₂) *N-(2-cyanoethyl)dehydroabietylamine*		—	625	
palm kernel oil amine	steam bath		*mono cyanoethyl deriv. of palm kernel oil amine*		—	963	
RNH₂ⓖ *tallow amine*	35° reflux	0.5 1.0	RNHCH₂CH₂CN		—	344	
coconut oil amine	steam bath		*mono cyanoethyl derivative of coconut oil amine*		—	963	

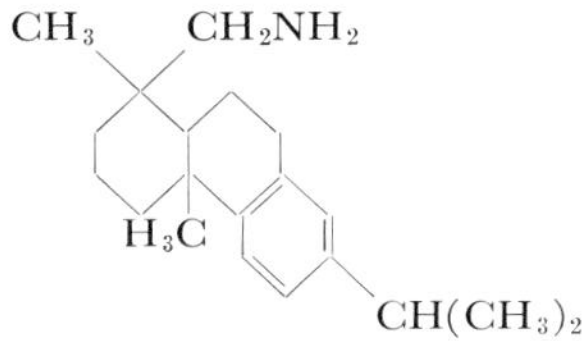

(B) Secondary Aliphatic Amines

Reactants	Reaction Temperature (°C.)	Reaction Time (Hr.)	Products	% Yield	M.P. or B.P. (°C.)	References — This Exam.	References — See Also:
(CH₃)₂NH *dimethylamine*	—	—	(CH₃)₂NCH₂CH₂CN *3-dimethylaminopropionitrile*	~100	—	963	815, 265, 664, 801, 1069, 933, 1068, 266, 1065, 1355

TABLE XIX—Continued

(B) Secondary Aliphatic Amines

Reactants	Reaction Time (Hr.)	Reaction Temperature (°C.)	Products	% Yield	M.P. or B.P. (°C.)	References: This Exam.	See Also:
CH₃NHCH₂CH₂CN _3-methylaminopropionitrile_	16.0	90°	CH₃N(CH₂CH₂CN)₂ _3,3'-methyliminodipropionitrile_	95	B.P. 159.5-169°/5 mm.	815	
CH₃CH₂CH₂NHCH₃ _N-methylpropylamine_	O.N.	95°	CH₃CH₂CH₂N(CH₃)CH₂CH₂CN _3-(methylpropylamino)propionitrile_	93	B.P. 102-106°/26 mm.	272	
(CH₃)₂CHNHCH₃ _N-methylisopropylamine_	O.N.	95°	(CH₃)₂CHN(CH₃)CH₂CH₂CN _3-(isopropylmethylamino)propionitrile_	76	B.P. 94-96°/32 mm.	272	
(C₂H₅)₂NH _diethylamine_	—	—	(C₂H₅)₂NCH₂CH₂CN _3-diethylaminopropionitrile_	96-98	B.P. 65°/2 mm. B.P. 76°/9 mm. B.P. 87°/20 mm. B.P. 197.3°/755 mm.	664	1145, 1244, 1068, 1355, 1120
HOCH₂CH₂NHC₂H₅ _N-ethylaminoethanol_	O.N.	50° R.T.	HOCH₂CH₂N(CH₂CH₃)CH₂CH₂CN _3-(ethyl-2-hydroxyethylamino)propionitrile_	72	B.P. 133-134°/7 mm.	195	1040
(HOCH₂CH₂)₂NH _2,2'-iminodiethanol_	—	60°	(HOCH₂CH₂)₂NCH₂CH₂CN _3-bis(2-hydroxyethyl)aminopropionitrile_	~100	—	567 569	521, 1145, 266, 249
CH₃CH₂CH₂CH₂NHCH₃ _N-methylbutylamine_	O.N.	95°	CH₃CH₂CH₂CH₂N(CH₃)CH₂CH₂CN _3-(butylmethylamino)propionitrile_	83	B.P. 108-112°/40 mm.	272	
(CH₃)₂CHCH₂NHCH₃ _N-methyl-2-methylpropylamine_	O.N.	95°	(CH₃)₂CHCH₂N(CH₃)CH₂CH₂CN _3-(isobutylmethylamino)propionitrile_	78	B.P. 103-105°/33 mm.	272	
C₂H₅CH(CH₃)NHCH₃ _N-methyl-1-methylpropylamine_	O.N.	95°	CH₃CH₂CH(CH₃)N(CH₃)CH₂CH₂CN _3-(sec-butylmethylamino)propionitrile_	87	B.P. 111-112°/32 mm.	272	
(CH₃)₂CHNHC₂H₅ _1-methyldiethylamine_	O.N.	95°	(CH₃)₂CHN(CH₂CH₃)CH₂CH₂CN _3-(ethylisopropylamino)propionitrile_	31	B.P. 98-101°/29 mm.	272	
HN(CH₂CH₂CN)₂ _3,3'-iminodipropionitrile_	60	160-180°	N(CH₂CH₂CN)₃ _3,3',3''-nitrilotripropionitrile_	40	M.P. 57-58°	1065	

TABLE XIX—Continued

(B) Secondary Aliphatic Amines

Reactants	Reaction Time (Hr.)	Reaction Temperature (°C.)	Products	% Yield	M.P. or B.P. (°C.)	References This Exam.	References See Also:
(cyclopentyl)—$NHCH_3$ *N-methylcyclopentylamine*	O.N.	95°	(cyclopentyl)—$N(CH_3)CH_2CH_2CN$ *3-(cyclopentylmethylamino)propionitrile*	96	B.P. 134-135°/33 mm.	272	
$CH_3CH_2CH_2CH(CH_3)NHCH_3$ *N-methyl-1-methylbutylamine*	O.N.	95°	$CH_3CH_2CH_2CH(CH_3)N(CH_3)CH_2CH_2CN$ *3-(methyl-1-methylbutylamino)propionitrile*	89	B.P. 101-103°/18 mm.	272	
$(C_2H_5)_2CHNHCH_3$ *N-methyl-1-ethylpropylamine*	O.N.	95°	$(C_2H_5)_2CHN(CH_3)CH_2CH_2CN$ *3-[(1-ethylpropyl)methylamino]propionitrile*	81	B.P. 111-114°/17 mm.	272	
$(CH_3)_2CHCH_2NHC_2H_5$ *N-ethyl-2-methylpropylamine*	O.N.	95°	$(CH_3)_2CHCH_2N(CH_2CH_3)CH_2CH_2CN$ *3-(ethylisobutylamino)propionitrile*	56	B.P. 114-115°/35 mm.	272	
$(C_3H_7)_2NH$ *dipropylamine*	O.N.	50° R.T.	$(C_3H_7)_2NCH_2CH_2CN$ *3-dipropylaminopropionitrile*	90	B.P. 104-105°/1 mm.	195	1145, 1120
$(CH_3)_2CHNH(C_3H_7)$ *N-propyl-1-methylethylamine*	O.N.	95°	$(CH_3)_2CHN[(CH_2)_2CH_3]CH_2CH_2CN$ *3-(isopropylpropylamino)propionitrile*	80	B.P. 110-113°/31-32 mm.	272	
$[(CH_3)_2CH]_2NH$ *diisopropylamine*	O.N.	50° R.T.	$[(CH_3)_2CH]_2NCH_2CH_2CN$ *3-diisopropylaminopropionitrile*	12	B.P. 100-102°/13 mm.	195	
$(CH_3)_2CHCH(CH_3)NHCH_3$ *N,1,2-trimethylpropylamine*	O.N.	95°	$(CH_3)_2CHCH(CH_3)N(CH_3)CH_2CH_2CN$ *3-[(1,2-dimethylpropyl)methylamino]propionitrile*	92	B.P. 131-134°/40 mm.	272	
$CH_3(CH_2)_3NHCH_2CH_2OH$ *N-butyl-2-hydroxyethylamine*	O.N.	50° R.T.	$HOCH_2CH_2N[(CH_2)_3CH_3]CH_2CH_2CN$ *3-(butyl-2-hydroxyethylamino)propionitrile*	61	B.P. 147-148°/7 mm.	195	1040
$CH_3CH_2NHCH_2Si(CH_3)_3$ *N-[(trimethylsilyl)methyl]ethylamine*	12	60°	$(CH_3)_3SiCH_2N[(CH_3CH_2)]CH_2CH_2CN$ *3-[ethyl(trimethylsilylmethyl)amino]propionitrile*	77.4	B.P. 83.5°/3 mm.	1346	
(cyclohexyl)—$NHCH_3$ *N-methylcyclohexylamine*	O.N.	95°	(cyclohexyl)—$N(CH_3)CH_2CH_2CN$ *3-(cyclohexylmethylamino)propionitrile*	61	B.P. 145-148°/40 mm.	272	
(cyclopentyl)—NHC_2H_5 *N-ethylcyclopentylamine*	O.N.	95°	(cyclopentyl)—$N(C_2H_5)CH_2CH_2CN$ *3-(cyclopentylethylamino)propionitrile*	48	B.P. 130-133°/20 mm.	272	

TABLE XIX—Continued

(B) Secondary Aliphatic Amines

Reactants	Reaction Time (Hr.)	Reaction Temperature (°C.)	Products	% Yield	M.P. or B.P. (°C.)	References	
						This Exam.	See Also:
$CH_3CH_2CH(CH_3)NHC_3H_7$ *1-methyldipropylamine*	O.N.	95°	$CH_3CH_2CH(CH_3)N[(CH_2)_2CH_3]CH_2CH_2CN$ *3-[(1-methylpropyl)propylamino]propionitrile*	34	B.P. 105-111°/22-25 mm.	272	
$n\text{-}C_4H_9NHC_3H_7$ *N-propylbutylamine*	O.N.	95°	$CH_3CH_2CH_2CH_2N[(CH_2)_2CH_3]CH_2CH_2CN$ *3-(butylpropylamino)propionitrile*	61	B.P. 128-129°/35 mm.	272	
$(CH_3)_2CHCH_2NHC_3H_7$ *2-methyldipropylamine*	O.N.	95°	$(CH_3)_2CHCH_2N[(CH_2)_2CH_3]CH_2CH_2CN$ *3-(isobutylpropylamino)propionitrile*	49	B.P. 105-110°/21 mm.	272	
C_6H_5—CH_2NHCH_3 *N-methylbenzylamine*	36.0	steam cone	C_6H_5—$CH_2N(CH_3)CH_2CH_2CN$ *3-(benzylmethylamino)propionitrile*	75-93	B.P. 163-164°/14 mm.	633	
$(n\text{-}C_3H_7)_2CHNHCH_3$ *N-methyl-1-propylbutylamine*	O.N.	95°	$[CH_3(CH_2)_2]_2CHN(CH_3)CH_2CH_2CN$ *3-(methyl-1-propylbutylamino)propionitrile*	65	B.P. 152-153°/38 mm.	272	
$[CH_3(CH_2)_3]_2NH$ *dibutylamine*	O.N.	50° R.T.	$[CH_3(CH_2)_3]_2NCH_2CH_2CN$ *3-dibutylaminopropionitrile*	96	B.P. 127-131°/11 mm.	195	1145, 568, 963, 566, 579, 1120, 520
$[(CH_3)_2CHCH_2]_2NH$ *diisobutylamine*	O.N.	50° R.T.	$[(CH_3)_2CHCH_2]_2NCH_2CH_2CN$ *3-diisobutylaminopropionitrile*	51	B.P. 116-117°/10 mm.	195	
$(CH_3)_2CHCH_2NHC_4H_9$ *N-butyl-2-methylpropylamine*	O.N.	95°	$(CH_3)_2CHCH_2N[(CH_2)_2CH_3]CH_2CH_2CN$ *3-(butylisobutylamino)propionitrile*	42	B.P. 135-138°/28 mm.	272	
$CH_3CH_2NHSi(CH_2CH_3)_3$ *N,1,1,1-tetraethylsilylamine*	61	77-80°	$(CH_3CH_2)_3SiN(CH_2CH_3)CH_2CH_2CN$ *3-(tetraethylsilylamino)propionitrile*	13.6	B.P. 262-265°/740 mm.	1346	
C_6H_5—$CH_2NHC_2H_5$ *N-ethylbenzylamine*	10	110°	C_6H_5—$CH_2N(CH_2CH_3)CH_2CH_2CN$ *3-(benzylethylamino)propionitrile*	94	B.P. 148°/3 mm.	1205	
$CH_3(CH_2)_3NH$—(cyclopentyl) *N-butylcyclopentylamine*	O.N.	95°	(cyclopentyl)—$N(CH_2CH_2CN)CH_2CH_2CH_2CH_3$ *3-(butylcyclopentylamino)propionitrile*	68	B.P. 142-143°/17 mm.	272	

TABLE XIX—Continued

(B) Secondary Aliphatic Amines

Reactants	Reaction Temperature (°C.)	Reaction Time (Hr.)	Products	% Yield	M.P. or B.P. (°C.)	References — This Exam.	References — See Also:
[C₆H₅]—NHCH₂Si(CH₃)₃ *N-[(trimethylsilyl)methyl]aniline*	130°	24	[C₆H₅]—N(CH₂CH₂CN)CH₂Si(CH₃)₃ *3-[N-trimethylsilylmethyl)anilino]propionitrile*	68.6	B.P. 199-200°/6 mm.	1346	
[CH₃(CH₂)₄]₂NH *diamylamine*	50° R.T.	O.N.	[CH₃(CH₂)₄]₂NCH₂CH₂CN *3-diamylaminopropionitrile*	90	B.P. 136°/6 mm.	525	1145, 1120
[CH₃(CH₂)₅]₂NH *dihexylamine*	—	—	[CH₃(CH₂)₅]₂NCH₂CH₂CN *3-dihexylaminopropionitrile*	85	B.P. 145-146°/2 mm.	1145	
[(C₂H₅)₂NCH₂CH₂CH₂]₂NH *3,3′-bis(diethylamino)dipropylamine*	—	—	[(C₂H₅)₂NCH₂CH₂CH₂]₂NCH₂CH₂CN *3-[bis(3-diethylaminopropyl)amino]propionitrile*	70	B.P. 153°/3 mm.	1145	
[CH₃(CH₂)₇]₂NH *dioctylamine*	steam bath	100.0	[CH₃(CH₂)₇]₂NCH₂CH₂CN *3-dioctylaminopropionitrile*	80	B.P. 180-182°/2 mm.	195	
[CH₃(CH₂)₃CH(C₂H₅)CH₂]₂NH *2,2′-diethyldihexylamine*	steam bath	100.0	[CH₃(CH₂)₃CH(C₂H₅)CH₂]₂NCH₂CH₂CN *3-[bis(2-ethylhexyl)amino]propionitrile*	65	B.P. 163-164°/2 mm.	195	

(C) Heterocyclic Amines

Reactants	Reaction Temperature (°C.)	Reaction Time (Hr.)	Products	% Yield	M.P. or B.P. (°C.)	References — This Exam.	References — See Also:
CH₂\CH₂/NH *ethylenimine*	R.T.	O.N.	CH₂\CH₂/NCH₂CH₂CN *1-aziridinepropionitrile*	90	B.P. 80-82°/10 mm.	113	608
[pyrrole] NH *pyrrole*	steam bath	O.N.	NCH₂CH₂CN *1-pyrrolepropionitrile*	86	B.P. 135-150°/8-10 mm.	273	572, 124, 912
(CH₃)₂C—CH₂ N H *2,2-dimethylaziridine*	reflux	34.0	(CH₃)₂C\CH₂/NCH₂CH₂CN *2,2-dimethyl-1-aziridinepropionitrile*	66	B.P. 79-83°/8 mm. 198-199°/752 mm.	1053	

TABLE XIX—Continued

(C) Heterocyclic Amines

Reactants	Reaction Time (Hr.)	Reaction Temperature (°C.)	Products	% Yield	M.P. or B.P. (°C.)	References This Exam.	References See Also:
 pyrrolidine (NH)	0.5	100°	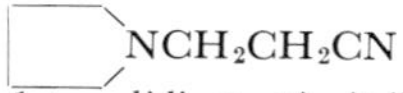 NCH$_2$CH$_2$CN — *1-pyrrolidinepropionitrile*	86	B.P. 78-80°/8 mm.	1205	273
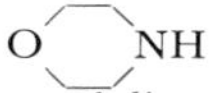 morpholine (O NH)	—	—	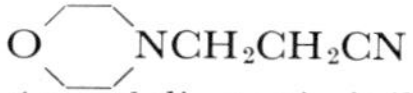 O NCH$_2$CH$_2$CN — *4-morpholinepropionitrile*	95	B.P. 149°/20 mm.	1145	912
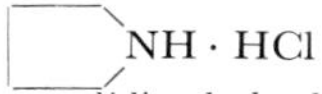 pyrrolidine hydrochloride (NH·HCl)	72	reflux	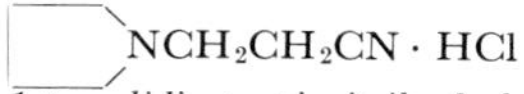 NCH$_2$CH$_2$CN · HCl — *1-pyrrolidinepropionitrile, hydrochloride*	90	M.P. 168-170°	1280	
 piperazine (HN NH · 6H$_2$O)	2.0	40-50°	 NCCH$_2$CH$_2$N NCH$_2$CH$_2$CN — *1,4-piperazinedipropionitrile*	—	—	100	912, 572
 4-pyridone (O= NH)	5.0	60-65°	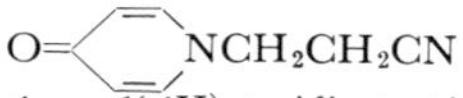 O= NCH$_2$CH$_2$CN — *4-oxo-1(4H)-pyridinepropionitrile*	42.5	M.P. 109-111°	8	
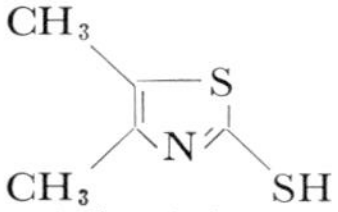 4,5-dimethyl-2-thiazolethiol	11.0	R.T.	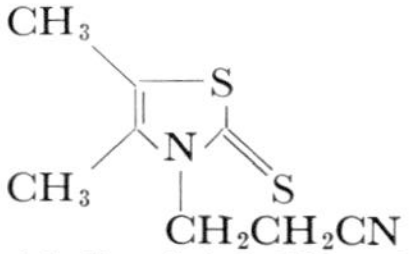 CH$_2$CH$_2$CN — *4,5-dimethyl-2-thioxo-4-thiazoline-3-propionitrile*	22	M.P. 158-159°	1029	
 piperidine (N H)	4.0	100°	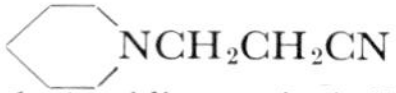 NCH$_2$CH$_2$CN — *1-piperidinepropionitrile*	99	B.P. 114-115°/18 mm.	1069, 665	1070, 664, 1079, 1145, 572, 273, 912

TABLE XIX—Continued

(C) Heterocyclic Amines

Reactants	Reaction Time (Hr.)	Reaction Temperature (°C.)	Products	% Yield	M.P. or B.P. (°C.)	References This Exam.	See Also:
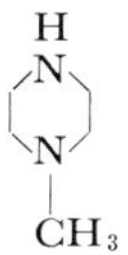 N-methylpiperazine	several hours O.N.	reflux 25°	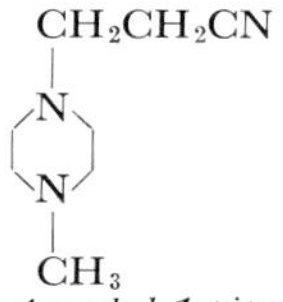 4-methyl-1-piperazinepropionitrile	79.5	B.P. 68-72°/0.3 mm.	1391	
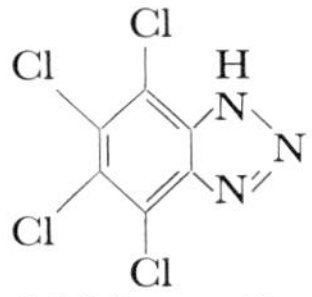 4,5,6,7-tetrachlorobenzotriazole	18	75°	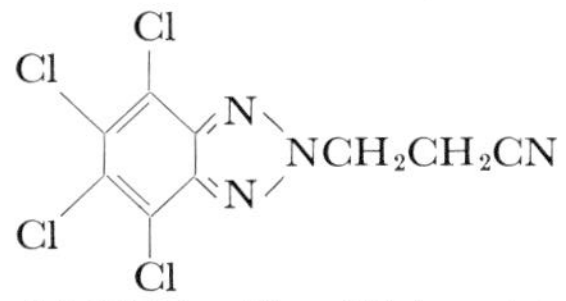 4,5,6,7-tetrachloro-2H-benzotriazole-2-propionitrile	52	M.P. 195-198°	1447	
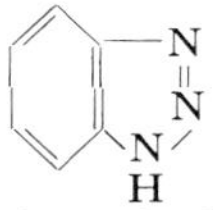 benzotriazole	5.0	water bath	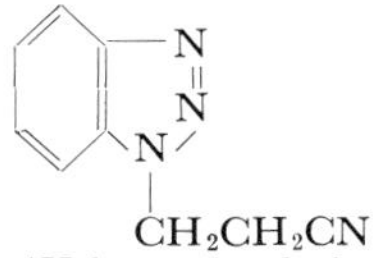 1H-benzotriazole-1-propionitrile	23-25	M.P. 79-80°	1157	
 2-ethylpyrrole	—	—	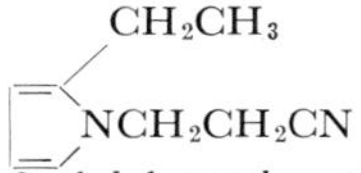 2-ethyl-1-pyrrolepropionitrile	—	—	912	
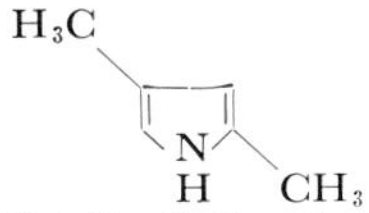 2,4-dimethylpyrrole	4.5	40°	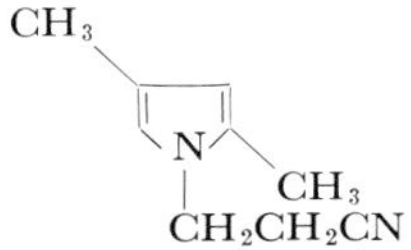 2,4-dimethyl-1-pyrrolepropionitrile	58	B.P. 152-153°/18 mm.	1420	

TABLE XIX—Continued

(C) Heterocyclic Amines

Reactants	Reaction Time (Hr.)	Reaction Temperature (°C.)	Products	% Yield	M.P. or B.P. (°C.)	References This Exam.	References See Also:
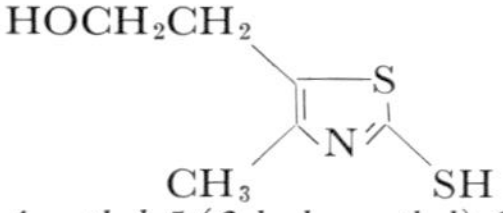 HOCH₂CH₂ ... SH (thiazole structure) *4-methyl-5-(2-hydroxyethyl)-2-thiazolethiol*	10	R.T.	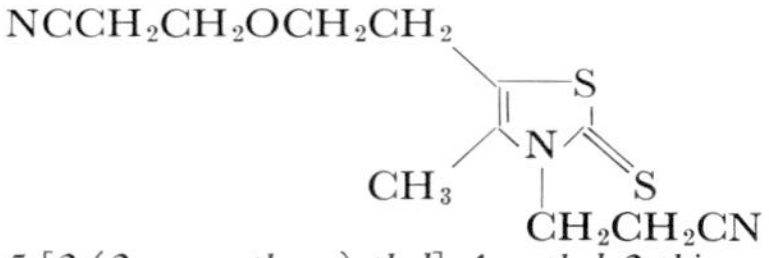 NCCH₂CH₂OCH₂CH₂ ... (thiazoline structure with CH₃, S, CH₂CH₂CN) *5-[2-(2-cyanoethoxy)ethyl]-4-methyl-2-thioxo-4-thiazoline-3-propionitrile*	—	M.P. 62-63°	1181	
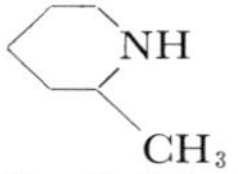 NH ... CH₃ *2-methylpiperidine*	O.N.	steam bath	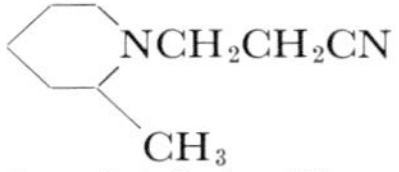 NCH₂CH₂CN ... CH₃ *2-methyl-1-piperidinepropionitrile*	99	B.P. 137-140°/30 mm.	273	
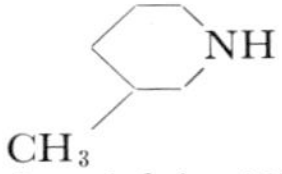 NH ... CH₃ *3-methylpiperidine*	O.N.	steam bath	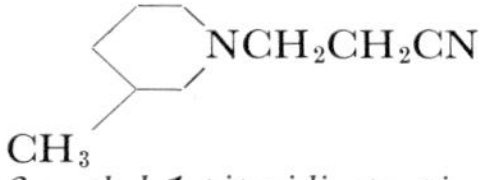 NCH₂CH₂CN ... CH₃ *3-methyl-1-piperidinepropionitrile*	97	B.P. 126-128°/28 mm.	273	
 H₃C ... NH *4-methylpiperidine*	O.N.	steam bath	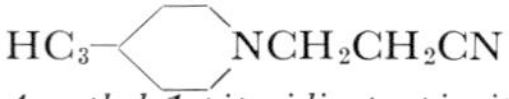 H₃C ... NCH₂CH₂CN *4-methyl-1-piperidinepropionitrile*	87	B.P. 127-130°/27-28 mm.	273	
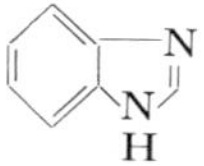 benzimidazole (N ... N–H)	2.0 0.5	28-35° 80°	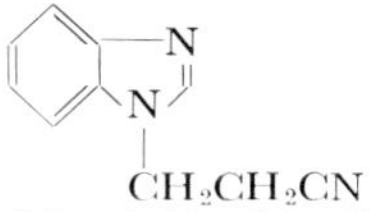 CH₂CH₂CN *1-benzimidazolepropionitrile*	94	M.P. 112°	572	912

TABLE XIX—Continued

(C) Heterocyclic Amines

Reactants	Reaction Time (Hr.)	Reaction Temperature (°C.)	Products	% Yield	M.P. or B.P. (°C.)	References This Exam.	See Also:
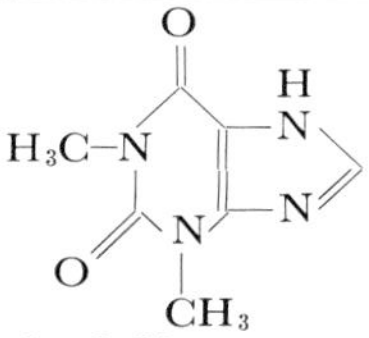 theophylline	—	reflux	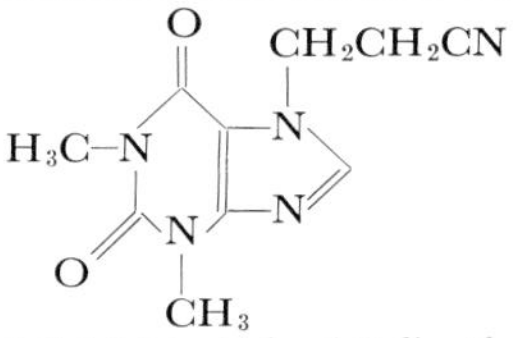 1,2,3,6-tetrahydro-1,3-dimethyl-2,6-dioxo-7-purinepropionitrile	~100	M.P. 160°	882	
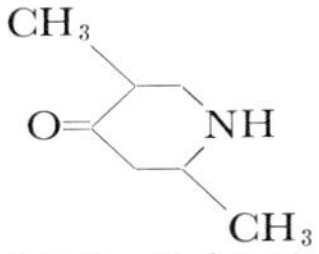 2,5-dimethyl-4-piperidone	3.0 O.N.	95-97° R.T.	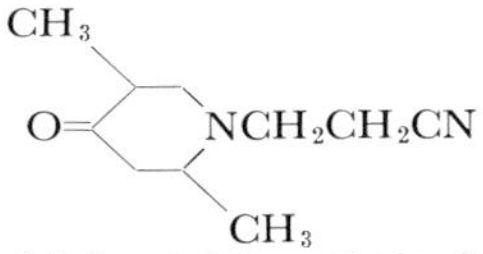 2,5-dimethyl-4-oxo-1-piperidinepropionitrile	96(II)	B.P. 143-145°/5.5 mm.	815	
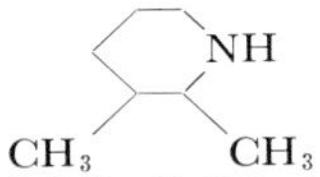 2,3-dimethylpiperidine	O.N.	steam bath	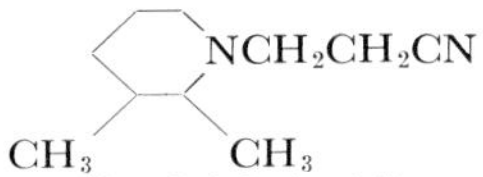 2,3-dimethyl-1-piperidinepropionitrile	99	B.P. 140-142°/35 mm.	273	
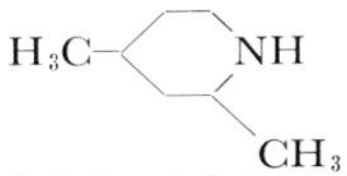 2,4-dimethylpiperidine	O.N.	steam bath	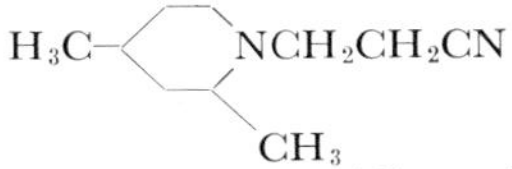 2,4-dimethyl-1-piperidinepropionitrile	68	B.P. 130-133°/29 mm.	273	
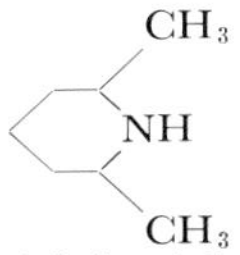 2,6-dimethylpiperidine	O.N.	steam bath	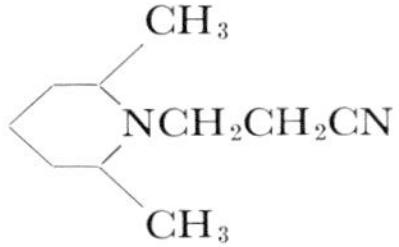 2,6-dimethyl-1-piperidinepropionitrile	82	B.P. 121-125°/26-28 mm.	273	

TABLE XIX—Continued

(C) Heterocyclic Amines

Reactants	Reaction Time (Hr.)	Reaction Temperature (°C.)	Products	% Yield	M.P. or B.P. (°C.)	This Exam.	See Also:
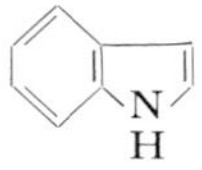 indole	1-2	exo-thermic	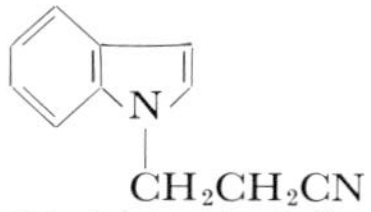 CH_2CH_2CN 1-indolepropionitrile	95	B.P. 168-180°/3 mm. M.P. 47°	1424	912, 572
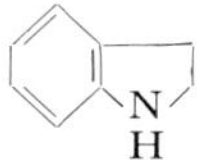 2,3-dihydroindole	—	—	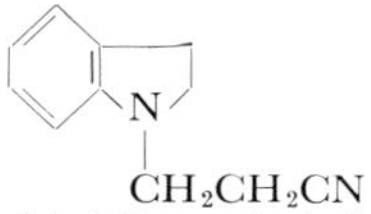 CH_2CH_2CN 1-indolinepropionitrile	—	—	912	
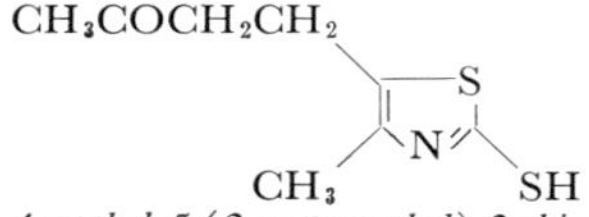 $CH_3COCH_2CH_2$ ... 4-methyl-5-(2-acetoxyethyl)-2-thiazolethiol	10.0	R.T.	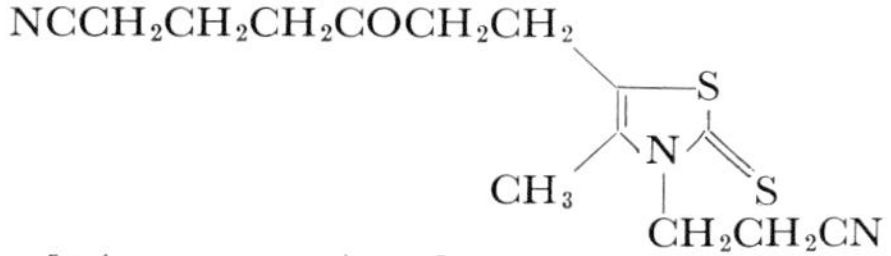 $NCCH_2CH_2CH_2COCH_2CH_2$ ... 5-[2-(2-cyanoethoxy)ethyl]-4-methyl-2-thioxo-4-thiazoline-3-propionitrile	20.2	M.P. 62-63°	1181	
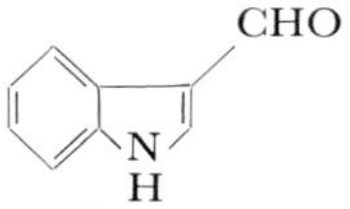 3-indolecarboxaldehyde	24.0	R.T.	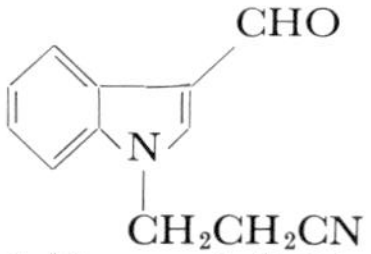 CHO CH_2CH_2CN 1-(2-cyanoethyl)-3-indolecarboxaldehyde	68.2	M.P. 127-127.5°	124	
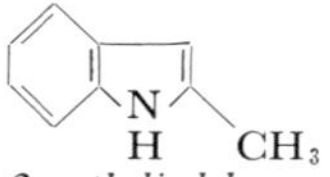 2-methylindole	12	130°	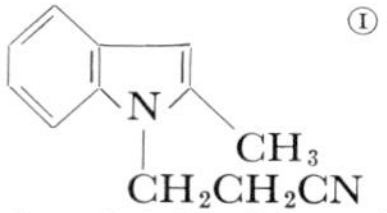 CH_2CH_2CN 2-methyl-1-indolepropionitrile	74	B.P. 180-194°/2 mm. M.P. 82°	572	912

TABLE XIX—Continued

(C) Heterocyclic Amines

Reactants	Reaction Time (Hr.)	Reaction Temperature (°C.)	Products	% Yield	M.P. or B.P. (°C.)	References This Exam.	References See Also:
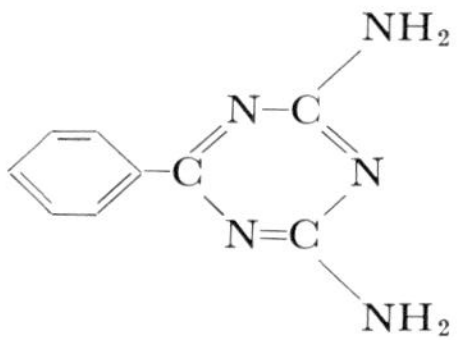 2,4-diamino-6-phenyl-s-triazine	1.0	75°	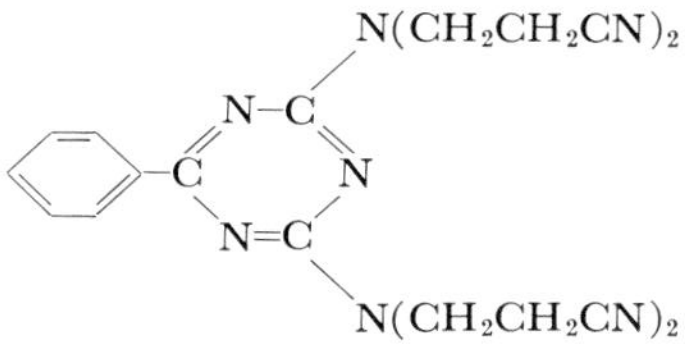 2,4-bis[bis(2-cyanoethyl)amino]-6-phenyl-s-triazine	98	M.P. 162-163°	826	
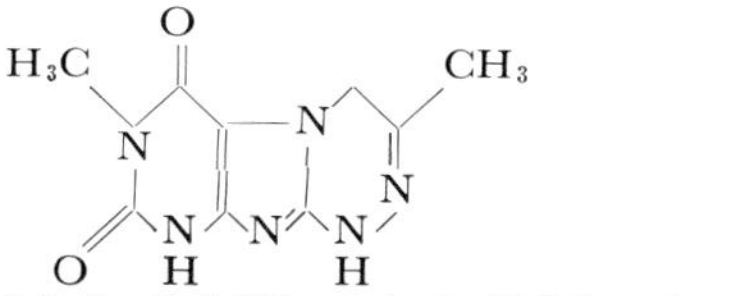 3,7-dimethyl-1H-as-triazino[4,3-f]purine-6,8(7H,9H)-dione	0.3	reflux	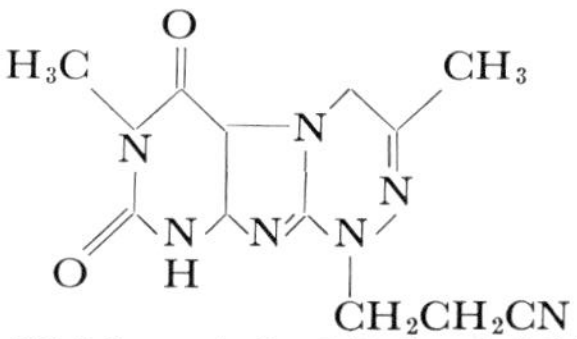 6,7,8,9-tetrahydro-3,7-dimethyl-6,8-dioxo-1H-as-triazino[4,3-f]purine-1-propionitrile	60	M.P. 210-211°	1454	
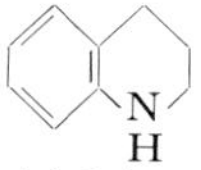 1,2,3,4-tetrahydroquinoline	3.0 6.0	108-125° reflux	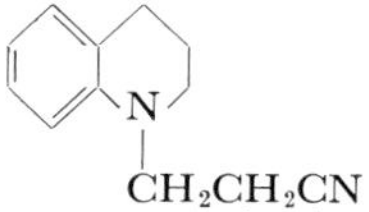 3,4-dihydro-1(2H)-quinolinepropionitrile	75.5	B.P. 192°/10 mm.	1145	740, 573, 912
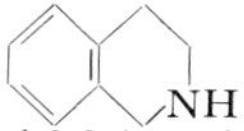 1,2,3,4-tetrahydroisoquinoline	—	—	 3,4-dihydro-2(1H)-isoquinolinepropionitrile	—	—	912	

TABLE XIX—Continued

(C) Heterocyclic Amines

Reactants	Reaction Time (Hr.)	Reaction Temperature (°C.)	Products	% Yield	M.P. or B.P. (°C.)	References This Exam.	See Also:
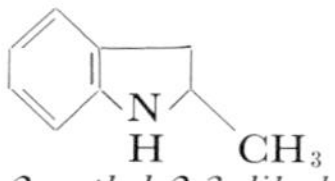 2-methyl-2,3-dihydroindole	—	120-140°	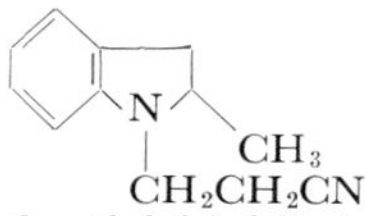 2-methyl-1-indolinepropionitrile	—	B.P. 140-142°/1 mm.	573	912
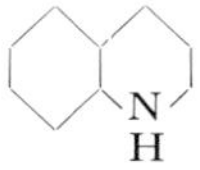 decahydroquinoline	2.0	200°	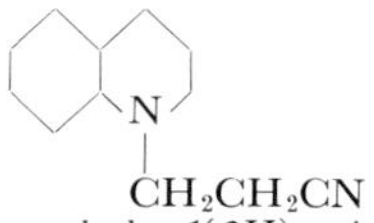 octahydro-1(2H)-quinolinepropionitrile	61	B.P. 160-167°/15 mm.	572	912
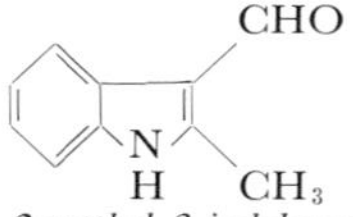 2-methyl-3-indolecarboxaldehyde	24.0	R.T.	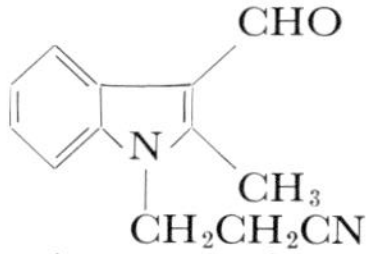 1-(2-cyanoethyl)-2-methyl-3-indolecarboxaldehyde	—	M.P. 148-149°	124	
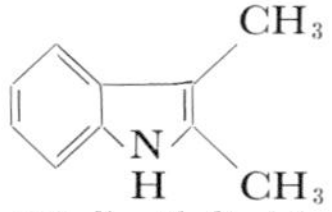 2,3-dimethylindole	12.0	130-140°	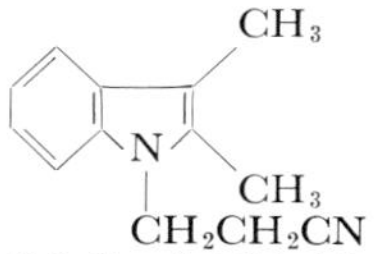 2,3-dimethyl-1-indolepropionitrile	83.5	M.P. 80°	572	912
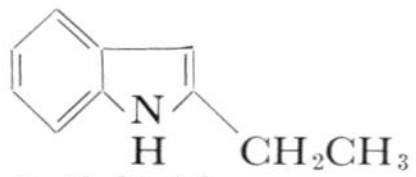 2-ethylindole	—	—	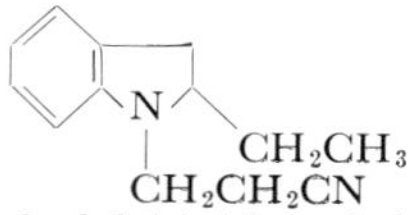 2-ethyl-1-indolepropionitrile	—	—		912

TABLE XIX—Continued

(C) Heterocyclic Amines

Reactants	Re-action Time (Hr.)	Reaction Temperature (°C.)	Products	% Yield	M.P. or B.P. (°C.)	References This Exam.	References See Also:
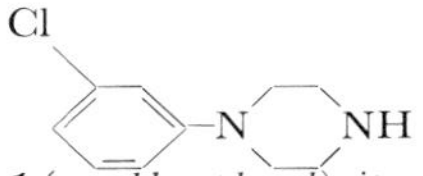 1-(m-chlorophenyl)piperazine	—	—	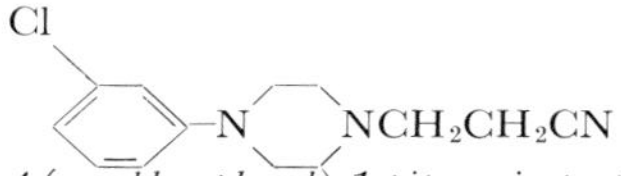 4-(m-chlorophenyl)-1-piperazinepropionitrile	48.7	B.P. 210.6-212.6°/1.3 mm.	881	
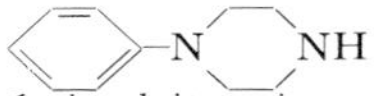 1-phenylpiperazine	1.5	55°	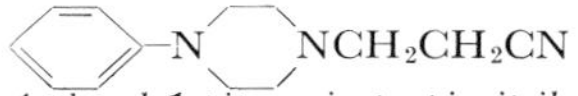 4-phenyl-1-piperazinepropionitrile	86	M.P. 71.3-72.1°	881	
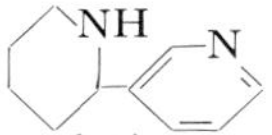 anabasine	0.5	50-60°	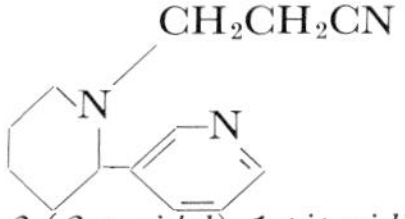 2-(3-pyridyl)-1-piperidinepropionitrile	95-98	B.P. 163-165°/0.5 mm. B.P. 172-173°/2 mm. B.P. 212-215°/10 mm.	1090	
 4,4'-bipiperidine	1.75	reflux	 [4,4'-bipiperidine]-1,1'-dipropionitrile	—	M.P. 109°	433	
 perimidine	1.50	reflux	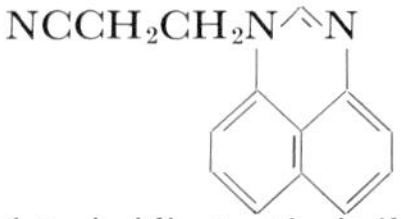 1-perimidinepropionitrile	—	M.P. 136-139°	572	912
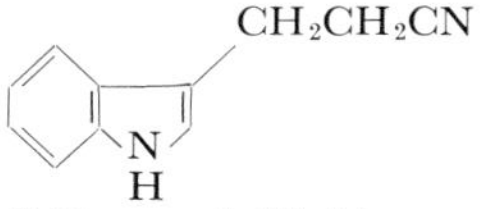 3-(2-cyanoethyl)indole	1.2	exo-thermic	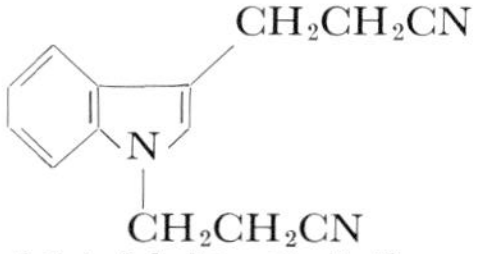 1,3-indoledipropionitrile	97	M.P. 96-97°	1424	912

TABLE XIX—Continued

(C) Heterocyclic Amines

Reactants	Reaction Time (Hr.)	Reaction Temperature (°C.)	Products	% Yield	M.P. or B.P. (°C.)	References This Exam.	References See Also:
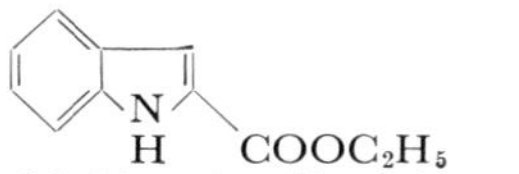 2-indoleacetic acid, ethyl ester	O.N.	50°	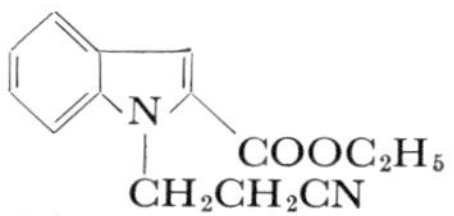 1-(2-cyanoethyl)-2-indolecarboxylic acid, ethyl ester	90	M.P. 86-87°	102	
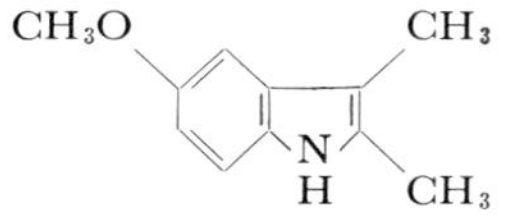 2,3-dimethyl-5-methoxyindole	1.0 / 1.0	120-130° / 140°	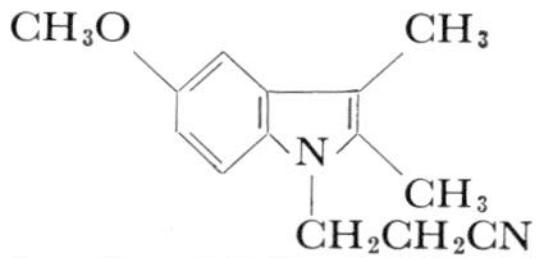 5-methoxy-2,3-dimethyl-1-indolepropionitrile	81.3	M.P. 93°	572	
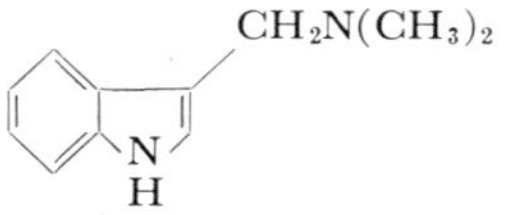 gramine	O.N.	50°	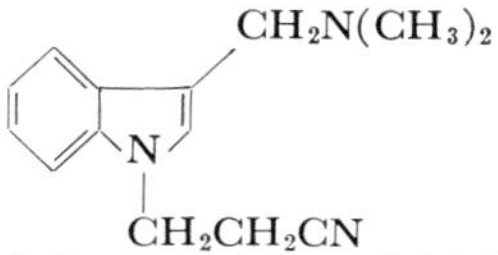 3-dimethylaminomethyl-1-indolepropionitrile	90	M.P. of picrate 140-142°	102	
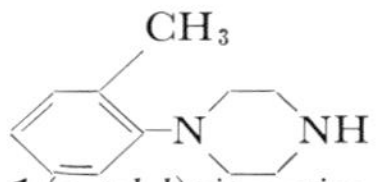 1-(o-tolyl)piperazine	—	—	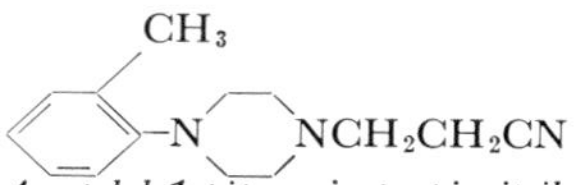 4-o-tolyl-1-piperazinepropionitrile	~100	M.P. 78.4-79.4°	881	
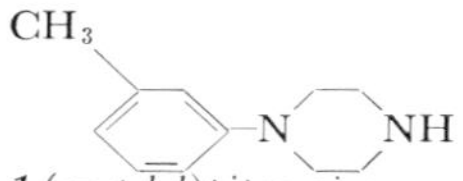 1-(m-tolyl)piperazine	—	—	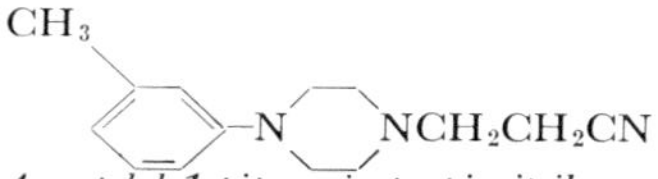 4-m-tolyl-1-piperazinepropionitrile	77.5	B.P. 197-199°/1.3 mm.	881	

TABLE XIX—Continued

(C) Heterocyclic Amines

Reactants	Reaction Time (Hr.)	Reaction Temperature (°C.)	Products	% Yield	M.P. or B.P. (°C.)	References	
						This Exam.	See Also:
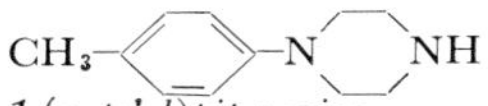 CH_3—⬡—N⬡NH *1-(p-tolyl)piperazine*	—	—	 CH_3—⬡—N⬡NCH$_2$CH$_2$CN *4-p-tolyl-1-piperazinepropionitrile*	86.0	M.P. 70.4-71.4°	881	
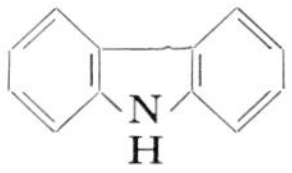 carbazole	—	0°	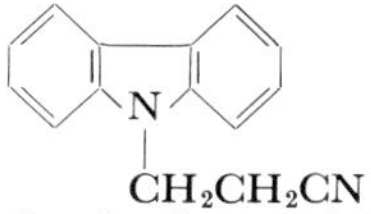 CH$_2$CH$_2$CN *9-carbazolepropionitrile*	89	M.P. 156.5°	1077	1145, 572, 912
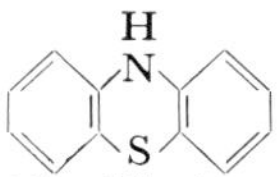 *phenothiazine*	0.5	0-5° reflux	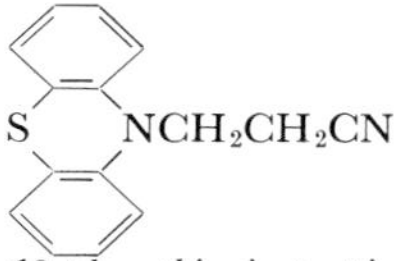 NCH$_2$CH$_2$CN *10-phenothiazinepropionitrile*	92	M.P. 156-157°	1270	264
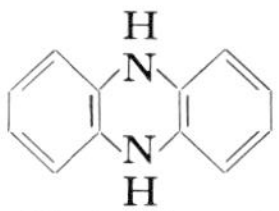 *dihydrophenazine*	—	—	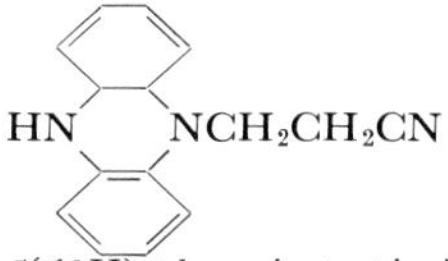 NCH$_2$CH$_2$CN *5(10H)-phenazinepropionitrile*	—	—	264	
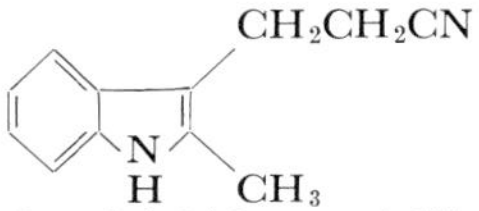 CH$_2$CH$_2$CN CH$_3$ *2-methyl-3-(2-cyanoethyl)indole*	—	—	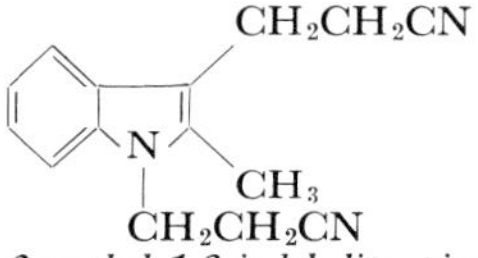 CH$_2$CH$_2$CN CH$_3$ CH$_2$CH$_2$CN *2-methyl-1,3-indoledipropionitrile*	—	—	912	

TABLE XIX—Continued

(C) Heterocyclic Amines

Reactants	Reaction Time (Hr.)	Reaction Temperature (°C.)	Products	% Yield	M.P. or B.P. (°C.)	References — This Exam.	References — See Also:
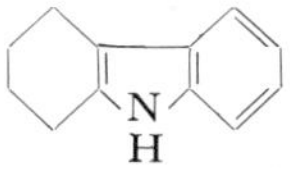 1,2,3,4-tetrahydrocarbazole	1.0	—	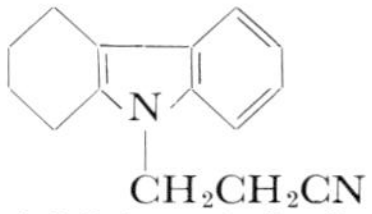 CH₂CH₂CN 1,2,3,4-tetrahydro-9-carbazolepropionitrile	53	M.P. 115-116°	1006	
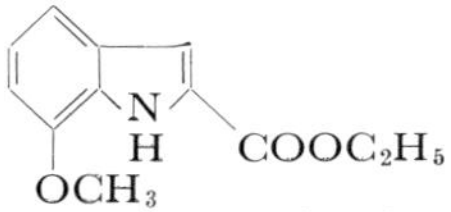 COOC₂H₅ OCH₃ 7-methoxy-2-indolecarboxylic acid, ethyl ester	O.N.	50°	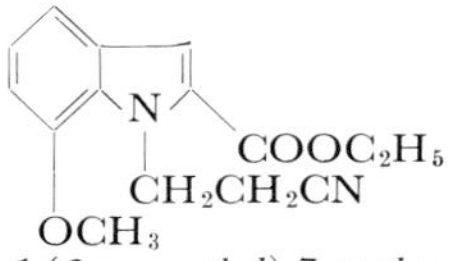 COOC₂H₅ CH₂CH₂CN OCH₃ 1-(2-cyanoethyl)-7-methoxy-2-indolecarboxylic acid, ethyl ester	72	M.P. 110-112°	102	
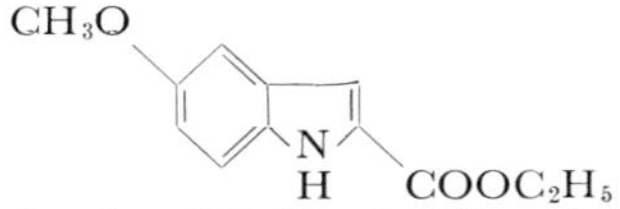 CH₃O COOC₂H₅ 5-methoxy-2-indolecarboxylic acid, ethyl ester	O.N.	50°	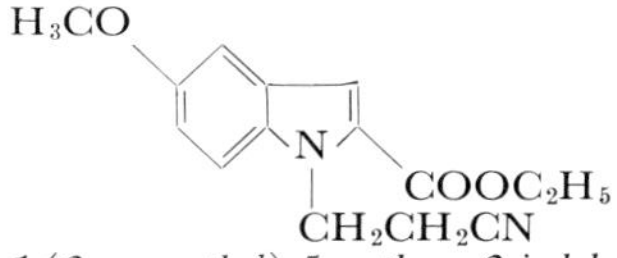 H₃CO COOC₂H₅ CH₂CH₂CN 1-(2-cyanoethyl)-5-methoxy-2-indolecarboxylic acid, ethyl ester	82.7	M.P. 112°	102	
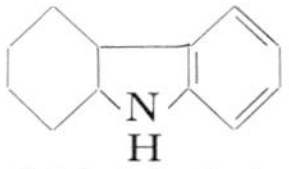 1,2,3,4,4a,9a-hexahydrocarbazole	—	120-140°	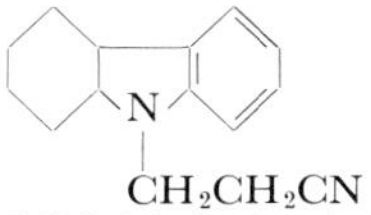 CH₂CH₂CN 1,2,3,4,4a,9a-hexahydro-9-carbazolepropionitrile	—	B.P. 180-200°/2 mm.	573	912
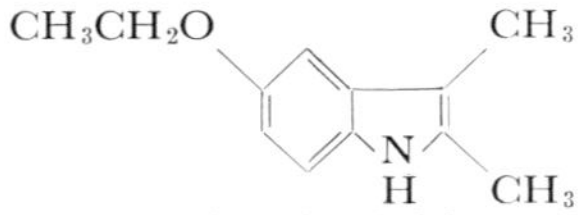 CH₃CH₂O CH₃ CH₃ 2,3-dimethyl-5-ethoxyindole	—	—	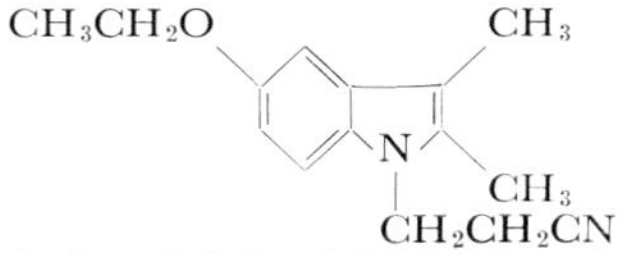 CH₃CH₂O CH₃ CH₃ CH₂CH₂CN 5-ethoxy-2,3-dimethyl-1-indolepropionitrile	—	—	912	

TABLE XIX—Continued

(C) Heterocyclic Amines

Reactants	Reaction Time (Hr.)	Reaction Temperature (°C.)	Products	% Yield	M.P. or B.P. (°C.)	References This Exam.	References See Also:
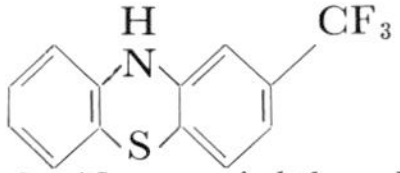 2-trifluoromethylphenothiazine	1.0	steam bath	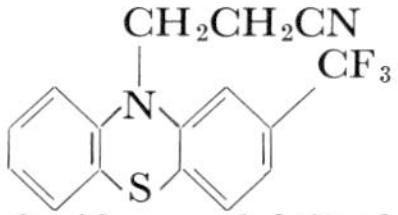 2-trifluoromethyl-10-phenothiazinepropionitrile	67	M.P. 159.5-160°	1007	
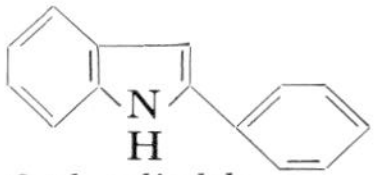 2-phenylindole	2-3.0	reflux	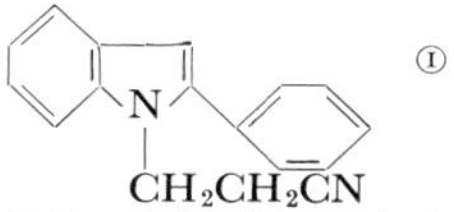 2-phenyl-1-indolepropionitrile	~100	M.P. 90°	572	1077, 124, 912
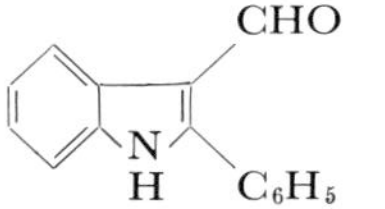 2-phenyl-3-indolecarboxaldehyde	3 days	R.T.	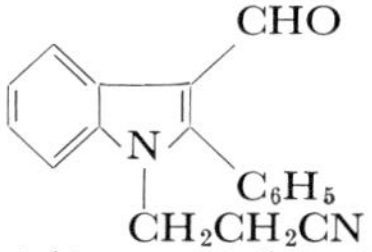 1-(2-cyanoethyl)-2-phenyl-3-indolecarboxaldehyde	90	M.P. 155-156.5°	124	
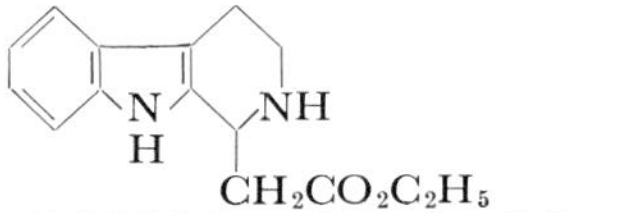 ethyl 1,2,3,4-tetrahydro-β-carboline-1-acetate	18.0	reflux	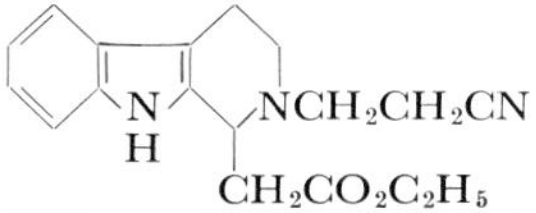 2-(2-cyanoethyl)-1,2,3,4-tetrahydro-9H-pyrid[3,4-b]-indole-1-acetic acid, ethyl ester	39	M.P. 179.5-180.5°	452	
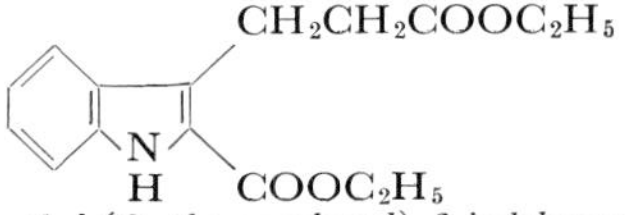 ethyl (2-ethoxycarbonyl)-3-indolepropionate	10.0	R.T.	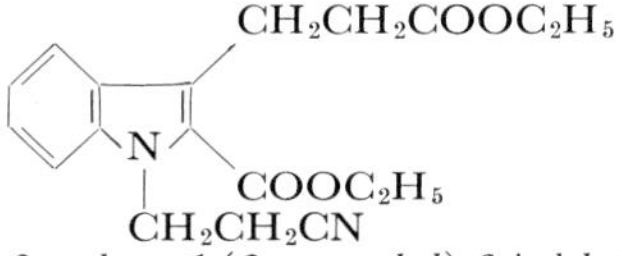 2-carboxy-1-(2-cyanoethyl)-3-indolepropionic acid, diethyl ester	80	M.P. 70-71°	1326	

TABLE XIX—Continued

(C) Heterocyclic Amines

Reactants	Reaction Time (Hr.)	Reaction Temperature (°C.)	Products	% Yield	M.P. or B.P. (°C.)	References This Exam.	References See Also:
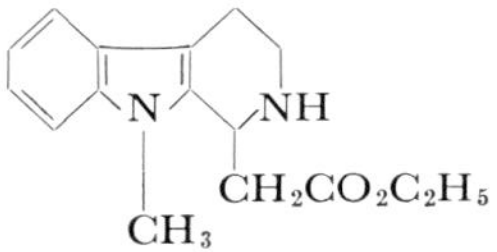 ethyl 1,2,3,4-tetrahydro-9-methyl-β-carboline-1-acetate	20.0	115° (sealed tube)	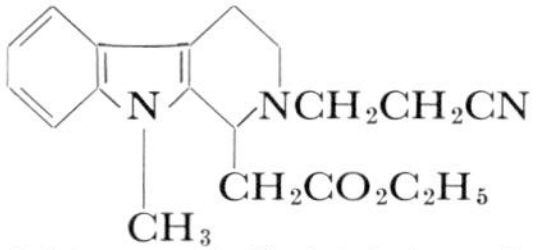 2-(2-cyanoethyl)-1,2,3,4-tetrahydro-9-methyl-9H-pyrid-[3,4-b]indole-1-acetic acid, ethyl ester	8	M.P. 116-117°	452	
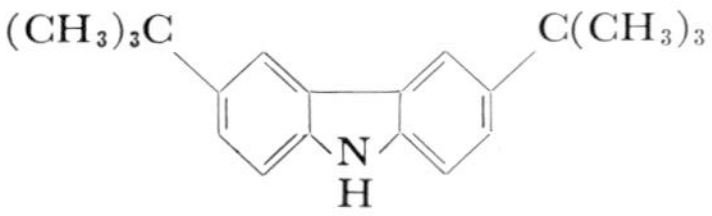 3,6-di-t-butylcarbazole	1.0	steam bath	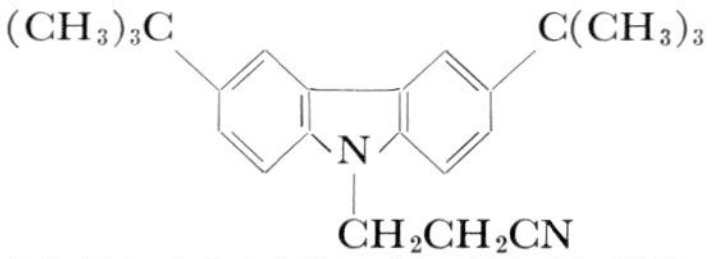 3,6-di-tert-butyl-9-carbazolepropionitrile	59	M.P. 190-190.5°	1006	

(D) Aromatic Amines

Reactants	Reaction Time (Hr.)	Reaction Temperature (°C.)	Products	% Yield	M.P. or B.P. (°C.)	References This Exam.	References See Also:
 p-bromoaniline	1.0	reflux	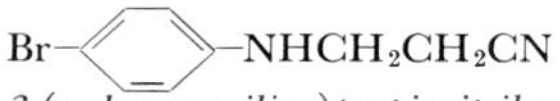 3-(p-bromoanilino)propionitrile	96	M.P. 96.5-97.5°	1279	
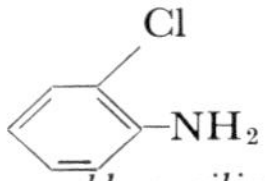 o-chloroaniline	3.0	reflux	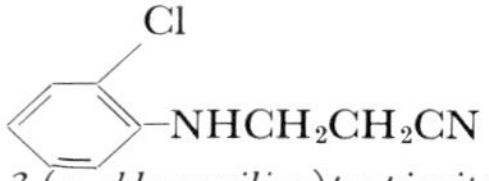 3-(o-chloroanilino)propionitrile	62	B.P. 139-141°/0.3 mm.	1279	1282
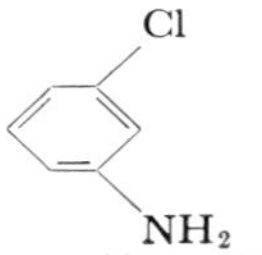 m-chloroaniline	2.0	reflux	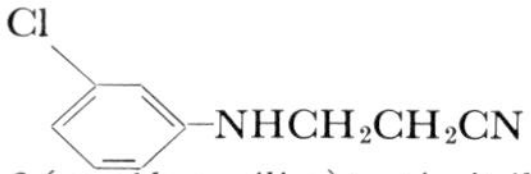 3-(m-chloroanilino)propionitrile	65	B.P. 146-149°/0.3 mm. M.P. 48-49°	1279	

TABLE XIX—Continued

(D) Aromatic Amines

Reactants	Reaction Time (Hr.)	Reaction Temperature (°C.)	Products	% Yield	M.P. or B.P. (°C.)	References This Exam.	References See Also:
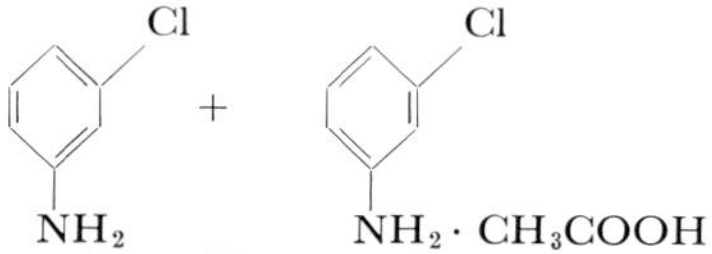 Cl...NH₂ + Cl...NH₂ · CH₃COOH m-chloroaniline + m-chloroaniline acetate	14.0	130-140°	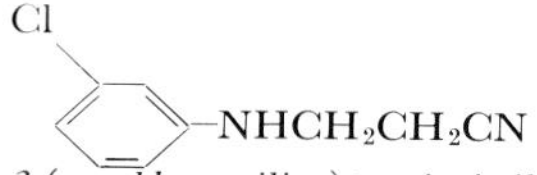 Cl...NHCH₂CH₂CN 3-(m-chloroanilino)propionitrile	81	B.P. 187-189°/9 mm. M.P. 48°	101	
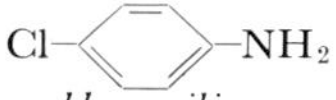 Cl—NH₂ p-chloroaniline	1.25	reflux	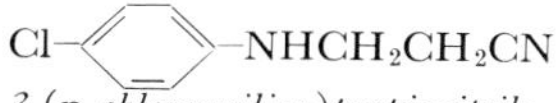 Cl—NHCH₂CH₂CN 3-(p-chloroanilino)propionitrile	78	B.P. 168-169°/1.0 mm. M.P. 73.5-75°	1279	101, 1206
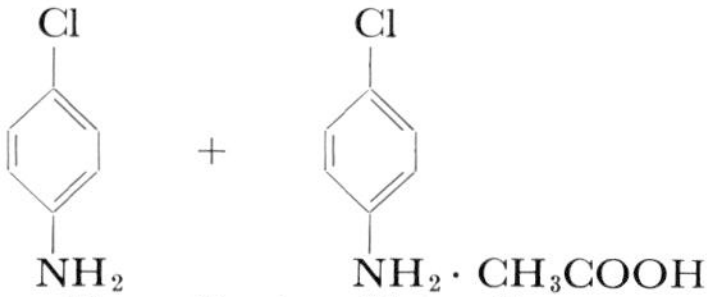 Cl—NH₂ · CH₃COOH + Cl—NH₂ p-chloroaniline + p-chloroaniline acetate	14.0	130-140°	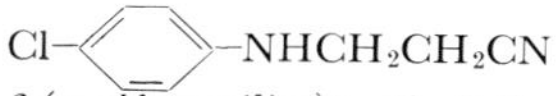 Cl—NHCH₂CH₂CN 3 (p-chloroanilino)propionitrile	72	M.P. 72-73° B.P. 182-185°/4 mm.	101	137, 136, 135
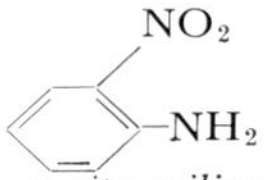 NO₂...NH₂ o-nitroaniline	12.0	reflux	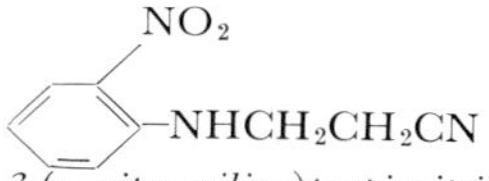 NHCH₂CH₂CN 3-(o-nitroanilino)propionitrile	—	—	1279	
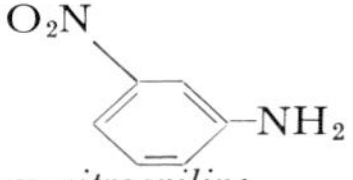 O₂N...NH₂ m-nitroaniline	12.0	reflux	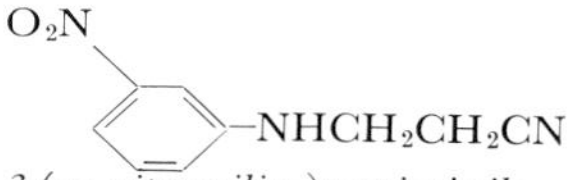 O₂N...NHCH₂CH₂CN 3-(m-nitroanilino)propionitrile	81	M.P. 95-96°	1279	137
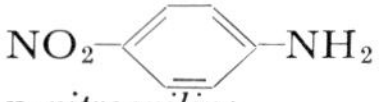 NO₂—NH₂ p-nitroaniline	12.0	reflux	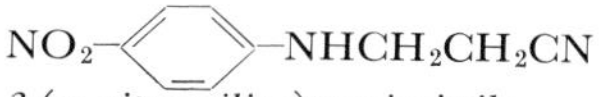 NO₂—NHCH₂CH₂CN 3-(p-nitroanilino)propionitrile	6	M.P. 128-130°	136	1279

TABLE XIX—Continued

(D) Aromatic Amines

Reactants	Reaction Time (Hr.)	Reaction Temperature (°C.)	Products	% Yield	M.P. or B.P. (°C.)	References This Exam.	References See Also:
 NO_2—NH$_2$ p-nitroaniline	18.0	40° 25°	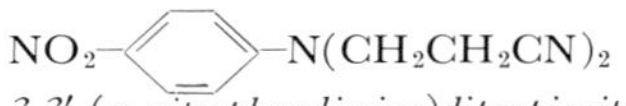 NO_2—N(CH$_2$CH$_2$CN)$_2$ 3,3'-(p-nitrophenylimino)dipropionitrile	69.7	M.P. 163-164°	1219	
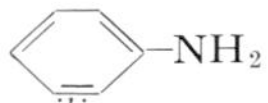 —NH$_2$ aniline + NH$_2$ · CH$_3$COOH aniline + aniline acetate	1.0	reflux	 3-NHCH$_2$CH$_2$CN 3-anilinopropionitrile	73	B.P. 114-116°/0.3 mm. M.P. 52-53°	1279	1206, 1409
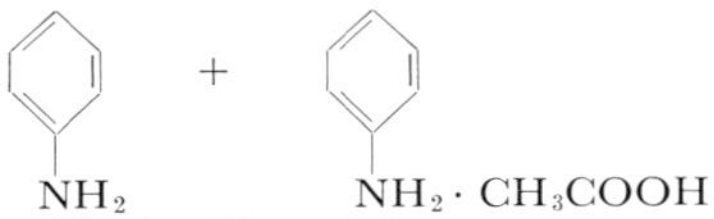	14.0	120-140°	 —NHCH$_2$CH$_2$CN 3-anilinopropionitrile	98	B.P. 160°/6 mm. M.P. 40°	101	1008, 136, 135, 270, 885, 963, 1418
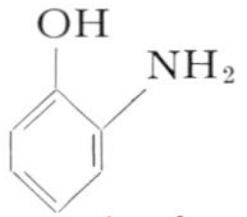 OH NH$_2$ o-aminophenol	24.0	reflux	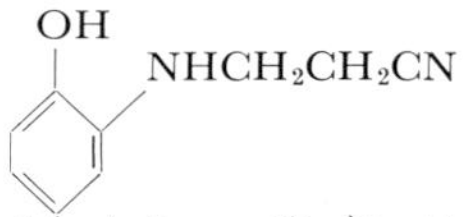 OH NHCH$_2$CH$_2$CN 3-(o-hydroxyanilino)propionitrile	78	M.P. 110-111°	1279	
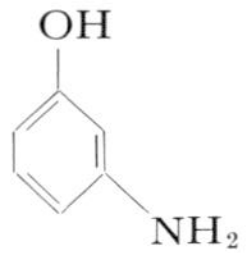 OH NH$_2$ m-aminophenol	24.0	reflux	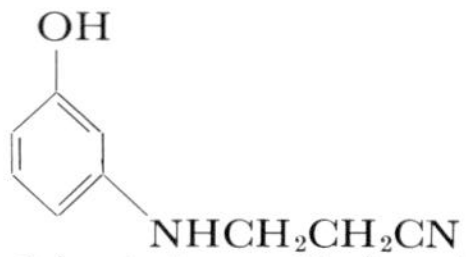 NHCH$_2$CH$_2$CN 3-(m-hydroxyanilino)propionitrile	69	—	1279	
 HO—NH$_2$ p-aminophenol	24.0	reflux	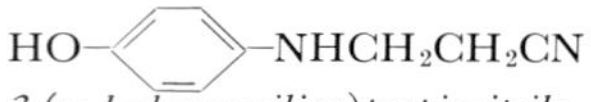 HO—NHCH$_2$CH$_2$CN 3-(p-hydroxyanilino)propionitrile	22	M.P. 86-88°	1279	

TABLE XIX—Continued

(D) Aromatic Amines

Reactants	Reaction Time (Hr.)	Reaction Temperature (°C.)	Products	% Yield	M.P. or B.P. (°C.)	References — This Exam.	References — See Also:
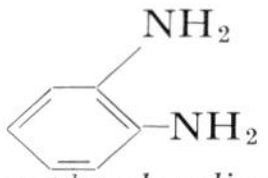 o-phenylenediamine	14.0	reflux	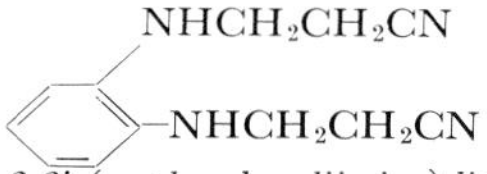 3,3'-(o-phenylenediimino)dipropionitrile	63	M.P. 115-118°	1279	1205, 136
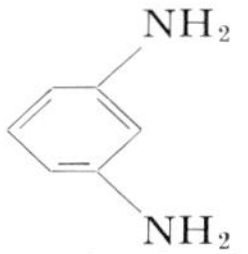 m-phenylenediamine	0.67	reflux	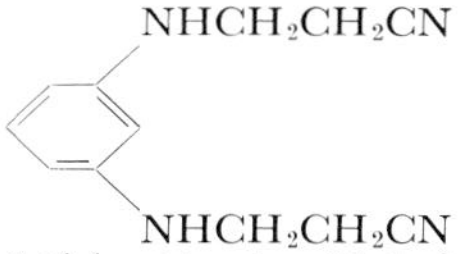 3,3'-(m-phenylenediimino)dipropionitrile	95	—	1279	
 p-phenylenediamine	—	—	 3,3'-(p-phenylenediimino)dipropionitrile	22	M.P. 140°	699	1205
 p-phenylenediamine	14.0	120° (pressure)	 3,3',3'',3'''-(p-phenylenedinitrilo)tetrapropionitrile	83	M.P. 141-142°	136	699
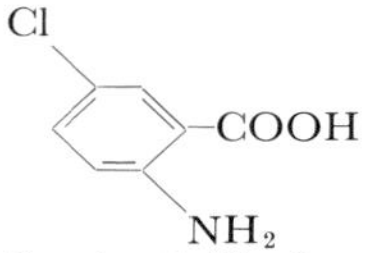 2-amino-5-chlorobenzoic acid	—	—	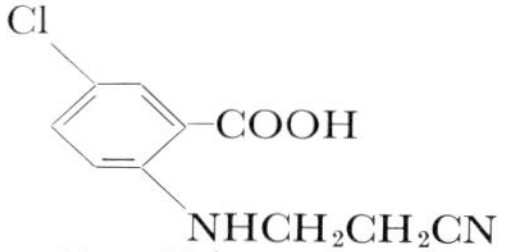 5-chloro-N-(2-cyanoethyl)anthranilic acid	89.7	—	1207	
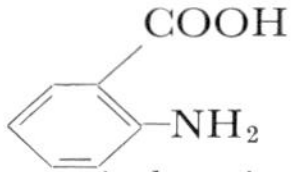 o-aminobenzoic acid	—	—	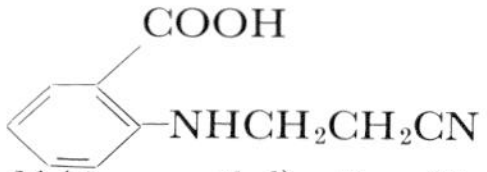 N-(2-cyanoethyl)anthranilic acid	89.7	M.P. 169.5°	1207	1384

TABLE XIX—Continued

(D) Aromatic Amines

Reactants	Reaction Time (Hr.)	Reaction Temperature (°C.)	Products	% Yield	M.P. or B.P. (°C.)	References This Exam.	References See Also:
NH₂—⬡—CO₂H *p-aminobenzoic acid*	7.0	150° (pressure)	NCCH₂CH₂NH—⬡—COOH *p-(2-cyanoethylamino)benzoic acid*	35	M.P. 221.5-222.5°	136	
o-toluidine (CH₃, NH₂)	12.0	reflux	—NHCH₂CH₂CN *3-o-toluidinopropionitrile*	65	B.P. 125-126°/0.2 mm.	136	
			—N(CH₂CH₂CN)₂ *3,3'-(o-tolylimino)dipropionitrile*	35	B.P. 173°/0.2 mm.	136	1279
m-toluidine	0.33	reflux	—NHCH₂CH₂CN *3-m-toluidinopropionitrile*	71	B.P. 143-146°/0.5 mm. M.P. 49.5-50.5°	1279	
m-toluidine	20.0	reflux	—N(CH₂CH₂CN)₂ *3,3'-(m-tolylimino)dipropionitrile*	75	M.P. 87-88°	136	135
p-toluidine	12.0	reflux	—NHCH₂CH₂CN *3 p-toluidinopropionitrile*	56	B.P. 148-155°/1.0 mm. M.P. 103.5-105°	1279	135, 136, 1206
			—N(CH₂CH₂CN)₂ *3,3'-(p-tolylimino)dipropionitrile*	36	M.P. 61-62°		

TABLE XIX—Continued

(D) Aromatic Amines

Reactants	Reaction Time (Hr.)	Reaction Temperature (°C.)	Products	% Yield	M.P. or B.P. (°C.)	References This Exam.	References See Also:
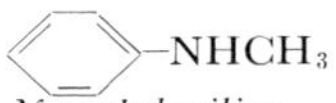 —NHCH$_3$ *N-methylaniline*	22.0	reflux	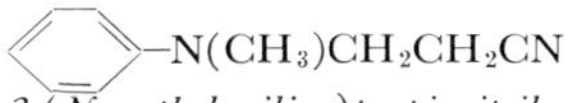 —N(CH$_3$)CH$_2$CH$_2$CN *3-(N-methylanilino)propionitrile*	84	B.P. 170-171°/19 mm.	1279	1145, 573, 25
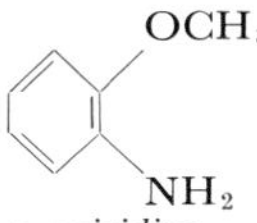 OCH$_3$ NH$_2$ *o-anisidine*	18.0	reflux	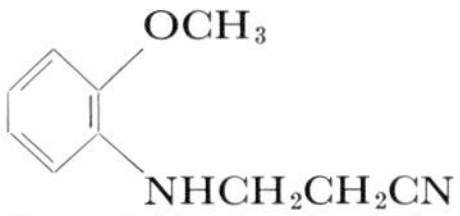 NHCH$_2$CH$_2$CN OCH$_3$ *3-o-anisidinopropionitrile*	33	B.P. 140-141°/1.0 mm.	1279	
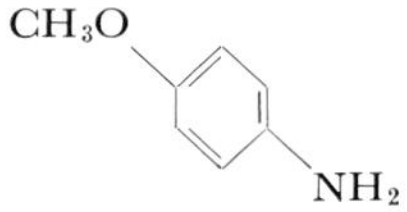 CH$_3$O—⟨ ⟩—NH$_2$ *p-anisidine*	15.0	reflux	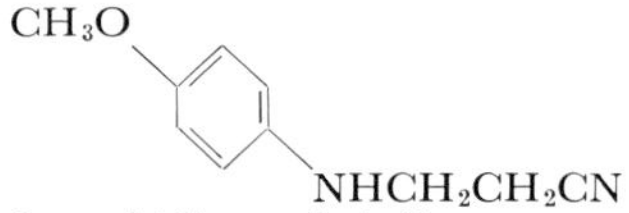 CH$_3$O—NHCH$_2$CH$_2$CN *3-p-anisidinopropionitrile*	84	B.P. 154-155°/0.8 mm. M.P. 59-61°	1279	135, 136, 359, 1206, 1244
			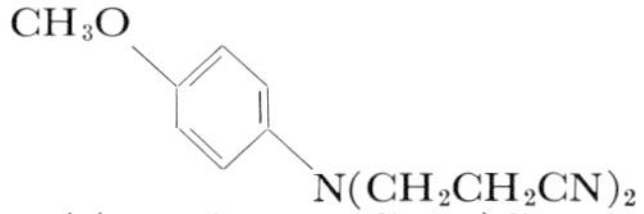 CH$_3$O—N(CH$_2$CH$_2$CN)$_2$ *3,3'-(p-methoxyphenylimino)dipropionitrile*	14	B.P. 210-211°/0.7 mm. M.P. 100-101°		
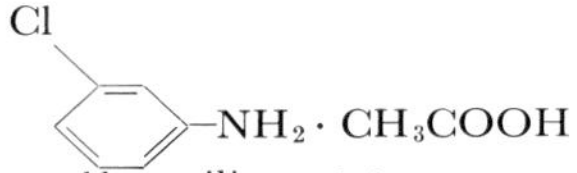 Cl—⟨ ⟩—NH$_2$·CH$_3$COOH *m-chloroaniline acetate*	14.0	120-140°	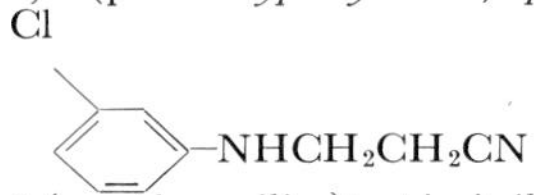 Cl—NHCH$_2$CH$_2$CN *3-(m-chloroanilino)propionitrile*	81 ⓕ	B.P. 187-189°/9 mm. M.P. 48°	101	
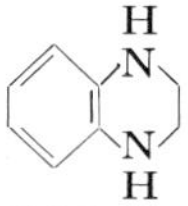 H N N H *1,2,3,4-tetrahydroquinoxaline*	7.0	reflux	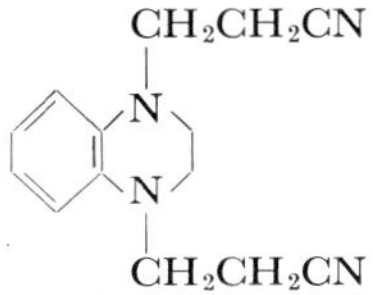 CH$_2$CH$_2$CN N N CH$_2$CH$_2$CN *2,3-dihydro-1,4-quinoxalinedipropionitrile*	80	M.P. 88.5-89°	26	

TABLE XIX—Continued

(D) Aromatic Amines

Reactants	Re-action Time (Hr.)	Reaction Tem-perature (°C.)	Products	% Yield	M.P. or B.P. (°C.)	References: This Exam.	References: See Also:
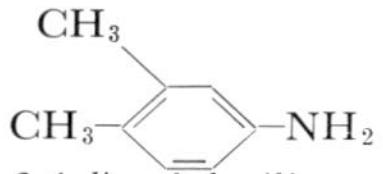 CH_3 CH_3 NH_2 *3,4-dimethylaniline*	12.0	reflux	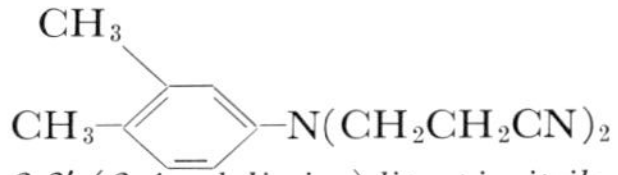 CH_3 CH_3 $N(CH_2CH_2CN)_2$ *3,3′-(3,4-xylylimino)dipropionitrile*	11	M.P. 84°	136	
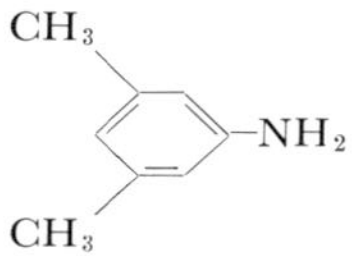 CH_3 NH_2 CH_3 *3,5-dimethylaniline*	4.0	reflux	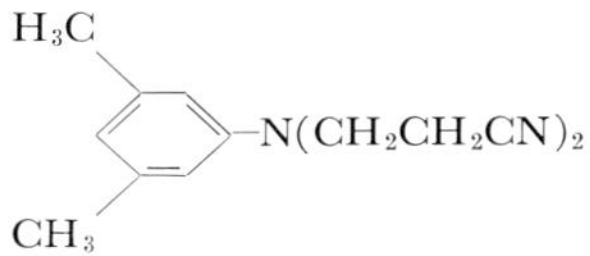 H_3C $N(CH_2CH_2CN)_2$ CH_3 *3,3′-(3,5-xylylimino)dipropionitrile*	79	M.P. 130°	1292	
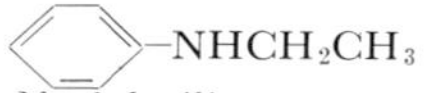 $NHCH_2CH_3$ *N-ethylaniline*	100.0	100°	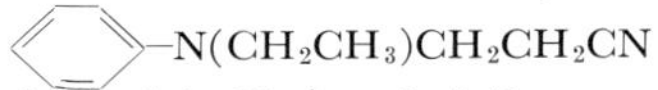 $N(CH_2CH_3)CH_2CH_2CN$ *3-(N-ethylanilino)propionitrile*	70	—	664	1078, 1077, 665, 520, 566, 568, 519, 1279
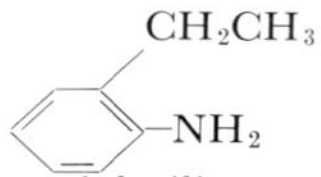 CH_2CH_3 NH_2 o-*ethylaniline*	12.0	reflux	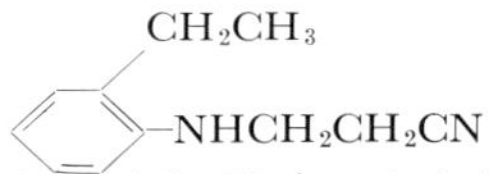 CH_2CH_3 $NHCH_2CH_2CN$ *3-(*o*-ethylanilino)propionitrile*	53	B.P. 125-132°/0.3 mm.	1279	
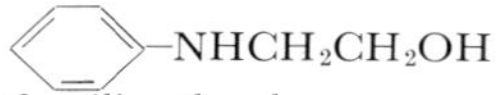 $NHCH_2CH_2OH$ *2-anilinoethanol*	150.0	reflux	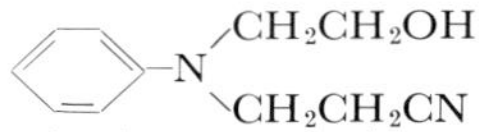 N CH_2CH_2OH CH_2CH_2CN *3-[N-(2-hydroxyethyl)anilino]propionitrile*	91	B.P. 305-307°/8 mm.	327	
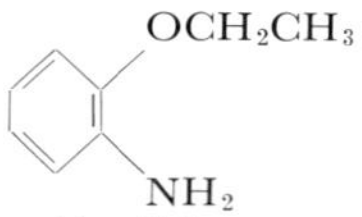 OCH_2CH_3 NH_2 o-*phenetidine*	22.0	reflux	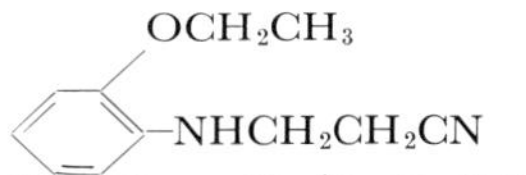 OCH_2CH_3 $NHCH_2CH_2CN$ *3-(*o*-ethoxyanilino)propionitrile*	45	B.P. 141-143°/0.7 mm.	1279	912

TABLE XIX—Continued

(D) Aromatic Amines

Reactants	Reaction Time (Hr.)	Reaction Temperature (°C.)	Products	% Yield	M.P. or B.P. (°C.)	References — This Exam.	References — See Also:
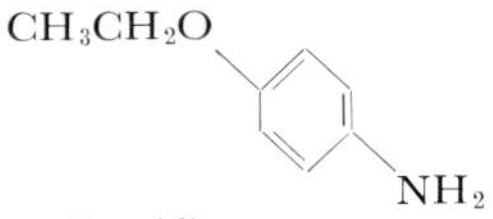 CH_3CH_2O—[ring]—NH_2 *p-phenetidine*	22.0	reflux	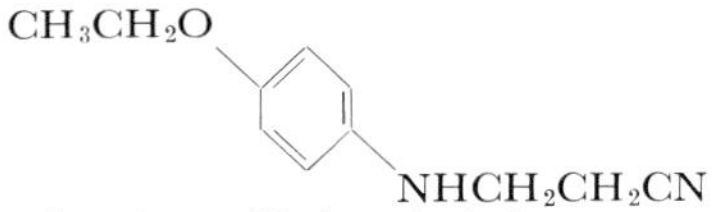 CH_3CH_2O—[ring]—$NHCH_2CH_2CN$ *3-(p-ethoxyanilino)propionitrile*	90	B.P. 165-166°/0.7 mm. M.P. 73-75°	1279	912, 1206
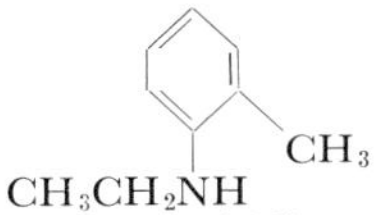 CH_3CH_2NH—[ring-CH_3] *N-ethyl-o-toluidine*	—	—	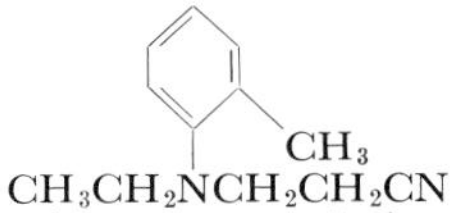 $CH_3CH_2NCH_2CH_2CN$ [ring-CH_3] *3-(N-ethyl-o-toluidino)propionitrile*	—	—	912	
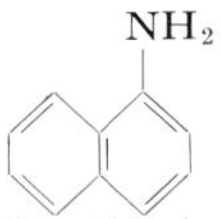 [1-naphthyl]—NH_2 *1-naphthylamine*	5.5	reflux	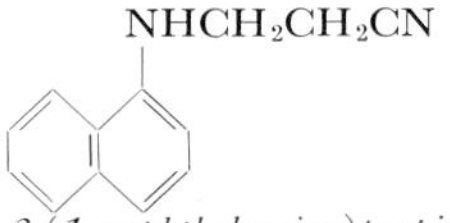 [1-naphthyl]—$NHCH_2CH_2CN$ *3-(1-naphthylamino)propionitrile*	89	B.P. 180-210°/0.5 mm. M.P. 69-70°	1279	136
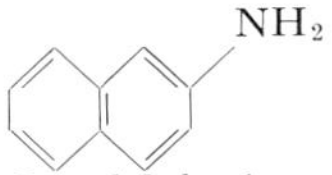 [2-naphthyl]—NH_2 *2-naphthylamine*	4.0	reflux	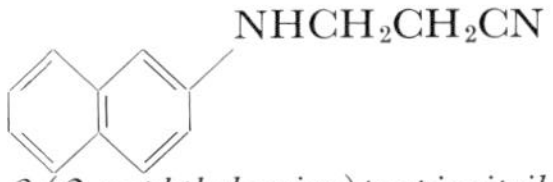 [2-naphthyl]—$NHCH_2CH_2CN$ *3-(2-naphthylamino)propionitrile*	—	M.P. 99-100°	137	
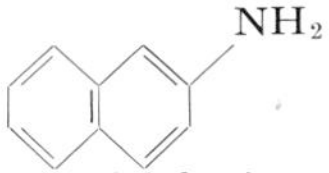 [2-naphthyl]—NH_2 *2-naphthylamine*	12.0	reflux	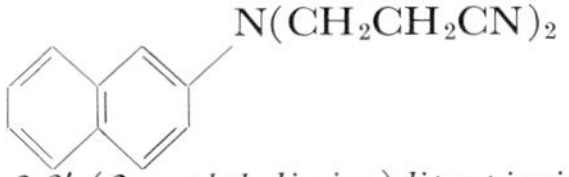 [2-naphthyl]—$N(CH_2CH_2CN)_2$ *3,3'-(2-naphthylimino)dipropionitrile*	25-35	M.P. 127.5-128.5°	136	
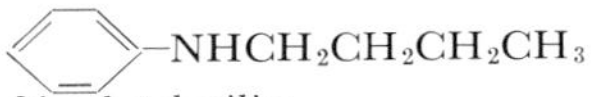 [ring]—$NHCH_2CH_2CH_2CH_3$ *N-n-butylaniline*	5.0	reflux	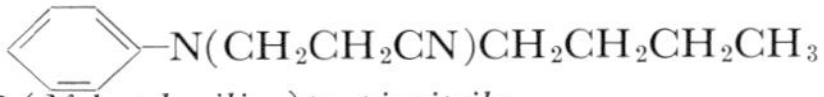 [ring]—$N(CH_2CH_2CN)CH_2CH_2CH_2CH_3$ *3-(N-butylanilino)propionitrile*	68	B.P. 145-148°/0.7 mm.	1279	912

TABLE XIX—Continued

(D) Aromatic Amines

Reactants	Reaction Temperature (°C.)	Reaction Time (Hr.)	Products	% Yield	M.P. or B.P. (°C.)	References	
						This Exam.	See Also:
 C6H5—NHCH2CH2CH2CH2CH3 *N-n-amylaniline*	reflux	3.0	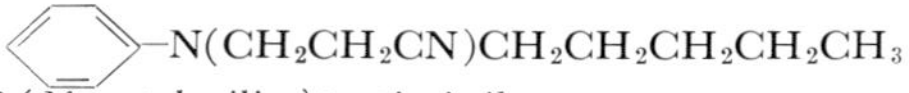 C6H5—N(CH2CH2CN)CH2CH2CH2CH2CH3 *3-(N-pentylanilino)propionitrile*	66	B.P. 172-180°/0.8 mm.	1279	
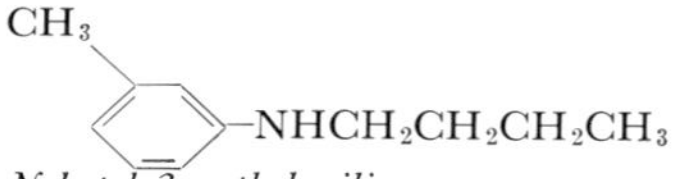 CH3—C6H4—NHCH2CH2CH2CH3 *N-butyl-3-methylaniline*	—	—	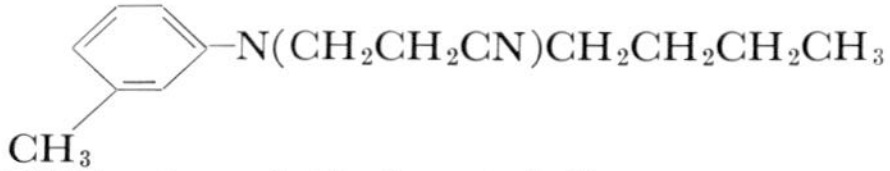 CH3—C6H4—N(CH2CH2CN)CH2CH2CH2CH3 *3-(N-butyl-m-toluidino)propionitrile*	—	—	912	
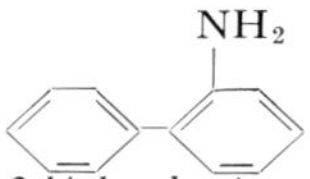 *2-biphenylamine*	reflux	12.0	NHCH2CH2CN *3-(2-biphenylamino)propionitrile*	65	M.P. 86°	136	
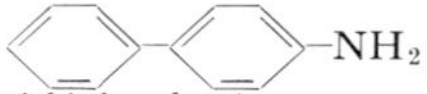 *4-biphenylamine*	reflux	12.0	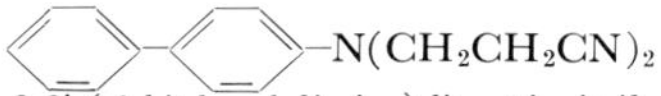 —N(CH2CH2CN)2 *3,3'-(4-biphenylimino)dipropionitrile*	80	M.P. 165.5-166°	136	1279
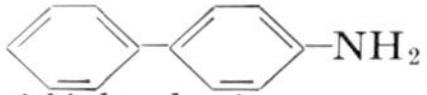 *4-biphenylamine*	150° (sealed tube)	4.0	—NHCH2CH2CN *3-(4-biphenylamino)propionitrile*	13	M.P. 174-177°	90	
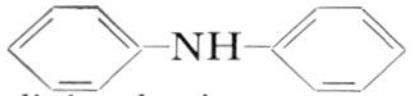 *diphenylamine*	150°	8.0	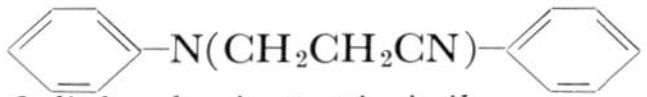 —N(CH2CH2CN)—C6H5 *3-diphenylaminopropionitrile*	22.8	B.P. 133°/0.05 mm. M.P. 41°	270	
NH2—C6H4—C6H4—NH2 *benzidine*	reflux	8.0	 (NCCH2CH2NH—C6H4—)2 *3,3'-(4,4'-biphenylenediimino)dipropionitrile*	~100	M.P. 245-245.5°	136	1279

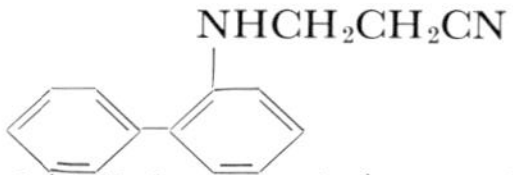

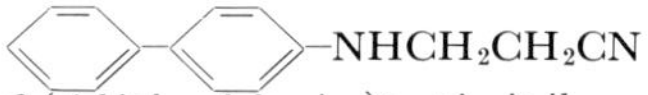

TABLE XIX—Continued

(D) Aromatic Amines

Reactants	Reaction Time (Hr.)	Reaction Temperature (°C.)	Products	% Yield	M.P. or B.P. (°C.)	References This Exam.	See Also:
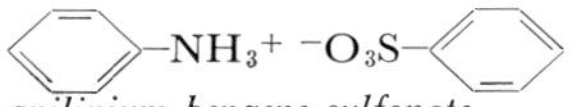 C_6H_5-NH_3^+ ^-O_3S-C_6H_5 *anilinium benzene sulfonate*	1.0	180°	$(C_2H_5)_2NCH_2CH_2CN$ *3-diethylaminopropionitrile*	—	B.P. 35-40°/0.07 mm.	—	
		120-140°	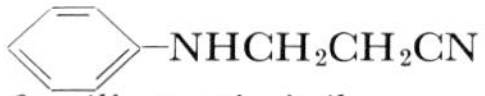 C_6H_5-$NHCH_2CH_2CN$ *3-anilinopropionitrile*	2.5	B.P. 120-125°/0.07 mm.	90	
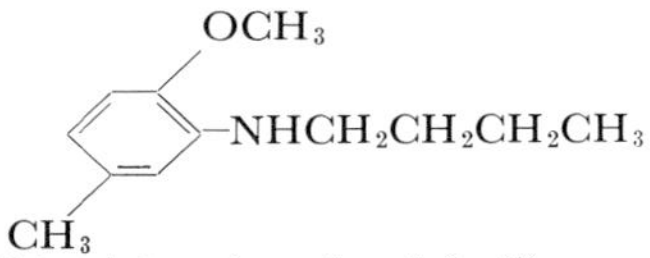 (OCH₃, CH₃ benzene)-$NHCH_2CH_2CH_3$ *N-butyl-2-methoxy-5-methylaniline*	—		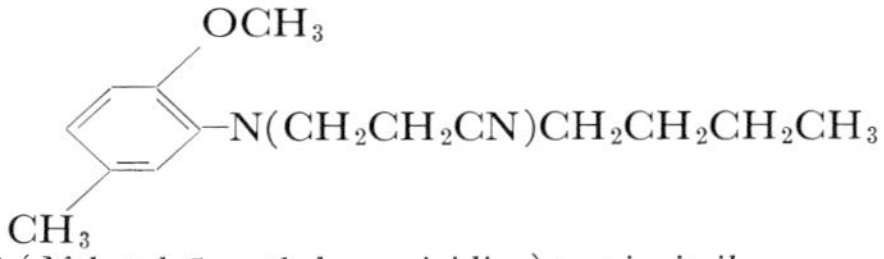 $N(CH_2CH_2CN)CH_2CH_2CH_2CH_3$ (OCH₃, CH₃ ring) *3-(N-butyl-5-methyl-o-anisidino)propionitrile*	—	B.P. 160-165°/2 mm.	573	912
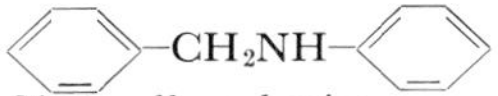 $C_6H_5CH_2NH$-C_6H_5 *N-phenylbenzylamine*	—	—	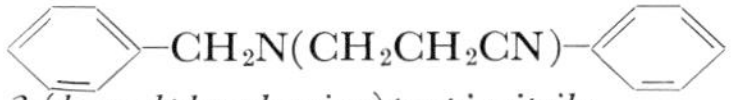 $C_6H_5CH_2N(CH_2CH_2CN)$-C_6H_5 *3-(benzylphenylamino)propionitrile*	—	—	912	
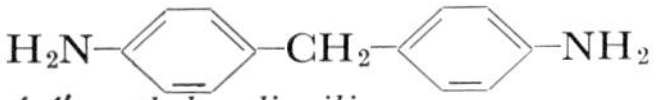 H_2N-C_6H_4-CH_2-C_6H_4-NH_2 *4,4'-methylenedianiline*	3.0	reflux	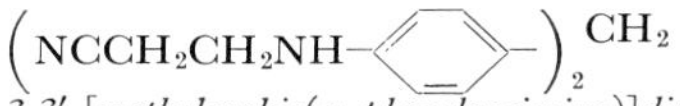 $\left(NCCH_2CH_2NH\text{-}C_6H_4\right)_2CH_2$ *3,3'-[methylenebis(p-phenyleneimino)]dipropionitrile*	96	M.P. 115-117°	1279	
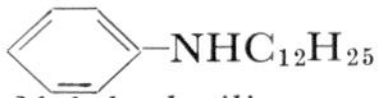 C_6H_5-$NHC_{12}H_{25}$ *N-dodecylaniline*	3.0	reflux	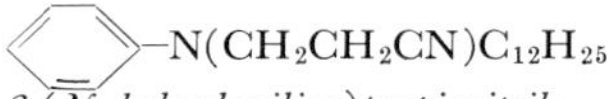 C_6H_5-$N(CH_2CH_2CN)C_{12}H_{25}$ *3-(N-dodecylanilino)propionitrile*	64	B.P. 197-202°/0.3 mm.	1279	

(E) Amino Acids and Derivatives

Reactants	Reaction Time (Hr.)	Reaction Temperature (°C.)	Products	% Yield	M.P. or B.P. (°C.)	References This Exam.	See Also:
$HO_2CCH_2NH_2$ *glycine*	18.0 / 2.0	25° / 50°	$HO_2CCH_2N(CH_2CH_2CN)_2$ *N,N-bis(2-cyanoethyl)glycine*	90	M.P. 77.8-78.8°	729 / 726	
$HO_2CCH_2NH_2$ *glycine*	O.N.	R.T.	$HO_2CCH_2NHCH_2CH_2CN$ *N-(2-cyanoethyl)glycine*	87	M.P. 190-191° (dec.)	728 / 726	

TABLE XIX—Continued

(E) Amino Acids and Derivatives

Reactants	Reaction Time (Hr.)	Reaction Temperature (°C.)	Products	% Yield	M.P. or B.P. (°C.)	References This Exam.	References See Also:
CH₃OCOCH₂NH₂ glycine, methyl ester	72.0 / 5.0	25° reflux	CH₃OCOCH₂NHCH₂CN N-(2-cyanoethyl)glycine, methyl ester	55.2	B.P. 142-143°/12 mm.	1062	
CH₃CH(NH₂)COOH dl-alanine	18.0 / 4.0	25° 50°	HOOCCH(CH₃)N(CH₂CH₂CN)₂ N,N-bis(2-cyanoethyl)alanine	97	M.P. 75.5-76.8°	729 726	728
CH₃CH(NH₂)COOH dl-alanine	O.N.	R.T.	HOOCCH(CH₃)NHCH₂CN N-(2-cyanoethyl)-dl-alanine	82.5	M.P. 249-250° (dec.)	728 726	
HOCH₂CH(NH₂)COOH dl-serine	—	50°	NCCH₂CH₂OCH₂CH(NHCH₂CH₂CN)COOH 3-(2-cyanoethoxy)-N-(2-cyanoethyl)-dl-alanine	51	M.P. 210-215° (dec.)	1453	
			CH₃OCOCH₂NHCH₂CH₂CN N-(2-cyanoethyl)glycine, methyl ester	17.8	—	1062	
CH₃OCOCH₂NH₂ · HCl glycine, methyl ester, hydrochloride	10.0	75°	CH₃OCOCH₂N(CH₂CH₂CN)₂ N,N-bis(2-cyanoethyl)glycine, methyl ester	21.9	B.P. 218-219°/12 mm. M.P. 59.5-60°	1062	729
KO₂CCH₂CH(NH₂)CO₂K dipotassium dl-aspartate	18.0 / 2.0	25° 50°	KO₂CCH₂CH(NHCH₂CH₂CN)CO₂K N-(2-cyanoethyl)-dl-aspartic acid, dipotassium salt	~100	—	728 726	
HO₂CCH(NH₂)CH₂CO₂H dl-aspartic acid	18.0 / 4.0	25° reflux	HO₂CCH[N(CH₂CH₂CN)₂]CH₂CO₂H N,N-bis(2-cyanoethyl)-dl-aspartic acid	88	M.P. 136-137°	729 726	
HO₂CCH₂NHCOCH₂NH₂ glycylglycine	18.0	R.T.	HO₂CCH₂NHCOCH₂NHCH₂CH₂CN N-[N-(2-cyanoethyl)glycyl]glycine	78.5	M.P. 144°	1063	
C₂H₅OCOCH₂NH₂ glycine, ethyl ester	72.0 / 5.0	25° reflux	C₂H₅OCOCH₂NHCH₂CH₂CN N-(2-cyanoethyl)glycine, ethyl ester	70.5	B.P. 148-149/12 mm.	1062	254
			C₂H₅OCOCH₂NHCH₂CH₂CN N-(2-cyanoethyl)glycine, ethyl ester	23.2	—	1062	
C₂H₅OCOCH₂NH₂ glycine, ethyl ester	10.0	75°	C₂H₅OCOCH₂N(CH₂CH₂CN)₂ N,N-bis(2-cyanoethyl)glycine, ethyl ester	29.3	B.P. 221-222°/12 mm.	1062	

TABLE XIX—Continued

(E) Amino Acids and Derivatives

Reactants	Reaction Temperature (°C.)	Reaction Time (Hr.)	Products	% Yield	M.P. or B.P. (°C.)	References This Exam.	References See Also:
$KO_2CCH_2CH_2CH(NH_2)CO_2K$ dipotassium l-glutamate	25°	24.0	$KO_2CCH_2CH_2CH(NHCH_2CH_2CN)COOK$ N-(2-cyanoethyl)glutamic acid, dipotassium salt	~100	—	728 726	
(ring structure CO_2H, NH) l-proline	25°	48.0	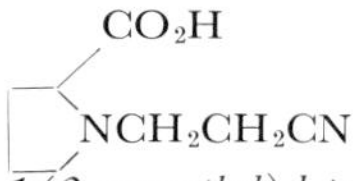 (ring structure CO_2H, NCH_2CH_2CN) 1-(2-cyanoethyl)-l-proline	17	M.P. 137-140°	728 726	
$HO_2CCH_2CH_2CH(NH_2)CO_2H$ glutamic acid	25°	24.0	$HO_2CCH_2CH_2CH(NHCH_2CH_2CN)CO_2H$® N-(2-cyanoethyl)glutamic acid	>97	—	727	
$HO_2CCH(NH_2)CH_2CH_2CO_2H$ l-glutamic acid	25° 60°	18.0 20.0	$HO_2CCH[N(CH_2CH_2CN)_2]CH_2CH_2CO_2H$ N,N-bis(2-cyanoethyl)-l-glutamic acid	88.4	M.P. 71.5-72.8°	729	728
$HO_2CCH(NH_2)CH(CH_3)_2$ dl-valine	25° reflux	18 20	$HO_2CCH[N(CH_2CH_2CN)_2]CH(CH_3)_2$ N,N-bis(2-cyanoethyl)-dl-valine	84	M.P. 54-55°	729	
$HO_2CCH(NH_2)CH(CH_3)_2$ dl-valine	R.T.	O.N.	$(CH_3)_2CHCH(NHCH_2CH_2CN)COOH$ N-(2-cyanoethyl)-dl-valine	—	M.P. 252-253° (dec.)	728	
$HO_2CCH(NH_2)CH_2CH_2SCH_3$ dl-methionine	25° 50-60°	18.0 2.0	$HO_2CCH(NHCH_2CH_2CN)CH_2CH_2SCH_3$ N-(2-cyanoethyl)-dl-methionine	98	M.P. 246-247° (dec.)	728	
$HO_2CCH(NH_2)CH_2CH_2SCH_3$ dl-methionine	25° reflux	18.0 19.0	$HO_2CCH[N(CH_2CH_2CN)_2]CH_2CH_2SCH_3$ N,N-bis(2-cyanoethyl)-dl-methionine	91	M.P. 65-66°	729	
$CH_3CH(NH_2)COOC_2H_5 \cdot HCl$ alanine hydrochloride, ethyl ester	65-70°	4-5	$CH_3CH(NHCH_2CH_2CN)COOC_2H_5$ N-(2-cyanoethyl)alanine, ethyl ester	68	B.P. 157-158°/20 mm.	1417	
(imidazole structure) $CH_2CH(NH_2)CO_2H$ histidine	25° 50-60°	18.0 2.0	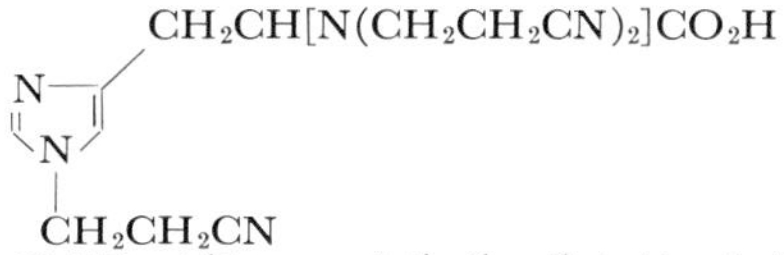 (imidazole structure with $CH_2CH[N(CH_2CH_2CN)_2]CO_2H$ and CH_2CH_2CN) N,N,1-tris(2-cyanoethyl)-4(or 5)-imidazolealanine	70	M.P. 184-186°	729	728

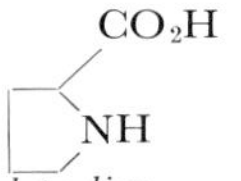

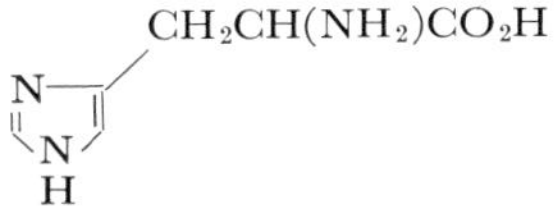

TABLE XIX—Continued

(E) Amino Acids and Derivatives

Reactants	Re-action Time (Hr.)	Reaction Temperature (°C.)	Products	% Yield	M.P. or B.P. (°C.)	References This Exam.	References See Also:
HO₂CCH(NH₂)CH₂CH(CH₃)₂ *l-leucine*	18.0 12.0	25° reflux	HO₂CCH[N(CH₂CH₂CN)₂]CH₂CH(CH₃)₂ *N,N-bis(2-cyanoethyl)-l-leucine*	95	M.P. 64-65°	729	
HO₂CCH(NH₂)CH₂CH(CH₃)₂ *l-leucine*	O.N. 2.0	R.T. reflux	(CH₃)₂CHCH₂CH(NHCH₂CH₂CN)COOH *N-(2-cyanoethyl)-l-leucine*	75	M.P. 249-250° (dec.)	728 726	
CH₃CH₂CH(CH₃)CH(NH₂)COOH *dl-isoleucine*	O.N. 2.0	R.T. reflux	CH₃CH₂CH(CH₃)CH(NHCH₂CH₂CN)COOH *N-(2-cyanoethyl)-dl-isoleucine*	86	M.P. 211-212° (dec.)	728	
NaO₂CCH(NH₂)CH₂⟨⟩OH *tyrosine, monosodium salt*	18.0 28.0	25° reflux	HO₂CCH[N(CH₂CH₂CN)₂]CH₂⟨⟩OH *N,N-bis(2-cyanoethyl)tyrosine*	—	M.P. 123-124°	729	
HO₂CCH(NH₂)CH₂⟨⟩OH *l-tyrosine*	O.N. 2.0	R.T. reflux	HO₂CCH(NHCH₂CH₂CN)CH₂⟨⟩OH *N-(2-cyanoethyl)-l-tyrosine*	93	M.P. 238-239° (dec.)	728 726	
⟨⟩CH₂CH(NH₂)COOH *dl-phenylalanine*	O.N.	R.T.	⟨⟩CH₂CH(NHCH₂CH₂CN)COOH *N-(2-cyanoethyl)-3-phenyl-dl-alanine*	92	M.P. 228-230° (dec.)	728 726	
C₂H₅OCOCH(NH₂)CH₂⟨⟩ *phenylalanine, ethyl ester*	5.0	75°	C₂H₅OCOCH(NHCH₂CH₂CN)CH₂⟨⟩ *N-(2-cyanoethyl)-3-phenylalanine, ethyl ester*	78.5	B.P. 191-192°/8 mm.	1062	
R–CH(NH₂)COOH ① *crude mixture of amino acids*	2.0 4.0	R.T. reflux	RCH(NHCH₂CH₂COOH)COOH	89	—	730	

(F) Miscellaneous Amino Compounds

Reactants	Re-action Time (Hr.)	Reaction Temperature (°C.)	Products	% Yield	M.P. or B.P. (°C.)	References This Exam.	References See Also:
NCNH₂ *cyanamide*	—	reflux	NCN(CH₂CH₂CN)₂ *3,3'-(cyanoimino)dipropionitrile*	98	M.P. 54°	485	
(NCNH)(NH₂)C=NH *cyanoguanidine (or dicyandiamide)*	3.0	reflux	*resinous syrup*	—	—	486 487	

TABLE XIX—Continued

(F) Miscellaneous Amino Compounds

Reactants	Reaction Time (Hr.)	Reaction Temperature (°C.)	Products	% Yield	M.P. or B.P. (°C.)	References This Exam.	References See Also:
$(CH_3)_2NNH_2$ *unsym-dimethylhydrazine*	2.0	reflux	$(CH_3)_2NNHCH_2CH_2CN$ *3-(2,2-dimethylhydrazino)propionitrile*	87	B.P. 80-90°/3 mm.	1285	
$(CH_3)_2C{=}NNH_2$ *acetone hydrazone*	0.5 24	40-45° reflux	$(CH_3)_2C{=}NNHCH_2CH_2CN$ *acetone, 2-cyanoethylhydrazone*	40.7	B.P. 123-127°/23 mm.	1283	
$(CH_3)_2CHCH{=}NNH_2$ *isobutyraldehyde hydrazone*	0.5 24	40-45° reflux	$(CH_3)_2CHCH{=}NNHCH_2CH_2CN$ *isobutyraldehyde, 2-cyanoethylhydrazone*	—	—	1283	
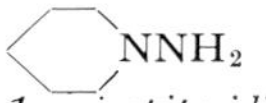 NNH_2 *1-aminopiperidine*	—	—	 N-NHCH₂CH₂CN *3-(piperidinoamino)propionitrile*	—	—	264	
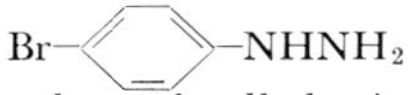 Br—$NHNH_2$ *p-bromophenylhydrazine*	6.0	reflux	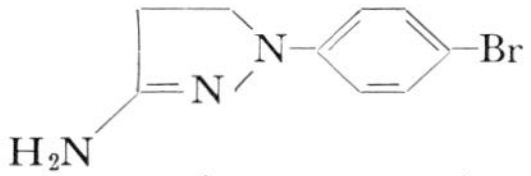 *3-amino-1-(p-bromophenyl)-2-pyrazoline*	—	M.P. 121°	1301	
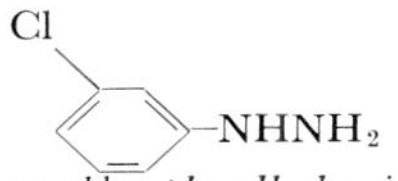 Cl—$NHNH_2$ *m-chlorophenylhydrazine*	4.0	reflux	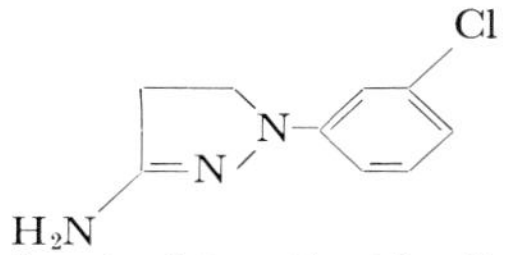 *3-amino-1-(m-chlorophenyl)-2-pyrazoline*	—	M.P. 142°	1301	
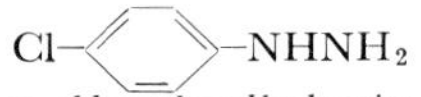 Cl—$NHNH_2$ *p-chlorophenylhydrazine*	6.0	reflux	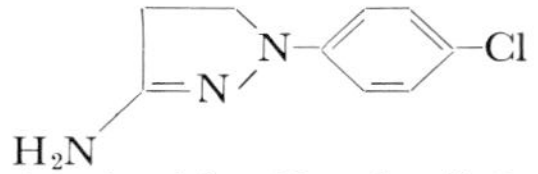 *3-amino-1-(p-chlorophenyl)-2-pyrazoline*	42	M.P. 135°	345	1301
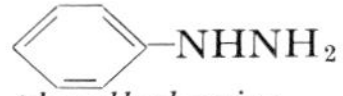 $NHNH_2$ *phenylhydrazine*	1.0	water bath	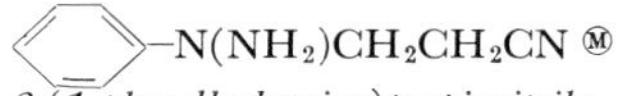 —$N(NH_2)CH_2CH_2CN$ *3-(1-phenylhydrazino)propionitrile*	—	—	870	1374

TABLE XIX—Continued

(F) Miscellaneous Amino Compounds

Reactants	Reaction Time (Hr.)	Reaction Temperature (°C.)	Products	% Yield	M.P. or B.P. (°C.)	References This Exam.	References See Also:
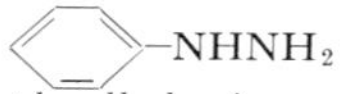 phenylhydrazine	2.0	water bath	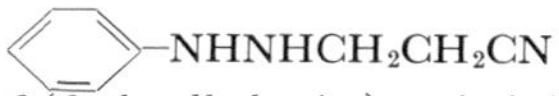 $-NHNHCH_2CH_2CN$ 3-(2-phenylhydrazino)propionitrile	74	B.P. 199°/3 mm.	870	345, 1375, 1281
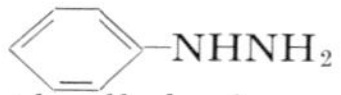 phenylhydrazine	6.0	reflux	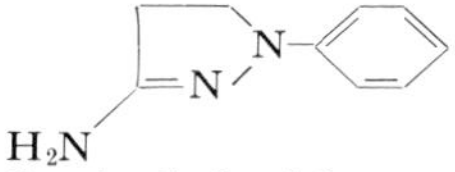 3-amino-1-phenyl-2-pyrazoline	74	M.P. 169°	345	1301
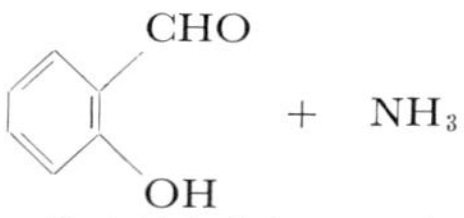 salicylaldehyde + ammonia	0.5 0.5 several days	25° steam bath 25°	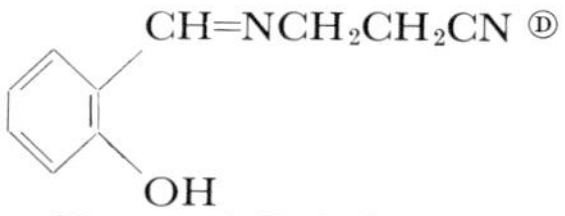 $CH=NCH_2CH_2CN$ α-(2-cyanoethylimino)-o-cresol	6	M.P. 74-75°	1059	
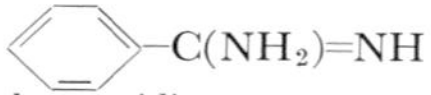 benzamidine $C(NH_2)=NH$	8.0	—	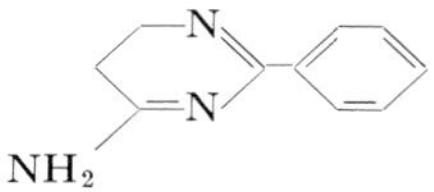 4-amino-5,6-dihydro-2-phenylpyrimidine	55	M.P. 177°	870	1374
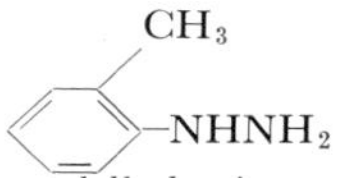 o-tolylhydrazine	6.0	reflux	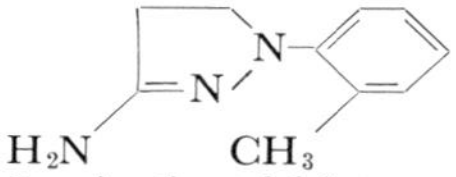 3-amino-1-o-tolyl-2-pyrazoline	8.5	M.P. 74°	345	1301
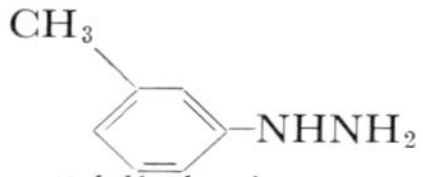 m-tolylhydrazine	6.0	reflux	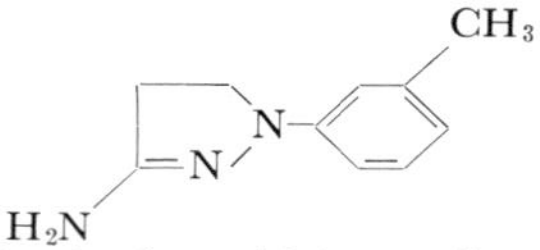 3-amino-1-m-tolyl-2-pyrazoline	47	M.P. 110°	345	1301

TABLE XIX—Continued

(F) Miscellaneous Amino Compounds

Reactants	Reaction Time (Hr.)	Reaction Temperature (°C.)	Products	% Yield	M.P. or B.P. (°C.)	References This Exam.	References See Also:
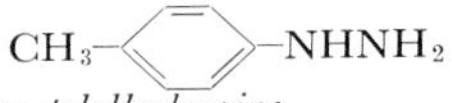 CH_3—C₆H₄—NHNH₂ p-tolylhydrazine	6.0	reflux	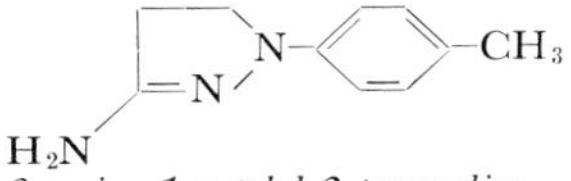 H₂N—pyrazoline—N=N—C₆H₄—CH₃ 3-amino-1-p-tolyl-2-pyrazoline	70	M.P. 143°	345	1301
 CH_3O—C₆H₄—NHNH₂ p-methoxyphenylhydrazine	4	reflux	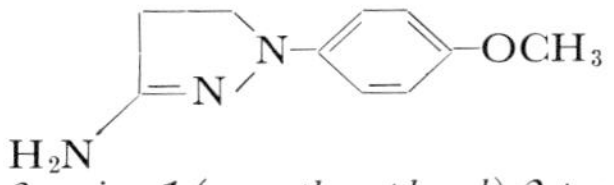 H₂N—pyrazoline—N=N—C₆H₄—OCH₃ 3-amino-1-(p-methoxyphenyl)-2-prazoline	—	M.P. 179-180°	1301	
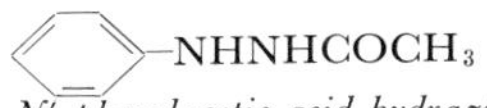 NHNHCOCH₃ N'-phenylacetic acid hydrazide	3.0	water bath	 C₆H₅—NHN(CH₂CH₂CN)COCH₃ acetic acid, 1-(2-cyanoethyl)-2-phenylhydrazide	25	M.P. 230°	870	
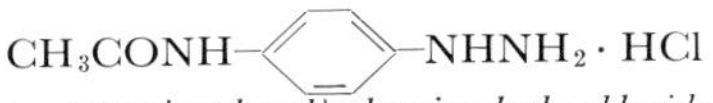 CH₃CONH—C₆H₄—NHNH₂·HCl p-acetamophenylhydrazine hydrochloride	3.5	reflux	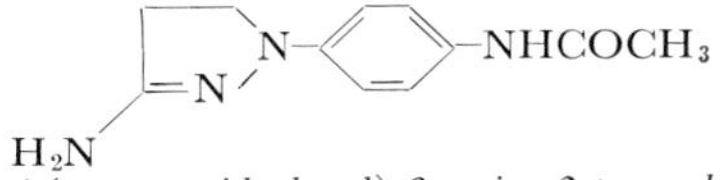 H₂N—pyrazoline—N=N—C₆H₄—NHCOCH₃ 1-(p-acetamidophenyl)-3-amino-2-pyrazoline	—	M.P. 204°	1301	
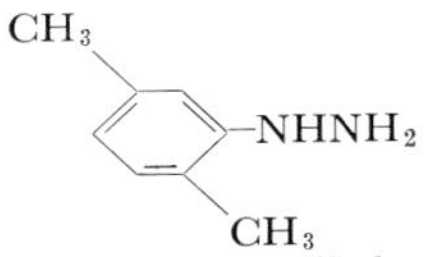 CH₃—C₆H₃(CH₃)—NHNH₂ 2,5-dimethylphenylhydrazine	4.0	reflux	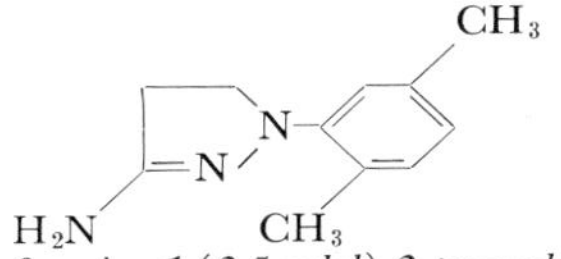 H₂N—pyrazoline—N=N—C₆H₃(CH₃)(CH₃) 3-amino-1-(2,5-xylyl)-2-pyrazoline	—	M.P. 99°	1301	
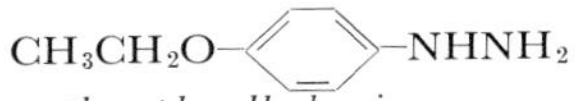 CH₃CH₂O—C₆H₄—NHNH₂ p-ethoxyphenylhydrazine	6.0	reflux	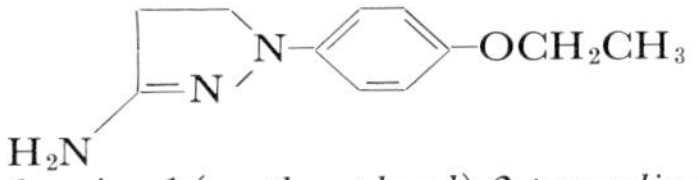 H₂N—pyrazoline—N=N—C₆H₄—OCH₂CH₃ 3-amino-1-(p-ethoxyphenyl)-2-pyrazoline	—	M.P. 192°	1301	

TABLE XIX—Continued

(F) Miscellaneous Amino Compounds

Reactants	Reaction Time (Hr.)	Reaction Temperature (°C.)	Products	% Yield	M.P. or B.P. (°C.)	References This Exam.	See Also:
 —NHNH— hydrazobenzene	0.5	—	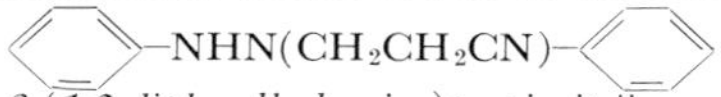 —NHN(CH₂CH₂CN)— 3-(1,2-diphenylhydrazino)propionitrile	73	M.P. 125°	870	1374
 —O—NHNH₂ p-phenoxyphenylhydrazine	24.0	reflux	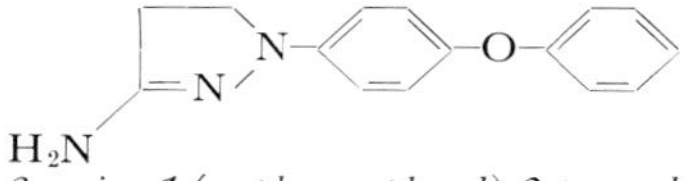 H₂N N—N— 3-amino-1-(p-phenoxyphenyl)-2-pyrazoline	—	M.P. 147°	1301	
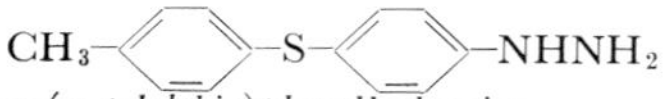 CH₃—S—NHNH₂ p-(p-tolylthio)phenylhydrazine	24.0	reflux	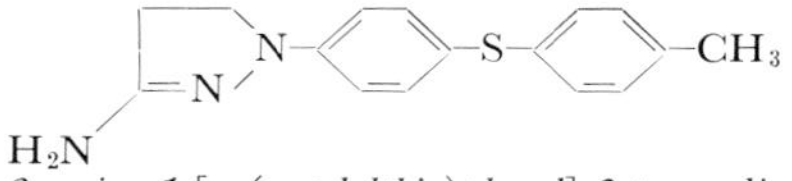 H₂N N—N— S—CH₃ 3-amino-1-[p-(p-tolylthio)phenyl]-2-pyrazoline	—	M.P. 123°	1301	
HN₃ hydrazoic acid	24-72.0	25°	N₃CH₂CH₂CN 3-azidopropionitrile	17.3	B.P. 64°/1 mm.	133	
HONH₂ hydroxylamine	2.0	10°-R.T.	HONHCH₂CH₂CN 3-hydroxyaminopropionitrile	~100	—⊗	520 568 566 519	
H₂NNH₂ · H₂O hydrazine hydrate	—	R.T.	H₂NNHCH₂CH₂CN 3-hydrazinopropionitrile	90	B.P. 108-112°/4 mm.	520 568 566 519	
H₂NNH₂ · H₂O hydrazine hydrate			H₂NNHCH₂CH₂CONH₂ 3-hydrazinopropionamide				
H₂NNH₂ · H₂O hydrazine hydrate	2 stored	35°	H₂NN(CH₂CH₂CN)₂ 3,3'-hydrazonodipropionitrile	80	B.P. 125-128°/ 0.1-0.3 mm.	1354	
H₂NNH₂ · H₂O hydrazine hydrate			NCCH₂CH₂HNNHCH₂CH₂CN 3,3'-hydrazodipropionitrile	9.1	B.P. 110-125°/ 0.1-0.3 mm.		
H₂NNH₂ · H₂O hydrazine hydrate	0.5 4.0	0° reflux	 N—N'—NH₂ · HCl 3-amino-2-pyrazoline hydrochloride	—	M.P. 196°	1301	

TABLE XIX—Continued

(G) Amides

Reactants	Reaction Time (Hr.)	Reaction Temperature (°C.)	Products	% Yield	M.P. or B.P. (°C.)	References This Exam.	References See Also:
HCONH₂ *formamide*	—	110-130°	HCON(CH₂CH(CN)CH₂CH(CN)CH₂CH₂CN / CH₂CH(CN)CH₂CH₂CN) *N-(2,4-dicyanobutyl)-N-(2,4,6-tricyanohexyl)formamide*	—	—	1134	
HCONH₂ *formamide*	—	85°	HCONHCH₂CH₂CN ⓞ *N-(2-cyanoethyl)formamide*; HCON(CH₂CH₂CN)₂ ⓟ *N,N-bis(2-cyanoethyl)formamide*	85	B.P. 150°/3 mm.	1135	1133, 63, 1334
NH₂CONH₂ *urea and derivatives*	—	—	*cyanoethylated urea and derivatives* ⓠ	—	—	1136	
HCONHCH₃ *N-methylformamide*	5.0	90-100°	HCON(CH₃)CH₂CH₂CN *N-(2-cyanoethyl)-N-methylformamide*	—	—	63	1133
CH₃CONH₂ *acetamide*	—	—	CH₃CONHCH₂CH₂CN *N-(2-cyanoethyl)acetamide*	84.5	M.P. 62° B.P. 132-135°/0.5-1 mm.	1135	843
CH₃CONH₂ *acetamide*	O.N.	<30°	CH₃CON(CH₂CH₂CN)₂ *N,N-bis(2-cyanoethyl)acetamide*	72 ⓡ	B.P. 210-225°/2 mm.	733	1135
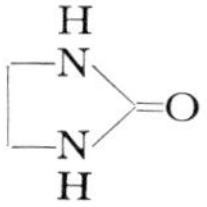 ethylene urea	3.0	40°	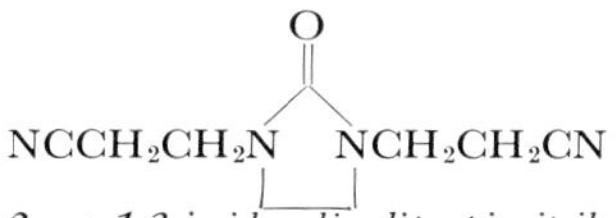 NCCH₂CH₂N–C(O)–NCH₂CH₂CN *2-oxo-1,3-imidazolinedipropionitrile*	95	—	1436	
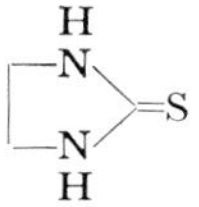 ethylene thiourea	2.5	40°	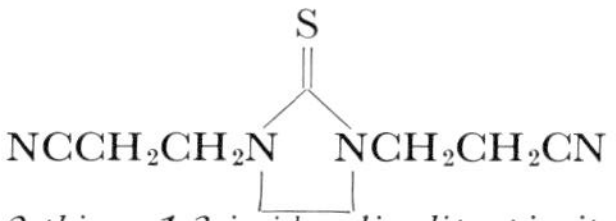 NCCH₂CH₂N–C(S)–NCH₂CH₂CN *2-thioxo-1,3-imidazolinedipropionitrile*	88.4	M.P. 134°	1436	

TABLE XIX—Continued

(G) Amides

Reactants	Products	Reaction Temperature (°C.)	Reaction Time (Hr.)	M.P. or B.P. (°C.)	% Yield	References This Exam.	See Also:
$CH_3CONHCH_3$ *N-methylacetamide*	$CH_3CON(CH_3)CH_2CH_2CN$ *N-(2-cyanoethyl)-N-methylacetamide*	—	—	B.P. 112°/1 mm. B.P. 160°/14 mm.	78	1135	577
$CH_3CH_2CONH_2$ *propionamide*	$CH_3CH_2CONHCH_2CH_2CN$ *N-(2-cyanoethyl)propionamide*	—	—	—	—	1135	
	$CH_3CH_2CON(CH_2CH_2CN)_2$ *N,N-bis(2-cyanoethyl)propionamide*	95°	—	M.P. 120°	97	1135	
(structure) *succinimide*	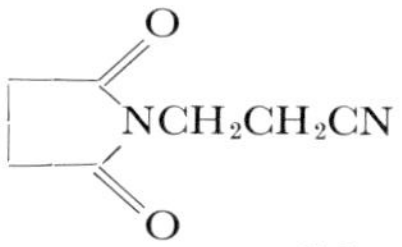 (structure) NCH_2CH_2CN *2,5-dioxo-1-pyrrolidinepropionitrile*	65–70°	1.5	M.P. 166°	64.9	1063	
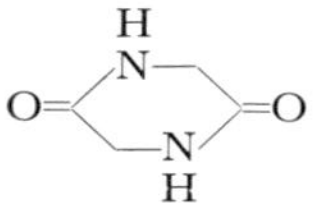 (structure) *2,5-piperazinedione*	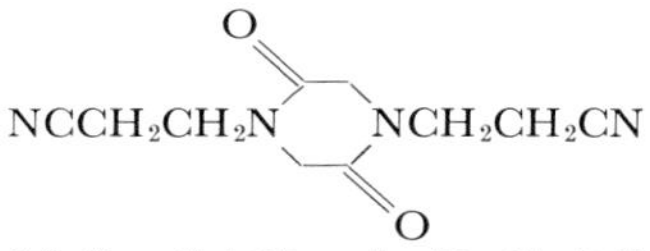 (structure) $NCCH_2CH_2N \cdots NCH_2CH_2CN$ *2,5-dioxo-1,4-piperazinedipropionitrile*	R.T.	2.0	M.P. 77°	17.4	173	
$CH_3CH=CHCONH_2$ *crotonamide*	$CH_3CH=CHCON(CH_2CH_2CN)_2$ *N,N-bis(2-cyanoethyl)crotonamide*	—	—	B.P. 122°/0.7 mm.	86	1135	577
(structure) *2-pyrrolidinone*	(structure) NCH_2CH_2CN *2-oxo-1-pyrrolidinepropionitrile*	—	—				
$HCONHCH_2CH_2CH_3$ *N-propylformamide*	$HCON(CH_2CH_2CN)CH_2CH_2CH_3$ *N-(2-cyanoethyl)-N-propylformamide*	—	—	—	—	1135	

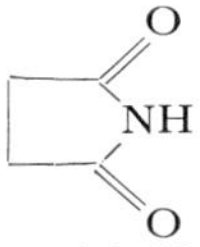

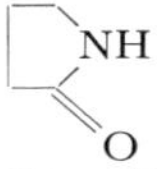

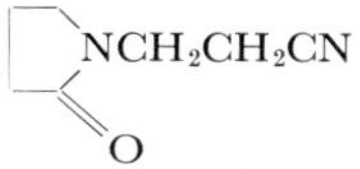

TABLE XIX—Continued

(G) Amides

Reactants	Reaction Temperature (°C.)	Reaction Time (Hr.)	Products	% Yield	M.P. or B.P. (°C.)	References This Exam.	References See Also:
CH₃CH₂CONHCH₃ N-methylpropionamide	—	—	CH₃CH₂CON(CH₃)CH₂CH₂CN N-(2-cyanoethyl)-N-methylpropionamide	66–74	B.P. 114–115°/1 mm.	1135	577
CH₃CH₂CH₂SO₂NH₂ 1-butanesulfonamide	<30°	O.N.	CH₃CH₂CH₂SO₂N(CH₂CH₂CN)₂ N,N-bis(2-cyanoethyl)butanesulfonamide	55	B.P. 225–233°/2 mm. M.P. 46–49°	733	
CH₃CH₂CH₂SO₂NH₂ 1-butanesulfonamide	<30°	O.N.	CH₃CH₂CH₂SO₂NHCH₂CH₂CN N-(2-cyanoethyl)butanesulfonamide	51	B.P. 195–206°/3 mm.	733	
CH₃CH₂CH₂SO₂NHCH₃ N-methyl-1-propylsulfonamide	—	—	CH₃CH₂CH₂SO₂N(CH₃)CH₂CH₂CN N-(2-cyanoethyl)-N-methylpropanesulfonamide	—	B.P. 146–148°/ 0.7–1.0 mm.	1135	
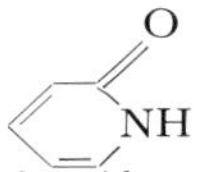 2-pyridone	steam cone	0.5	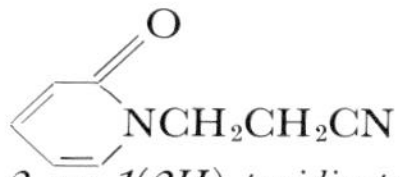 NCH₂CH₂CN 2-oxo-1(2H)-pyridinepropionitrile	90	M.P. 93–94°	9	
HCONH(CH₂)₃CH₃ N-butylformamide	—	—	HCON(CH₂CH₂CN)CH₂CH₂CH₂CH₃ N-butyl-N-(2-cyanoethyl)formamide	87	B.P. 129–130°/0.5 mm.	1135	1133, 63
HCONHCH(CH₃)CH₂CH₃ N-(1-methylpropyl)formamide	—	—	HCON(CH₂CH₂CN)CH(CH₃)CH₂CH₃ N-sec.-butyl-N-(2-cyanoethyl)formamide	—	B.P. 129–130°/0.5 mm.	63	
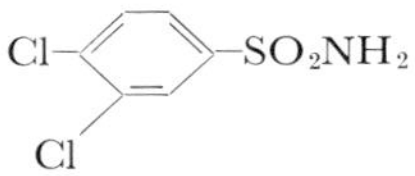 Cl—⟨benzene⟩—SO₂NH₂ (Cl) 3,4-dichlorobenzenesulfonamide	—	—	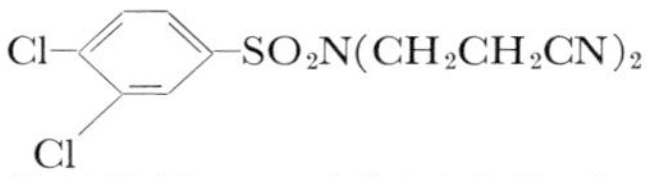 Cl—⟨benzene⟩—SO₂N(CH₂CH₂CN)₂ (Cl) N,N-bis(2-cyanoethyl)3,4-dichlorobenzene-sulfonamide	93	M.P. 158°	1135	
Br—⟨benzene⟩—SO₂NH₂ p-bromobenzenesulfonamide	25°	48.0	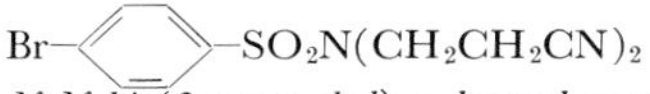 Br—⟨benzene⟩—SO₂N(CH₂CH₂CN)₂ N,N-bis(2-cyanoethyl)-p-bromobenzenesulfonamide	66	M.P. 133°	1348	

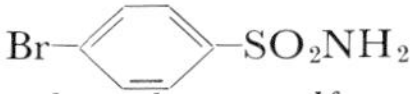

TABLE XIX—Continued

(G) **Amides**

Reactants	Reaction Time (Hr.)	Reaction Temperature (°C.)	Products	% Yield	M.P. or B.P. (°C.)	References This Exam.	References See Also:
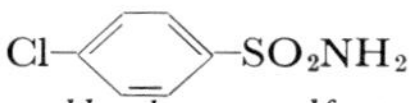 Cl—[C₆H₄]—SO_2NH_2 *p-chlorobenzenesulfonamide*	48.0	25°	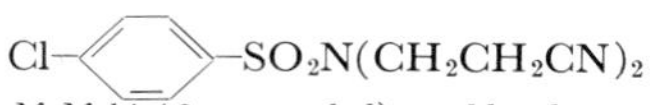 Cl—[C₆H₄]—$SO_2N(CH_2CH_2CN)_2$ *N,N-bis(2-cyanoethyl)-p-chlorobenzenesulfonamide*	87	M.P. 132°	1348	
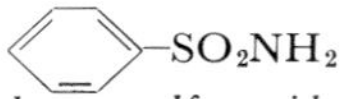 [C₆H₅]—SO_2NH_2 *benzenesulfonamide*	—	—	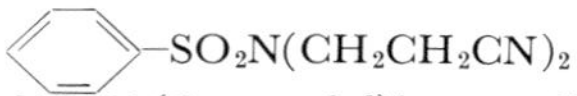 [C₆H₅]—$SO_2N(CH_2CH_2CN)_2$ *N,N-bis(2-cyanoethyl)benzenesulfonamide*	87	M.P. 92°	1135	1348
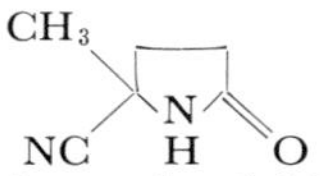 *5-cyano-5-methyl-2-pyrrolidinone*	0.5	steam bath	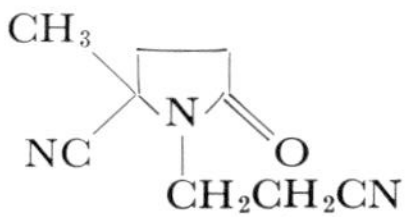 *2-cyano-2-methyl-5-oxo-1-pyrrolidinepropionitrile*	43.9	M.P. 75–77°	432	
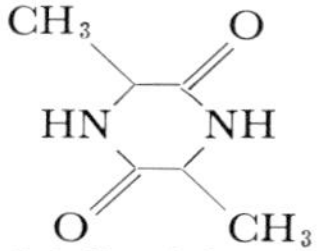 *3,6-dimethyl-2,5-piperazinedione*	1.5	65–70°	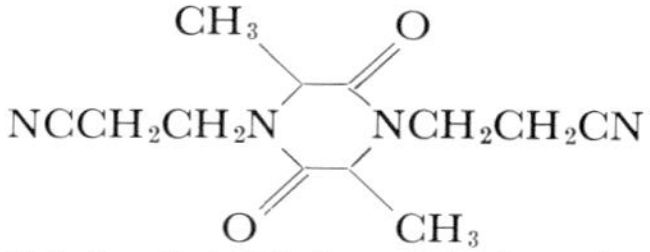 $NCCH_2CH_2N$ ... NCH_2CH_2CN *2,5-dimethyl-3,6-dioxo-1,4-piperazinedipropionitrile*	—	M.P. 185°	1063	
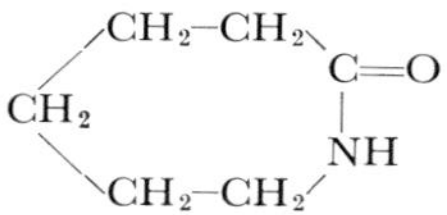 *2-oxohexamethylenimine (ε-caprolactam)*	2.0 63.0	30–35° R.T.	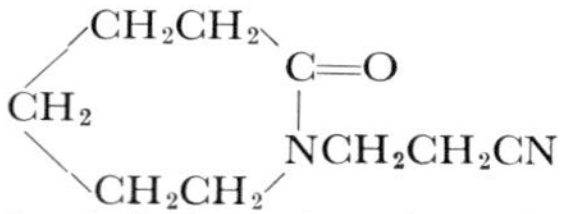 NCH_2CH_2CN *hexahydro-2-oxo-1-azepinepropionitrile*	65	M.P. 32–34° B.P. 153–158°/ 1.5–1.8 mm.	106	577, 1135

TABLE XIX—Continued

(G) Amides

Reactants	Reaction Time (Hr.)	Reaction Temperature (°C.)	Products	% Yield	M.P. or B.P. (°C.)	This Exam.	See Also:
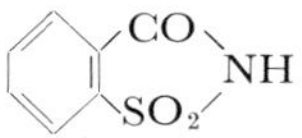 CO–NH–SO_2 (saccharin)	—	—	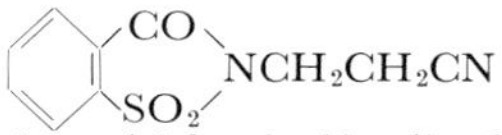 CO–NCH_2CH_2CN–SO_2 3-oxo-1,2-benzisothiazoline-2-propionitrile,1,1-dioxide	—	—	1135	
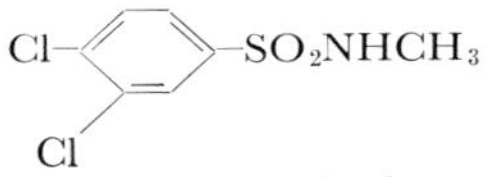 Cl–SO_2NHCH_3 (Cl) N-methyl-3,4-dichlorobenzenesulfonamide	—	—	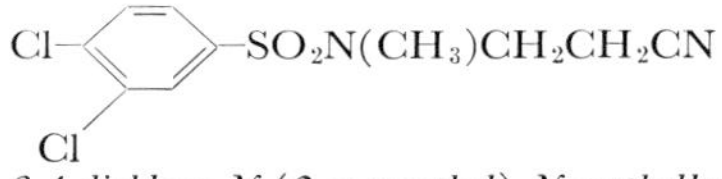 Cl–$SO_2N(CH_3)CH_2CH_2CN$ (Cl) 3,4-dichloro-N-(2-cyanoethyl)-N-methylbenzenesulfonamide	88	M.P. 134.5°	1135	
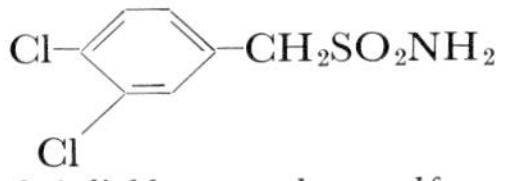 Cl–$CH_2SO_2NH_2$ (Cl) 3,4-dichloro-α-toluenesulfonamide	48.0	35° R.T.	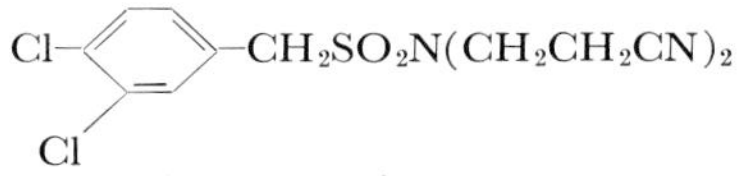 Cl–$CH_2SO_2N(CH_2CH_2CN)_2$ (Cl) N,N-bis(2-cyanoethyl)-3,4-dichloro-α-toluenesulfonamide	75	M.P. 150°	1350	
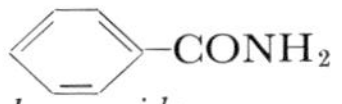 $CONH_2$ benzamide	—	—	 $CONHCH_2CH_2CN$ N-(2-cyanoethyl)benzamide	~50	M.P. 92-93°	1135	577
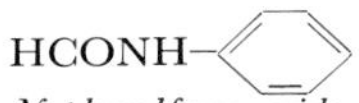 $HCONH$– N-phenylformamide	—	—	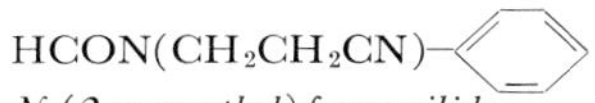 $HCON(CH_2CH_2CN)$– N-(2-cyanoethyl)formanilide	88	B.P. 159-161°/2 mm.	1135	63, 1133
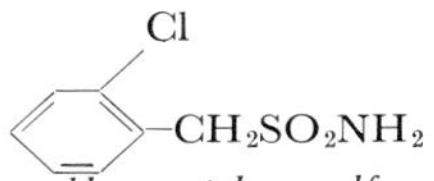 Cl–$CH_2SO_2NH_2$ o-chloro-α-toluenesulfonamide	48.0	35° R.T.	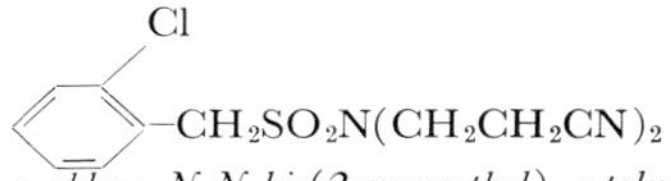 Cl–$CH_2SO_2N(CH_2CH_2CN)_2$ o-chloro-N,N-bis(2-cyanoethyl)-α-toluenesulfonamide	77	M.P. 92-93°	1350	

TABLE XIX—Continued

(G) Amides

Reactants	Reaction Temperature (°C.)	Reaction Time (Hr.)	Products	% Yield	M.P. or B.P. (°C.)	References — This Exam.	References — See Also:
Cl—[ring]—CH₂SO₂NH₂ *m-chloro-α-toluenesulfonamide*	35° R.T.	48.0	Cl—[ring]—CH₂SO₂N(CH₂CH₂CN)₂ *m-chloro-N,N-bis(2-cyanoethyl)-α-toluenesulfonamide*	82.5	M.P. 85-86°	1350	
Cl—[ring]—CH₂SO₂NH₂ *p-chloro-α-toluenesulfonamide*	R.T.	48.0	Cl—[ring]—CH₂SO₂N(CH₂CH₂CN)₂ *p-chloro-N,N-bis(2-cyanoethyl)-α-toluenesulfonamide*	90	M.P. 121-22°	1350	
H₂N—[ring]—NHCHO *p-aminoformanilide*	—	—	H₂N—[ring]—N(CH₂CH₂CN)CHO *4'-amino-N-(2-cyanoethyl)formanilide*	—	—	1218	
H₃C—[ring]—SO₂NH₂ *p-toluenesulfonamide*	25°	48	H₃C—[ring]—SO₂N(CH₂CH₂CN)₂ *N,N-bis(2-cyanoethyl)-p-toluenesulfonamide*	88	M.P. 105-106°	1348	1303
[ring]—CH₂SO₂NH₂ *α-toluenesulfonamide*	R.T.	24.0	[ring]—CH₂SO₂N(CH₂CH₂CN)₂ *N,N-bis(2-cyanoethyl)-α-toluenesulfonamide*	97.5	M.P. 103-104°	179 184	
[ring]—SO₂NHCH₃ *N-methylbenzenesulfonamide*	—	—	[ring]—SO₂N(CH₃)CH₂CH₂CN *N-(2-cyanoethyl)-N-methylbenzenesulfonamide*	85	M.P. 72°	1135	
[cyclohexyl]—HCONH  *N-cyclohexylformamide*	—	—	brown oil	—	—	63	1135
HCONH(CH₂)₅CH₃ *N-hexylformamide*	—	—	HCON(CH₂CH₂CN)CH₂(CH₂)₃CH₂CH₃ *N-(2-cyanoethyl)-N-hexylformamide*	—	—	1135	

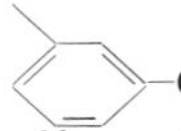

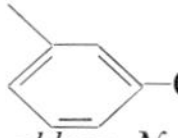

TABLE XIX—Continued

(G) Amides

Reactants	Reaction Time (Hr.)	Reaction Temperature (°C.)	Products	% Yield	M.P. or B.P. (°C.)	References This Exam.	References See Also:
$HCONHCH_2(CH_2)_2CH(CH_3)_2$ *N-(4-methylpentyl)formamide*	—	—	$HCON(CH_2CH_2CN)CH_2(CH_2)_2CH(CH_3)_2$ *N-(2-cyanoethyl)-N-isohexylformamide*	80	B.P. 131°/0.8 mm.	1135	63, 1133
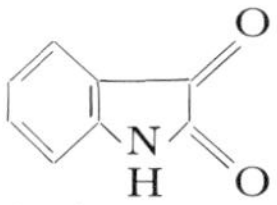 *isatin*	several days	R.T.	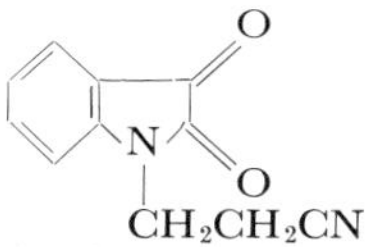 CH_2CH_2CN *2,3-dioxo-1-indolinepropionitrile*	50	M.P. 130-131° M.P. 133°	326	
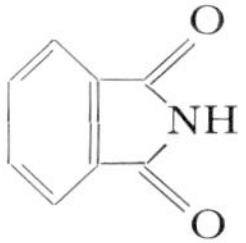 *phthalimide*	0.33	reflux	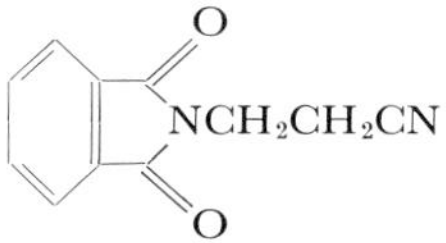 NCH_2CH_2CN *N-(2-cyanoethyl)phthalimide*	100	M.P. 154-155.5°	412	1135, 928
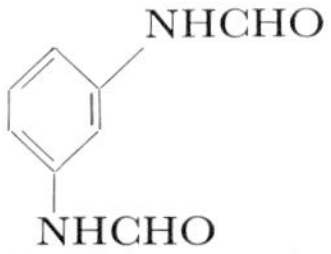 NHCHO NHCHO *N,N'-(m-phenylene)bis(formamide)*	O.N.	50° 25°	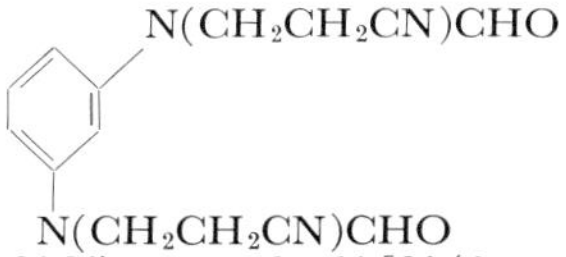 $N(CH_2CH_2CN)CHO$ $N(CH_2CH_2CN)CHO$ *N,N'-m-phenylenebis[N-(2-cyanoethyl)formamide]*	~100	M.P. 114-117°	1218	
 $HCONH$—$NHCHO$ *N,N'-(p-phenylene)bis(formamide)*	O.N.	50° 25°	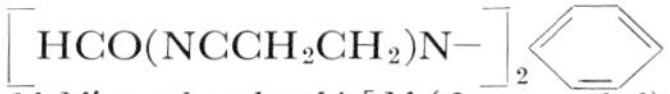 $\left[HCO(NCCH_2CH_2)N- \right]_2$ *N,N'-p-phenylenebis[N-(2-cyanoethyl)formamide]*	87	—	1218	

TABLE XIX—Continued

(G) Amides

Reactants	Reaction Time (Hr.)	Reaction Temperature (°C.)	Products	% Yield	M.P. or B.P. (°C.)	References This Exam.	References See Also:
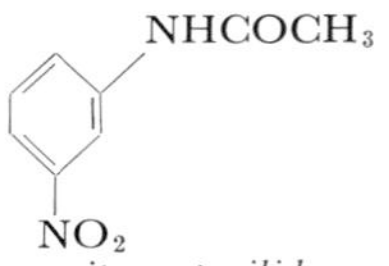 $NHCOCH_3$ / NO_2 m-nitroacetanilide	16	reflux	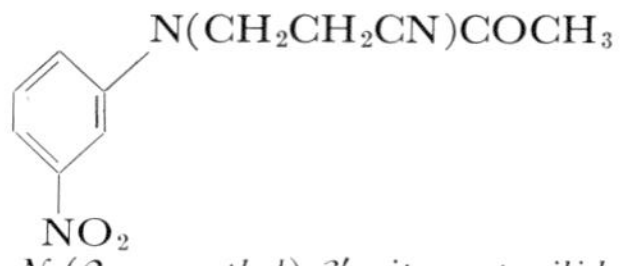 $N(CH_2CH_2CN)COCH_3$ / NO_2 *N-(2-cyanoethyl)-3'-nitroacetanilide*	91	M.P. 81-82.5°	1218	
CH_3CONH⟨⟩ *acetanilide*	—	—	$N(CH_2CH_2CN)COCH_3$ *N-(2-cyanoethyl)acetanilide*	64	M.P. 60-61°	1135	577, 135
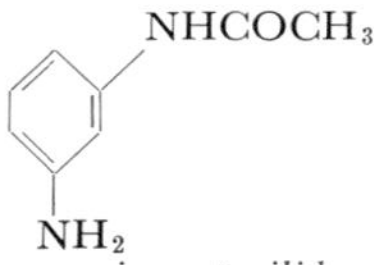 $NHCOCH_3$ / NH_2 m-aminoacetanilide	2.5 O.N.	35° 25°	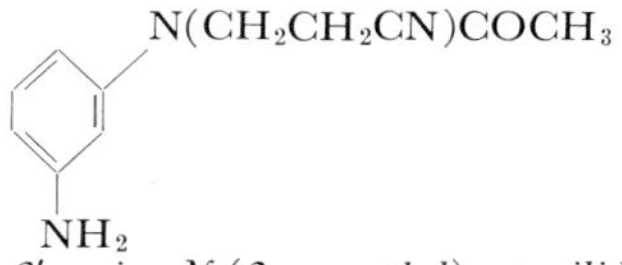 $N(CH_2CH_2CN)COCH_3$ / NH_2 *3'-amino-N-(2-cyanoethyl)acetanilide*	81.2	—	1218	
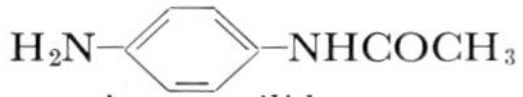 H_2N—⟨⟩—$NHCOCH_3$ *p-aminoacetanilide*	24.0	reflux	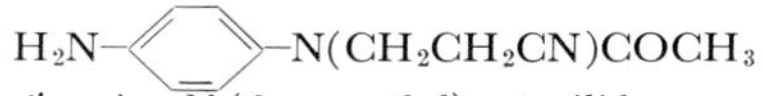 H_2N—⟨⟩—$N(CH_2CH_2CN)COCH_3$ *4'-amino-N-(2-cyanoethyl)acetanilide*	95.6	—	1218	
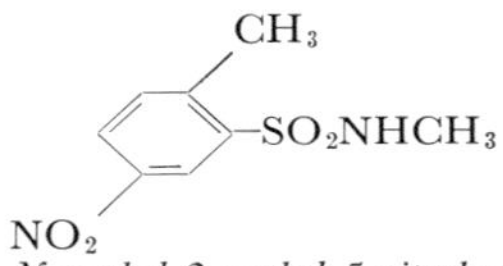 CH_3 / SO_2NHCH_3 / NO_2 *N-methyl-2-methyl-5-nitrobenzene-sulfonamide*	—	—	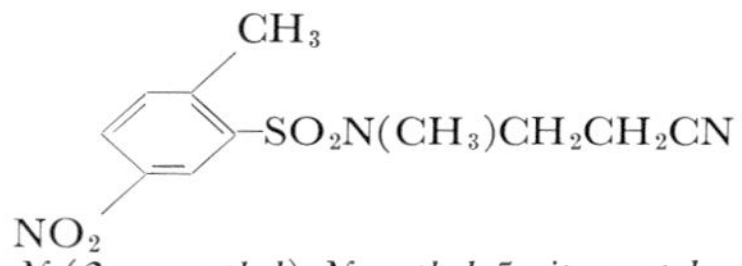 CH_3 / $SO_2N(CH_3)CH_2CH_2CN$ / NO_2 *N-(2-cyanoethyl)-N-methyl-5-nitro-o-toluene-sulfonamide*	—	M.P. 119°	1135	

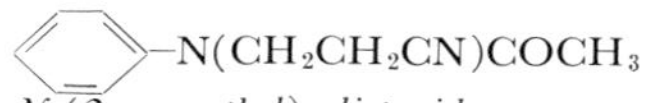

TABLE XIX—Continued

(G) Amides

Reactants	Reaction Time (Hr.)	Reaction Temperature (°C.)	Products	% Yield	M.P. or B.P. (°C.)	References	
						This Exam.	See Also:
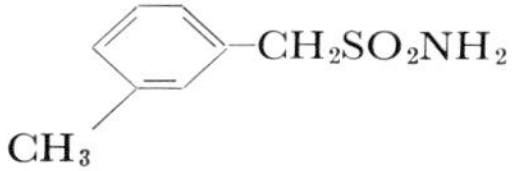 ⬡—$CH_2SO_2NH_2$ with CH_3 m-toluenemethanesulfonamide	48.0	35° R.T.	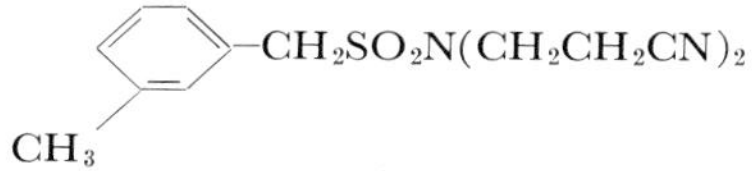 ⬡—$CH_2SO_2N(CH_2CH_2CN)_2$ with CH_3 N,N-bis(2-cyanoethyl)-m-tolylmethanesulfonamide	80	M.P. 94-95°	1350	
 CH_3CH_2—⬡—SO_2NH_2 p-ethylbenzenesulfonamide	48.0	25°	 CH_3CH_2—⬡—$SO_2N(CH_2CH_2CN)_2$ N,N-bis(2-cyanoethyl)-p-ethylbenzenesulfonamide	80	M.P. 75-76°	1348	
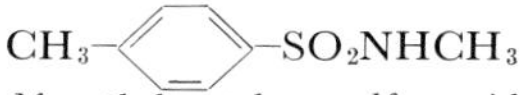 CH_3—⬡—SO_2NHCH_3 N-methyl-p-toluenesulfonamide	48.0	25°	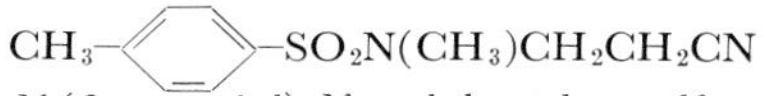 CH_3—⬡—$SO_2N(CH_3)CH_2CH_2CN$ N-(2-cyanoethyl)-N-methyl-p-toluenesulfonamide	87	M.P. 105-106°	1348	
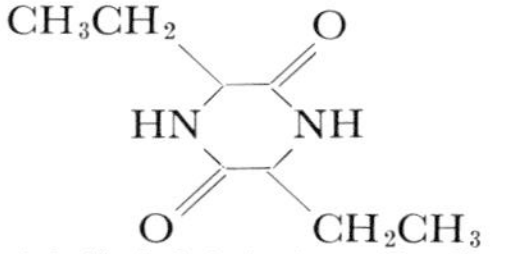 3,6-diethyl-2,5-piperazinedione	1.5	65-70°	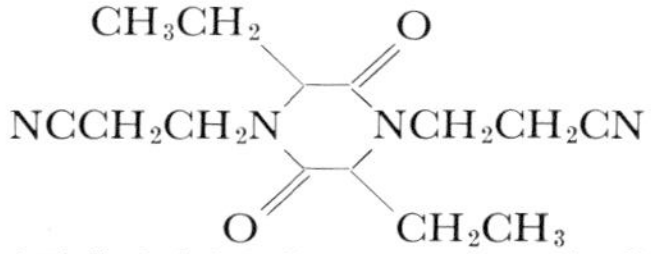 2,5-diethyl-3,6-dioxo-1,4-piperazinedipropionitrile	—	M.P. 176.5°	1063	
$CH_3NHCO(CH_2)_4CONHCH_3$ N,N'-dimethylhexanediamide	—	—	$[NCCH_2CH_2N(CH_3)CO]_2(CH_2)_4$ N,N'-bis(2-cyanoethyl)-N,N'-dimethylhexanediamide	—	—	577	
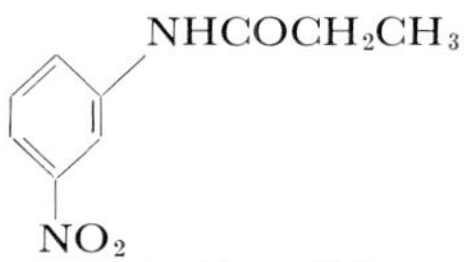 ⬡—$NHCOCH_2CH_3$ with NO_2 m-nitropropionanilide	—	—	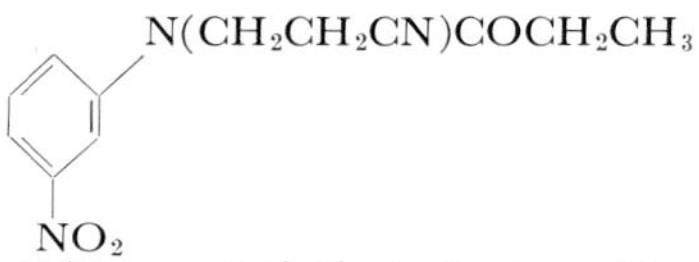 ⬡—$N(CH_2CH_2CN)COCH_2CH_3$ with NO_2 N-(2-cyanoethyl)-3'-nitropropionanilide	—	—	1218	

TABLE XIX—Continued

(G) Amides

Reactants	Reaction Time (Hr.)	Reaction Temperature (°C.)	Products	% Yield	M.P. or B.P. (°C.)	References	
						This Exam.	See Also:
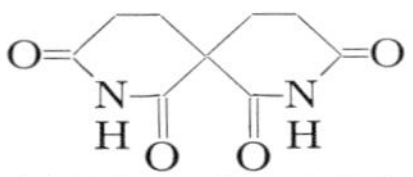 1,3,7,9-tetraketo-2,8-diazaspiro[5.5]-hendecane	—	—	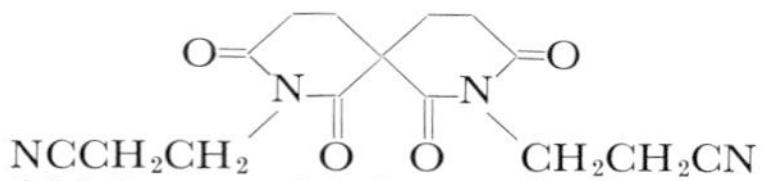 1,3,7,9-tetraoxo-2,8-diazaspiro[5.5]undecane-2,8-dipropionitrile	35	M.P. 122°	1331	
 CH_3CONH—SO_2NHCH_3 4-acetylamino-N-methylbenzenesulfonamide	—	—	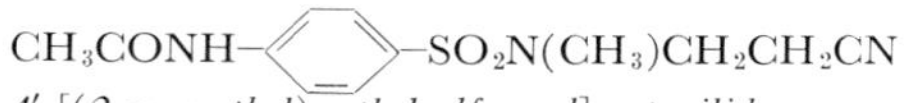 CH_3CONH—$SO_2N(CH_3)CH_2CH_2CN$ 4'-[(2-cyanoethyl)methylsulfamoyl]acetanilide	73	M.P. 142-143°	1135	
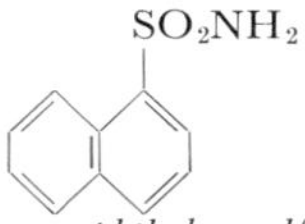 SO_2NH_2 α-naphthalenesulfonamide	48.0	25°	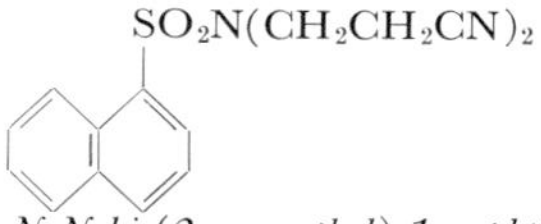 $SO_2N(CH_2CH_2CN)_2$ N,N-bis(2-cyanoethyl)-1-naphthalenesulfonamide	66	M.P. 120-121°	1348	
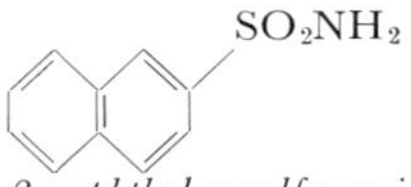 SO_2NH_2 β-naphthalenesulfonamide	48.0	25°	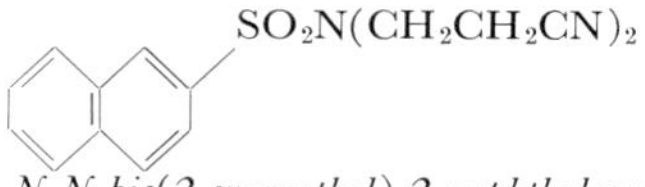 $SO_2N(CH_2CH_2CN)_2$ N,N-bis(2-cyanoethyl)-2-naphthalenesulfonamide	78	M.P. 109-110°	1348	
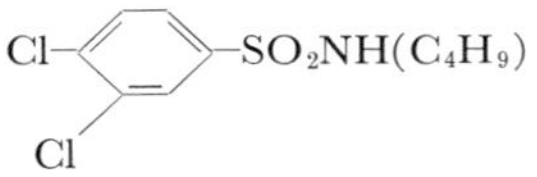 Cl—$SO_2NH(C_4H_9)$ Cl N-butyl-3,4-dichlorobenzenesulfonamide	—	—	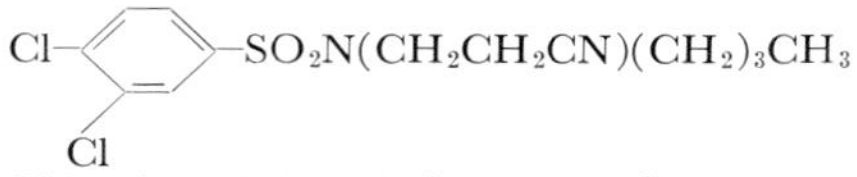 Cl—$SO_2N(CH_2CH_2CN)((CH_2)_3CH_3$ Cl N-butyl-3,4-dichloro-N-(2-cyanoethyl)benzene-sulfonamide	85	M.P. 91°	1135	
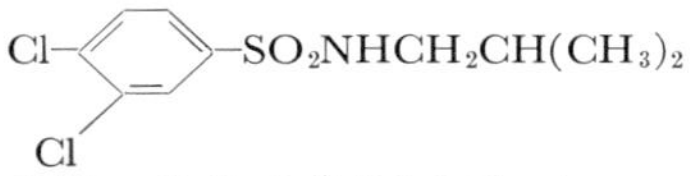 Cl—$SO_2NHCH_2CH(CH_3)_2$ Cl N-(2-methylpropyl)-3,4-dichlorobenzene-sulfonamide	—	—	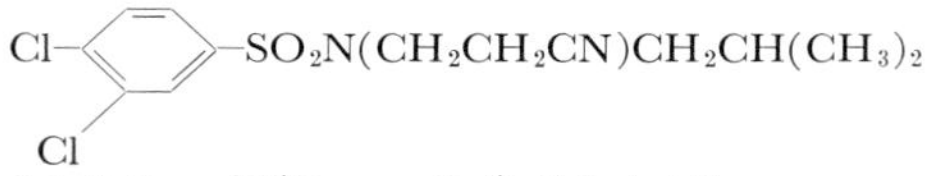 Cl—$SO_2N(CH_2CH_2CN)CH_2CH(CH_3)_2$ Cl 3,4-dichloro-N-(2-cyanoethyl)-N-isobutylbenzene-sulfonamide	82	M.P. 104°	1135	

TABLE XIX—Continued

Reactants	Re-action Time (Hr.)	Reaction Tem-perature (°C.)	Products	% Yield	M.P. or B.P. (°C.)	References: This Exam.	References: See Also:
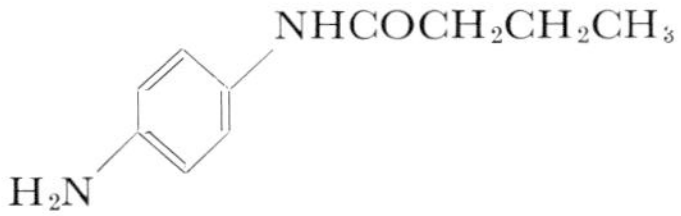NHCOCH₂CH₂CH₃ H₂N p-*aminobutyranilide*	—	—	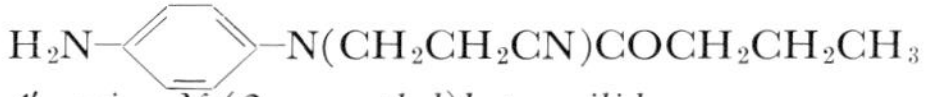H₂N N(CH₂CH₂CN)COCH₂CH₂CH₃ *4′-amino-N-(2-cyanoethyl)butyranilide*	—	—	1218	
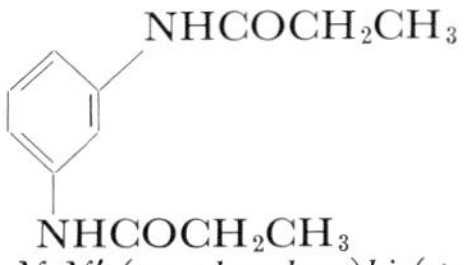NHCOCH₂CH₃ NHCOCH₂CH₃ *N,N′-*(m-*phenylene)bis(propionamide)*	—	—	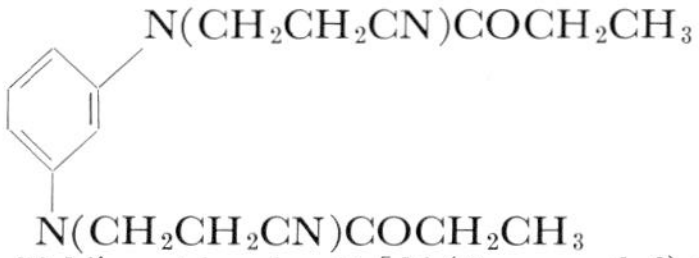N(CH₂CH₂CN)COCH₂CH₃ N(CH₂CH₂CN)COCH₂CH₃ *N,N′-*m-*phenylenebis[N-(2-cyanoethyl)propionamide]*	—	—	1218	
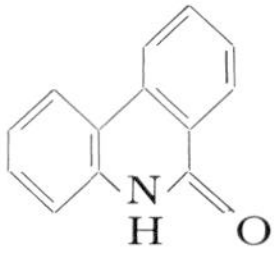N H O *6,5H-phenanthridone*	4.0	reflux	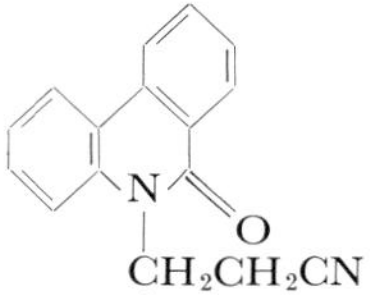N O CH₂CH₂CN *6-oxo-5(6H)-phenanthridinepropionitrile*	98	M.P. 170-170.5°	89	
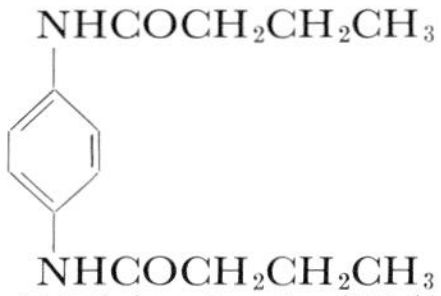NHCOCH₂CH₂CH₃ NHCOCH₂CH₂CH₃ *N,N′-*(p-*phenylene)bis(butyramide)*	—	—	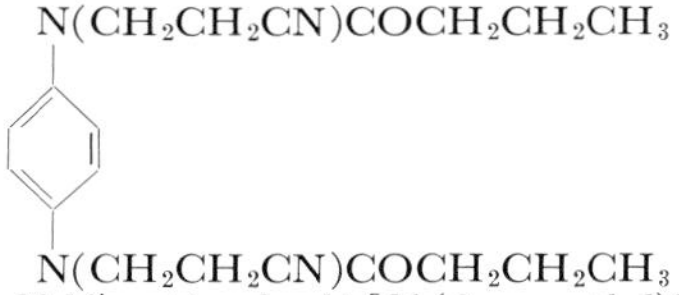N(CH₂CH₂CN)COCH₂CH₂CH₃ N(CH₂CH₂CN)COCH₂CH₂CH₃ *N,N′-*p-*phenylenebis[N-(2-cyanoethyl)butyramide]*	—	—	1218	

TABLE XIX—Continued

(G) Amides

Reactants	Reaction Time (Hr.)	Reaction Temperature (°C.)	Products	% Yield	M.P. or B.P. (°C.)	References This Exam.	See Also:
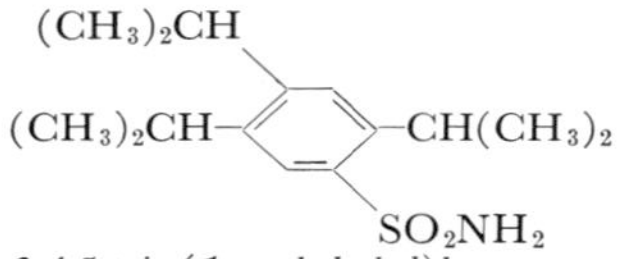 $(CH_3)_2CH$—[benzene ring with $CH(CH_3)_2$ and SO_2NH_2]—$CH(CH_3)_2$ 2,4,5-*tris*-(1-methylethyl)benzene-sulfonamide	—	—	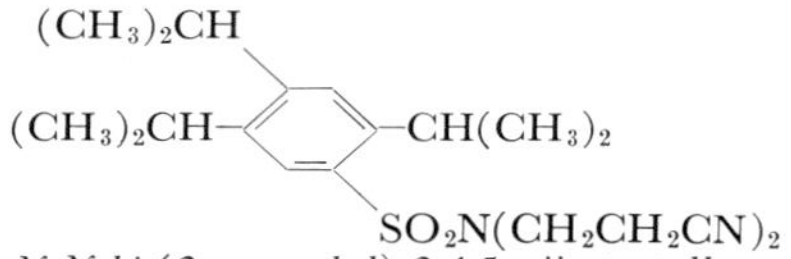 $(CH_3)_2CH$—[benzene ring with $CH(CH_3)_2$ and $SO_2N(CH_2CH_2CN)_2$]—$CH(CH_3)_2$ *N,N-bis*(2-cyanoethyl)-2,4,5-triisopropylbenzene-sulfonamide	—	M.P. 140–145°	1135	
$C_{16}H_{31}SO_2NHCH_3$ ⑤ mixed *N-methylalkanesulfonamides*	—	—	$C_{16}H_{31}SO_2N(CH_3)CH_2CH_2CN$ mixed *N-(2-cyanoethyl)-N-methylalkanesulfonamides*	—	—	1135	

NOTES:

Ⓐ Mole ratio, ammonia: acrylonitrile = 6:1.
Ⓑ Mole ratio, ammonia: acrylonitrile = 0.53:1.
Ⓒ Added after stirring acrylonitrile and amine.
Ⓓ Structure uncertain.
Ⓔ Product decomposes on heating—even at 0.01 mm.
Ⓕ Product not positively identified.
Ⓖ Mixed alkyl groups derived from tallow fatty acids.
Ⓗ Based on unrecovered piperidone.
Ⓘ A small amount of 1,3-cyanoethyl derivative was also produced.
Ⓙ Yield based on unrecovered aniline.
Ⓚ Product isolated after refluxing in acetone was—

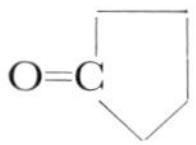

Ⓛ Principally leucine, isoleucine and methionine.
Ⓜ On heating with HCl, this gives 1-phenyl-3-pyrazolidoneimine.
Ⓝ Decomposes during attempted distillation.
Ⓞ Using excess formamide.
Ⓟ Using excess acrylonitrile.
Ⓠ Whitmore et al. (ref. 1145) were unable to obtain a reaction between acrylonitrile and urea.
Ⓡ Based on unrecovered acetamide.
Ⓢ Mixture of hydrocarbons, from 11-17 carbon atoms obtained from Fischer-Tropsch synthesis.
Ⓣ Acrylonitrile and formaldehyde dropped into heated reaction chamber over 3-5 hours, then ammonia added over 5 hours at a rate of 25 liters per hour.

TABLE XX—"O" Cyanoethylation

(A) Water and Aliphatic Monohydric Alcohols

Reactants	Reaction Time (Hr.)	Reaction Temperature (°C.)	Products	% Yield	M.P. or B.P. (°C.)	References This Exam.	References See Also:
H_2O *water*	3.0	30-40°	$O(CH_2CH_2CN)_2$ *3,3'-oxydipropionitrile*	77	B.P. 119-120°/1 mm.	962	165, 179, 885
CH_3OH *methanol*	—	—	$CH_3OCH_2CH_2CN$ *3-methoxypropionitrile*	90	B.P. 164°	716	1106, 248, 53, 27, 1364, 1103
CH_3CH_2OH *ethyl alcohol*	2.0	20-30°	$CH_3CH_2OCH_2CH_2CN$ *3-ethoxypropionitrile*	95.5	B.P. 167-173°	248	586, 1106, 962, 1012, 716, 1103, 53, 27, 655, 1355
$CH_3CH_2OH + Na$ *ethyl alcohol + sodium*	—	—	$CH_3CH_2OCH_2CH_2CH_2NH_2$ *3-ethoxypropylamine*	30	B.P. 49-50°/30 mm.	1179	668
$CH_3CH_2OH + HCO_2C_2H_5$ *ethyl alcohol + ethyl formate*	—	—	$CH_3OCH_2C(CN){=}CHOCH_3$ *3-methoxy-2-(methoxymethyl)acrylonitrile*	26.4	B.P. 94-96°/3 mm.	1431	
$CH_2{=}CHCH_2OH$ *allyl alcohol*	1.0 1.0	45° 50-55°	$CH_2{=}CHCH_2OCH_2CH_2CN$ *3-allyloxypropionitrile*	95	B.P. 77-79°/9 mm.	586	242, 155, 240, 27, 53
$HOCH_2CH(NH_2)COOH$ *dl-serine*	—	50°	$NCCH_2CH_2OCH_2CH(NHCH_2CH_2CN)COOH$ *dl-3-(2-cyanoethoxy)-N-(2-cyanoethyl)alanine*	51	M.P. 210-215° (dec.)	1453	
$CH_3CH_2CH_2OH$ *propyl alcohol*	18.0	25°	$CH_3CH_2CH_2OCH_2CH_2CN$ *3-propoxypropionitrile*	95	B.P. 85-89°/24 mm.	1355	690, 27, 1120, 240, 242
$(CH_3)_2CHOH$ *isopropyl alcohol*	2.0	20-30°	$(CH_3)_2CHOCH_2CH_2CN$ *3-isopropoxypropionitrile*	91	B.P. 83-85°/24 mm.	248	716, 1106, 586, 53, 1334

TABLE XX—Continued

(A) Water and Aliphatic Monohydric Alcohols

Reactants	Reaction Time (Hr.)	Reaction Temperature (°C.)	Products	% Yield	M.P. or B.P. (°C.)	References — This Exam.	References — See Also:
$CH_3CHOHC{\equiv}CH$ *3-butyn-2-ol*	O.N.	<30°	$CH_3CH(C{\equiv}CH)OCH_2CH_2CN$ *3-(1-methyl-2-propynyloxy)propionitrile*	—	B.P. 94-96°/16 mm.	1357	
$CH_2{=}C(CH_3)CH_2OH$ *2-methyl-2-propen-1-ol*	6.0	15-25°	$CH_2{=}C(CH_3)CH_2OCH_2CH_2CN$ *3-(2-methylallyloxy)propionitrile*	63.2	B.P. 209-212°	155	15
$CH_3(CH_2)_2CH_2OH$ *butyl alcohol*	—	80°	$CH_3(CH_2)_3OCH_2CH_2CN$ *3-butyloxypropionitrile*	88	B.P. 206°	716	1334, 1355, 903, 1103, 53, 27, 1421
$CH_3CH_2CH_2CH_2OH$ + Na *butyl alcohol + sodium*	—	—	$CH_3CH_2CH_2CH_2OCH_2CH_2CH_2NH_2$ *3-butoxypropylamine*	44.3 59.6	B.P. 78-79°/23 mm. B.P. 71-72°/19 mm.	117	668, 1452
$(CH_3)_2CHCH_2OH$ *isobutyl alcohol*	3.25	<35°	$(CH_3)_2CHCH_2OCH_2CH_2CN$ *3-isobutoxypropionitrile*	90	B.P. 193-195°	248	242, 240
$(CH_3)_2CHCH_2OH$ + Na *isobutyl alcohol + sodium*	—	reflux	$(CH_3)_2CHCH_2O(CH_2)_3NH_2$ *3-isobutoxypropylamine*	63.1	B.P. 72-73°/34 mm.	668	1179
$CH_3CH_2CH(CH_3)OH$ *sec-butyl alcohol*	3 days	22-30°	$CH_3CH_2CH(CH_3)OCH_2CH_2CN$ *3-sec-butoxypropionitrile*	86	—	248	242, 240
$(CH_3)_3COH$ *tert-butyl alcohol*	—	—	$(CH_3)_3COCH_2CH_2CN$ *3-tert-butoxypropionitrile*	—	B.P. 87°/10 mm.	27	
$(CH_3)_3SiCH_2OH$ *trimethylsilylmethanol*	24.0	<50°	$(CH_3)_3SiCH_2OCH_2CH_2CN$ *3-[(trimethylsilyl)methoxy]propionitrile*	79	B.P. 201.5°	1370	
$HC{\equiv}CC(OH)(CH_3)_2$ *2-methyl-3-butyne-2-ol*	6.0 O.N.	R.T. R.T.	$HC{\equiv}CC(OCH_2CH_2CN)(CH_3)_2$ *3-(1,1-dimethyl-2-propynyloxy)propionitrile*	84	B.P. 96-96.5°/18 mm.	814	155, 1321
$CH_3CH_2CHOHC{\equiv}CH$ *1-pentyn-3-ol*	O.N.	<30°	$C_2H_5CH(C{\equiv}CH)OCH_2CH_2CN$ *3-(1-ethyl-2-propynyloxy)propionitrile*	—	B.P. 104-105°/15 mm.	1357	
$H_2C{=}CHC(OH)(CH_3)_2$ *2-methyl-3-buten-2-ol*	6.0 O.N.	R.T. R.T.	$CH_2{=}CHC(OCH_2CH_2CN)(CH_3)CH_3$ *3-(1,1-dimethylallyloxy)propionitrile*	95 Ⓐ	B.P. 98-100°/24 mm.	814	155

TABLE XX—Continued

(A) Water and Aliphatic Monohydric Alcohols

Reactants	Reaction Time (Hr.)	Reaction Temperature (°C.)	Products	% Yield	M.P. or B.P. (°C.)	References This Exam.	References See Also:
⬠—OH *cyclopentanol*	18.0	20–35° 20–25°	⬠—OCH$_2$CH$_2$CN *3-cyclopentyloxypropionitrile*	81	B.P. 122°/22 mm.	156	
CH$_3$(CH$_2$)$_3$CH$_2$OH *amyl alcohol*	—	—	CH$_3$(CH$_2$)$_4$OCH$_2$CH$_2$CN *3-pentyloxypropionitrile*	92	B.P. 218°	716	27
(CH$_3$)$_2$CHCH$_2$CH$_2$OH *isopentyl alcohol*	—	—	(CH$_3$)$_2$CHCH$_2$CH$_2$OCH$_2$CH$_2$CN *3-isopentyloxypropionitrile*	82	B.P. 99°/13 mm.	240 242	
(CH$_3$)$_2$CHCH$_2$CH$_2$OH + Na *isopentyl alcohol + sodium*	—	—	(CH$_3$)$_2$CHCH$_2$CH$_2$OCH$_2$CH$_2$CH$_2$NH$_2$ *3-isopentyloxypropylamine*	41.4	B.P. 78.5–80°/18 mm.	1179	668
CH$_3$CH$_2$CH$_2$CH(CH$_3$)OH *1-methyl-1-butanol*	—	—	CH$_3$CH$_2$CH$_2$CH(CH$_3$)OCH$_2$CH$_2$CN *3-(1-methylbutoxy)propionitrile*	70	B.P. 98°/16 mm.	240 242	
CH$_3$CH$_2$C(OH)(CH$_3$)$_2$ *2-methyl-2-butanol*	4.0 O.N.	R.T. R.T.	CH$_3$CH$_2$C(OCH$_2$CH$_2$CN)(CH$_3$)$_2$ *3-(1,1-dimethylpropoxy)propionitrile*	10	B.P. 92–97°/18 mm.	814	
C$_2$H$_5$Si(CH$_3$)$_2$CH$_2$OH *dimethylethylsilylmethanol*	24.0	<50°	CH$_3$CH$_2$Si(CH$_3$)$_2$CH$_2$OCH$_2$CH$_2$CN *3-[(ethyldimethylsilyl)methoxy]propionitrile*	82.8	B.P. 225.8°	1370	
CH$_3$CH$_2$CH$_2$CH(OH)C≡CH *1-hexyn-3-ol*	24.0	R.T.	CH$_3$CH$_2$CH$_2$CH(OCH$_2$CH$_2$CN)C≡CH *3-(1-ethyl-2-propynyloxy)propionitrile*	82	B.P. 90–91°/6.5 mm.	816	
(CH$_3$)$_2$CHCH(OH)C≡CH *4-methyl-1-pentyn-3-ol*	24.0	R.T.	(CH$_3$)$_2$CHCH(OCH$_2$CH$_2$CN)C≡CH *3-(1-isopropyl-2-propynyloxy)propionitrile*	61	B.P. 83–85°/5.5 mm.	816	
CH$_3$CH$_2$C(CH$_3$)(OH)C≡CH *3-methyl-1-pentyn-3-ol*	24.0	R.T.	CH$_3$CH$_2$C(CH$_3$)(OCH$_2$CH$_2$CN)C≡CH *3-(1-ethyl-1-methyl-2-propynyloxy)propionitrile*	96	B.P. 67–68°/3.5 mm. B.P. 64°/2.5 mm.	816	
⬡—OH *cyclohexanol*	6.0 O.N.	R.T. R.T.	⬡—OCH$_2$CH$_2$CN *3-cyclohexyloxypropionitrile*	97 Ⓐ	B.P. 130–132°/20 mm.	815	586, 156, 962
CH$_3$(CH$_2$)$_4$CH$_2$OH *1-hexanol*	18.0	reflux	CH$_3$(CH$_2$)$_5$OCH$_2$CH$_2$CN *3-hexyloxypropionitrile*	31	B.P. 115.5°/9 mm.	1120	

TABLE XX—Continued

(A) Water and Aliphatic Monohydric Alcohols

Reactants	Reaction Time (Hr.)	Reaction Temperature (°C.)	Products	% Yield	M.P. or B.P. (°C.)	References — This Exam.	References — See Also:
$(CH_3)_3SiCH_2CH_2OH$ *3-trimethylsilyl-1-propanol*	24.0	<50°	$(CH_3)_3Si(CH_2)_3OCH_2CH_2CN$ *3-[3-(trimethylsilyl)propxy]propionitrile*	53.6	B.P. 242°	1370	
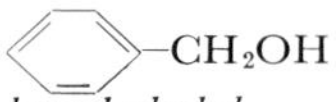 —CH_2OH *benzyl alcohol*	—	—	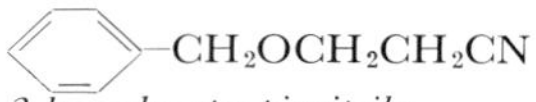 —$CH_2OCH_2CH_2CN$ *3-benzyloxypropionitrile*	94	B.P. 114-116°/0.5 mm.	1106	1334, 586. 53
$H_2C=CHC≡CC(OH)(CH_3)_2$ *2-methyl-5-hexene-3-yn-2-ol*	6.0 O.N.	R.T. R.T.	$H_2C=CHC≡CC(OCH_2CH_2CN)(CH_3)_2$ *3-(1,1-dimethyl-4-penten-2-ynyloxy)propionitrile*	80	B.P. 93-94°/6 mm.	814	1321
$(CH_3CH_2)_2C(OH)C≡CH$ *3-ethyl-1-pentyn-3-ol*	O.N.	<30°	$(C_2H_5)_2C(C≡CH)OCH_2CH_2CN$ *3-(1,1-diethyl-2-propynyloxy)propionitrile*	—	B.P. 111-113°/15 mm.	1357	
$CH_3CH_2CH_2C(OH)(CH_3)C≡CH$ *3-methyl-1-hexyn-3-ol*	O.N.	<30°	$CH_3CH_2CH_2C(C≡CH)(CH_3)OCH_2CH_2CN$ *3-(1-ethynyl-1-methylbutoxy)propionitrile*	—	B.P. 112-114°/15 mm.	1357	
$(CH_3)_2C(C≡CH)OCH_2CH_2OH$ *3-(2-hydroxyethoxy)-3-methylbutyne*	3.0	80°	$HC≡CC(CH_3)_2OCH_2CH_2OCH_2CH_2CN$ *3-[2-(1,1-dimethyl-2-propynyloxy)ethoxy]propionitrile*	65.8	B.P. 144-145.5/25 mm.	1321	
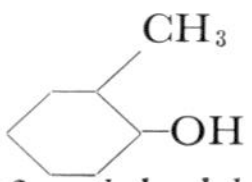 CH_3 / —OH *2-methylcyclohexanol*	—	R.T.	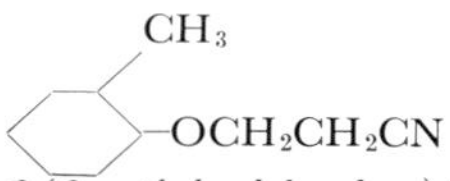 CH_3 / —OCH₂CH₂CN *3-(2-methylcyclohexyloxy)propionitrile*	Ⓐ 93	B.P. 134-137°/18 mm.	815	
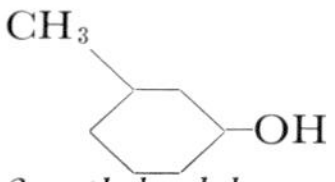 CH_3 —OH *3-methylcyclohexanol*	—	R.T.	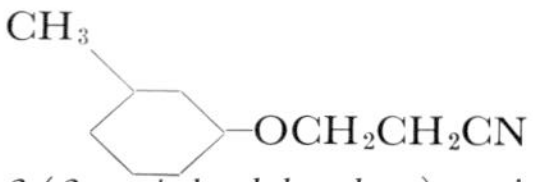 CH_3 —OCH₂CH₂CN *3-(3-methylcyclohexyloxy)propionitrile*	Ⓐ 98	B.P. 133-136°/16 mm.	815	
$(CH_3)_2CH(CH_2)_3CH_2OH$ *5-methyl-1-hexanol*	—	<50°	$(CH_3)_2CH(CH_2)_3CH_2OCH_2CH_2CN$ *3-(5-methylhexyloxy)propionitrile*	—	B.P. 120°/15 mm.	427	
$CH_3(CH_2)_3C(OH)(CH_3)_2$ *2-methyl-2-hexanol*	2.0	25-45°	$CH_3(CH_2)_3C(OCH_2CH_2CN)(CH_3)_2$ *3-(1,1-dimethylpentyloxy)propionitrile*	20	B.P. 105-107°/11 mm.	814	

TABLE XX—Continued

(A) Water and Aliphatic Monohydric Alcohols

Reactants	Reaction Temperature (°C.)	Reaction Time (Hr.)	Products	% Yield	M.P. or B.P. (°C.)	References This Exam.	References See Also:
$C_6H_5CHOHCH_3$ 1-phenyl-1-ethanol	40-45°	1.5	$C_6H_5CH(OCH_2CH_2CN)CH_3$ 3-(α-methylbenzyloxy)propionitrile	79	B.P. 72-74°/1 mm.	378	
$(CH_3)_2C=CHC(CH_3)(OH)C\equiv CH$ 3,5-dimethyl-4-hexen-1-yn-3-ol	R.T.	24.0	$(CH_3)_2C=CHC(CH_3)(OCH_2CH_2CN)C\equiv CH$ 3-(1-ethynyl-1,3-dimethyl-2-butenyloxy)propionitrile	73	B.P. 98-100°/5 mm.	816	
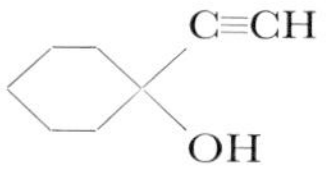 1-ethynylcyclohexanol	R.T.	24.0	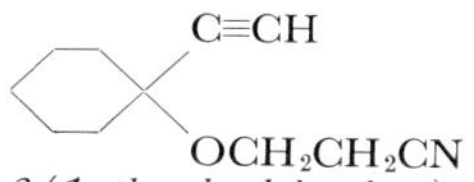 3-(1-ethynylcyclohexyloxy)propionitrile	93	B.P. 92-95°/3 mm.	816	1357
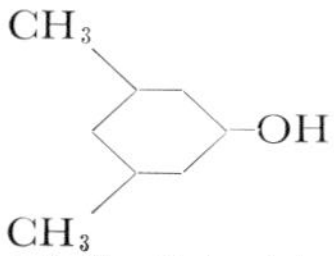 3,5-dimethylcyclohexanol	—	—	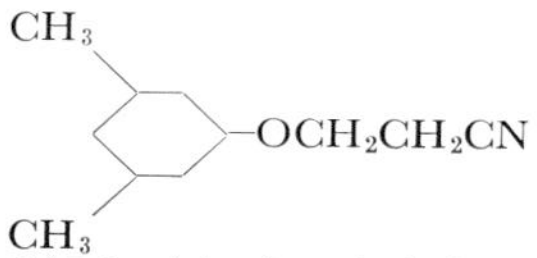 3-(3,5-xylyloxy)propionitrile	51	B.P. 95-96°/0.5 mm.	1106	
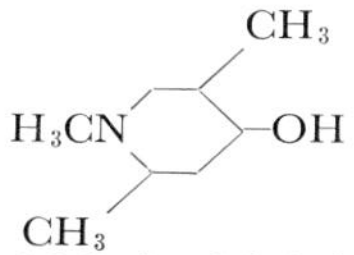 1,2,5-trimethyl-4-piperidinol	R.T. R.T.	4.0 O.N.	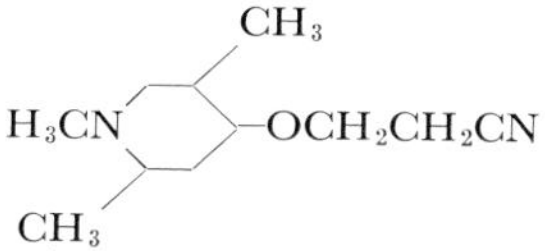 3-(1,2,5-trimethyl-4-piperidyloxy)propionitrile	68.7	B.P. 117°/4 mm.	815	
$CH_3(CH_2)_6CH_2OH$ 1-octanol	40° reflux	1.0 —	$CH_3(CH_2)_6CH_2OCH_2CH_2CN$ 3-octyloxypropionitrile	80	B.P. 150°/20 mm.	716	
$(CH_3)_2CH(CH_2)_4CH_2OH$ 6-methyl-1-heptanol	—	—	$(CH_3)_2CH(CH_2)_4CH_2OCH_2CH_2CN$ 3-(6-methylheptyloxy)propionitrile	—	—	413	
$CH_3(CH_2)_3CH(CH_2CH_3)CH_2OH$ 2-ethyl-1-hexanol	40° reflux	1.0 —	$CH_3(CH_2)_3CH(CH_2CH_3)CH_2OCH_2CH_2CN$ 3-(2-ethylhexyloxy)propionitrile	88	B.P. 100-110°/2 mm.	716	1106, 27

TABLE XX—Continued

(A) Water and Aliphatic Monohydric Alcohols

Reactants	Reaction Time (Hr.)	Reaction Temperature (°C.)	Products	% Yield	M.P. or B.P. (°C.)	References This Exam.	See Also:
 (benzene)—CH=CHCH$_2$OH *cinnamyl alcohol*	6.5	25°	 (benzene)—CH=CHCH$_2$OCH$_2$CH$_2$CN *3-cinnamyloxypropionitrile*	59	B.P. 160-170°/1-2 mm.	155	
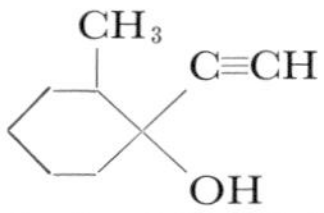 (cyclohexane: CH$_3$, C≡CH, OH) *1-ethynyl-2-methylcyclohexanol*	O.N.	<30°	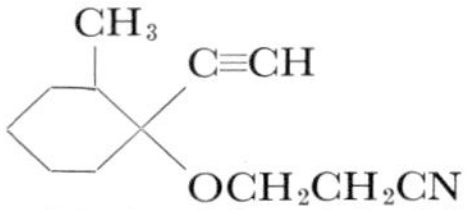 OCH$_2$CH$_2$CN (cyclohexane: CH$_3$, C≡CH) *3-(1-ethynyl-2-methylcyclohexyloxy)propionitrile*	—	B.P. 135-136°/10 mm.	1357	
[(CH$_3$)$_2$CH]$_2$C(OH)C≡CH *3-isopropyl-4-methyl-1-pentyn-3-ol*	O.N.	<30°	[(CH$_3$)$_2$CH]$_2$C(C≡CH)OCH$_2$CH$_2$CN *3-(1-diisopropyl-2-propynyloxy)propionitrile*	—	B.P. 126-128°/13 mm.	1357	
(CH$_3$CH$_2$CH$_2$)$_2$C(OH)C≡CH *3-propyl-1-hexyn-3-ol*	24.0	R.T.	(CH$_3$CH$_2$CH$_2$)$_2$C(OCH$_2$CH$_2$CN)C≡CH *3-(1-ethynyl-1-propylbutoxy)propionitrile*	95	B.P. 98-99°/4 mm. B.P. 102-103°/5 mm.	816	
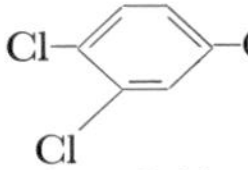 Cl—(dichlorophenyl)—C(OH)(CH$_3$)C≡CH *2-(3,4-dichlorophenyl)-3-butyn-2-ol*	1.5 O.N.	+40-50° R.T.	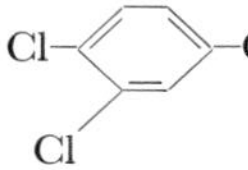 Cl—(dichlorophenyl)—C(C≡CH)(CH$_3$)OCH$_2$CH$_2$CN *3-(3,4-dichloro-α-ethynyl-α-methylbenzyloxy)-propionitrile*	92	B.P. 158-159°/1 mm.	1358	
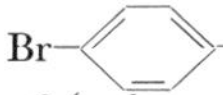 Br—(phenyl)—C(OH)(CH$_3$)C≡CH *2-(p-bromophenyl)-3-butyn-2-ol*	1.5 O.N.	40-50° R.T.	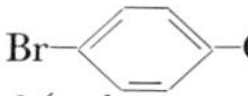 Br—C(C≡CH)(CH$_3$)OCH$_2$CH$_2$CN *3-(p-bromo-α-ethynyl-α-methylbenzyloxy)propionitrile*	90	B.P. 153-154°/2 mm.	1358	
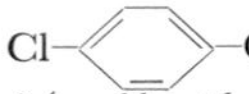 Cl—(phenyl)—C(OH)(CH$_3$)C≡CH *2-(p-chlorophenyl)-3-butyn-2-ol*	1.5 O.N.	40-50° R.T.	 Cl—C(C≡CH)(CH$_3$)OCH$_2$CH$_2$CN *3-(p-chloro-α-ethynyl-α-methylbenzyloxy)propionitrile*	93	B.P. 140-141°/1 mm.	1358	
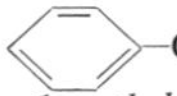 (phenyl)—C(CH$_3$)(OH)C≡CH *1-methyl-1-phenyl-2-propyn-1-ol*	24.0	R.T.	 (phenyl)—C(CH$_3$)(OCH$_2$CH$_2$CN)C≡CH *3-(α-ethynyl-α-methylbenzyloxy)propionitrile*	97	B.P. 115-118°/3.5 mm.	816	1358

TABLE XX—Continued

(A) Water and Aliphatic Monohydric Alcohols

Reactants	Reaction Time (Hr.)	Reaction Temperature (°C.)	Products	% Yield	M.P. or B.P. (°C.)	References: This Exam.	See Also:
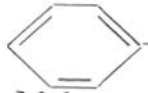 $\langle\rangle$—CONHCH(COOH)CH$_2$OH *N-benzoyl-dl-serine*	—	50°	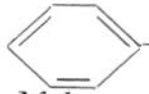 —CONHCH(COOH)CH$_2$OCH$_2$CH$_2$CN *N-benzoyl-3-(2-cyanoethoxy)-dl-alanine*	80	M.P. 143°	1453	
 $\langle\rangle$—CONHCH(COOH)CH$_2$OH *N-benzoyl-l-serine*	—	50°	 —CONHCH(COOH)CH$_2$OCH$_2$CH$_2$CN$_2$ *N-benzoyl-3-(2-cyanoethoxy)-l-alanine*	50	M.P. 95°	1453	
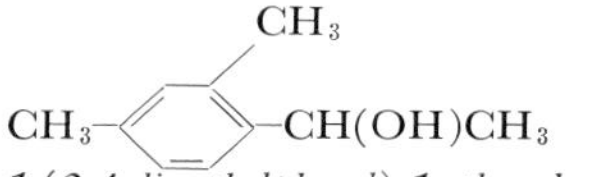 CH$_3$—$\langle\rangle$—CH(OH)CH$_3$ CH$_3$ *1-(2-4-dimethylphenyl)-1-ethanol*	1.5	40–45°	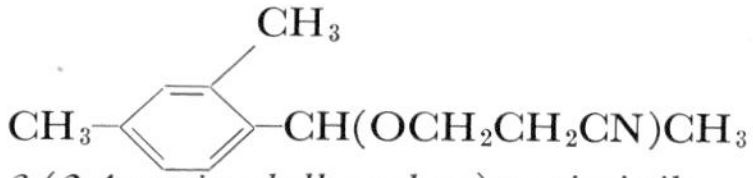 CH$_3$—$\langle\rangle$—CH(OCH$_2$CH$_2$CN)CH$_3$ CH$_3$ *3-(2,4,α-trimethylbenzyloxy)propionitrile*	72	B.P. 150–151°/1–2 mm.	378	
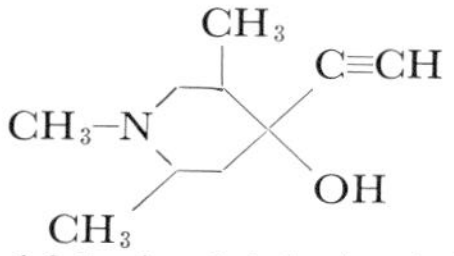 CH$_3$ C≡CH CH$_3$—N OH CH$_3$ *1,2,5-trimethyl-4-ethynyl-4-piperidinol*	O.N.	<30°	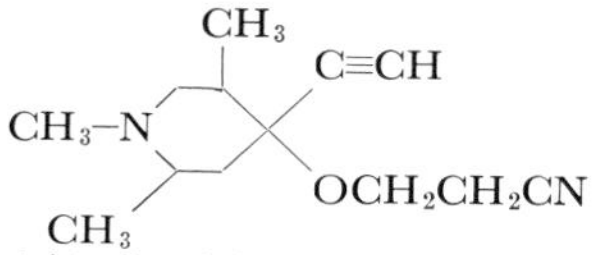 CH$_3$ C≡CH CH$_3$—N OCH$_2$CH$_2$CN CH$_3$ *3-(4-ethynyl-1,2,5-trimethyl-4-piperidyloxy)-propionitrile*	—	B.P. 135–137°/3 mm.	1357	
CH$_3$(CH$_2$)$_5$C(CH$_3$)(OH)C≡CH *3-methyl-1-nonyn-3-ol*	O.N.	<30°	CH$_3$(CH$_2$)$_5$C(C≡CH)(CH$_3$)OCH$_2$CH$_2$CN *3-(1-ethynyl-1-methylheptyloxy)propionitrile*	—	B.P. 115–116°/2.5 mm.	1357	
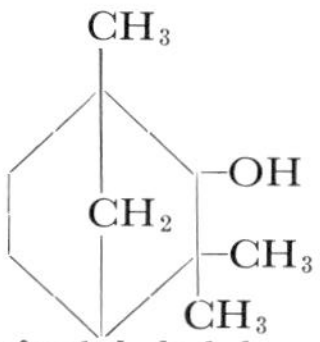 CH$_3$ —OH CH$_2$ CH$_3$ CH$_3$ *fenchyl alcohol*	— 2.25 2.0	25–35° R.T. 45–50°	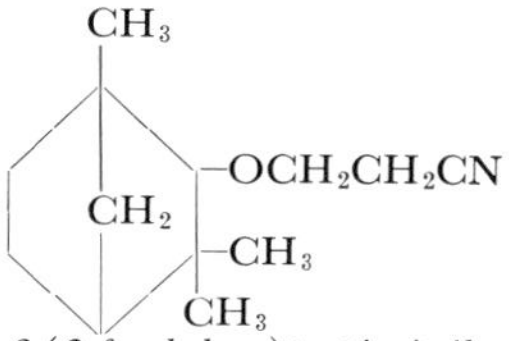 CH$_3$ —OCH$_2$CH$_2$CN CH$_2$ CH$_3$ CH$_3$ *3-(2-fenchyloxy)propionitrile*	—	B.P. 135–137°/9 mm.	156	

TABLE XX—Continued

(A) Water and Aliphatic Monohydric Alcohols

Reactants	Reaction Temperature (°C.)	Reaction Time (Hr.)	Products	% Yield	M.P. or B.P. (°C.)	References This Exam.	References See Also:
(CH$_3$)$_2$CH— ring with OH and CH$_3$ *menthol*	30-40°	several hours	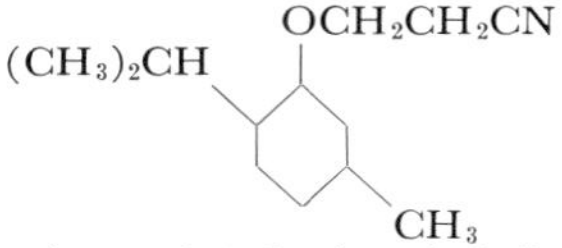 (CH$_3$)$_2$CH— ring with OCH$_2$CH$_2$CN and CH$_3$ *3-(p-menth-3-yloxy)propionitrile*	—	B.P. 149°/10 mm.	156	
CH$_3$(CH$_2$)$_8$CH$_2$OH *1-decanol*	40° reflux	1.0 —	CH$_3$(CH$_2$)$_8$CH$_2$OCH$_2$CH$_2$CN *3-decyloxypropionitrile*	37	B.P. 283°	716	
C$_6$H$_5$—CH$_2$CH$_2$CH(OH)C≡CH *5-phenyl-1-pentyne-3-ol*	R.T.	24.0	C$_6$H$_5$—CH$_2$CH$_2$CH(OCH$_2$CH$_2$CN)C≡CH *3-(1-phenethyl-2-propynyloxy)propionitrile*	80	B.P. 141-143°/3 mm.	816	
C$_6$H$_5$—C(OH)(C$_2$H$_5$)C≡CH *3-phenyl-1-pentyn-3-ol*	40-50° R.T.	1.5 O.N.	C$_6$H$_5$—C(C≡CH)(C$_2$H$_5$)OCH$_2$CH$_2$CN *3-(α-ethyl-α-ethynylbenzyloxy)propionitrile*	97	B.P. 127-129°/2 mm.	1358	
H$_3$C—C$_6$H$_4$—C(OH)(CH$_3$)C≡CH 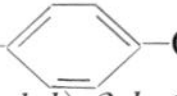 *2-(p-tolyl)-3-butyn-2-ol*	40-50° R.T.	1.5 O.N.	H$_3$C—C$_6$H$_4$—C(C≡CH)(CH$_3$)OCH$_2$CH$_2$CN *3-(α-ethynyl-p,α-dimethylbenzyloxy)propionitrile*	97.4	B.P. 134-136°/2 mm.	1358	
H$_3$CO—C$_6$H$_4$—C(OH)(CH$_3$)C≡CH  *2-(p-methoxyphenyl)-3-butyn-2-ol*	40-50° R.T.	1.5 O.N.	H$_3$CO—C$_6$H$_4$—C(C≡CH)(CH$_3$)OCH$_2$CH$_2$CN *3-(α-ethynyl-p-methoxy-α-methylbenzyloxy)- propionitrile*	97	M.P. 65-66°	1358	
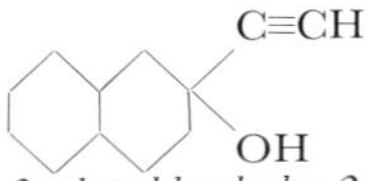 decahydronaphthyl with C≡CH and OH *2-ethynyldecahydro-2-naphthol*	R.T.	24.0	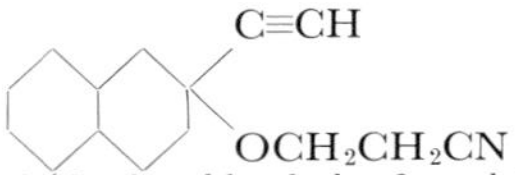 decahydronaphthyl with C≡CH and OCH$_2$CH$_2$CN *3-(2-ethynyldecahydro-2-naphthyloxy)propionitrile*	89	B.P. 150-153°/4.5 mm.	816	

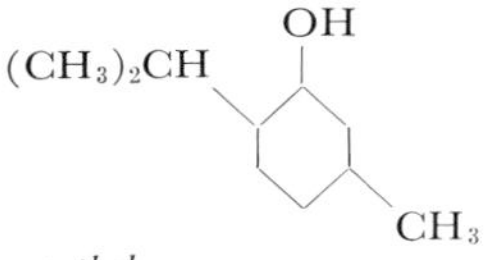

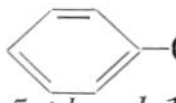

TABLE XX—Continued

(A) Water and Aliphatic Monohydric Alcohols

Reactants	Reaction Time (Hr.)	Reaction Temperature (°C.)	Products	% Yield	M.P. or B.P. (°C.)	This Exam.	See Also:
(structure) OH 2-cyclohexylcyclohexanol	3.0	30-40°	(structure) OCH$_2$CH$_2$CN 3-(2-cyclohexylcyclohexyloxy)propionitrile	—	B.P. 154-156°/1 mm.	156	
CH$_3$(CH$_2$)$_{10}$CH$_2$OH 1-dodecanol	—	—	CH$_3$(CH$_2$)$_{10}$CH$_2$OCH$_2$CH$_2$CN 3-(dodecyloxy)propionitrile	—	B.P. 140-143°/1 mm.	27	
CH$_3$(CH$_2$)$_8$C(OH)(CH$_3$)C≡CH 3-methyl-1-dodecyn-3-ol	O.N.	<30°	CH$_3$(CH$_2$)$_8$C(C≡CH)(CH$_3$)OCH$_2$CH$_2$CN 3-(1-ethynyl-1-methyldecyloxy)propionitrile	—	B.P. 148-150°/3.5 mm.	1357	
(CH$_3$)$_3$CCH$_2$C(CH$_3$)$_2$—(structure)OH 4-(1,1,3,3-tetramethylbutyl)cyclohexanol	4.0	25° 40°	(CH$_3$)$_3$CCH$_2$C(CH$_3$)$_2$—(structure)—OCH$_2$CH$_2$CN 3-[4-(1,1,3,3-tetramethylbutyl)cyclohexyloxy]-propionitrile	—	B.P. 165-170°/2 mm.	156	
$\left(\mathrm{C_6H_5}\right)_2$—C(OH)C≡CH 1,1-diphenyl-2-propyn-1-ol	1.5 O.N.	40-50° R.T.	$\left(\mathrm{C_6H_5}\right)_2$—C(C≡CH)OCH$_2CH_2$CN 3-(1,1-diphenyl-2-propynyloxy)propionitrile	99	M.P. 84-85°	1358	816
CH$_3$(CH$_2$)$_7$CH=CH(CH$_2$)$_7$CH$_2$OH 9-octadecenol	2.0	75-80°	CH$_3$(CH$_2$)$_7$CH=CH(CH$_2$)$_7$CH$_2$OCH$_2$CH$_2$CN 3-(9-octadecenyloxy)propionitrile	85	M.P. 16°	586	155
CH$_3$(CH$_2$)$_{16}$CH$_2$OH 1-octadecanol	—	—	CH$_3$(CH$_2$)$_{16}$CH$_2$OCH$_2$CH$_2$CN 3-octadecyloxypropionitrile	—	M.P. 50°	27	1103
leuna alcohol ®	—	50-60°	cyanoethylated leuna alcohol	—		427	

Additional examples of reactions involving complex monohydric alcohols are contained in the following references: 155, 156.

(B) Monohydric Ether Alcohols

Reactants	Reaction Time (Hr.)	Reaction Temperature (°C.)	Products	% Yield	M.P. or B.P. (°C.)	This Exam.	See Also:
CH$_3$OCH$_2$CH$_2$OH 2-methoxyethanol	—	—	CH$_3$OCH$_2$CH$_2$OCH$_2$CH$_2$CN 3-(2-methoxyethoxy)propionitrile	87	B.P. 98-100°/9 mm.	1106	157, 53

TABLE XX—Continued

(B) Monohydric Ether Alcohols

Reactants	Reaction Temperature (°C.)	Reaction Time (Hr.)	Products	% Yield	M.P. or B.P. (°C.)	References This Exam.	See Also:
$CH_3CH_2OCH_2CH_2OH$ 2-ethoxyethanol	15° 25°	0.75 8.0	$CH_3CH_2OCH_2CH_2OCH_2CH_2CN$ 3-(2-ethoxyethoxy)propionitrile	75	B.P. 128°/26 mm.	157	
(furan)CH_2OH furfuryl alcohol	25-45°	5.0	(furan)$CH_2OCH_2CH_2CN$ 3-furfuryloxypropionitrile	74	B.P. 145-149°/20 mm.	53	155
(tetrahydrofuran)CH_2OH tetrahydrofurfuryl alcohol	—	—	(tetrahydrofuran)$CH_2OCH_2CH_2CN$ 3-tetrahydrofurfuryloxypropionitrile	80	B.P. 100°/15 mm.	1106	157
$CH_2=CHCH_2OCH_2CH_2OH$ 2-(allyloxy)ethanol	18-20°	3.0	$CH_2=CHCH_2OCH_2CH_2OCH_2CH_2CN$ 3-(2-allyloxyethoxy)propionitrile	80	B.P. 110°/2 mm.	980	
$CH_3OCH_2CH_2OCH_2CH_2OH$ 2-(2-methoxyethoxy)ethanol	25-30° 25°	0.75 7.0	$CH_3OCH_2CH_2OCH_2CH_2OCH_2CH_2CN$ 3-[2-(2-methoxyethoxy)ethoxy]propionitrile	64	B.P. 145-150°/10 mm.	157	
$(CH_3OCH_2)_2CHOH$ 1,3-dimethoxy-2-propanol	25-35° —	0.67 6.0	$(CH_3OCH_2)_2CHOCH_2CH_2CN$ 3-[2-methoxy-1-(methoxymethyl)ethoxy]propionitrile	80.4	B.P. 110°/0.5 mm.	157	
$CH_2=CHCH_2OCH_2CH_2CH_2OH$ 3-allyloxy-1-propanol	15-25° 20°	3.0 0.5	$CH_2=CHCH_2O(CH_2)_3OCH_2CH_2CN$ 3-(3-allyloxypropoxy)propionitrile	78	B.P. 138-142°/12 mm.	980	
$CH_2=CHCH_2OCH_2CH(CH_3)OH$ 1-allyloxy-2-propanol	15-25° 20°	3.0 0.5	$CH_2=CHCH_2OCH_2CH(CH_3)OCH_2CH_2CN$ 3-(allyloxy-1-methylethoxy)propionitrile	77	B.P. 140-142°/12 mm.	980	
$CH_3(CH_2)_3OCH_2CH_2OH$ 2-butoxyethanol	30-45° R.T.	— 1.0	$CH_3(CH_2)_3OCH_2CH_2OCH_2CH_2CN$ 3-(2-butoxyethoxy)propionitrile	78.3	B.P. 130°/10 mm.	157	
(furan)$CH_2OCH_2CH_2OH$ 2-(2-furfuryloxy)ethanol	<25° 25°	2.0 0.5	(furan)$CH_2OCH_2CH_2OCH_2CH_2CN$ 3-(2-furfuryloxyethoxy)propionitrile	52	B.P. 152-154°/1 mm.	980	

TABLE XX—Continued

(B) Monohydric Ether Alcohols

Reactants	Reaction Time (Hr.)	Reaction Temperature (°C.)	Products	% Yield	M.P. or B.P. (°C.)	References This Exam.	See Also:
 [C₆H₅]—OCH₂CH₂OH *2-phenoxyethanol*	1.0 18.0	25–50° 25°	 [C₆H₅]—OCH₂CH₂OCH₂CH₂CN *3-(2-phenoxyethoxy)propionitrile*	77.5	B.P. 160°/1 mm.	157	
$CH_3(CH_2)_3OCH_2CH_2OCH_2CH_2OH$ *2-(2-butoxyethoxy)ethanol*	0.58 8.0	10–15° 25°	$CH_3(CH_2)_3O(CH_2CH_2O)_2CH_2CH_2CN$ *3-[2-(2-butoxyethoxy)ethoxy]propionitrile*	70	B.P. 165–175°/10 mm.	157	
 [C₆H₅]—CH₂OCH₂CH₂OH *2-benzyloxyethanol*	0.5 4.0	25–30° 25–30°	 [C₆H₅]—CH₂OCH₂CH₂OCH₂CH₂CN *3-(2-benzyloxyethoxy)propionitrile*	76	B.P. 146°/1 mm.	157	
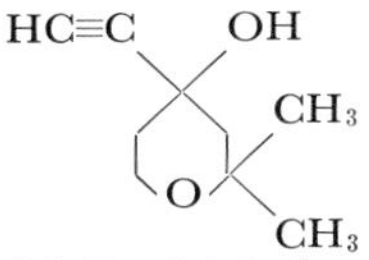 $HC{\equiv}C$ — OH structure with CH₃ groups *2,2-dimethyl-4-ethynyltetrahydropyran-4-ol*	24.0	R.T.	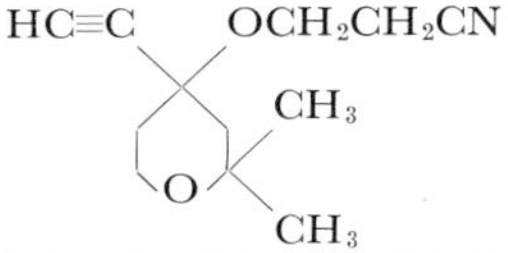 $HC{\equiv}C$ — OCH₂CH₂CN structure with CH₃ groups *3-(4-ethynyltetrahydro-2,2-dimethyl-4-pyranyloxy)-propionitrile*	72	B.P. 122–125°/3 mm.	816	
 [C₆H₅]—CH(CH₃)OCH₂CH₂OH *2-(α-methylbenzyloxy)ethanol*	1.5	40–45°	 [C₆H₅]—CH(CH₃)OCH₂CH₂OCH₂CH₂CN *3-[2-(α-methylbenzyloxy)ethoxy]propionitrile*	73	B.P. 102–104°/1 mm.	378	

Additional examples of reactions involving complex monohydric ether alcohols are contained in reference 157.

(C) Hemiformals (ROH + HCHO)

Reactants	Reaction Time (Hr.)	Reaction Temperature (°C.)	Products	% Yield	M.P. or B.P. (°C.)	References This Exam.	See Also:
$CH_3OH + CH_2O$ *methanol + formaldehyde*	— 4.0 3.0	25–35° R.T. 45°	$CH_3OCH_2OCH_2CH_2CN$ *3-(methoxymethoxy)propionitrile*	44	B.P. 103–106°/26 mm. B.P. 200°/775 mm.	185	
$CH_3CH_2OH + CH_2O$ *ethyl alcohol + formaldehyde*	5 days	R.T.	$CH_3CH_2OCH_2OCH_2CH_2CN$ *3-(ethoxymethoxy)propionitrile*	65.7	B.P. 94–98°/15 mm.	764	

TABLE XX—Continued

(C) Hemiformals (ROH + HCHO)

Reactants	Reaction Temperature (°C.)	Reaction Time (Hr.)	Products	% Yield	M.P. or B.P. (°C.)	References This Exam.	References See Also:
$CH_2=CHCH_2OH + CH_2O$ *allyl alcohol + formaldehyde*	25-50°	3.0	$CH_2=CHCH_2OCH_2OCH_2CH_2CN$ *3-(allyloxymethoxy)propionitrile*	32	B.P. 100-110°/11-12 mm.	185	
$(CH_3)_3COH + CH_2O$ *t-butyl alcohol + formaldehyde*	25-45° 35-40°	0.44 1.5	$(CH_3)_3COCH_2OCH_2CH_2CN$ *3-(tert.-butoxymethoxy)propionitrile*	40	B.P. 75-80°/1-3 mm.	185	
⬡—$CH_2OH + CH_2O$ *benzyl alcohol + formaldehyde*	R.T.	6.0	⬡ $CH_2OCH_2OCH_2CH_2CN$ *3-(benzyloxymethoxy)propionitrile*	40	B.P. 133-135°/0.5 mm.	185	
$CH_3(CH_2)_5CH(CH_3)OH + CH_2O$ *2-octanol + formaldehyde*	30-45° 40-43°	0.33 1.0	$CH_3(CH_2)_5CH(CH_3)OCH_2OCH_2CH_2CN$ *3-[(1-methylheptyloxy)methoxy]propionitrile*	47	B.P. 160°/10 mm.	185	

(D) Dihydric Alcohols

Reactants	Reaction Temperature (°C.)	Reaction Time (Hr.)	Products	% Yield	M.P. or B.P. (°C.)	References This Exam.	References See Also:
$CH_2O \cdot H_2O$ *methylene glycol*	reflux	7-8	$CH_2(OCH_2CH_2CN)_2$ *3,3'-(methylenedioxy)dipropionitrile*	—	B.P. 155-160°/2 mm.	1123	347
$HOCH_2CH_2OH$ *ethylene glycol*	30° R.T.	6.0 22.0	$NCCH_2CH_2OCH_2CH_2OCH_2CH_2CN$ *3,3'-(ethylenedioxy)dipropionitrile*	97.1	—	1360	53, 170, 962, 698, 427, 287, 179, 164, 885, 663, 210, 27, 248, 1097, 1421
$HOCH_2CH_2CH_2OH$ *1,3-propanediol*	20-42° 25°	— 6.5	$NCCH_2CH_2OCH_2CH_2CH_2OCH_2CH_2CN$ *3,3'-(trimethylenedioxy)dipropionitrile*	87.5	B.P. 165-170°/1-2 mm.	170	179, 164
$HOCH_2CH(CH_3)OH$ *1,2-propanediol*	25-28° R.T.	2.0 6.0	$NCCH_2CH_2OCH_2CH(CH_3)OCH_2CH_2CN$ *3,3'-(propylenedioxy)dipropionitrile*	78	B.P. 160-170°/1-2 mm.	170 164	179, 663
$HOCH_2-C{\equiv}C-CH_2OH$ *2-butyne-1,4-diol*	R.T.	48.0	$NCCH_2CH_2OCH_2C{\equiv}CCH_2OCH_2CH_2CN$ *3,3'-(2-butynylenedioxy)dipropionitrile*	96	B.P. 189-195°/3 mm.	814	

TABLE XX—Continued

(D) Dihydric Alcohols

Reactants	Reaction Time (Hr.)	Reaction Temperature (°C.)	Products	% Yield	M.P. or B.P. (°C.)	References — This Exam.	References — See Also:
HO(CH₂)₄OH 1,4-butanediol	1.5 / 1.0	<50° / 50°	NCCH₂CH₂O(CH₂)₄OCH₂CH₂CN 3,3'-(tetramethylenedioxy)dipropionitrile	85	B.P. 165°/0.2 mm. M.P. 36-39°	586	663, 885, 1097, 1360
HO(CH₂)₄OH 1,4-butanediol	1.5 / 1.0	<50° / 50°	HO(CH₂)₄OCH₂CH₂CN 3-(4-hydroxybutoxy)propionitrile	—	B.P. 115°/0.3 mm.	586	
HOCH₂CH₂CH(CH₃)OH 1,3-butanediol	1.0 / 7.0	25-40° / 25°	NCCH₂CH₂OCH₂CH₂CH(CH₃)OCH₂CH₂CN 3,3'-(1-methyltrimethylenedioxy)dipropionitrile	68.1	B.P. 170-175°/1 mm.	170	427, 885, 1097, 164, 1360
HOCH(CH₃)CH(CH₃)OH 2,3-butanediol	— / 6.0	10-20° / 20-25°	[NCCH₂CH₂OCH(CH₃)—]₂ 3,3'-(1,2-dimethylethylenedioxy)dipropionitrile	67.2	B.P. 165-175°/2 mm. M.P. 53-54°	170	179, 1161, 885
(CH₃)₂C(OH)CH₂OH 2-methyl-1,2-propanediol	— / 5.5	23-35° / 25°	(CH₃)₂C(OCH₂CH₂CN)CH₂OCH₂CH₂CN 3,3'-(1,1-dimethylethylenedioxy)dipropionitrile	71	B.P. 126-130°/10 mm.	170	
HOCH₂CH₂OCH₂CH₂OH diethylene glycol	5.0	10-20°	NCCH₂CH₂(OCH₂CH₂)₂OCH₂CH₂CN 3,3'-[oxybis(ethyleneoxy)]dipropionitrile	92	B.P. 185-195°/1-2 mm.	170	663, 1161, 179, 164, 427, 1146, 1360
HOCH₂CH₂OCH₂CH₂CH₂OH diethylene glycol	—	—	HOCH₂CH₂OCH₂CH₂CH₂OCH₂CH₂CN 3-[2-(2-hydroxyethoxy)ethoxy]propionitrile	—	B.P. 186°/9 mm.	1161	
HOCH₂(CH₂)₃CH(OH)CH₃ 1,4-pentanediol	—	—	NCCH₂CH₂O(CH₂)₃CH(CH₃)OCH₂CH₂CN 3,3'-(1-methyltetramethylenedioxy)dipropionitrile	83	B.P. 157°/1 mm.	240 241	
HOCH₂CH₂CH₂CH₂CH₂OH 1,5-pentanediol	1.0 / 6.0	18-38° / 25°	NCCH₂CH₂O(CH₂)₅OCH₂CH₂CN 3,3'-(pentamethylenedioxy)dipropionitrile	80	B.P. 180-190°/1-2 mm.	170	179
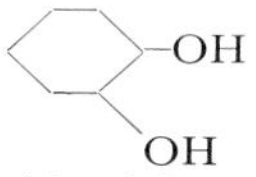 [cyclohexane ring with] —OH, OH 1,2-cyclohexanediol	0.67 / 7.0	35-50° / 25°	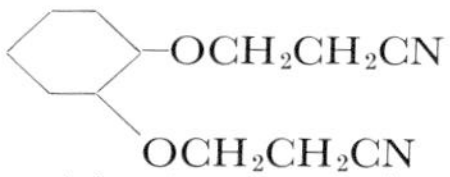 [cyclohexane ring with] —OCH₂CH₂CN, OCH₂CH₂CN 3,3'-(o-phenylenedioxy)dipropionitrile	58	B.P. 180-190°/1 mm.	170	170

TABLE XX—Continued

(D) Dihydric Alcohols

Reactants	Reaction Time (Hr.)	Reaction Temperature (°C.)	Products	% Yield	M.P. or B.P. (°C.)	References — This Exam.	References — See Also:
HO-⟨C₆H₁₀⟩-OH *1,4-cyclohexanediol*	1.5	reflux	NCCH₂CH₂O-⟨C₆H₄⟩-OCH₂CH₂CN *3,3'-(p-phenylenedioxy)dipropionitrile*	—	M.P. 112°	753 754 755	
HO(CH₂)₆OH *1,6-hexanediol*	—	—	NCCH₂CH₂O(CH₂)₆OCH₂CH₂CN *3,3'-(hexamethylenedioxy)dipropionitrile*	—	B.P. 190-200°/1.5 mm.	663	418, 698
HOCH(CH₃)CH₂OCH₂CH(CH₃)OH *dipropylene glycol*	— 17.0	25-45° 25°	O[CH₂CH(CH₃)OCH₂CH₂CN]₂ *3,3'-[oxybis(1,2-propyleneoxy)]dipropionitrile*	73	B.P. 185-195°/1-2 mm.	170	164
HO(CH₂CH₂O)₂CH₂CH₂OH *triethylene glycol*	1.5 16.0	20-30° 25°	NCCH₂CH₂(OCH₂CH₂)₃OCH₂CH₂CN *3,3'-[ethylenebis(oxyethyleneoxy)]dipropionitrile*	77	B.P. 210-220°/1-2 mm.	170	179, 164, 885, 427
HO(CH₂)₃C(OH)(CH₃)C≡CH *3-methyl-1-hexyne-3,6-diol*	O.N.	<30°	NC(CH₂)₂O(CH₂)₃C(OH)(CH₃)C≡CH *3-(4-hydroxy-4-methyl-5-hexynyloxy)propionitrile*	—	B.P. 148-150°/3 mm.	1357	
HOC(CH₃)₂C≡CC(CH₃)₂OH *1,1,4,4-tetramethyl-2-butyne-1,4-diol*	—	35-50°	HOC(CH₃)₂C≡CC(CH₃)₂OCH₂CH₂CN *3-(4-hydroxy-1,1,4-trimethyl-2-pentynyloxy)-propionitrile*	48	B.P. 119-121°/0.3 mm.	1284	814, 1321
HOC(CH₃)₂C≡CC(CH₃)₂OH *1,1,4,4-tetramethyl-2-butyne-1,4-diol*	0.5	105°	[NCCH₂CH₂OC(CH₃)₂]₂C≡C *3,3'-(1,1,4,4-tetramethyl-2-butynylenedioxy)-dipropionitrile*	37	B.P. 149-152°/0.3 mm.		
HOCH₂CH₂(OCH₂CH₂)₃OH *tetraethylene glycol*	1.5 16.0	20-30° 25°	NCCH₂CH₂(OCH₂CH₂)₄OCH₂CH₂CN *3,3'-[oxybis(ethyleneoxyethyleneoxy)]dipropionitrile*	61	B.P. 220-230°/1-2 mm.	170	
[C₂H₅C(OH)(CH₃)-]₂C≡C *3,5-dimethyl-4-octyne-3,5-diol*	0.5 O.N.	reflux R.T.	C≡C[C₂H₅C(CH₃)OCH₂CH₂CN]₂ *3,3'-(1,4-diethyl-1,4-dimethyl-2-butynlenedioxy)-dipropionitrile* — C₂H₅C(CH₃)OH / C≡C / C₂H₅C(CH₃)OCH₂CH₂CN *3-(1-ethyl-4-hydroxy-1,4-dimethyl-2-hexynyloxy)-propionitrile*	40 / 19.5	B.P. 161-162°/0.5 mm. / B.P. 124-130/0.5 mm.	1284	

TABLE XX—Continued

(D) Dihydric Alcohols

(E) Polyhydric Alcohols

Reactants	Reaction Time (Hr.)	Reaction Temperature (°C.)	Products	% Yield	M.P. or B.P. (°C.)	References	
						This Exam.	See Also:
$HO(CH_2)_{10}OH$ *1,10-decanediol*	18.0	25-35°	$NCCH_2CH_2O(CH_2)_{10}OCH_2CH_2CN$ *3,3'-(decamethylenedioxy)dipropionitrile*	—	B.P. 225°/1 mm.	179	170
$(HOCH_2CH_2OCH_2CH_2OCH_2)_2$ *pentaethylene glycol*	—	—	$CH_2OCH_2CH_2OCH_2CH_2OCH_2CH_2CN)_2$ *3,3'-[ethylenebis(oxyethyleneoxyethyleneoxy)]-dipropionitrile*	—	B.P. 215-225°/4 mm.	885	
$HOCH_2CH_2(OCH_2CH_2)_5OH$ *hexaethylene glycol*	17.0	20-28° 25°	$NCCH_2CH_2(OCH_2CH_2)_6OCH_2CH_2CN$ *3,3'-[oxybis(ethyleneoxyethyleneoxy)]-dipropionitrile*	94	—	170	
$HOCH_2CH_2(OCH_2CH_2)_xOH$ *polyethylene glycol*	5.0	30° 30°	$NCCH_2CH_2(OCH_2CH_2)_xOCH_2CH_2CN$ *3,3'-[oxybis(ethyleneoxy)x]dipropionitrile*	94	—	170	427
$HOCH_2CH(OH)CH_2OH$ *glycerol*	2.5 6.0	25-30° 25°	$NCCH_2CH_2OCH(CH_2OCH_2CH_2CN)_2$ *3,3',3''-glyceryltrioxytripropionitrile*	71.3	B.P. 250-260°/1-2 mm.	170	1161, 179, 164
$C(CH_2OH)_4$ *pentaerythritol*	7.0 24.0	40-50° R.T.	$C(CH_2OCH_2CH_2CN)_4$ *3,3'-[2,2-bis(2-cyanoethoxymethyl)trimethylenedioxy]-dipropionitrile*	79	—	170	164
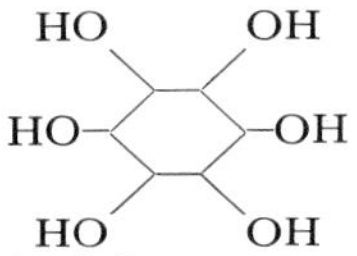 *inositol*	5.0	40-50°	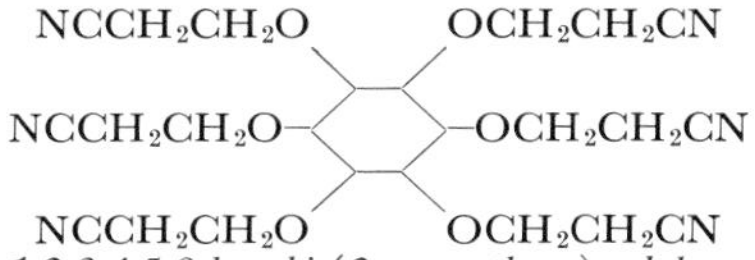 *1,2,4,5,6-hexakis(2-cyanoethoxy)cyclohexane*	—	—	170	
$O{=}CH(CHOH)_4CH_2OH$ *glucose*	18.0	—	$O{=}CH(CHOH)_4CH_2OCH_2CH_2CN$ *6-O-(2-cyanoethyl)glucose*	—	—	427	
$HOCH_2(CHOH)_4CH_2OH$ *mannitol*	10-12	—	$HOCH_2(CHOH)_4CH_2OCH_2CH_2CN$ *3-(2,3,4,5,6-pentahydroxyhexyloxy)propionitrile*	—	—	427	562

TABLE XX—Continued

(E) Polyhydric Alcohols

Reactants	Reaction Time (Hr.)	Reaction Temperature (°C.)	Products	% Yield	M.P. or B.P. (°C.)	References: This Exam.	References: See Also:
$HOCH_2(CHOH)_4CH_2OH$ *mannitol*	5.0	40-50°	$CH_2OCH_2CH_2CN$ | $(CHOCH_2CH_2CN)_4$ | $CH_2OCH_2CH_2CN$ *1,2,3,4,5,6-hexakis(2-cyanoethoxy)hexane*	—	—	170	562, 164
$HOCH_2(CHOH)_4CH_2OH$ *sorbitol*	16-20	—	$HOCH_2(CHOH)_4CH_2OCH_2CH_2CN$ *2-(2,3,4,5,6-pentahydroxyhexyloxy)propionitrile*	—	—	427	
$HOCH_2(CHOH)_4CH_2OH$ *sorbitol*	—	20-30°	$CH_2OCH_2CH_2CN$ | $(CHOCH_2CH_2CN)_4$ | $CH_2OCH_2CH_2CN$ *1,2,3,4,5,6-hexakis(2-cyanoethoxy)hexane*	—	—	164	
$C_{12}H_{22}O_{11}$ *sucrose*	—	—	*colorless viscous oil*	—	—	234	427

(F) Miscellaneous Aliphatic Alcohols

Reactants	Reaction Time (Hr.)	Reaction Temperature (°C.)	Products	% Yield	M.P. or B.P. (°C.)	References: This Exam.	References: See Also:
$HOCH_2SO_3Na$ *hydroxymethanesulfonic acid, sodium salt*	1.0 2.0	60-70° 70-80°	$NCCH_2CH_2OCH_2SO_3Na$ *(2-cyanoethoxy)methanesulfonic acid, sodium salt*	—	—	591	
$NaHSO_3+CH_2O$ *sodium bisulfite+formaldehyde*	—	20-25°	Ⓓ	—	—	591	
$HOCH_2CN$ *glycolonitrile*	0.75	80-90°	$NCCH_2OCH_2CH_2CN$ *3-(cyanomethoxy)propionitrile*	—	B.P. 125°/5 mm.	465	
$ClCH_2CH_2OH$ *2-chloroethanol*	10.0	40°	$ClCH_2CH_2OCH_2CH_2CN$ *3-(2-chloroethoxy)propionitrile*	—	B.P. 126-127°/16 mm.	533	
FCH_2CH_2OH *2-fluoroethanol*	—	—	$FCH_2CH_2OCH_2CH_2CN$ *3-(2-fluoroethoxy)propionitrile*	—	—	952	

TABLE XX—Continued

(F) Miscellaneous Aliphatic Alcohols

Reactants	Reaction Temperature (°C.)	Reaction Time (Hr.)	Products	% Yield	M.P. or B.P. (°C.)	This Exam.	See Also:
$HOCH_2CH_2SH$ *2-mercaptoethanol*	25°	16.0	$NCCH_2CH_2OCH_2CH_2SCH_2CH_2CN$ *3-[2-(2-cyanoethylthio)ethoxy]propionitrile*	98.3	B.P. 218-219°/7 mm.	557	
$NCCH_2CH_2OH$ *hydracrylonitrile (ethylene cyanohydrin)*	—	—	$O(CH_2CH_2CN)_2$ *3,3'-oxydipropionitrile*	88.7	—	667	165, 662, 465, 1096, 210, 27
$CH_3CHOHCN$ *lactonitrile*	90°	0.5	$CH_3CH(CN)OCH_2CH_2CN$ *2,3'-oxydipropionitrile*	—	B.P. 150-155°/20 mm.	465	
$CH_3CH(OH)COONa$ *lactic acid, sodium salt*	50° 50-55°	1.0 2.0	$CH_3CH(OCH_2CH_2CN)COOH$ *2-(2-cyanoethoxy)propionic acid*	—	B.P. 145-155°/0.6 mm. (E)	586	
$FCH_2CH_2CH_2OH$ *3-fluoro-1-propanol*	—	—	$FCH_2CH_2CH_2OCH_2CH_2CN$ *3-(3-fluoropropoxy)propionitrile*	—	—	952	
$CH_3CH(OH)CO_2CH_3$ *lactic acid, methyl ester*	25°	18.0	$CH_3CH(OCH_2CH_2CN)CO_2CH_3$ *2-(2-cyanoethoxy)propionic acid, methyl ester*	51	B.P. 90°/1.2 mm.	900 902	
$ClCH_2CH_2OCH_2CH_2OH$ *2-(2-chloroethoxy)ethanol*	20-25° 25-30°	0.5 2.0	$ClCH_2CH_2OCH_2CH_2OCH_2CH_2CN$ *3-[2-(2-chloroethoxy)ethoxy]propionitrile*	67.7	B.P. 133-137°/1 mm.	157	557
$S(CH_2CH_2OH)_2$ *2,2'-thiodiethanol*	20-25° 25°	1.0 7.0	$S(CH_2CH_2OCH_2CH_2CN)_2$ *3,3'-[thiobis(ethyleneoxy)]dipropionitrile*	92	B.P. 220-230°/1-2 mm.	170	557
$HOCH_2CH_2SCH_2CH_2CN$ *β-(2-hydroxyethylmercapto)propionitrile*	25°	16.0	$NCCH_2CH_2OCH_2CH_2SCH_2CH_2CN$ *3-[2-(2-cyanoethylthio)ethoxy]propionitrile*	88	B.P. 224-225°/9 mm.	557	422
$C_2H_5OCOCH(OH)CH_3$ *lactic acid, ethyl ester*	25° 100°	18.0 1.0	$CH_3CH(OCH_2CH_2CN)CO_2C_2H_5$ *2-(2-cyanoethoxy)propionic acid, ethyl ester*	(F)	B.P. 95°/1 mm.	902	900
$CH_3N(CH_2CH_2OH)_2$ *2,2'-methyliminodiethanol*	<50°	—	$CH_3N(CH_2CH_2OCH_2CH_2CN)_2$ *3,3'-[methyliminobis(ethyleneoxy)]dipropionitrile*	—	—	427	
$HOCH_2$–[S]–CH_2OH *2,5-bis(hydroxymethyl)thiophene*	45° R.T.	6.0 16.0	$NCCH_2CH_2OCH_2$–[S]–$CH_2OCH_2CH_2CN$ *2,5-bis(2-cyanoethoxymethyl)thiophene*	31.8	B.P. 210-212°/0.45 mm.	450	

TABLE XX—Continued

(F) Miscellaneous Aliphatic Alcohols

Reactants	Reaction Temperature (°C.)	Reaction Time (Hr.)	Products	% Yield	M.P. or B.P. (°C.)	References This Exam.	See Also:
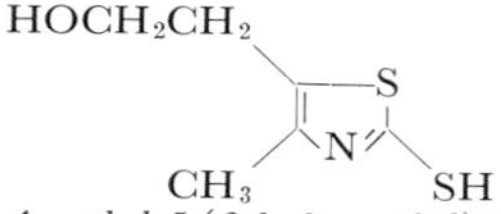 HOCH₂CH₂— [thiazole: CH₃, N, SH] 4-methyl-5-(2-hydroxyethyl)-2-thiazolethiol	R.T.	10.0	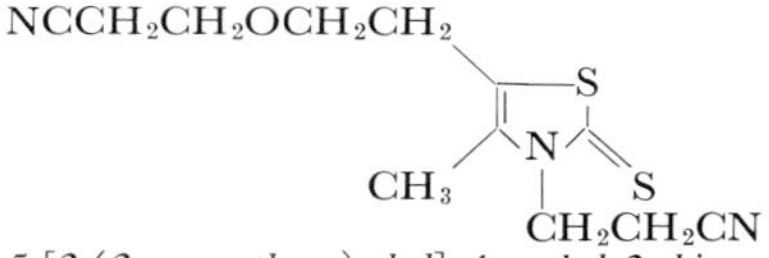 NCCH₂CH₂OCH₂CH₂— [thiazoline: S, N, CH₃, =S, CH₂CH₂CN] 5-[2-(2-cyanoethoxy)ethyl]-4-methyl-2-thioxo-4-thiazoline-3-propionitrile	—	M.P. 62-63°	1181	
HOCH₂CH₂SCH₂CH₂COOCH₃ 2-hydroxyethylmercaptopropionic acid, methyl ester	steam bath	24.0	NCCH₂CH₂OCH₂CH₂SCH₂CH₂COOCH₃ 3-[2-(2-cyanoethoxy)ethylthio]propionic acid, methyl ester	29	B.P. 178.5-180°/2 mm.	557	
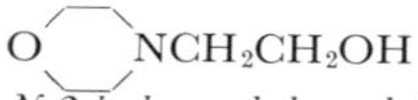 O[NCH₂CH₂OH morpholine] N-2-hydroxyethylmorpholine	25-35° 25°	0.33 18.0	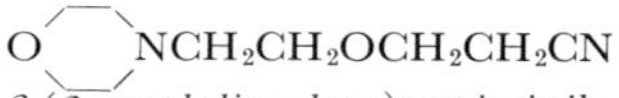 O[NCH₂CH₂OCH₂CH₂CN] 3-(2-morpholinoethoxy)propionitrile	61	B.P. 140-142°/1-2 mm.	161	
(CH₃CH₂)₂NCH₂CH₂OH 2-(diethylamino)ethanol	—	—	(CH₃CH₂)₂NCH₂CH₂OCH₂CH₂CN 3-(3-diethylaminoethoxy)propionitrile	83.5	B.P. 100-101°/5 mm.	59	1146, 161
(HOCH₂CH₂)₃N 2,2',2''-nitrilotriethanol	20-40° 25°	1.0 16.0	N(CH₂CH₂OCH₂CH₂CN)₃ 3,3',3''-[nitrilotris(ethyleneoxy)]tripropionitrile	97.7	—	161	
C₄H₉OCOCH(OH)CH₃ lactic acid, butyl ester	25° 100°	18.0 1.0	CH₃CH(OCH₂CH₂CN)CO₂C₄H₉ 2-(2-cyanoethoxy)propionic acid, butyl ester	50-80	B.P. 55°/0.04 mm. 77°/0.2 mm. 109°/1 mm.	902	900
(CH₃CH₂)₂NCH₂CH₂CH₂OH 3-diethylamino-1-propanol	—	—	(CH₃CH₂)₂NCH₂CH₂CH₂OCH₂CH₂CN 3-(3-diethylaminopropoxy)propionitrile	75.4	B.P. 148-150°/25 mm.	1146	
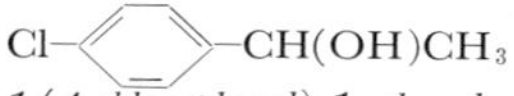 Cl—[phenyl]—CH(OH)CH₃ 1-(4-chlorophenyl)-1-ethanol	40-45°	1.5	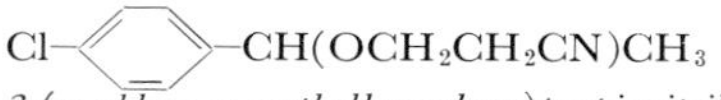 Cl—[phenyl]—CH(OCH₂CH₂CN)CH₃ 3-(p-chloro-α-methylbenzyloxy)propionitrile	83	B.P. 140-150°/6-7 mm.	378	

TABLE XX—Continued

(F) Miscellaneous Aliphatic Alcohols

Reactants	Reaction Time (Hr.)	Reaction Temperature (°C.)	Products	% Yield	M.P. or B.P. (°C.)	References This Exam.	References See Also:
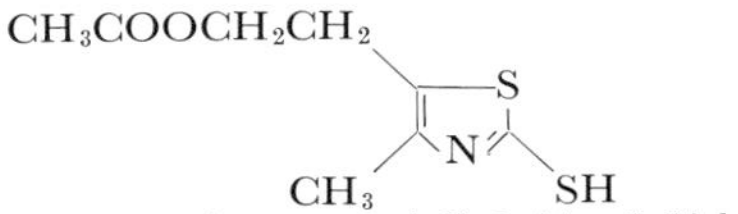 CH₃COOCH₂CH₂ — [thiazole] SH *4-methyl-5-(2-acetoxyethyl)-2-thiazolethiol*	10.0	R.T.	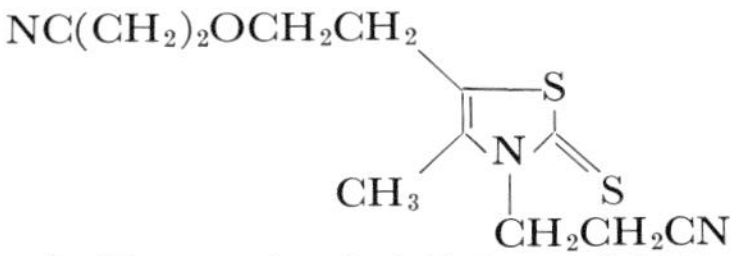 NC(CH₂)₂OCH₂CH₂ — [thiazoline] CH₂CH₂CN CH₃ *5-[2-(2-cyanoethoxy)ethyl]-4-methyl-2-thioxo-4-thiazoline-3-propionitrile*	20.2	M.P. 62-63°	1181	
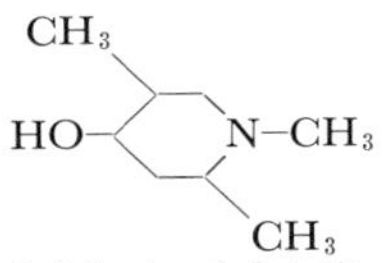 CH₃ [piperidinol] N—CH₃ HO *1,2,5-trimethyl-4-piperidinol*	4.0 O.N.	R.T. R.T.	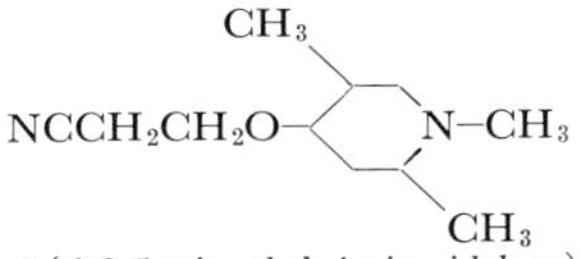 NCCH₂CH₂O — [ring] N—CH₃ CH₃ *3-(1,2,5-trimethyl-4-piperidyloxy)propionitrile*	99	B.P. 117°/4 mm.	815	
(CH₃CH₂CH₂)₂NCH₂CH₂OH *2-dipropylaminoethanol*	2.0	45°	(CH₃CH₂CH₂)₂NCH₂CH₂OCH₂CH₂CN *3-[2-(dipropylamino)ethoxy]propionitrile*	66.9	B.P. 123-125°/3 mm.	59	
CH₃(CH₂)₂CH₂N(CH₂CH₂OH)₂ *2,2'-butyliminodiethanol*	—	35-40°	CH₃CH₂CH₂CH₂N(CH₂CH₂OCH₂CH₂CN)₂ *3,3'-[butyliminobis(ethyleneoxy)]dipropionitrile*	—	—	427	
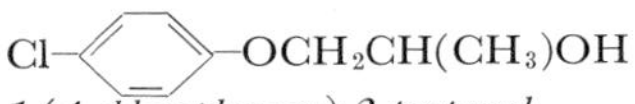 Cl—[benzene]—OCH₂CH(CH₃)OH *1-(4-chlorophenoxy)-2-propanol*	0.58 2.0	25-40° 25-30°	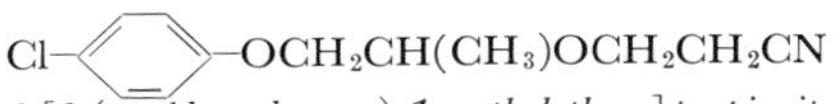 Cl—[benzene]—OCH₂CH(CH₃)OCH₂CH₂CN *3-[2-(p-chlorophenoxy)-1-methylethoxy]propionitrile*	72.2	B.P. 170°/1 mm.	157	
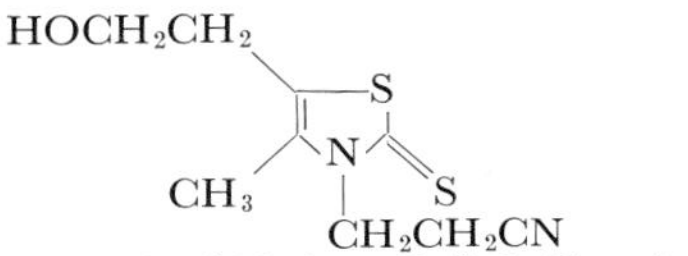 HOCH₂CH₂ — [thiazole] CH₃ CH₂CH₂CN *4-methyl-5-(2-hydroxyethyl)-2-thioxo-4-thiazoline-3-propionitrile*	12.0	R.T.	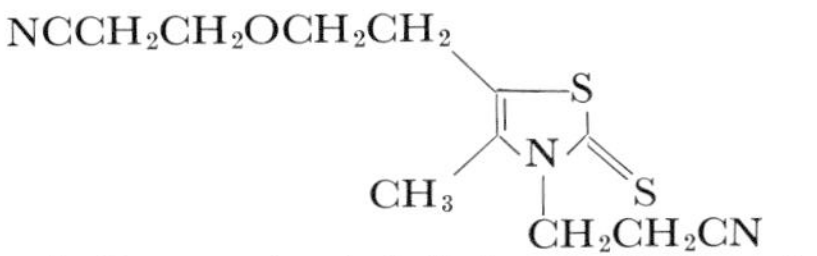 NCCH₂CH₂OCH₂CH₂ — [thiazole] CH₂CH₂CN CH₃ *5-[2-(2-cyanoethoxy)ethyl]-4-methyl-2-thioxo-4-thiazoline-3-propionitrile*	—	M.P. 62-63°	1181	

TABLE XX—Continued

(F) Miscellaneous Aliphatic Alcohols

Reactants	Reaction Time (Hr.)	Reaction Temperature (°C.)	Products	% Yield	M.P. or B.P. (°C.)	References — This Exam.	References — See Also:
$(CH_3CH_2)_2N(CH_2)_3CH(OH)CH_3$ *1-diethylamino-4-pentanol*	—	—	$(CH_3CH_2)_2N(CH_2)_3CH(CH_3)OCH_2CH_2CN$ *3-[4-(diethylamino)-1-methylbutoxy]propionitrile*	66	B.P. 125-130°/3 mm.	1146	
$[HOCH(CH_3)CH_2]_3N$ *1,1',1''-nitrilotri-2-propanol*	18.0	30-40° 25°	$[NCCH_2OCH(CH_3)CH_2]_3N$ *3,3',3''-[nitrilotris(1,2-propyleneoxy)](tripropionitrile)*	ⓖ 100	—	161	
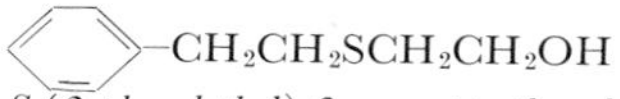 (C₆H₅)CH₂CH₂SCH₂CH₂OH *S-(2-phenylethyl)-2-mercaptoethanol*	18.0	25°	 (C₆H₅)CH₂CH₂SCH₂CH₂OCH₂CH₂CN *3-[2-(phenethylthio)ethoxy]propionitrile*	86.5	B.P. 177-185°/1-2 mm.	316 317	
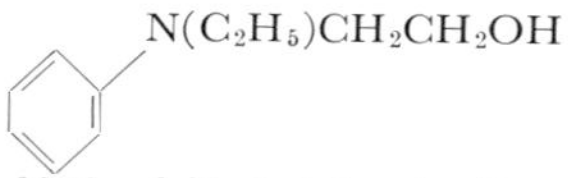 $N(C_2H_5)CH_2CH_2OH$ (N-phenyl) *N-phenyl-N-ethyl-2-aminoethanol*	—	20-30° 25°	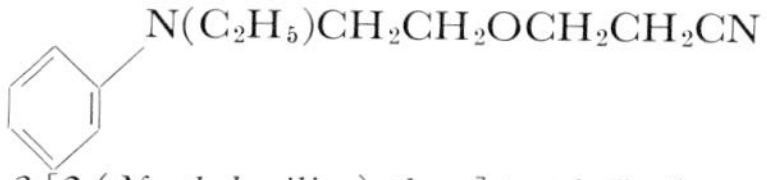 $N(C_2H_5)CH_2CH_2OCH_2CH_2CN$ (N-phenyl) *3-[2-(N-ethylanilino)ethoxy]propionitrile*	66.6	B.P. 180-185°/4 mm.	161	
$ClCH_2(CH_2)_8CH_2OH$ *10-chloro-1-decanol*	2.0	25°	$ClCH_2(CH_2)_8CH_2OCH_2CH_2CN$ *3-(10-chlorodecyloxy)propionitrile*	70	B.P. 170-174°/5 mm.	24	
$[CH_3CH(CH_3)CH_2]_2NCH_2CH_2OH$ *2-di-(2-methylpropyl)aminoethanol*	—	—	$[CH_3CH(CH_3)CH_2]_2NCH_2CH_2OCH_2CH_2CN$ *3-[2-(diisobutylamino)ethoxy]propionitrile*	61.5	B.P. 129-130°/3 mm.	59	
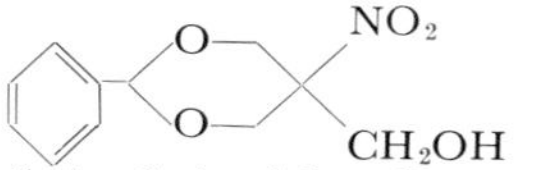 (m-dioxane, NO₂ and CH₂OH) *5-nitro-2-phenyl-m-dioxanemethanol*	O.N.	—	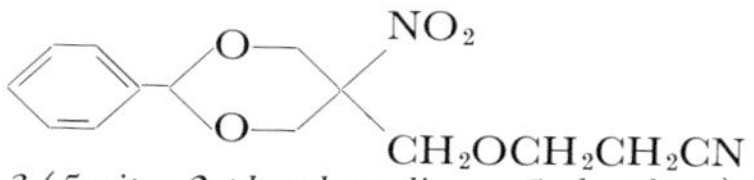 (m-dioxane, NO₂ and CH₂OCH₂CH₂CN) *3-(5-nitro-2-phenyl-m-dioxan-5-ylmethoxy)-propionitrile*	—	M.P. 77.7°	954	
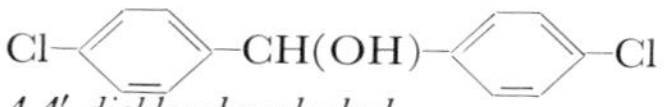 Cl—C₆H₄—CH(OH)—C₆H₄—Cl *4,4'-dichlorobenzhydrol*	—	—	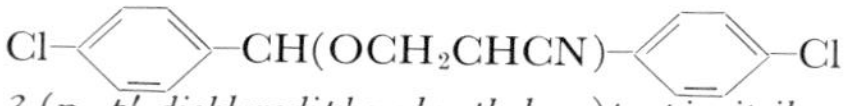 Cl—C₆H₄—CH(OCH₂CHCN)—C₆H₄—Cl *3-(p,p'-dichlorodiphenylmethyloxy)propionitrile*	67	M.P. 75-76.5°	453	

TABLE XX—Continued

(G) Phenois

Reactants	Reaction Time (Hr.)	Reaction Temperature (°C.)	Products	% Yield	M.P. or B.P. (°C.)	References This Exam.	References See Also:
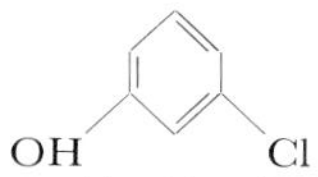 m-chlorophenol (OH, Cl)	3.0	120-130°	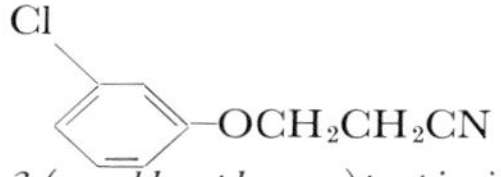 Cl—OCH₂CH₂CN 3-(m-chlorophenoxy)propionitrile	—	—	1104 404	58, 1103
 p-chlorophenol (Cl, OH)	—	reflux	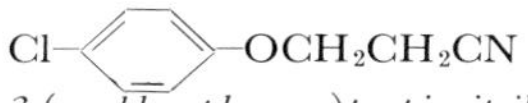 Cl—OCH₂CH₂CN 3-(p-chlorophenoxy)propionitrile	10	—	58	
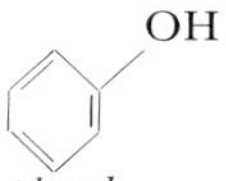 phenol (OH)	5.0	130-140°	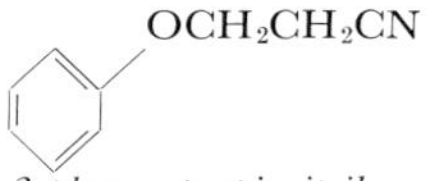 OCH₂CH₂CN 3-phenoxypropionitrile	70	M.P. 61-62°	268	58, 404, 1104, 1103, 1334
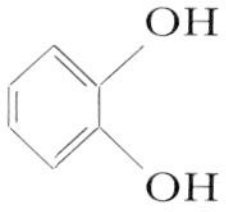 pyrocatechol (OH, OH)	24.0	85°	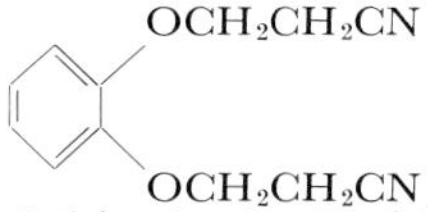 OCH₂CH₂CN OCH₂CH₂CN 3,3'-(o-phenylenedioxy)dipropionitrile	24.7	M.P. 123°	268	
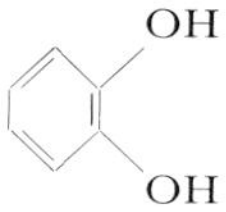 pyrocatechol (OH, OH)	5.0	130-140°	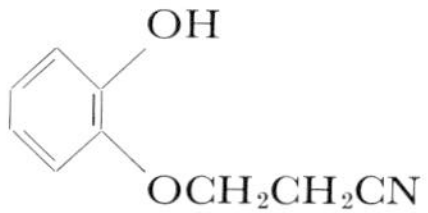 OCH₂CH₂CN OH 3-(2-hydroxyphenoxy)propionitrile	—	—	1104 404	
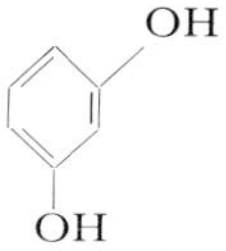 resorcinol (OH, OH)	24.0	85°	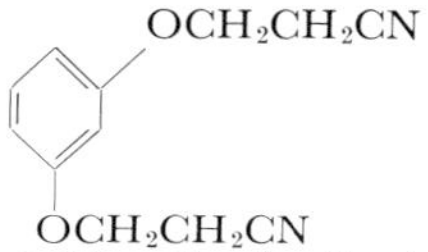 OCH₂CH₂CN OCH₂CH₂CN 3,3'-(m-phenylenedioxy)dipropionitrile	53	M.P. 112°	268	58

3-$(m$-$chlorophenoxy)propionitrile$

3-$(p$-$chlorophenoxy)propionitrile$

3-$phenoxypropionitrile$

$3,3'$-$(o$-$phenylenedioxy)dipropionitrile$

3-$(2$-$hydroxyphenoxy)propionitrile$

$3,3'$-$(m$-$phenylenedioxy)dipropionitrile$

TABLE XX—Continued

Reactants	Re-action Time (Hr.)	Reaction Temperature (°C.)	Products	% Yield	M.P. or B.P. (°C.)	References This Exam.	References See Also:
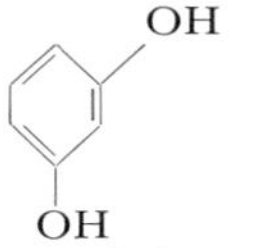 OH — OH — OH resorcinol	—	—	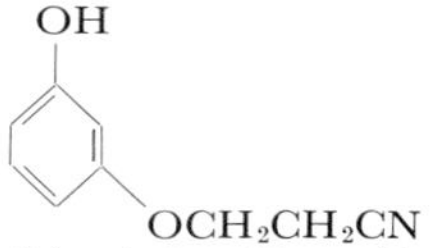 OCH₂CH₂CN 3-(m-hydroxyphenoxy)propionitrile	—	—	1103	
 HO — OH hydroquinone	—	—	 NCCH₂CH₂O — OCH₂CH₂CN 3,3'-(p-phenylenedioxy)dipropionitrile	70	—	44	268, 404, 1104, 1103
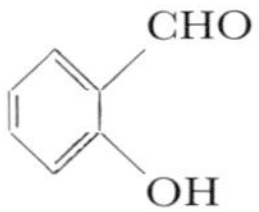 CHO — OH salicylaldehyde	72.0	—	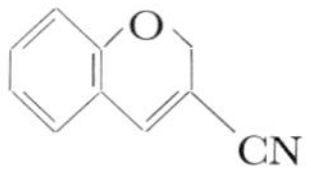 CN 2H-1-benzopyran-3-carbonitrile	19	M.P. 50°	1059	58
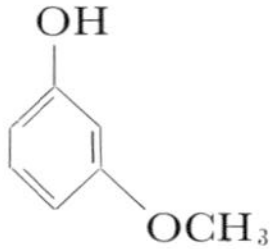 OCH₃ — OH 3-methoxyphenol	20.0	reflux	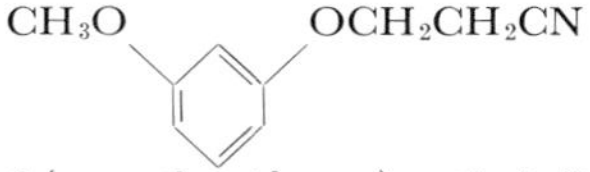 CH₃O — OCH₂CH₂CN 3-(m-methoxyphenoxy)propionitrile	76	B.P. 145-146°/3 mm. M.P. 29.5-30.5°	58	
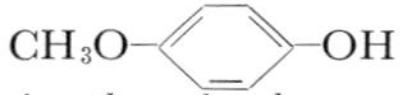 CH₃O — OH 4-methoxyphenol	—	—	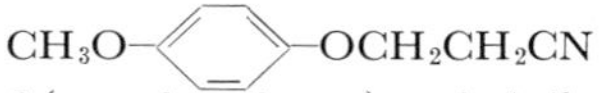 CH₃O — OCH₂CH₂CN 3-(p-methoxyphenoxy)propionitrile	50	M.P. 63-64.5°	879	
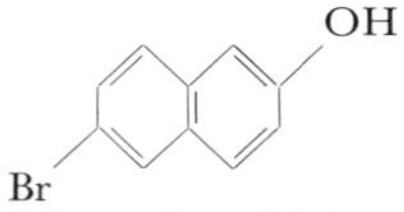 Br — OH 6-bromo-2-naphthol	20.0	reflux	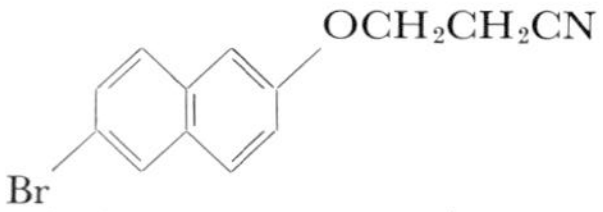 OCH₂CH₂CN Br 3-(6-bromo-2-naphthyloxy)propionitrile	10	—	58	

TABLE XX—Continued

(G) Phenols

Reactants	Reaction Time (Hr.)	Reaction Temperature (°C.)	Products	% Yield	M.P. or B.P. (°C.)	References This Exam.	References See Also:
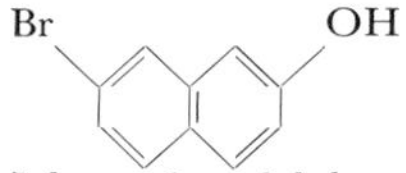 7-bromo-2-naphthol	20.0	reflux	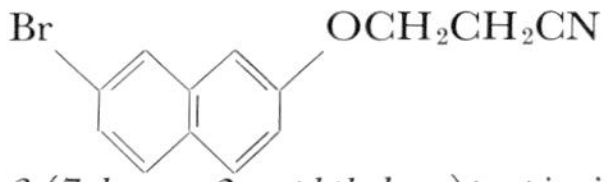 3-(7-bromo-2-naphthyloxy)propionitrile	10	M.P. 120°	58	
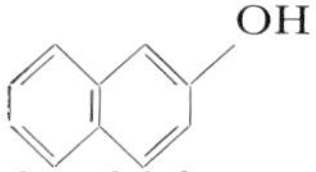 2-naphthol	2.0	reflux	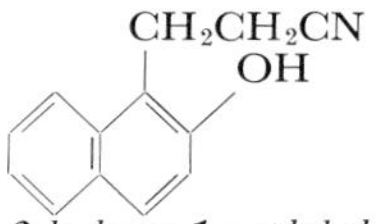 2-hydroxy-1-naphthalenepropionitrile	94	M.P. 142°	467 485	57, 1103, 1104, 404
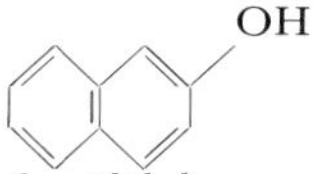 2-naphthol	24.0	reflux	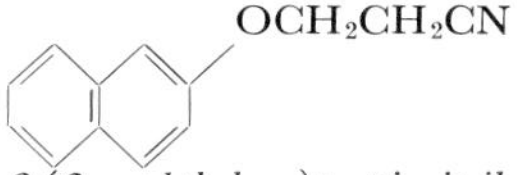 3-(2-naphthyloxy)propionitrile	—	M.P. 108–109°	1349	
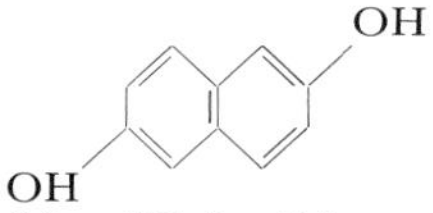 2,6-naphthalenediol	—	—	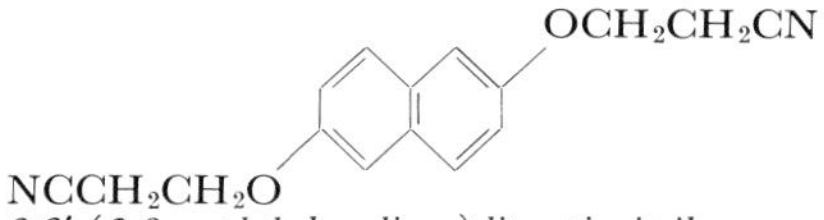 3,3'-(2,6-naphthylenedioxy)dipropionitrile	—	M.P. 194°	268	
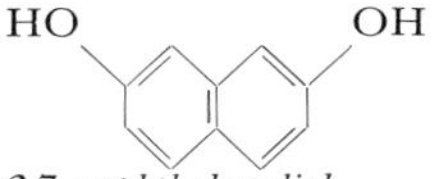 2,7-naphthalenediol	—	—	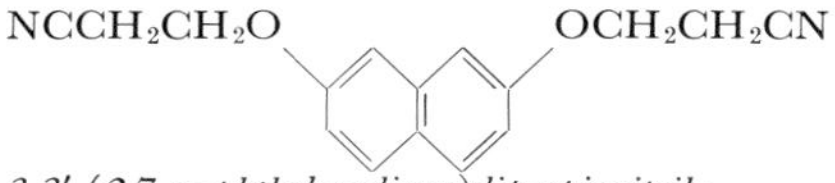 3,3'-(2,7-naphthylenedioxy)dipropionitrile	—	M.P. 153°	268	
 4,4'-dihydroxydiphenyl	—	—	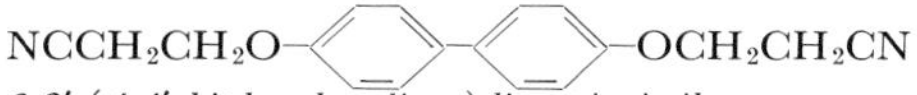 3,3'-(4,4'-biphenylenedioxy)dipropionitrile	47	M.P. 188–189°	268	

TABLE XX—Continued

(G) Phenols

Reactants	Reaction Temperature (°C.)	Reaction Time (Hr.)	Products	% Yield	M.P. or B.P. (°C.)	References This Exam.	See Also:
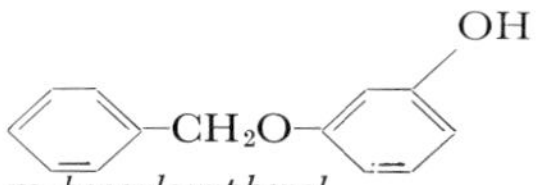 m-benzyloxyphenol (OH)	95-105°	30.0	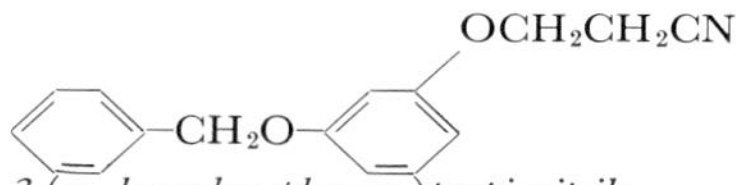 3-(m-benzyloxyphenoxy)propionitrile (OCH_2CH_2CN)	95	M.P. 89-90°	1273	

(H) Oximes

Reactants	Reaction Temperature (°C.)	Reaction Time (Hr.)	Products	% Yield	M.P. or B.P. (°C.)	References This Exam.	See Also:
$(CH_3)_2C=NOH$ acetone oxime	25-30°	14.0	$(CH_3)_2C=NOCH_2CH_2CN$, acetone, O-(2-cyanoethyl)oxime	60.5	B.P. 85°/10 mm.	179	181
$CH_3-C=NOH$ dimethylglyoxamine	25-38° R.T.	0.83 24.0	$CH_3-C=NOCH_2CH_2CN$ $CH_3-C=NOCH_2CH_2CN$ dimethylglyoxime, O,O-(2-cyanoethyl)diether	60	M.P. 123°	181	179
CH_3/C_2H_5 $C=NOH$ methyl ethyl ketoxime	R.T.	14.0	CH_3/C_2H_5 $C=NOCH_2CH_2CN$, 2-butanone, O-(2-cyanoethyl)oxime	71	B.P. 109°/21 mm.	179	181
$CH=NOH$ 2-furaldehydeoxime	30-40° R.T.	0.5 2.0	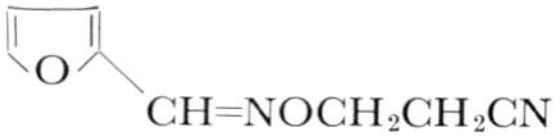 $CH=NOCH_2CH_2CN$, 2-furaldehyde, O-(2-cyanoethyl)oxime	45.7	M.P. 116°	181	179
$=NOH$ cyclohexanone oxime	25-46° 25°	0.25 24.0	 $=NOCH_2CH_2CN$, cyclohexanone, O-(2-cyanoethyl)oxime	—	B.P. 130-135°/8 mm.	181	
$C(CH_3)=NOH$ acetophenone oxime	R.T. 40-50°	2.0 2.0	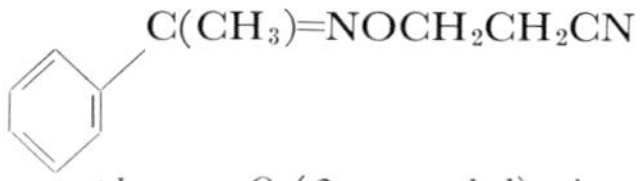 $C(CH_3)=NOCH_2CH_2CN$, acetophenone, O-(2-cyanoethyl)oxime	92	M.P. 44°	179	181

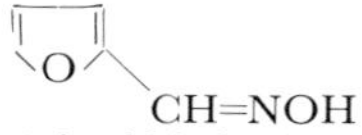

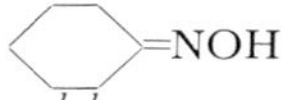

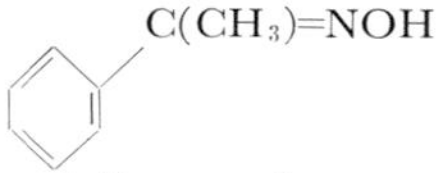

TABLE XX—Continued

(H) Oximes

Reactants	Reaction Time (Hr.)	Reaction Temperature (°C.)	Products	% Yield	M.P. or B.P. (°C.)	References	
						This Exam.	See Also:
$CH_3(CH_2)_2CH=C(C_2H_5)CH=NOH$ *2-ethyl-2-hexenaldoxime*	18.0 0.75	25° 90°	$CH_3(CH_2)_2CH=C(C_2H_5)CH=NOCH_2CH_2CN$ *2-ethyl-2-hexenal, O-(2-cyanoethyl)oxime*	80.7	B.P. 105-115°/1 mm.	181	
$CH_3(CH_2)_3CH(CH_2CH_3)CH=NOH$ *2-ethylhexyldoxime*	— 4.0	25.57° R.T.	$CH_3(CH_2)_3CH(CH_2CH_3)CH=NOCH_2CH_2CN$ *2-ethylhexanal, O-(2-cyanoethyl)oxime*	—	B.P. 90°/0.5 mm.	181	
$CH_3(CH_2)_6C(CH_3)=NOH$ *2-nonanone oxime*	— 20.0	30-40° 25-30°	$CH_3(CH_2)_6C(CH_3)=NOCH_2CH_2CN$ *2-nonanone, O-(2-cyanoethyl)oxime*	84.6	B.P. 102-104°/1 mm.	181	
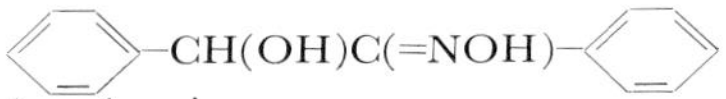 [phenyl]—CH(OH)C(=NOH)—[phenyl] *benzoin oxime*	24.0	R.T.	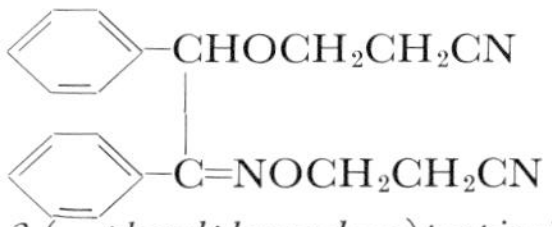 [phenyl]—CHOCH₂CH₂CN / C=NOCH₂CH₂CN—[phenyl] *3-(α-phenylphenacyloxy)propionitrile, O-(2-cyanoethyl)oxime*	96	M.P. 72-73°	179	

(I) Hydroperoxides

Reactants	Reaction Time (Hr.)	Reaction Temperature (°C.)	Products	% Yield	M.P. or B.P. (°C.)	References	
CH_3CH_2OOH *ethyl hydroperoxide*	—	20-25°	$CH_3CH_2OOCH_2CH_2CN$ *(2-cyanoethyl) ethyl peroxide*	—	—	470	
$(CH_3)_3COOH$ *t-butyl hydroperoxide*	1.0	30-35°	$(CH_3)_3COOCH_2CH_2CN$ *tert-butyl (2-cyanoethyl) peroxide*	—	—	470	

NOTES:
(A) Based on unrecovered carbinol.
(B) Leuna alcohol—a mixture of medium molecular weight alcohols boiling in the range of 160-220°C.
(C) Condensation product of 9 moles of ethylene oxide and p-tert-octyl-o-cresol.
(D) Structure not given.
(E) Boiling point of the free acid.
(F) Yields varied unaccountably.
(G) Yield of crude product.

TABLE XXI—"S" Cyanoethylation

(A) Inorganic Sulfur Compounds

Reactants	Reaction Time (Hr.)	Reaction Temperature (°C.)	Products	% Yield	M.P. or B.P. (°C.)	References This Exam.	References See Also:
H₂S *hydrogen sulfide*	—	65-70°	S(CH₂CH₂CN)₂ *3,3'-thiodipropionitrile*	86-93	B.P. 191-194°/7 mm.	421	629, 142, 576, 698, 526
H₂S *hydrogen sulfide*	—	reflux	S(CH₂CH₂CSNH₂)₂ *3,3'-thiobis[thionopropionamide]*	46	—	295	
NaSx *sodium polysulfide*	1.0	25°	NCCH₂CH₂SSCH₂CH₂CN *3,3'-dithiodipropionitrile*	19 Ⓐ	M.P. 47.6°	1037	
NaHSO₃ *sodium bisulfite*	24.0	25°	NaO₂SCH₂CH₂CN *2-cyanoethanesulfonic acid, sodium salt*	96 Ⓑ	—	958	209
KHSO₃ *potassium bisulfite*	16.0	50° 25°	KO₃SCH₂CH₂CN *2-cyanoethanesulfonic acid, potassium salt*	72	—	209	
Na₂SO₃ + H₂O *sodium sulfite + water*	—	15-45°	NCCH₂CH₂SO₃Na *2-cyanoethanesulfonic acid, sodium salt*	—	—	795	
Na₂S₂O₃ + H₂O *sodium thiosulfate + water*	—	reflux	(NCCH₂CH₂SSO₃Na) Ⓒ *2-cyanoethanethiosulfonic acid, sodium salt*	—	—	937	
Na₂CS₃ + H₂O *sodium thiocarbonate + water*	—	—	S(CH₂CH₂CN)₂ *3,3'-thiodipropionitrile*	—	—	526	

(B) Alkyl Mercaptans

Reactants	Reaction Time (Hr.)	Reaction Temperature (°C.)	Products	% Yield	M.P. or B.P. (°C.)	References This Exam.	References See Also:
CH₃SH *methanethiol*	16.0	R.T.	CH₃SCH₂CH₂CN *3-methylthiopropionitrile*	91	B.P. 97°/15 mm.	557	1047
CH₃CH₂SH *ethanethiol*	18.0	25°	CH₃CH₂SCH₂CH₂CN *3-ethylthiopropionitrile*	95	B.P. 100°/13 mm.	1355	557, 469, 448, 449
CH₃CH₂CH₂SH *1-propanethiol*	1.0	<30°	CH₃CH₂CH₂SCH₂CH₂CN *3-propylthiopropionitrile*	78	B.P. 95-100°/4 mm.	469	

TABLE XXI—Continued

(B) Alkyl Mercaptans

Reactants	Reaction Temperature (°C.)	Reaction Time (Hr.)	Products	% Yield	M.P. or B.P. (°C.)	References This Exam.	See Also:
$(CH_3)_2CHSH$ *2-propanethiol*	R.T.	16.0	$(CH_3)_2CHSCH_2CH_2CN$ *3-isopropylthiopropionitrile*	95	B.P. 102.5-103°/12 mm.	557	
$CH_3CH_2CH_2CH_2SH$ *1-butanethiol*	35-40°	0.5	$CH_3CH_2CH_2CH_2SCH_2CH_2CN$ *3-butylthiopropionitrile*	98	B.P. 117°/3 mm.	1131	557, 469
$(CH_3)_2CHCH_2SH$ *2-methyl-1-propanethiol*	R.T.	1.0	$(CH_3)_2CHCH_2SCH_2CH_2CN$ *3-isobutylthiopropionitrile*	85	B.P. 132.5-133°/30 mm. B.P. 106°/6 mm.	557	
$(CH_3)_3CSH$ *2-methyl-2-propanethiol*	—	—	$(CH_3)_3CSCH_2CH_2CN$ *3-tert-butylthiopropionitrile*	95	B.P. 113.5-114°/17 mm.	557	
$(CH_3)_3SiCH_2SH$ *trimethylsilylmethanethiol*	—	—	$(CH_3)_3SiCH_2SCH_2CH_2CN$ *3-(trimethylsilylmethylthio)propionitrile*	88.5	B.P. 250°	1347	
$CH_3Si(C_2H_5)_2CH_2SH$ *diethylmethylsilylmethanethiol*	—	—	$CH_3Si(C_2H_5)_2CH_2SCH_2CH_2CN$ *3-(diethylmethylsilylmethylthio)propionitrile*	79.5	B.P. 100.5°/2 mm.	1347	
$(CH_3)_3SiCH_2CH_2CH_2SH$ *3-trimethylsilyl-1-propanethiol*	—	—	$(CH_3)_3SiCH_2CH_2CH_2SCH_2CH_2CN$ *3-(3-trimethylsilylpropylthio)propionitrile*	71	B.P. 108.5°/1 mm.	1347	
 ⬡—CH_2SH *α-toluenethiol*	—	—	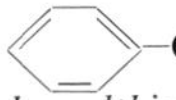 ⬡—$CH_2SCH_2CH_2CN$ *benzylthiopropionitrile*	95	B.P. 131°/0.9 mm.	1047	557, 449
$CH_3(CH_2)_7SH$ *1-octanethiol*	40-50° R.T.	1.0 O.N.	$CH_3(CH_2)_7SCH_2CH_2CN$ *3-octylthiopropionitrile*	63	—	897	
octanethiol ①	<50° 50-60°	during addn. 2.0	—	—	—	1009	
$CH_3Si(CH_2CH_2CH_3)_2CH_2SH$ *dipropylmethylsilylmethanethiol*	—	—	$CH_3Si(C_3H_7)_2CH_2SCH_2CH_2CN$ *3-[(methyldipropylsilyl)methylthio]propionitrile*	70.5	B.P. 124-125°/2 mm.	1347	

TABLE XXI—Continued

(B) Alkyl Mercaptans

Reactants	Reaction Time (Hr.)	Reaction Temperature (°C.)	Products	% Yield	M.P. or B.P. (°C.)	References This Exam.	See Also:
$CH_3(CH_2)_8SH$ *1-nonanethiol*	1.0 O.N.	40-50° R.T.	$CH_3(CH_2)_8SCH_2CH_2CN$ *3-nonylthiopropionitrile*	48	—	897	
$CH_3(CH_2)_9SH$ *1-decanethiol*	0.5 1.0	40-50° —	$CH_3(CH_2)_9SCH_2CH_2CN$ *3-decylthiopropionitrile*	69	B.P. 154-156°/3 mm.	994	
$CH_3(CH_2)_{10}CH_2SH$ *1-dodecanethiol*	—	—	$CH_3(CH_2)_{10}CH_2SCH_2CH_2CN$ *3-dodecylthiopropionitrile*	81	B.P. 197-198°/4 mm. M.P. 21°	994	897, 469
dodecanethiol Ⓔ	dur- ing addn. 2.0	<50° 50-60°	—	—	—	1009	
$CH_3(CH_2)_{17}SH$ *1-octadecanethiol*	—	—	$CH_3(CH_2)_{17}SCH_2CH_2CN$ *3-octadecylthiopropionitrile*	70	M.P. 50-51°	994	

(C) Miscellaneous Mercaptans

Reactants	Reaction Time (Hr.)	Reaction Temperature (°C.)	Products	% Yield	M.P. or B.P. (°C.)	References This Exam.	See Also:
CH_3COSH *thioacetic acid*	2.0	38-105°	$CH_3COSCH_2CH_2CN$ *thiolacetic acid, 2-cyanoethyl ester*	88.6	—	289 288	
$HSCH_2COOH$ *thiolacetic acid*	—	—	$HOOCCH_2SCH_2CH_2CN$ *(2-cyanoethylthio)acetic acid*	77	—	1398	791
$HOCH_2CH_2SH$ *2-mercaptoethanol*	0.5 16.0	55-60° R.T.	$HOCH_2CH_2SCH_2CH_2CN$ *3-(2-hydroxyethylthio)propionitrile*	92-94	B.P. 178-180°/14 mm.	422	557, 448, 449
$HSCH_2CH_2SH$ *1,2-ethanedithiol*	1.0 —	40-50°	$NCCH_2CH_2SCH_2CH_2SH$ *3-(2-mercaptoethylthio)propionitrile*	26	B.P. 139-141°/6 mm.	449	448
$HSCH_2CH_2SH$ *1,2-ethanedithiol*	1.0 —	40-50°	$NCCH_2CH_2SCH_2CH_2SCH_2CH_2CN$ Ⓔ *3,3'-(ethylenedithio)dipropionitrile*	—	M.P. 151°	448	449

TABLE XXI—Continued

(C) Miscellaneous Mercaptans

Reactants	Reaction Time (Hr.)	Reaction Temperature (°C.)	Products	% Yield	M.P. or B.P. (°C.)	References This Exam.	References See Also:
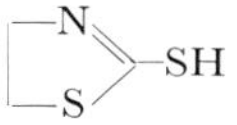 [thiazoline structure] SH *2-thiazoline-2-thiol*	2.0	<30°	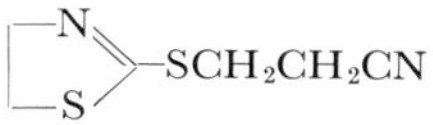 [structure]—SCH$_2$CH$_2$CN *3-(2-thiazolin-2-ylthio)propionitrile*	70	—	469	
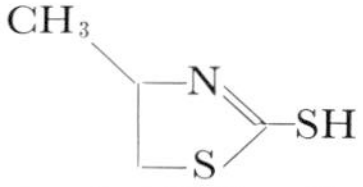 CH$_3$ [thiazoline structure] SH *4-methyl-2-thiazoline-2-thiol*	2.0	<30°	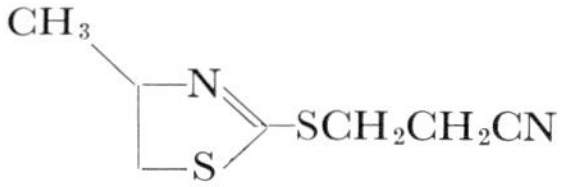 CH$_3$ [structure]—SCH$_2$CH$_2$CN *3-(4-methyl-2-thiazolin-2-ylthio)propionitrile*	—	—	469	
CH$_3$CH$_2$OOCCH$_2$SH *thiolacetic acid, ethyl ester*	0.5	R.T.	CH$_3$CH$_2$OOCCH$_2$SCH$_2$CH$_2$CN *(2-cyanoethylthio)acetic acid, ethyl ester*	89	B.P. 169°/16 mm.	557	791
(C$_2$H$_5$O)$_2$PSSH *phosphorodithioic acid, O,O'-diethyl ester*	22.0	R.T.	(C$_2$H$_5$O)$_2$PSSCH$_2$CH$_2$CN *phosphorodithioic acid, S-(2-cyanoethyl) O,O-diethyl ester*	—	—	87	
 [thiophene structure] CH$_2$SH *2-thiomethylthiophene*	1.0	reflux	 [thiophene structure] CH$_2$SCH$_2$CH$_2$CN *3-(2-thenylthio)propionitrile*	47	B.P. 127-130°/2.5 mm.	635	
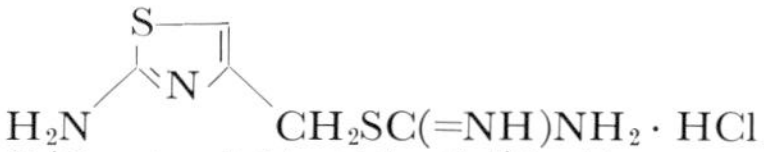 H$_2$N—[thiazole structure]—CH$_2$SC(=NH)NH$_2$ · HCl *S-(2-amino-4-thiazolylmethyl)isothiourea hydrochloride*	3 min.	R.T.	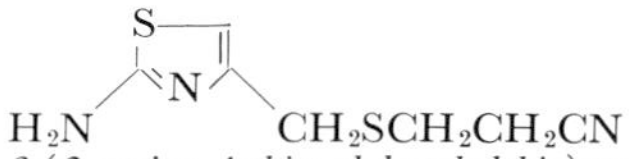 H$_2$N—[thiazole structure]—CH$_2$SCH$_2$CH$_2$CN *3-(2-amino-4-thiazolylmethylthio)propionitrile*	—	M.P. 110-111°	1017	
(C$_2$H$_5$)$_2$NCH$_2$CH$_2$SH *2-diethylaminoethanethiol*	O.N.	R.T.	(C$_2$H$_5$)$_2$NCH$_2$CH$_2$SCH$_2$CH$_2$CN *3-(2-diethylaminoethylthio)propionitrile*	92	B.P. 111°/2.5 mm.	253	

TABLE XXI—Continued

(C) Miscellaneous Mercaptans

Reactants	Reaction Temperature (°C.)	Reaction Time (Hr.)	Products	% Yield	M.P. or B.P. (°C.)	References This Exam.	References See Also:
[structure] 2-benzoxazolethiol	R.T.	45.0	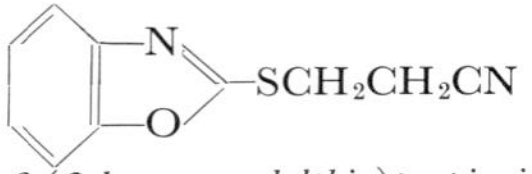 [structure] SCH_2CH_2CN 3-(2-benzoxazolylthio)propionitrile	88	M.P. 173-173.5°	557	
[structure] 2-benzothiazolethiol	R.T.	16.0	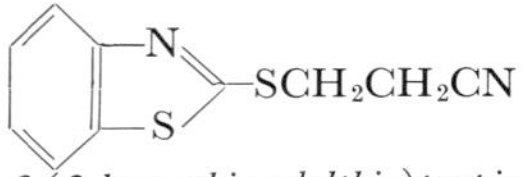 [structure] SCH_2CH_2CN 3-(2-benzothiazolylthio)propionitrile	87	M.P. 167°	557	250, 469
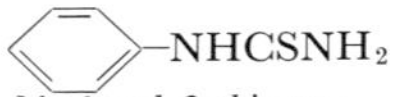 $NHCSNH_2$ N-phenyl-2-thiourea	—	—	—	—	—	376	
$CH_3OOC(CH_2)_3CH(SH)COOCH_3$ 2-thiol-1,6-hexanedioic acid, dimethyl ester	reflux	2.0	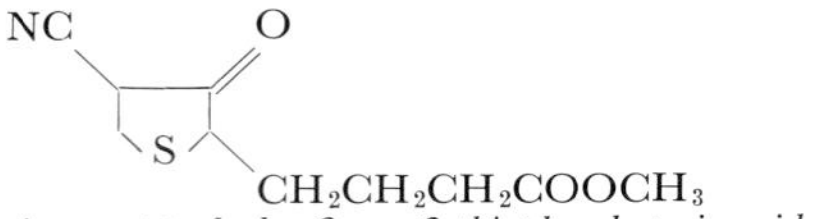 [structure] $CH_2CH_2CH_2COOCH_3$ 4-cyanotetrahydro-3-oxo-2-thiophenebutyric acid, methyl ester	81	—	68	
 NHCSNH [phenyl] thiocarbanilide	—	2.0	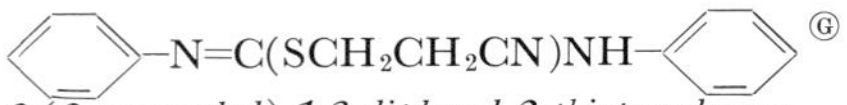 $-N{=}C(SCH_2CH_2CN)NH-$ 2-(2-cyanoethyl)-1,3-diphenyl-2-thiopseudourea	—	—	469	
HS–R–SH dimercaptans	—	—	$NCCH_2CH_2S-R-SCH_2CH_2CN$	—	—	142	

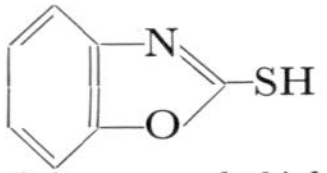

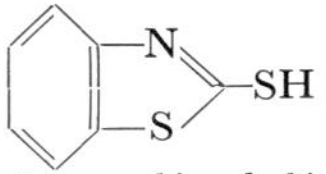

TABLE XXI—Continued

(D) Thiophenols

Reactants	Reaction Time (Hr.)	Reaction Temperature (°C.)	Products	% Yield	M.P. or B.P. (°C.)	This Exam.	See Also:
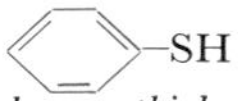 benzenethiol (SH on benzene)	16.0	R.T.	 $—SCH_2CH_2CN$ 3-phenylthiopropionitrile	97	B.P. 154°/8 mm.	557	469, 49
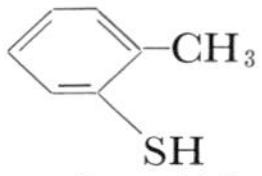 o-toluenethiol (CH_3, SH)	16.0	R.T.	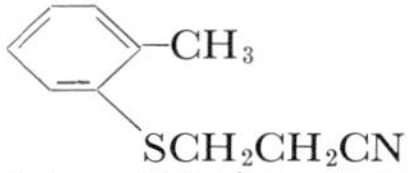 $—SCH_2CH_2CN$ (CH_3) 3-(o-tolylthio)propionitrile	81	B.P. 177.5°/16 mm.	557	
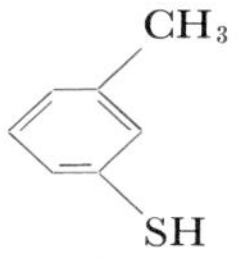 m-toluenethiol (CH_3, SH)	16.0	R.T.	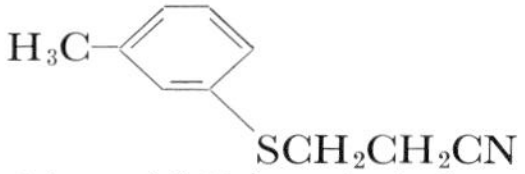 H_3C— SCH_2CH_2CN 3-(m-tolylthio)propionitrile	97	B.P. 177.5°/18 mm.	557	
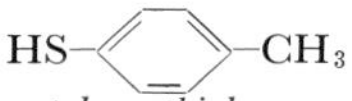 p-toluenethiol (HS—CH_3)	16.0	R.T.	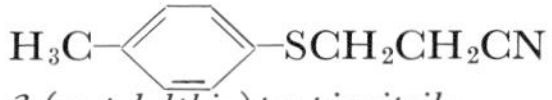 H_3C—SCH_2CH_2CN 3-(p-tolylthio)propionitrile	95	B.P. 178.5°/17 mm.	557	469
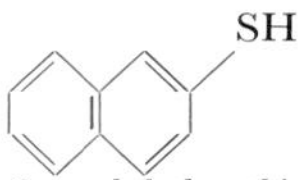 2-naphthalenethiol (SH)	1.0	65°	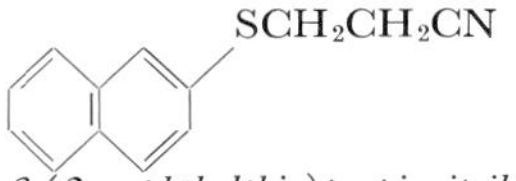 SCH_2CH_2CN 3-(2-naphthylthio)propionitrile	92	B.P. 178-179°	57	469

(E) Thiocarbamates

Reactants	Reaction Time (Hr.)	Reaction Temperature (°C.)	Products	% Yield	M.P. or B.P. (°C.)	This Exam.	See Also:
H_2NCSNH_2 thiourea	— 3.0	<30° —	$H_2NC(=NH)SCH_2CH_2CN$ ⊙ 2-(2-cyanoethyl)-2-thiopseudourea	94	—	469	
$H_2NCSSNH_4$ ammonium dithiocarbamate	— —	20-30° 50°	(II)	—	B.P. 150°	604	

TABLE XXI—Continued

(E) Thiocarbamates

Reactants	Reaction Time (Hr.)	Reaction Temperature (°C.)	Products	% Yield	M.P. or B.P. (°C.)	References This Exam.	See Also:
$(CH_3)_2NCSSNa$ *N,N-dimethyldithiocarbamic acid, sodium salt*	—	R.T.	$(CH_3)_2NCSSCH_2CH_2CN$ *dimethyldithiocarbamic acid, 2-cyanoethyl ester*	—	M.P. 37–38°	318	
$(CH_3)_2NCSSH$ *N,N-dimethyldithiocarbamic acid*	3.0	<30°	$(CH_3)_2NCSSCH_2CH_2CN$ *dimethyldithiocarbamic acid, 2-cyanoethyl ester*	—	M.P. 40–42°	469	
O⟨⟩NCSSNa *morpholinodithiocarbamic acid, sodium salt*	—	R.T.	O⟨⟩NCSSCH$_2$CH$_2$CN *4-morpholinecarbodithioic acid, 2-cyanoethyl ester*	—	M.P. 86.5°	318	
$(CH_3CH_2)_2NCSSNa$ *N,N-diethyldithiocarbamic acid, sodium salt*	—	R.T.	$(CH_3CH_2)_2NCSSCH_2CH_2CN$ *diethyldithiocarbamic acid, 2-cyanoethyl ester*	—		318	
NaSSCN⟨⟩NCSSNa *piperazinobis(dithiocarbamic) acid, disodium salt*	—	30°	NCCH$_2$CH$_2$SSCN⟨⟩NCSSCH$_2$CH$_2$CN *1,4-piperazinedicarbodithioic acid, bis(2-cyanoethyl) ester*	—	M.P. 140°	319	
⟨⟩NCSSNa *piperidinodithiocarbamic acid, sodium salt*	—	R.T.	⟨⟩NCSSCH$_2$CH$_2$CN *1-piperidinecarbodithioic acid, 2-cyanoethyl ester*	—	M.P. 79.5°	318	
$(CH_2)_2[N(CH_3)CSSNa]_2$ *N,N'-dimethylethylenediaminebisdithiocarbamic acid, disodium salt*	—	30°	$(CH_2)_2[N(CH_3)CSSCH_2CH_2CN]_2$ *ethylenebis[methyldithiocarbamic acid], bis(2-cyanoethyl) ester*	—	M.P. 151°	319	
⟨⟩NCSSH *piperidinodithiocarbamic acid*	3.0	<40°	⟨⟩NCSSCH$_2$CH$_2$CN *1-piperidinecarbodithioic acid, 2-cyanoethyl ester*	61	M.P. 80–82°	469	
$(CH_2)_3[N(CH_3)CSSNa]_2$ *N,N'-dimethyltrimethylenediaminebisdithiocarbamic acid, disodium salt*	—	30°	$(CH_2)_3[N(CH_3)CSSCH_2CH_2CN]_2$ *trimethylenebis[methyldithiocarbamic acid], bis(2-cyanoethyl) ester*	—	M.P. 93°	319	

TABLE XXI—Continued

(E) Thiocarbamates

Reactants	Reaction Time (Hr.)	Reaction Temperature (°C.)	Products	% Yield	M.P. or B.P. (°C.)	References This Exam.	See Also:
$(CH_2)_2[N(C_2H_5)CSSNa]_2$ *N,N′-diethylethylenediaminebisdithio-carbamic acid, disodium salt*	—	30°	$(CH_2)_2[N(C_2H_5)CSSCH_2CH_2CN]_2$ *ethylenebis[ethyldithiocarbamic acid], bis(2-cyanoethyl) ester*	—	M.P. 102°	319	
 CH_3NHCSS^- H_3NCH_2—[benzene] *N-methyldithiocarbamic acid, benzylammonium salt*	—	—	$CH_3NHCSSCH_2CH_2CN$ *methyldithiocarbamic acid, 2-cyanoethyl ester*	—	M.P. 38°	1248	
$(CH_2)_3[N(C_2H_5)CSSNa]_2$ *N,N′-diethyltrimethylenediaminebisdithio-carbamic acid, disodium salt*	—	30°	$(CH_2)_3[N(C_2H_5)CSSCH_2CH_2CN]_2$ *trimethylenebis[2-ethyldithiocarbamic acid], bis(2-cyanoethyl) ester*	—	M.P. 56°	319	
$(n\text{-}C_4H_9)_2NCSSH$ *dibutyldithiocarbamic acid*	—	<30°	$(n\text{-}C_4H_9)_2NCSSCH_2CH_2CN$ *dibutyldithiocarbamic acid, 2-cyanoethyl ester*	82.5	—	469	
 $CH_3CH_2NHCSS^-$ $^+H_3NCH_2$—[benzene] *N-ethyldithiocarbamic acid, benzylammonium salt*	—	—	$CH_3CH_2NHCSSCH_2CH_2CN$ *ethyldithiocarbamic acid, 2-cyanoethyl ester*	—	M.P. 91°	1248	
$(CH_2)_6[N(CH_3)CSSNa]_2$ *N,N′-dimethylhexamethylenediamine-bisdithiocarbamic acid, disodium salt*	—	30°	$(CH_2)_6[N(CH_3)CSSCH_2CH_2CN]$ *hexamethylenebis[methyldithiocarbamic acid], bis(2-cyanoethyl) ester*	—	M.P. 72.5°	319	
$(CH_2)_6[N(C_2H_5)CSSNa]_2$ *N,N′-diethylhexamethylenediamine-bisdithiocarbamic acid, disodium salt*	—	30°	$(CH_2)_6[N(C_2H_5)CSSCH_2CH_2CN]_2$ *hexamethylenebis[ethyldithiocarbamic acid], bis(2-cyanoethyl) ester*	—	M.P. 93.5°	319	
  [benzene]—CH_2NHCSS^- $^+H_3NCH_2$—[benzene] *N-benzyldithiocarbamic acid, benzylammonium salt*	—	—	 [benzene]—$CH_2NHCSSCH_2CH_2CN$ *benzyldithiocarbamic acid, 2-cyanoethyl ester*	—	M.P. 54°	1248	

TABLE XXI—Continued

(E) Thiocarbamates

Reactants	Reaction Time (Hr.)	Reaction Temperature (°C.)	Products	% Yield	M.P. or B.P. (°C.)	References This Exam.	See Also:
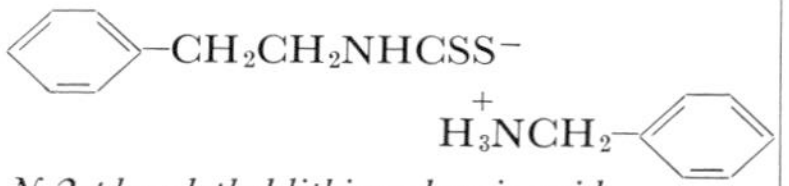 —CH₂CH₂NHCSS⁻ ⁺H₃NCH₂— *N-2-phenylethyldithiocarbamic acid, benzylammonium salt*	—	—	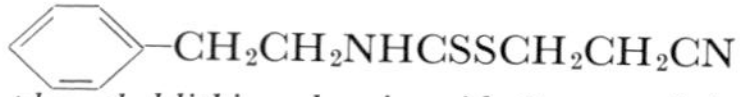 —CH₂CH₂NHCSSCH₂CH₂CN *phenethyldithiocarbamic acid, 2-cyanoethyl ester*	—	M.P. 54°	1248	
(CH₂)₂[N(CH₂C₆H₅)CSSNa]₂ *N,N'-dibenzylethylenediaminebisdithio- carbamic acid, disodium salt*	—	30°	(CH₂)₂[N(CH₂C₆H₅)CSSCH₂CH₂CN]₂ *ethylenebis[benzyldithiocarbamic acid], bis(2-cyanoethyl) ester*	—	M.P. 119.5°	319	

(F) Sulfinic Acids

Reactants	Reaction Time (Hr.)	Reaction Temperature (°C.)	Products	% Yield	M.P. or B.P. (°C.)	References This Exam.	See Also:
CH₃CH₂SO₂H *ethylsulfinic acid*	—	—	CH₃CH₂SO₂CH₂CH₂CN *3-ethylsulfonylpropionitrile*	—	—	1192	
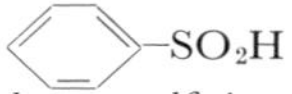 —SO₂H *benzenesulfinic acid*	—	—	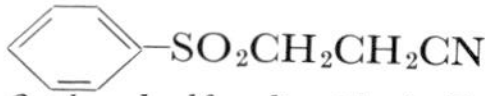 —SO₂CH₂CH₂CN *3-phenylsulfonylpropionitrile*	97	M.P. 95-96°	1192	
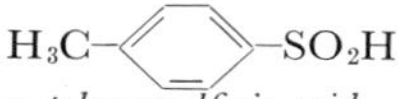 H₃C—SO₂H *p-toluenesulfinic acid*	—	—	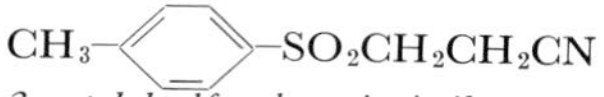 CH₃—SO₂CH₂CH₂CN *3-p-tolylsulfonylpropionitrile*	98	M.P. 93.5-94°	1192	
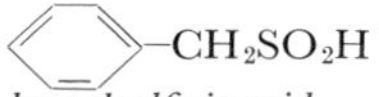 —CH₂SO₂H *benzylsulfinic acid*	—	—	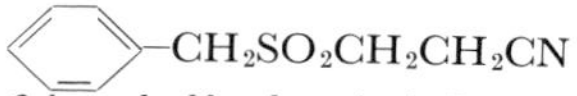 —CH₂SO₂CH₂CH₂CN *3-benzylsulfonylpropionitrile*	84	M.P. 115-116°	1192	
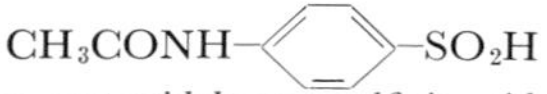 CH₃CONH—SO₂H *p-acetamidobenzenesulfinic acid*	—	—	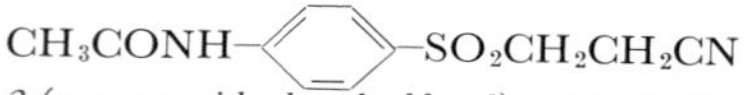 CH₃CONH—SO₂CH₂CH₂CN *3-(p-acetamidophenylsulfonyl)propionitrile*	95	M.P. 208-209°	1192	

TABLE XXI—Continued

(F) Sulfinic Acids

Reactants	Reaction Time (Hr.)	Reaction Temperature (°C.)	Products	% Yield	M.P. or B.P. (°C.)	References This Exam.	See Also:
SO₂H ![structure] *2-naphthylsulfinic acid*	—	—	SO₂CH₂CH₂CN ![structure] *3-(2-naphthylsulfonyl)propionitrile*	90	M.P. 137-138°	1192	

NOTES: Ⓐ Based on unrecovered acrylonitrile.
Ⓑ By analysis an 89% recovery was obtained; HSO₃ is the reacting species.
Ⓒ Products have not been isolated; structure uncertain.
Ⓓ No structure given; prepared from diisobutylene.
Ⓔ No structure given; prepared from triisobutylene.
Ⓕ Isolated as the dicarboxylic acid.
Ⓖ Structure uncertain.
Ⓗ Product not identified.

TABLE XXII—Boron, Phosphorus, Arsenic, Silicon and Tin Cyanoethylation

Reactants	Reaction Time (Hr.)	Reaction Temperature (°C.)	Products	% Yield	M.P. or B.P. (°C.)	References This Exam.	See Also:
B₂H₆ *diborane*	20.0	25°	red solid possibly B(CH₂CH₂CN)₃ *tris(2-cyanoethyl)boron*	—	—	1032	
(CH₃O)₂P(O)H *dimethyl phosphonate*	—	60-70°	(CH₃O)₂P(O)CH₂CH₂CN *(2-cyanoethyl)phosphonic acid, dimethyl ester*	86.3	B.P. 158°/11 mm.	893	
(CH₃CH₂O)₂P(O)H *diethyl phosphonate*	—	—	(CH₃CH₂O)₂P(O)CH₂CH₂CN *(2-cyanoethyl)phosphonic acid, diethyl ester*	83	B.P. 159-160°/10 mm.	893	
[(CH₃)₂CHO]₂P(O)H *diisopropyl phosphonate*	—	—	[(CH₃)₂CHO]₂P(O)CH₂CH₂CN *(2-cyanoethyl)phosphonic acid, diisopropyl ester*	46.4	B.P. 160°/13 mm.	893	
(n-C₄H₉O)₂P(O)H *di-n-butyl phosphonate*	—	20-25°	(CH₃CH₂CH₂CH₂O)₂P(O)CH₂CH₂CN *(2-cyanoethyl)phosphonic acid, dibutyl ester*	84	—	125	893, 1295
[(CH₃)₂CHCH₂O]₂P(O)H *diisobutyl phosphonate*	—	—	[(CH₃)₂CHCH₂O]₂P(O)CH₂CH₂CN *(2-cyanoethyl)phosphonic acid, diisobutyl ester*	71	B.P. 171°/11 mm.	893	
[(CH₃)₂CHCH₂CH₂O]₂P(O)H *diisoamyl phosphonate*	—	—	[(CH₃)₂CHCH₂CH₂O]₂P(O)CH₂CH₂CN *(2-cyanoethyl)phosphonic acid, diisopentyl ester*	55	B.P. 168-170°/3 mm.	1388	

TABLE XXII—Continued

Boron, Phosphorus, Arsenic, Silicon and Tin Cyanoethylation

Reactants	Reaction Temperature (°C.)	Reaction Time (Hr.)	Products	% Yield	M.P. or B.P. (°C.)	This Exam.	See Also:
$[CH_3(CH_2)_5O]_2P(O)H$ di-n-hexyl phosphonate	—	—	$[CH_3(CH_2)_5O]_2P(O)CH_2CH_2CN$ (2-cyanoethyl)phosphonic acid, dihexyl ester	61.1	B.P. 198-200°/1 mm.	1388	
$[CH_3(CH_2)_7O]_2P(O)H$ di-n-octyl phosphonate	—	—	$[CH_3(CH_2)_7O]_2P(O)CH_2CH_2CN$ (2-cyanoethyl)phosphonic acid, dioctyl ester	63.2	B.P. 218-220°/2 mm.	1388	
$(C_2H_5O)(CH_3CH_2)P(O)H$ ethyl ethylphosphinate	steam bath	0.5	$(CH_3CH_2O)(CH_3CH_2)P(O)CH_2CH_2CN$ (2-cyanoethyl)ethylphosphinic acid, ethyl ester	67	B.P. 171-171.5°/12 mm.	1389	
$[CH_3(CH_2)_3O][(CH_3CH_2)P(O)H$ butyl ethylphosphinate	steam bath	0.5	$[CH_3(CH_2)_3O][(CH_3CH_2)P(O)CH_2CH_2CN$ (2-cyanoethyl)ethylphosphinic acid, butyl ester	53	B.P. 192°/13 mm.	1389	
$CH_3CH_2OP(O)H$(phenyl) ethyl phenylphosphinate	steam bath	0.5	$(CH_3CH_2O)(NCCH_2CH_2)P(O)$(phenyl) (2-cyanoethyl)phenylphosphinic acid, ethyl ester	48	B.P. 162-163°/1 mm.	1389	
$CH_3(CH_2)_3OP(O)H$(phenyl) butyl phenylphosphinate	15-18°	—	$[CH_3(CH_2)_3O](NCCH_2CH_2)P(O)$(phenyl) (2-cyanoethyl)phenylphosphinic acid, butyl ester	67	B.P. 111-114°/0.01 mm.	1215	
(benzyl)$CH_2P(O)HCH_2$(benzyl) dibenzylphosphine oxide	50-60° 0°	18.0	(benzyl)$CH_2P(O)(CH_2CH_2CN)CH_2$(benzyl) 3-(dibenzylphosphoroso)propionitrile	66	M.P. 109-110°	1344	
$[CH_3(CH_2)_7]_2P(O)H$ di-n-octylphosphine oxide	—	1-2	$[CH_3(CH_2)_7]_2P(O)CH_2CH_2CN$ 3-(dioctylphosphoroso)propionitrile	39	M.P. 53.4-54.2°	1344	
(phenyl)$-PH_2$ phenyl phosphine	130-135°	6.0	(phenyl)$-P(CH_2CH_2CN)_2$ 3,3'-(phenylphosphinidene)dipropionitrile	62	M.P. 72-73° B.P. 195-205°/0.2 mm.	739	
(phenyl)PH(phenyl) diphenyl phosphine	130°	7.0	(phenyl)$P(CH_2CH_2CN)$(phenyl) 3-(diphenylphosphino)propionitrile	71	M.P. 64-64.5°	739	
$(CH_3O)_2P(S)H$ dimethyl phosphonothioate	steam bath	0.5	$(CH_3O)_2P(S)CH_2CH_2CN$ (2-cyanoethyl)phosphonothioic acid, O,O-dimethyl ester	59	B.P. 138-139°/14 mm.	1389	

TABLE XXII—Continued

Boron, Phosphorus, Arsenic, Silicon and Tin Cyanoethylation

Reactants	Reaction Time (Hr.)	Reaction Temperature (°C.)	Products	% Yield	M.P. or B.P. (°C.)	This Exam.	See Also:
$(CH_3CH_2O)_2P(S)H$ *diethyl phosphonothioate*	0.5	steam bath	$(CH_3CH_2O)_2P(S)CH_2CH_2CN$ *(2-cyanoethyl)phosphonothioic acid, O,O-diethyl ester*	74	B.P. 134–135°/7 mm.	1389	
$[CH_3(CH_2)_3O]_2P(S)H$ *dibutyl phosphonothioate*	0.5	steam bath	$[CH_3(CH_2)_3O]_2P(S)CH_2CH_2CN$ *(2-cyanoethyl)phosphonothioic acid, O,O-dibutyl ester*	68	B.P. 167°/5 mm.	1389	
$[(CH_3)_2CHCH_2O]_2P(S)H$ *diisobutyl phosphonothioate*	0.5	steam bath	$[(CH_3)_2CHCH_2O]_2P(S)CH_2CH_2CN$ *(2-cyanoethyl)phosphonothioic acid, O,O-diisobutyl ester*	67	B.P. 174°/14 mm.	1389	
CH_3AsH_2 *methyl arsine*	2 wks. 2 hrs.	R.T. reflux	$CH_3As(CH_2CH_2CN)_2$ *3,3′-(methylarsylene)dipropionitrile*	53	B.P. 148–149°/0.1 mm.	270	
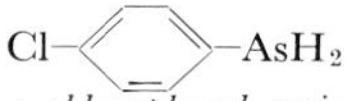 Cl—⟨⟩—AsH₂ *p-chlorophenyl arsine*	2.0	reflux	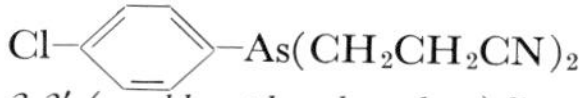 Cl—⟨⟩—As(CH₂CH₂CN)₂ *3,3′-(p-chlorophenylarsylene)dipropionitrile*	92	M.P. 71–72°	269	
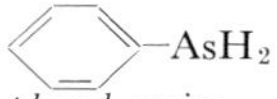 ⟨⟩—AsH₂ *phenyl arsine*	5.0	reflux	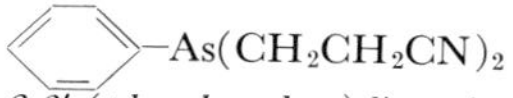 ⟨⟩—As(CH₂CH₂CN)₂ *3,3′-(phenylarsylene)dipropionitrile*	77	B.P. 200–210°/0.1 mm. M.P. 59–60°	269	783
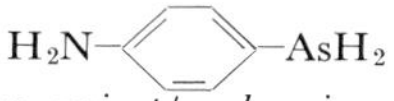 H₂N—⟨⟩—AsH₂ *p-aminophenyl arsine*	1.0 4.0	55° 100°	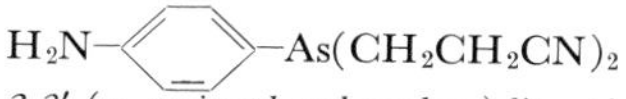 H₂N—⟨⟩—As(CH₂CH₂CN)₂ *3,3′-(p-aminophenylarsylene)dipropionitrile*	96	M.P. 77.5–78.5°	269	
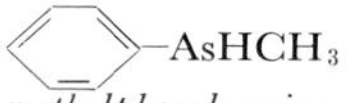 ⟨⟩—AsHCH₃ *methylphenyl arsine*	4.0	reflux	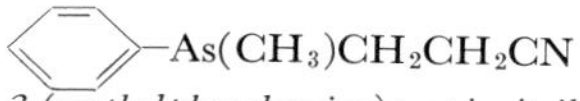 ⟨⟩—As(CH₃)CH₂CH₂CN *3-(methylphenylarsino)propionitrile*	85	B.P. 172–174°/14 mm.	1330	
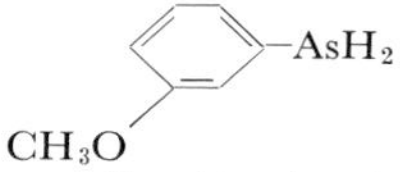 CH₃O—⟨⟩—AsH₂ *m-methoxyphenyl arsine*	6.0	100°	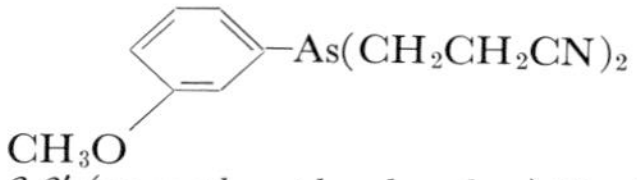 CH₃O—⟨⟩—As(CH₂CH₂CN)₂ *3,3′-(m-methoxyphenylarsylene)dipropionitrile*	100	B.P. 206–212°/0.03 mm.	1330	

Boron, Phosphorus, Arsenic, Silicon and Tin Cyanoethylation

TABLE XXII—Continued

Reactants	Reaction Time (Hr.)	Reaction Temperature (°C.)	Products	% Yield	M.P. or B.P. (°C.)	References This Exam.	References See Also:
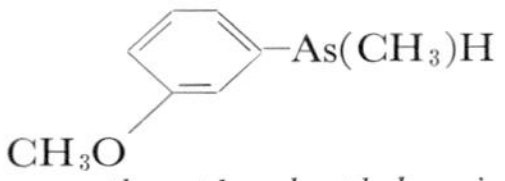 (structure) $-As(CH_3)H$ CH_3O m-methoxyphenylmethyl arsine	6.0	100°	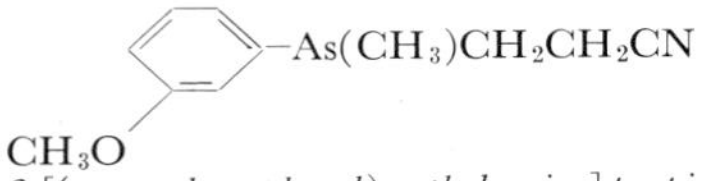 (structure) $-As(CH_3)CH_2CH_2CN$ CH_3O 3-[(m-methoxyphenyl)methylarsino]propionitrile	90	B.P. 148-152°/1 mm.	1330	
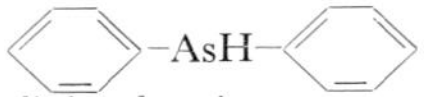 $-AsH$ diphenyl arsine	1.5	reflux	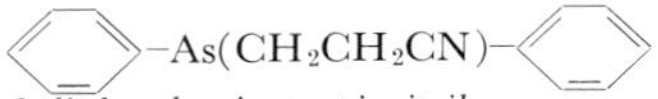 $-As(CH_2CH_2CN)$ 3-diphenylarsinopropionitrile	83	M.P. 37-39°	269	
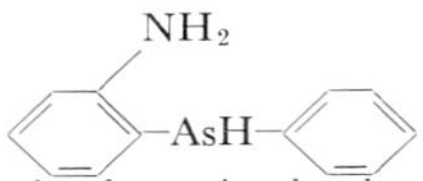 NH_2 $-AsH$ phenyl-o-aminophenyl arsine	4.0	reflux	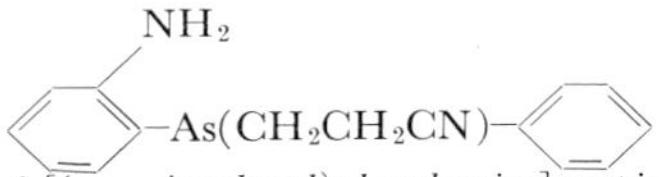 NH_2 $-As(CH_2CH_2CN)$ 3-[(o-aminophenyl)phenylarsino]propionitrile	46	B.P. 197-200°/0.35 mm.	270	
Cl_3SiH trichlorosilane	20.0	100°	$Cl_3SiCH(CH_3)CN$ 2-(trichlorosilyl)propionitrile	31	B.P. 70°/8 mm.	1271	837
Cl_3SiH trichlorosilane	5.0	160°	$Cl_3SiCH_2CH_2CN$ 3-(trichlorosilyl)propionitrile	76	M.P. 34.6-35.1° B.P. 109°/30 mm.	836	837, 1371
CH_3SiHCl_2 methyldichlorosilane	26.0	75°	$NCCH(CH_3)SiCl_2CH_3$ 2-(dichloromethylsilyl)propionitrile	26	B.P. 60-62.5°/4 mm.	1271	
$(CH_3CH_2CH_2)_3SnH$ tripropyltin hydride	4	100°	$(CH_3CH_2CH_2)_3SnCH_2CH_2CN$ 3-(tripropylstannyl)propionitrile	70	B.P. 157-160°/12 mm.	1435	
$(CH_3CH_2CH_2CH_2)_3SnH$ tributyltin hydride	—	—	$(CH_3CH_2CH_2CH_2)_3SnCH_2CH_2CN$ 3-(tributylstannyl)propionitrile	70	B.P. 126-134°/0.2 mm.	1115	
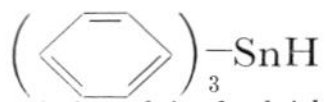 $\left(\text{phenyl}\right)_3-SnH$ triphenyltin hydride	—	80°	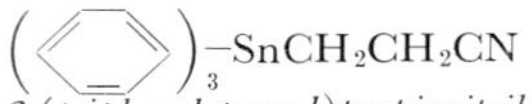 $\left(\text{phenyl}\right)_3-SnCH_2CH_2CN$ 3-(triphenylstannyl)propionitrile	94	M.P. 93-94°	1115	1435

TABLE XXIII—"Cl" and "Br" Cyanoethylation

Reactants	Re-action Time (Hr.)	Reaction Tem-perature (°C.)	Products	% Yield	M.P. or B.P. (°C.)	References	
						This Exam.	See Also:
HBr *hydrobromic acid*	—	—	BrCH₂CH₂CN *3-bromopropionitrile*	91	B.P. 92°/25 mm.	803	
HCl *hydrochloric acid*	18.0	25°	ClCH₂CH₂CN *3-chloropropionitrile*	97.2	B.P. 91-93°/41 mm.	800	388, 890, 364, 800, 1028

BIBLIOGRAPHY

1. American Cyanamid Company, unpublished results. Reference has been made to unpublished work by American Cyanamid Company only in those cases where the published data are either meager or not readily available.
2. ABE, *Rept. Osaka Municipal Inst. Ind. Research* No. 12, 46, (1948). C.A. 44, 2274 (1950).
3. ABBOTT AND OTTO, U. S. Patent 2,707,205 (1955).
4. ABRAMS AND SHERWOOD, *Am. Dyestuff Reptr.* 42, 777-82 (1953).
5. ABRAMS AND SHERWOOD, *Am. Dyestuff Reptr.* 43, 780-84 (1954).
6. ACARA AND LEVINE, *J. Am. Chem. Soc.* 72, 2864-66 (1950).
7. ADAMS, U. S. Patent 2,655,496 (1953).
8. ADAMS AND JOHNSON, *J. Am. Chem. Soc.* 71, 705 (1949).
9. ADAMS AND JONES, *J. Am. Chem. Soc.* 69, 1803 (1947).
10. AHLBRECHT, REID AND HUSTED, U. S. Patent 2,642,416 (1953).
11. ALBERTSON, *J. Am. Chem. Soc.* 72, 2594-99 (1950).
12. ALBERTSON, U. S. Patent 2,585,210 (1952).
13. ALBERTSON AND ARCHER, U. S. Patent 2,496,326 (1950).
14. ALBERTSON AND ARCHER, U. S. Patent 2,553,737 (1951).
15. ALBISETTI, JR. AND FISHER, U. S. Patent 2,641,607 (1953).
16. ALDER, CHAMBERS AND TRIMBORN, *Ann.* 566, 27 (1950).
17. ALDER, KRIEGER AND WEISS, *Chem. Ber.* 88, 144-55 (1955).
18. ALDER AND RUHMANN, *Ann.* 566, 1-27 (1950).
19. ALDER AND VOGT, *Ann.* 564, 109-40 (1949).
20. ALEKSEEVA AND MEZHOV, *J. Gen. Chem.* (*U.S.S.R.*) 22, 1813-16 (1952).
21. ALFREY, BOHRER, HAAS AND LEWIS, *J. Polymer Sci.* 5, 719-26 (1950).
22. ALFREY AND PRICE, *J. Polymer Sci.* 2, 101 (1947).
23. ALLEN AND DREWITT, U. S. Patent 2,502,548 (1950).
24. ALLEN AND VAN ALLAN, *J. Org. Chem.* 14, 754-60 (1949).
25. ALLISON, BRAUNHOLTZ AND MANN, *J. Chem. Soc.* 1954, 403-08.
26. ALMOND AND MANN, *J. Chem. Soc.* 1951, 1906-09.
27. American Cyanamid Company, British Patent 544,421 (1942); C.A. 36, 6548 (1942).
28. American Cyanamid Company, Paper Chemicals Dept., *Tech. Bulletin No. 20, The Bardac Process* (1948).
29. American Cyanamid Company, British Patent 631,592 (1949); C.A. 44, 4494 (1950).
30. American Cyanamid Company, Swiss Patent 259,439 (1949); *Chem. Zentr. 1950*, I, 917.
31. American Cyanamid Company, *New Product Bulletin No. 12, β-Substituted Propionitriles* (1950).
32. American Cyanamid Company, *New Product Bulletin No. 13, Substituted Propylamines* (1950).
33. American Cyanamid Company, *New Product Bulletin No. 14, Dipropionitriles* (1950).
34. American Cyanamid Company, British Patent 642,409 (1950); C.A. 46, 146 (1952).
35. American Cyanamid Company, British Patent 686,692; C.A. 48, 8251 (1954).
36. American Cyanamid Company, British Patent 717,041.
37. American Cyanamid Company, British Patent 722,451 (1955).
38. American Cyanamid Company, British Patent 723,638 (1955).
39. *Am. Textile Reptr.* 69, 17, 44 (1955).
40. AMOS, MCCURDY AND MCINTIRE, U. S. Patent 2,694,692 (1954).
41. ANDERSAG, *Chem. Ber.* 81, 499 (1948).
42. ANSELL AND HEY, *J. Chem. Soc. 1950*, 1683-86.
43. ANTHEIL, U. S. Patent 2,631,961 (1953).
44. ARBUZOV AND ISAEVA, *J. Gen. Chem.* (*U.S.S.R.*) 22, 1685 (1952).
45. ARBUZOV AND KATAEV, *J. Gen. Chem.* (*U.S.S.R.*) 20, 68-81 (1950); C.A. 44, 5827 (1950).
46. ARBUZOV AND KATAEV, *J. Gen. Chem.* (*U.S.S.R.*) 20, 931-35 (1950), English Translation 20, 971; C.A. 44, 9364-65 (1950).
47. ARBUZOV AND VIL'CHINSKAYA, *J. Gen. Chem.* (*U.S.S.R.*) 21, 1872-76 (1951), English Translation 21, 2079; C.A. 46, 6617d (1952).
48. ARMATYS, U. S. Patent 2,663,696 (1953).
49. ARNDT, LOEWE AND AYCA, *Chem. Ber.* 84, 329-32 (1951).
50. ARNOLD, U. S. Patent 2,408,402 (1946).
51. ARNOLD, U. S. Patent 2,491,471 (1946).
52. ARNOLD, BUCKLEY AND DODSON, *J. Am. Chem. Soc.* 72, 3153-55 (1950).
53. ASTLE AND ETHERINGTON, *Ind. Eng. Chem.* 44, 2871-72 (1952).
54. ASTHANA AND MISRA, *J. Indian Chem. Soc.* 31, 459-60 (1954).
55. AZORLOSA, U. S. Patent 2,654,671 (1953).
56. BACHMANN AND JOHNSON, *J. Am. Chem. Soc.* 71, 3463-68 (1949).
57. BACHMAN AND LEVINE, *J. Am. Chem. Soc.* 69, 2341 (1947).
58. BACHMAN AND LEVINE, *J. Am. Chem. Soc.* 70, 599 (1948).
59. BACHMAN AND MAYHEW, *J. Org. Chem.* 10, 243 (1945).
60. BACHMAN AND WICK, *J. Am. Chem. Soc.* 72, 3388-92 (1950).
61. BACON, *Trans. Faraday Soc.* 42, 140 (1946).
62. BACON, MORGAN and IMPERIAL CHEMICAL INDUSTRIES, LTD., British Patent 578,209 (1946); C.A. 41, 1881 (1947).

63. BADISCHE ANILIN- & SODA-FABRIK, French Patent 976,959 (1951); C.A. 47, 9348 (1953).
64. BADISCHE ANILIN, British Patent 710,973 (1954).
65. BADUM, U. S. Patent 2,297,194 (1942).
66. BAGLEY, U. S. Patent 2,623,026 (1952).
67. BAKELITE, LTD., British Patent 590,247 (1947); C.A. 42, 4400 (1948).
68. BAKER, U. S. Patent 2,440,659 (1948).
69. BAKER, SCHAUB, MCEVOY AND WILLIAMS, J. Org. Chem. 17, 132-40 (1952).
70. BALLAUF, PB 73894, frames 5269-78 (1942); Bib. 8, 962.
71. BAMFORD, Chemistry and Industry, No. 52, 1579-80 (1954).
72. BAMFORD, BARB AND JENKINS, Nature 169, 1044-46 (1952).
73. BAMFORD AND JENKINS, Proc. Roy. Soc. (London) A216, 515-39 (1953).
74. BAMFORD AND JENKINS, J. Polymer Sci. 14, 511 (1954).
75. BAMFORD AND JENKINS, Proc. Roy. Soc. (London) A228, 220 (1955).
76. BAMFORD, JENKINS, INGRAM AND SYMONS, Nature 175, 894-95 (1955).
77. BANES, YOUNG AND HUND, U. S. Patent 2,636,866 (1953).
78. BARE, J. Econ. Entomol. 41, 13 (1948).
79. BARE AND TENHET, Entomology and Plant Quarantine Bureau, Agr. Dept., E-794 (1950).
80. BARNES, KRAFT AND GORDON, J. Am. Chem. Soc. 71, 3523-28 (1949).
81. BARNES, LIDDEL AND WILLIAMS, Ind. Eng. Chem., Anal. Ed. 15, 83 (1943).
82. BARNES, LIDDEL AND WILLIAMS, Ind. Eng. Chem., Anal. Ed. 15, 699 (1943).
83. BARRER, Kolloid-Z. 120, No. 1-3, 177-90 (1951).
84. BARRICK, U. S. Patent 2,462,345 (1949).
85. BARRICK AND CRAMER, U. S. Patent 2,441,128 (1948).
86. BARRICK AND PAVLIC, U. S. Patent 2,506,571 (1950).
87. BARTLETT, RUDEL AND CYPHERS, U. S. Patent 2,611,728 (1952).
88. BASDEKIS, U. S. Patent 2,652,381 (1953).
89. BATES AND CYMERMAN-CRAIG, J. Chem. Soc. 1954, 1153-55.
90. BAUER, CYMERMAN AND SHELDON, J. Chem. Soc. 1951, 3311-15.
91. BAUER AND ESSER, U. S. Patent 2,220,033 (1940).
92. BAUM AND HERRMANN, German Patent 559,734 (1930); C.A. 27, 735 (1933).
93. BAUMGARTEN AND EIFERT, J. Am. Chem. Soc. 75, 3015-16 (1953).
94. BAXENDALE, EVANS AND PARK, Trans. Faraday Soc. 42, 155 (1946).
95. BAYER, Angew. Chem. 61, 229 (1949).
96. B. B. CHEMICAL CO. LTD., PUDDEFOOT AND SWIRE, British Patent 569,666 (1945); C.A. 41, 6438 (1947).
97. BEAN AND RUSSELL, U. S. Patent 2,604,388 (1952).
98. BECKBERGER, U. S. Patent 2,671,107 (1954).
99. BEESING, TYLER, KURTZ AND HARRISON, Anal. Chem. 21, 1073 (1949).
100. BEHR, KIRBY, MCDONALD AND TODD, J. Am. Chem. Soc. 68, 1296 (1946).
101. BEKHLI AND SEREBRENNIKOV, J. Gen. Chem. (U.S.S.R.) 19, 1553-57 (1949); C.A. 44, 3448 (1950).
102. BELL AND LINDWALL, J. Org. Chem. 13, 547 (1948).
103. BELLRINGER, BEWLEY AND STANLEY, British Patent 709,337; cf. J. Applied Chem. 4, 759 (1954).
104. BELLRINGER AND STANLEY, U. S. Patent 2,691,037 (1954).
105. BEMMELS, U. S. Patent 2,647,843 (1953).
106. BENSON AND CAIRNS, J. Am. Chem. Soc. 70, 2115 (1948).
107. BENSON AND CAIRNS, J. Am. Chem. Soc. 72, 5355-56 (1950).
108. BERGMANN, U. S. Patent 2,563,206 (1951).
109. BERGMANN, J. Appl. Chem. (London) 3, 145-46 (1953).
110. BERRY AND OSWIN, U. S. Patent 2,709,146 (1955).
111. BERRY, OSWIN AND ROSE, British Patent 669,907; Brit. Abst. 1952, B II, 998.
112. BERSTEIN, FARMER, ROTHSCHILD AND SPALDING, J. Chem. Phys. 21, 1303-05 (1953).
113. BESTIAN, Ann. 566, 210 (1950).
114. B. F. GOODRICH CHEMICAL CO., Hycar Blue Book.
115. B. F. GOODRICH CHEMICAL CO., Hycar Latices, Service Bulletin H-5 (1949).
116. BIEFELD AND MORRISON, U. S. Patent 2,673,823 (1954).
117. BIRD AND HALE, Anal. Chem. 24, 586-87 (1952).
118. BISSCHOPS, J. Polymer Sci. 12, 583-96, 597 (1954).
119. BISSCHOPS, J. Polymer Sci. 17, 81-88 (1955).
120. BISSCHOPS, J. Polymer Sci. 17, 89-98 (1955).
121. BIXLER AND FISHER, U. S. Patent 2,635,045 (1953).
122. BLOOD AND LINSTEAD, J. Chem. Soc. 1952, 2255-62.
123. BLOUT, MARK AND HOHENSTEIN, "Monomers," Interscience Publishers, Inc., New York, (1949), page 14.
124. BLUME AND LINDWALL, J. Org. Chem. 10, 255 (1945).
125. BOCHWIC AND MICHALSKI, Roczniki Chim. 25, 338-49 (1951); C.A. 48, 12013a.
126. BOCK AND HOUK, U. S. Patent 2,316,128 (1943).
127. BOCK AND HOUK, U. S. Patent 2,349,797 (1944).
128. BOEKELHEIDE AND GODFREY, J. Am. Chem. Soc. 75, 3679-85 (1953).
129. BOESE, U. S. Patent 2,438,894 (1948).

130.   BOESE, U. S. Patent 2,438,961 (1948).
131.   BOLAM, *Australian Plastics 10*, No. 107, 18-22 (1954); C.A. *48*, 11107a (1954).
132.   BOLTON, *Canadian J. Agri. Sci. 35*, No. 1, 51-57 (1955).
133.   BOYER, *J. Am. Chem. Soc. 73*, 5248-52 (1951).
134.   BRANT AND HASCHE, U. S. Patent 2,386,586 (1945).
135.   BRAUNHOLTZ AND MANN, *J. Chem. Soc. 1952*, 3046-51.
136.   BRAUNHOLTZ AND MANN, *J. Chem. Soc. 1953*, 1817-24.
137.   BRAUNHOLTZ AND MANN, *J. Chem. Soc. 1954*, 651-58.
138.   BRIEGER, RIEDERS AND HODES, *Arch. Ind. Hyg. Occup. Med. 6*, No. 2, 128-40 (1952).
139.   BRINTZINGER AND PFANNSTIEL, *Z. anorg. Chem. 255*, 325 (1948).
140.   BRINTZINGER, PFANNSTIEL AND KODDEBUSCH, *Angew. Chem. A60*, 311 (1948).
141.   BRINTZINGER AND SCHOLZ, *Chem. Ber. 83*, No. 2, 141-45 (1950).
142.   BRITISH CELANESE LTD., British Patent 631,020 (1949); C.A. *44*, 5641 (1950).
143.   BRITISH CELLOPHANE LTD., British Patent 682,689 (1952); C.A. *47*, 5169 (1953).
144.   BRITISH INSULATED CABLES, LTD. AND CHAPMAN, British Patent 530,512 (1940);
         C.A. *35*, 8154 (1941).
145.   BRITISH THOMSON-HOUSTON CO., LTD., British Patent 591,860 (1947); C.A. *42*,
         1316 (1948).
146.   BRITTON AND SEXTON, U. S. Patent 2,263,436 (1941).
147.   BROCKWAY, *Anal. Chem. 21*, 1207 (1949).
148.   BROCKWAY, U. S. Patent 2,547,686 (1951).
149.   BROCKWAY, U. S. Patent 2,666,782 (1954).
150.   BROOKS AND NAZZEWSKI, U. S. Patent 2,406,319 (1946).
151.   BROWN, U. S. Patent 2,554,482 (1951).
152.   BRUBAKER AND JACOBSON, U. S. Patent 2,462,354 (1949).
153.   BRUNNER AND PERGER, *Monatsh 79*, 187 (1948).
154.   BRUSON, U. S. Patent 2,280,058 (1942).
155.   BRUSON, U. S. Patent 2,280,790 (1942).
156.   BRUSON, U. S. Patent 2,280,791 (1942).
157.   BRUSON, U. S. Patent 2,280,792 (1942).
158.   BRUSON, *J. Am. Chem. Soc. 64*, 2457 (1942).
159.   BRUSON, U. S. Patent 2,287,510 (1942).
160.   BRUSON, U. S. Patent 2,311,183 (1943).
161.   BRUSON, U. S. Patent 2,326,721 (1943).
162.   BRUSON, U. S. Patent 2,352,515 (1944).
163.   BRUSON, U. S. Patent 2,361,259 (1944).
164.   BRUSON, U. S. Patent 2,372,808 (1945).
165.   BRUSON, U. S. Patent 2,382,036 (1945).
166.   BRUSON, U. S. Patent 2,383,444 (1945).
167.   BRUSON, U. S. Patent 2,386,736 (1945).
168.   BRUSON, U. S. Patent 2,386,737 (1945).
169.   BRUSON, U. S. Patent 2,394,962 (1946).
170.   BRUSON, U. S. Patent 2,401,607 (1946); U. S. Patent 2,437,905 (1948).
171.   BRUSON, U. S. Patent 2,435,552 (1948).
172.   BRUSON, U. S. Patent 2,466,680 (1949).
173.   BRUSON, "*Cyanoethylation*," *Organic Reactions, Volume V*, edited by R. Adams; John
         Wiley & Sons, Inc., New York (1949).
174.   BRUSON AND NIEDERHAUSER, U. S. Patent 2,440,140 (1948).
175.   BRUSON, NIEDERHAUSER, RIENER AND HESTER, *J. Am. Chem. Soc. 67*, 601 (1945).
176.   BRUSON AND RATERINK, U. S. Patent 2,466,678 (1949).
177.   BRUSON AND RIENER, *J. Am. Chem. Soc. 64*, 2850 (1942).
178.   BRUSON AND RIENER, *J. Am. Chem. Soc. 65*, 18 (1943).
179.   BRUSON AND RIENER, *J. Am. Chem. Soc. 65*, 23 (1943).
180.   BRUSON AND RIENER, *J. Am. Chem. Soc. 66*, 56 (1944).
181.   BRUSON AND RIENER, U. S. Patent 2,352,516 (1944).
182.   BRUSON AND RIENER, U. S. Patent 2,353,687 (1944).
183.   BRUSON AND RIENER, U. S. Patent 2,370,006 (1945).
184.   BRUSON AND RIENER, *J. Am. Chem. Soc. 70*, 214 (1948).
185.   BRUSON AND RIENER, U. S. Patent 2,435,869 (1948).
186.   BRUSON AND RIENER, *J. Am. Chem. Soc. 75*, 3585-86 (1953).
187.   BUC, *Organic Syntheses 27*, 3 (1947).
188.   BUC AND FORD, U. S. Patent 2,448,013 (1948).
189.   BUC, FORD AND WISE, *J. Am. Chem. Soc. 67*, 92 (1945).
190.   BUCHDAHL AND NIELSEN, *J. Polymer Sci. 15*, 1-8 (1955).
191.   BUCKLER AND HARRIS, *Inst. Rubber Ind. Transactions 31*, T2 (1955).
192.   BUCKLEY, ELLIOTT, HUNT AND LOWE, *J. Chem. Soc. 1947*, 1505.
193.   BUCKLEY AND LOWE, British Patent 584,086 (1947); C.A. *41*, 3478 (1947).
194.   BUCKLEY AND LOWE, British Patent 586,099 (1947); C.A. *42*, 201 (1948).
195.   BURCKHALTER, JONES, HOLCOMB AND SWEET, *J. Am. Chem. Soc. 65*, 2012 (1943).
196.   BURNELL AND TAYLOR, *J. Chem. Soc. 1954*, 3486-90.
197.   BURRELL, *Interchem. Rev. 14*, No. 1, 3-16 (1955).
198.   BUSSE, Part I; KOLB, STANLEY, BUSSE AND BILLMEYER, Part II, *Textile Research J. 23*,
         77-90 (1953).

199. CAIRNS, ENGELHARDT, JACKSON, KALB AND SAUER, *J. Am. Chem. Soc. 74,* 5636-40 (1952).
200. CAIRNS, GRAHAM, BARRICK AND SCHREIBER, *J. Org. Chem. 17,* 751-57 (1952).
201. CALIFORNIA RESEARCH CORP., British Patent 722,375.
202. CAMPBELL, U. S. Patent 2,415,414 (1947).
203. CAMPBELL, *J. Chem. Soc. 1954,* 1377-80.
204. CAMPBELL, CARTER AND SLATER, *J. Chem. Soc. 1948,* 1741.
205. CAMPBELL AND FAIRFULL, *J. Chem. Soc. 1949,* 1239.
206. CAMPBELL AND TUCKER, *J. Chem. Soc. 1949,* 2623.
207. CARLSON AND HOTCHKISS, U. S. Patent 2,335,997 (1943); U. S. Patent 2,377,401 (1945).
208. CAROSELLI AND GAGNON, U. S. Patent 2,686,737 (1954).
209. CARPENTER, U. S. Patent 2,312,878 (1943).
210. CARPENTER, U. S. Patent 2,404,164 (1946).
211. CARPENTER, U. S. Patent 2,434,606 (1948).
212. CARPENTER, U. S. Patent 2,646,444 (1953).
213. CARPENTER, U. S. Patent 2,676,977 (1954).
214. CARPENTER, DAVIS AND WIEDEMAN, U. S. Patent 2,404,163 (1946).
215. CARSON, U. S. Patent 2,575,581 (1951).
216. CASSELLA FARBWERKE, Swiss Patent 294,013 (1953).
217. CASTNER AND PETERS, U. S. Patent 2,481,080 (1949).
218. CATLIN, U. S. Patent 2,653,133 (1953).
219. CENTOLA AND PRATI, *Ricerca Sci. 23,* 1975-78 (1953); *C.A. 48,* 10376f (1954).
220. CHANDLER, FARIS, MAGAT, REITH AND SALSBURY, *Acid-Catalyzed Reactions of Nitriles,* presented at 117th meeting of Am. Chem. Soc. at Philadelphia, 1950.
221. CHAPIN, U. S. Patent 2,580,997 (1952).
222. CHAPIN AND HAM, U. S. Patent 2,520,083 (1950).
223. CHAPIN AND HAM, U. S. Patent 2,559,155 (1951).
224. CHAPIN, HAM AND MILLS, *J. Polymer Sci. 4,* 597 (1949).
225. CHAPIRO, *J. Chim. Phys. 47,* 764-75 (1950).
226. CHAPIRO, COUSIN, LANDLER AND MAGAT, *Rec. trav. Chim. 68,* 1037-68 (1949).
227. CHARLTON, JARRETT AND WALKER, U. S. Patent 2,406,453 (1946).
228. CHASE AND HEY, *J. Chem. Soc. 1952,* 553-72.
229. *Chem. Eng. 61,* No. 10, 112 (1954).
230. *Chem. Eng. News 29,* No. 53, 5530-31 (1951).
231. *Chem. Eng. News 32,* No. 38, 3798 (1954).
232. *Chem. Eng. News 32,* No. 41, 4066 (1954).
233. *Chem. Inds. 67,* No. 4 (1950) (Newsletter).
234. *Chem. Week 75,* 49 (1954).
235. *Chem. Week 75,* 97-98 (1954).
236. *Chem. Week 75,* 100-01 (1954).
237. *Chem. Week 76,* 96 (1955).
238. *Chem. Week 77,* 52, 54 (1955).
239. CHMIEL, U. S. Patent 2,491,477 (1949).
240. CHRISTIAN, *Iowa State Coll. J. Sci. 22,* 11 (1948).
241. CHRISTIAN, BROWN AND HIXON, *J. Am. Chem. Soc. 69,* 1961 (1947).
242. CHRISTIAN AND HIXON, *J. Am. Chem. Soc. 70,* 1333-36 (1948).
243. CIBA, LTD., British Patent 654,463 (1951); *C.A. 46,* 8152 (1952).
244. CIBA, LTD., Swiss Patent 275,798 (1951); *C.A. 47,* 1732 (1953).
245. CLAYTON, U. S. Patent 2,491,715 (1949).
246. CLELAND AND STOCKMAYER, *J. Polymer Sci. 17,* 473-77 (1955).
247. CLIFFORD AND D'IANNI, U. S. Patent 2,384,889 (1945).
248. CLIFFORD AND LICHTY, Canadian Patent 415,525 (1943).
249. CLIFFORD AND LICHTY, U. S. Patent 2,368,521 (1945).
250. CLIFFORD AND LICHTY, U. S. Patent 2,407,138 (1946).
251. CLIFFORD AND LICHTY, U. S. Patent 2,437,998 (1948).
252. CLIFFORD AND WOLFE, U. S. Patent 2,370,010 (1945).
253. CLINTON, SUTER, LASKOWSKI, JACKMAN AND HUBER, *J. Am. Chem. Soc. 67,* 594 (1945).
254. COCKER, CROSS AND McCORMICK, *J. Chem. Soc. 1953,* 1182-83.
255. COFFIELD, FILBEY, ECKE AND KOLKA, Presented at Meeting of the Am. Chem. Soc., Minneapolis, 1955.
256. COFFMAN, U. S. Patent 2,562,534 (1951).
257. COFFMAN, U. S. Patent 2,682,524 (1954).
258. COFFMAN, BARRICK, CRAMER AND RAASCH, *J. Am. Chem. Soc. 71,* 490 (1949).
259. COLLINSON AND DAINTON, *Disc. Faraday Soc. 12,* No. 12, 212-26.
260. COMPAGNIE DES MEULES NORTON (*Soc. anon.*), French Patent 851,036 (1940); *C.A. 36,* 1952 (1942).
261. COMPTON, MARTIN, WORD AND BARBER, *Textile Research J. 25,* No. 1, 58-75 (1955).
262. COMPTON, MARTIN, WORD AND THOMPSON, *Textile Ind. 117,* No. 10, 138-A–138-D, 188 (1953).
263. COMPTON AND WILSON, U. S. Patent 2,429,397 (1947).
264. CONROY, *Ph.D. Dissertation,* Pennsylvania State College (1946).
265. COOK AND MOSS, U. S. Patent 2,459,062 (1949).
266. COOK AND MOSS, U. S. Patent 2,589,674 (1952).

267. COOK AND REED, *J. Chem. Soc. 1945*, 399.
268. COOK AND REED, *J. Chem. Soc. 1945*, 920.
269. COOKSON AND MANN, *J. Chem. Soc. 1947*, 618.
270. COOKSON AND MANN, *J. Chem. Soc. 1949*, 67.
271. COOPER, *Chemistry and Industry 1953*, 407-08.
272. CORSE, BRYANT AND SHONLE, *J. Am. Chem. Soc. 68*, 1905 (1946).
273. CORSE, BRYANT AND SHONLE, *J. Am. Chem. Soc. 68*, 1911 (1946).
274. COSBY, U. S. Patent 2,481,826 (1949).
275. COTTON AND WALKDEN, *J. Econ. Entomol. 39*, 529 (1946).
276. COTTON AND YOUNG, *J. Econ. Entomol. 36*, 116 (1943).
277. COURTAULDS, LTD., Australian Patent 146,442 (1952).
278. COURTAULDS, LTD. AND MacGREGOR, British Patent 588,751 (1947); C.A. *41*, 6718 (1947).
279. COWAN, EVANS AND McKINNEY, U. S. Patent 2,594,293 (1952).
280. COWGILL, U. S. Patent 2,554,662 (1951); U. S. Patent 2,554,663 (1951).
281. COWGILL, U. S. Patent 2,554,899 (1951).
282. COWGILL, U. S. Patent 2,597,087 (1952).
283. COWLING, EGGERT AND ALEXANDER, *Ind. Eng. Chem. 46*, No. 9, 1977-85 (1954).
284. COYNER AND HILLMAN, *J. Am. Chem. Soc. 71*, 324 (1949).
285. CRANMER, *Corrosion 8*, 195-204 (1952).
286. CRATER, *India Rubber World 129*, No. 5, 629-31 (1954).
287. CREWS, U. S. Patent 2,495,214 (1950).
288. CROUCH AND WERKMAN, U. S. Patent 2,630,448 (1953).
289. CROUCH AND WERKMAN, U. S. Patent 2,630,452 (1953).
290. CRUZ, U. S. Patent 2,577,844 (1951).
291. CUMMINGS, *Ind. Eng. Chem. 46*, No. 9, 1985-91 (1954).
292. CUPERY, U. S. Patent 2,526,638 (1950).
293. CURD, HOGGARTH, LANDQUIST AND ROSE, *J. Chem. Soc. 1948*, 1766.
294. CYRIAX, *Chemistry and Industry 1952*, No. 37, 895-99.
295. DAHLBOM, *Acta Chem. Scand. 5*, 690-98 (1951).
296. DAINTON, *Nature 160*, 268 (1947).
297. DAINTON, *J. Phys. and Coll. Chem. 52*, 490 (1948).
298. DAINTON, *J. Chim. Phys. 48*, 182 (1951).
299. DAINTON, *J. Chem. Soc. 1952*, 1533.
300. DALBERT, *Rev. gen. caoutchouc 29*, 515-18 (1952); C.A. *46*, 10670 (1952).
301. D'ALCONTRES AND GRUNANGER, *Gazz. Chim. ital. 80*, 741-49 (1950).
302. D'ALELIO, U. S. Patent 2,437,421 (1948).
303. D'ALELIO, U. S. Patent 2,656,334 (1953).
304. DALY, U. S. Patent 2,439,202 (1948).
305. DALY, U. S. Patent 2,505,349 (1950).
306. DAMSCHRODER AND GATES, U. S. Patent 2,518,666 (1950).
307. DANIEL AND PETROPOULOS, U. S. Patent 2,600,623 (1952).
308. DAS, CHATTERJEE AND PALIT, *Proc. Roy. Soc.* (London) *A227*, 252-58 (1955).
309. DAUB AND DOYLE, *J. Am. Chem. Soc. 74*, 4449-50 (1952).
310. DAUL, REINHARDT, REID, *Textile Research J. 25*, No. 3, 246-53 (1955).
311. DAVIS, U. S. Patent 2,433,742 (1947).
312. DAVIS AND WIEDEMAN, *Ind. Eng. Chem. 37*, 482 (1945).
313. DAVIS AND WIEDEMAN, U. S. Patent 2,432,511 (1947).
314. DAVIS AND WIEDEMAN, Canadian Patent 460,690 (1949).
315. DAVISON AND BATES, *J. Chem. Soc. 1953*, 2607-11.
316. DAZZI, U. S. Patent 2,617,819 (1952).
317. DAZZI, U. S. Patent 2,658,047 (1953).
318. DELABY, DAMIENS AND SEYDEN-PENNE, *Compt. rend. 238*, 121 (1954).
319. DELABY, DAMIENS AND SEYDEN-PENNE, *Compt. rend. 239*, 1645-47 (1954).
320. DENTON AND PLANK, U. S. Patent 2,518,295 (1950).
321. DERMER AND EDMISON, *J. Am. Chem. Soc. 77*, 70-73 (1955).
322. DEUTSCHE CELLULOID-FABRIK, British Patent 470,969 (1937); C.A. *32*, 1119 (1938).
323. DEUTSCHE CELLULOID-FABRIK, French Patent 816,233 (1937).
324. D'IANNI, U. S. Patent 2,231,360 (1941).
325. D'IANNI, U. S. Patent 2,384,889 (1945).
326. DiCARLO AND LINDWALL, *J. Am. Chem. Soc. 67*, 199 (1945).
327. DICKEY, U. S. Patent 2,492,971 (1950); U. S. Patent 2,492,972 (1950).
328. DICKINSON, *Leather and Shoes 124*, No. 22, 6, 28 (1952).
329. DIECKMANN, MUSCOTT AND ROCHE, U. S. Patent 2,623,863 (1952).
330. DiMASI, U. S. Patent 2,510,090 (1950).
331. DISTILLERS CO., LTD., Australian Appln. 13,294 (1952).
332. DISTILLERS CO., LTD., Australian Patent 160,102 (1954).
333. DISTILLERS CO., LTD., Australian Patent 162,562 (1955).
334. DISTILLERS CO., LTD., Brazilian Appln. 64,295 (1952).
335. DITZ AND HUSSEY, U. S. Patent 2,578,518 (1951).
336. DOAK, *J. Am. Chem. Soc. 70*, 1525 (1948).
337. DOAK, quoted by Mayo and Walling, *Chem. Rev. 46*, 191 (1950).
338. DOUCET AND RUMPF, *Bull. soc. chim. France 1954*, 610-13.

339. DOUGLAS, PALMQUIST AND GROVE, U. S. Patent 2,647,848 (1953).
340. DOWNING, U. S. Patent 2,606,177 (1952).
341. DREISBACH, "Physical Properties of Chemical Substances," pp. 20-23, Dow Chemical
       Co., Midland, Mich. (1952).
342. DREYFUS, U. S. Patent 2,481,580 (1949).
343. DRUMMOND AND WATERS, J. Chem. Soc. 1955, 497-504.
344. DuBROW AND HARWOOD, J. Org. Chem. 17, 1043-46 (1952).
345. DUFFIN AND KENDALL, J. Chem. Soc. 1954, 408-415.
346. DUNN, U. S. Patent 2,606,176 (1952).
347. DuPONT, British Patent 576,800 (1946); C.A. 42, 3775 (1948).
348. DuPONT, British Patent 615,332 (1949).
349. DuPONT, Agricultural Newsletter (du Pont) 18, No. 5, 83-84 (1950).
350. DuPONT, Australian Patent 143,666 (1951).
351. DuPONT, British Patent 728,656 (1955).
352. DUTCHER AND WOLK, U. S. Patent 2,467,373 (1949).
353. DUTTA, J. Indian Chem. Soc. 31, 875-80 (1955).
354. EASTMAN, U. S. Patent 2,650,158 (1953).
355. EBERLY AND REID, U. S. Patent 2,537,626 (1951).
356. EDEN, J. Econ. Entomol. 44, 993-94 (1951).
357. EHRLICH AND DeLOLLIS, J. Research Nat. Bur. Standards 51, 145-54 (1953).
358. EHRLICH, TUCKER AND FRANKLIN, Ind. Eng. Chem. 47, 322-27 (1955).
359. ELDERFIELD, GENSLER, BEMBRY, KREMER, BRODY, HAGEMAN AND HEAD, J. Am.
       Chem. Soc. 68, 1259 (1946).
360. ELSTOW AND PLATT, Chemistry and Industry 1952, 449-50.
361. ENGEL, et al., U. S. Patent 2,592,550 (1952).
362. ENJAY Co., PERBUNAN, Compounding and Processing.
363. ERICKSON, U. S. Patent 2,459,420 (1949).
364. ERICKSON, U. S. Patent 2,524,011 (1950).
365. ERICKSON AND THOMAS, U. S. Patent 2,606,810 (1952).
366. ETIENNE, SPIRE AND TOROMANOFF, Bull. soc. chim. France 1952, 750-56.
367. EVANS, HIGGINSON AND WOODING, Rec. trav. chim. 68, 1069-78 (1949).
368. EVANS AND ROBERTSON, J. Chem. Soc. 1950, 2834-35.
369. EVANS, SANTAPPA AND URI, J. Polymer Sci. 7, 1243-60 (1951).
370. EVANS AND THURSTON-HOOKWAY, British Patent 616,904 (1949); C.A. 43, 5427 (1949)
371. EVANS AND URI, Nature 164, 404-05 (1949).
372. EWING AND BLACKMORE, U. S. Patent 2,681,292 (1954).
373. FALK, PB 35786; Bib. 9, 1085.
374. FARBENFABRIKEN BAYER, British Patent 678,614 (1952); Brit. Abstr. 1952, B II, 1292.
375. FARBENFABRIKEN BAYER, British Patent 719,330 (1954).
376. FABER AND WEGLER, unpublished results; quoted by Bayer, ref. 95.
377. FAULKNER, British Patent 636,866 (1950); C.A. 44, 8945 (1950).
378. FAULKNER, U. S. Patent 2,553,308 (1951).
379. FAULKNER AND STAUDINGER, U. S. Patent 2,590,834 (1952).
380. FAY, U. S. Patent 2,459,874 (1949).
381. FERRONI AND BERTE, Ann. chim. (Rome) 43, 76-79 (1953); C.A. 47, 7873 (1953).
382. FETSCHER, U. S. Patent 2,704,729 (1955).
383. FEUER AND PIER, J. Am. Chem. Soc. 76, 105-07 (1954).
384. FIELD, Modern Packaging 22, No. 4, 149 (1948).
385. FIELDS AND WESP, U. S. Patent 2,598,639 (1952).
386. FIKENTSCHER AND HEUCK, German Patent 654,989 (1938); C.A. 32, 3521 (1938).
387. FIKENTSCHER AND JACOBI, French Patent 715,893 (1931); C.A. 26, 1940 (1932).
388. FIKENTSCHER AND JACOBI, U. S. Patent 1,851,040 (1932).
389. FILANCHIONE et al., Rubber Age (N. Y.) 72, 631-37 (1953).
390. FINKELSTEIN, German Patent 496,372 (1930); C.A. 24, 3250 (1930).
391. FISCHER, U. S. Patent 2,710,821 (1955).
392. FISCHER AND COOK, U. S. Patent 2,552,775 (1951).
393. FISHER, Modern Plastics Encyclopedia 1947, 236A.
394. FISHER AND MAST, U. S. Patent 2,643,247 (1953).
395. FLORY, U. S. Patent 2,452,012 (1948).
396. FLOYD, J. Am. Chem. Soc. 71, 1746 (1949).
397. FLOYD, U. S. Patent 2,516,307 (1950).
398. FLUCK, U. S. Patent 2,536,050 (1951).
399. FORD, BUC AND GREINER, J. Am. Chem. Soc. 69, 844 (1947).
400. FORDYCE, CHAPIN AND HAM, J. Am. Chem. Soc. 70, 2489 (1948).
401. FOSTER, Materials and Methods 28, No. 9, 81-83 (1948).
402. FOX AND WENNER, U. S. Patent 2,465,307 (1949).
403. FRANCIS, J. Phys. Chem. 58, 1099-1114 (1954).
404. FRANK, EMMICK AND JOHNSON, J. Am. Chem. Soc. 69, 2313 (1947).
405. FRANK AND McPHERSON, J. Am. Chem. Soc. 71, 1387 (1949).
406. FRANK AND PIERLE, J. Am. Chem. Soc. 73, 724-30 (1951).
407. FRANKE AND THIELE, German Patent 811,350 (1951); C.A. 47, 3337 (1953).
408. FROST AND MARTELL, J. Org. Chem. 15, 51-53 (1950).
409. FUCHS, Kunststoffe 43, 409-15 (1953).

410. FULLER AND GAIRAUD, *Soil Sci. Soc. Amer. Proc. 18*, 35-40 (1954).
411. FUSON AND MILLER, *J. Org. Chem. 17*, 886-90 (1952).
412. GALAT, *J. Am. Chem. Soc. 67*, 1414 (1945).
413. GANS, U. S. Patent 2,394,542 (1946).
414. GARDNER, *J. Polymer Sci. 1*, 289 (1946).
415. GARVEY, U. S. Patent 2,443,678 (1948).
416. GATES AND LOWE, Canadian Patent 511,766 (1955).
417. GAYLER, U. S. Patent 2,672,456 (1954).
418. GEHLEN (Johann Wolfgang von Goethe Univ., Frankfort, Ger.), *Ann. 563*, 185-200 (1949).
419. GERBER, *Melliand Textilber 20*, 286 (1939).
420. GERKE, *J. Polymer Sci. 13*, 295-300 (1954).
421. GERSHBEIN AND HURD, *J. Am. Chem. Soc. 69*, 241 (1947).
422. GERSHBEIN AND HURD, *Org. Syntheses 29*, 52 (1949).
423. GESSLER, U. S. Patent 2,521,361 (1950).
424. GIDLEY, U. S. Patent 2,462,629 (1949).
425. GIDLEY, U. S. Patent 2,469,721 (1949).
426. GLASER, PB 73887, frames 6421-29 (1940); *Bib. 9*, 304.
427. GLASER, PB 73887, frames 6430-42 (1940-41); *Bib. 9*, 304.
428. GLASS, *J. Econ. Entomol. 37*, 74 (1944).
429. GLASS, *J. Econ. Entomol. 37*, 388 (1944).
430. GLASS AND CROSIER, *J. Econ. Entomol. 42*, 646 (1949).
431. GLEIM, U. S. Patent 2,630,420 (1953).
432. GLENN, FREIFELDER, STONE, HERTZ AND STRONG, *J. Am. Chem. Soc. 77*, 3080-82 (1955).
433. GOLDBERG AND JAMPOLSKY, U. S. Patent 2,624,734 (1953).
434. GOLDFINGER AND STEIDLITZ, *J. Polymer Sci. 3*, 786 (1948).
435. GOLDSCHMIDT AND STOECKL, *Chem. Ber. 85*, 630-34 (1952).
436. GORSKI, U. S. Patent 2,550,465 (1951).
437. GRADSTEN AND POLLOCK, *J. Am. Chem. Soc. 70*, 3079 (1948).
438. GRAHAM AND PICCARD, U. S. Patent 2,715,588 (1955); U. S. Patent 2,715,591 (1955).
439. GRANT, GREATHOUSE, REID AND WEAVER, *Textile Research J. 25*, No. 1, 76-83 (1955).
440. GRASSIE AND MELVILLE, *Proc. Roy. Soc.* (London) *A199*, 39-55 (1949).
441. GRAULICH, BECKER AND BAYER, U. S. Patent 2,678,924 (1954).
442. GREBENIUK AND TSUKERVANIK, *Zhur. Obshchei Khim. 25*, 286-93 (1955); *C.A. 50*, 1639a (1956).
443. GREEN AND TAYLOR, U. S. Patent 2,413,496 (1946).
444. GREENBERG, Canadian Patent 460,560 (1949).
445. GREENBURG, Canadian Patent 512,447 (1955).
446. GRESHAM AND STEADMAN, *J. Am. Chem. Soc. 71*, 1872 (1949).
447. GRESHAM AND STEADMAN, U. S. Patent 2,568,620 (1951).
448. GIBBINS, U. S. Patent 2,416,052 (1947).
449. GIBBINS, MILLER AND O'LEARY, U. S. Patent 2,397,960 (1946).
450. GIFFING AND SALISBURY, *J. Am. Chem. Soc. 70*, 3416 (1948).
451. GRIM, U. S. Patent 2,594,913 (1952).
452. GROVES AND SWAN, *J. Chem. Soc. 1952*, 650-61.
453. GRUMMITT AND MARSH, *J. Am. Chem. Soc. 71*, 4156 (1949).
454. GUNDERMANN AND MICHEEL, *Ann. 578*, 45-48 (1952).
455. HAAS AND KARLIN, *J. Polymer Sci. 9*, 588-92 (1952).
456. HAAS AND SIMON, *J. Polymer Sci. 9*, 309-14 (1952).
457. HAGEMEYER, U. S. Patent 2,701,260 (1955).
458. HAGER, U. S. Patent 2,644,842 (1953).
459. HALVERSON, STAMM AND WHALEN, *J. Chem. Phys. 16*, 808 (1948).
460. HAM, *J. Polymer Sci. 14*, 87-93 (1954).
461. HAM, U. S. Patent 2,559,154 (1951).
462. HAM, *Textile Research J. 24*, No. 7, 597-614 (1954).
463. HAMBURGER, PLATT AND MORGAN, *Textile Research J. 22*, No. 11, 695-729 (1952).
464. HANBY, WALEY, WATSON AND AMBROSE, *J. Chem. Soc. 1950*, 3239-49.
465. HANSLEY, U. S. Patent 2,333,782 (1943).
466. HANSON, U. S. Patent 2,463,032 (1949).
467. HARDMAN, U. S. Patent 2,421,837 (1947).
468. HARDMAN, *J. Am. Chem. Soc. 70*, 2119 (1948).
469. HARMAN, U. S. Patent 2,413,917 (1947).
470. HARMAN, U. S. Patent 2,508,256 (1950).
471. HARMAN, U. S. Patent 2,520,280 (1950).
472. HARMAN, U. S. Patent 2,649,470 (1953).
473. HARRIS, U. S. Patent 2,413,623 (1946).
474. HARRIS AND DEATLEY, U. S. Patent 2,423,186 (1947).
475. HARRIS AND SHARPLES, U. S. Patent 2,419,186 (1947).
476. HARRISON, U. S. Patent 2,471,742 (1949).
477. HASCHE AND McNALLY, PB 34813; *Bib. 3*, 10; *FIAT Final Report 836*.
478. HASLAM AND NEWLANDS, *Analyst 80*, 50-53 (1955).
479. HATFIELD AND OWEN, U. S. Patent 2,535,852 (1950).

480. HAUSER, U. S. Patent 2,462,185 (1949).
481. HAUSER, U. S. Patent 2,474,897 (1949).
482. HAUSER, U. S. Patent 2,525,671 (1950).
483. HAYES, *J. Polymer Sci.11*, 531-37 (1953).
484. HAZELDINE, *J. Chem. Soc. 1952*, 3490-98.
485. HECHENBLEIKNER, U. S. Patent 2,443,504 (1948).
486. HECHENBLEIKNER, U. S. Patent 2,489,181 (1949).
487. HECHENBLEIKNER, Canadian Patent 498,382 (1953).
488. HECHTMAN, U. S. Patent 2,714,562 (1955).
489. HECKERT, *Ind. Eng. Chem. 44*, 2103-09 (1952).
490. HEDRICK AND MOWRY, *Soil Sci. 73*, 427-41 (1952).
491. HEDRICK AND MOWRY, *Chemistry and Industry 1952*, 652-56.
492. HEDRICK AND MOWRY, U. S. Patent 2,651,885 (1953).
493. HEIDER, U. S. Patent 2,698,338 (1954).
494. HEIM, *Bull. soc. chim. Belg. 39*, 458 (1930); C.A. *25*, 2389 (1931).
495. HEINEMANN, Canadian 508,190 (1954).
496. HELD AND BLAINE, U. S. Patent 2,468,975 (1949).
497. HELLE, U. S. Patent 2,572,931 (1951).
498. HENDERSON AND MCLEOD, *Trans. Inst. Rubber Ind. 30*, No. 5, 115-28 (1954).
499. HENDRICKS AND DAHLQUIST, U. S. Patent 2,601,016 (1952).
500. HENECKA, *Chem. Ber. 81*, 197 (1948).
501. HENERY-LOGAN AND NICHOLLS, quoted by Simha and Wall, *J. Research Nat. Bur. Standards 41*, 521 (1948).
502. HENSON, *Official Digest Federation Paint and Varnish Production Clubs, No. 316*, 298-300 (1951).
503. HERNANDEZ AND NORD, *Experientia 3*, 489 (1947).
504. HERRENT, *J. Polymer Sci. 8*, 346-49 (1952).
505. HERSH AND MONTGOMERY, *Textile Research J. 25*, No. 4, 279-95 (1955).
506. HERZOG, GOLD AND GECKLER, *J. Am. Chem. Soc. 73*, 749-51 (1951).
507. HESSE AND BUECKING, *Ann. 563*, 31 (1949).
508. HESTER AND BRUSON, U. S. Patent 2,305,529 (1942).
509. HEUCK AND FREYTAG, U. S. Patent 2,230,776 (1941).
510. HEUCK AND FREYTAG, German Patent 711,919 (1941); C.A. *37*, 4503 (1943).
511. HEUSER, U. S. Patent 2,409,124 (1946).
512. HEY AND NAGDY, *J. Chem. Soc. 1954*, 1204-07.
513. HICKS AND MELVILLE, *Nature 171*, 300-01 (1953).
514. HICKS AND MELVILLE, *J. Polymer Sci. 12*, 461-468 (1954).
515. HICKS AND MELVILLE, *Proc. Roy. Soc.* (London) *A 226*, 314-35 (1954).
516. HILL, U. S. Patent 2,673,192 (1954).
517. HINDLE, *Am. Dyestuff Reptr. 43*, No. 18, 581-82 (1954).
518. HOCHBERG, U. S. Patent 2,681,324 (1954).
519. HOFFMANN AND JACOBI, German Patent 598,185 (1934); C.A. *28*, 5474 (1934).
520. HOFFMANN AND JACOBI, U. S. Patent 1,992,615 (1935).
521. HOFFMANN AND JACOBI, U. S. Patent 2,017,537 (1935).
522. HOFFMANN AND TAGMANN, *Helv. Chim. Acta 32*, 1470 (1949).
523. HOFRICHTER, U. S. Patent 2,711,996 (1955).
524. HOHENSTEIN, HOWARD AND ELLY, U. S. Patent 2,652,392 (1953).
525. HOLCOMB AND HAMILTON, *J. Am. Chem. Soc. 64*, 1309 (1942).
526. HOLLIHAN AND MOSS, *Ind. Eng. Chem. 39*, 222 (1947).
527. HOLLIHAN AND MOSS, *Ind. Eng. Chem. 39*, 929 (1947).
528. HOLLIHAN AND MOSS, U. S. Patent 2,499,501 (1950).
529. HOLLIHAN AND MOSS, U. S. Patent 2,511,060 (1950).
530. HOLMES, et al., *Can. J. Research 26B*, 248 (1948).
531. HOLST AND HERSAM, U. S. Patent 2,459,164 (1949).
532. HOOKWAY AND EVANS, U. S. Patent 2,468,015 (1949).
533. HOPFF, German Patent 743,224 (1943); C.A. *39*, 2766 (1945).
534. HOPFF, *Kunststoffe 42*, 423-26 (1952).
535. HOPFF AND SCHMIDT, U. S. Patent 2,102,179 (1937).
536. HORNER, JURGELEIT AND KLUEPFEL, *Ann. 591*, 108-17 (1955).
537. HORNER AND LINGNAU, *Ann. 573*, 30-35 (1951).
538. HORNER AND LINGNAU, *Ann. 591*, 21-52 (1955).
539. HORNER AND NAUMANN, *Ann. 587*, 93-102 (1954).
540. HORNER, SPIETSCHKA AND GROSS, *Ann. 573*, 17-30 (1951).
541. HORNER AND STOHR, *Chem. Ber. 86*, 1066-71 (1953).
542. HORNING AND FINELLI, *J. Am. Chem. Soc. 71*, 3204 (1949).
543. HORNING AND FINELLI, *Org. Syntheses 30*, 80-81 (1950).
544. HORNING AND SCHOCK, *J. Am. Chem. Soc. 70*, 2941 (1948).
545. HORNING AND SCHOCK, *J. Am. Chem. Soc. 70*, 2945 (1948).
546. HORNING AND SCHOCK, *J. Am. Chem. Soc. 71*, 1359 (1949).
547. HORSLEY, *Anal. Chem. 19*, 508 (1947).
548. HOTTA, *J. Colloid Sci. 9*, No. 6, 504-21 (1954).
549. HOUK AND BOCK, Canadian Patent 434,619 (1946).
550. HOUTZ, U. S. Patent 2,341,553 (1944).

551. Houtz, U. S. Patent 2,375,847 (1945).
552. Houtz, *Textile Research J. 20*, No. 11, 786-801 (1950).
553. Howe, U. S. Patent 2,637,664 (1953).
554. Huff, *U. S. Bur. Mines, Rept. Investigations 3669* (1942).
555. Humke, *Modern Plastics Encyclopedia 1947*, 592.
556. Hurd, U. S. Patent 2,645,628 (1953).
557. Hurd and Gershbein, *J. Am. Chem. Soc. 69*, 2328 (1947).
558. Hurd and Roedel, *Ind. Eng. Chem. 40*, 2078 (1948).
559. Hurdis and Smyth, *J. Am. Chem. Soc. 65*, 89 (1943).
560. Hussey and Wright, U. S. Patent 2,653,884 (1953).
561. Hutchinson, U. S. Patent 2,519,249 (1950).
562. Hutchinson, U. S. Patent 2,598,174 (1952).
563. I. G. Farbenind., A.-G., German Patent No. 580,351 (1929); C.A. *27*, 4816 (1933).
564. I. G. Farbenind., A.-G., British Patent 371,812 (1932); C.A. *27* 3346 (1933).
565. I. G. Farbenind., A.-G., French Patent 728,712 (1931); C.A. *26*, 6160 (1932); German Patent 571,665 (1933); C.A. *27*, 4419 (1933).
566. I. G. Farbenind., A.-G., British Patent 404,744 (1932); C.A. *28*, 4068 (1934).
567. I. G. Farbenind., A.-G., French Patent 740,410 (1932); C.A. *27*, 2318 (1933).
568. I. G. Farbenind., A.-G., French Patent 742,358 (1933); C.A. *27*, 3483 (1933).
569. I. G. Farbenind., A.-G., German Patent 570,677 (1933); C.A. *27*, 4246 (1933).
570. I. G. Farbenind., A.-G., French Patent 764,394 (1934); C.A. *28*, 5356 (1934).
571. I. G. Farbenind., A.-G., French Patent 806,715 (1936); C.A. *31*, 4991 (1937).
572. I. G. Farbenind., A.-G., British Patent 457,621 (1936); C.A. *31*, 3068 (1937).
573. I. G. Farbenind., A.-G., British Patent 466,316 (1937); C.A. *31*, 7887 (1937).
574. I. G. Farbenind., A.-G., British Patent 478,701 (1938); C.A. *32*, 5106 (1938).
575. I. G. Farbenind., A.-G., German Patent 666,466 (1938); C.A. *33*, 2149 (1939).
576. I. G. Farbenind., A.-G., German Patent 669,961 (1939); C.A. *33*, 5415 (1939).
577. I. G. Farbenind., A.-G., French Patent 877,120 (1942).
578. I. G. Farbenind., A.-G., Belgian Patent 452,384 (1943); *Chem. Zentr. 1945*, I, 1307.
579. I. G. Farbenind., A.-G., Belgian Patent 452,195 (1943); *Chem. Zentr. 1945* I, 1182.
580. I. G. Farbenind., A.-G., German Patent 753,863; PB 83606, frames 6612-14; *Bib. 9*, 994.
581. I. G. Farbenind., A.-G., German Patent Application I 51944.
582. I. G. Farbenind., A.-G., German Patent Application I 61340.
583. I. G. Farbenind., A.-G., German Patent Application I 66739 (1940).
584. I. G. Farbenind., A.-G., French Patent 898,275 (1945); *Chem. Zentr. 1946* I, 1084.
585. I. G. Farbenind, A.-G., German Patent Application I 67660; ADPA *13*, 138.
586. I. G. Farbenind., A.-G., German Patent Application I 69686 (1942); ADPA 1, 151; PB 83351, frames 5562-67; *Bib. 9*, 991.
587. I. G. Farbenind., A.-G., German Patent Application I 70733 (1941); PB 84041, frames 03231-32; French Patent 886,846 (1943).
588. I. G. Farbenind., A.-G., German Patent Application I 70772, quoted by Bayer, ref. 95.
589. I. G. Farbenind., A.-G., German Patent Application I 71937; PB 20545, frames 3065-66; ADPA *6*, 175.
590. I. G. Farbenind., A.-G., German Patent Application I 72334; ADPA *13*, 145.
591. I. G. Farbenind., A.-G., German Patent Application I 75276; ADPA 1, 222; PB 84030, frames 03831-32; *Bib. 9*, 991.
592. I. G. Farbenind., A.-G., German Patent Application I 76714.
593. I. G. Farbenind., A.-G., German Patent Application I 76717.
594. I. G. Farbenind., A.-G., PB 84064, frames 01293-301 (1941); *Bib. 9*, 991.
595. I. G. Farbenind., A.-G., French Patent 1,013,951 (1952); *Chem. Zentr. 124*, No. 37, 5933 (1953).
596. Imperial Chemical Industries, Ltd., British Patent 567,778 (1945); C.A. *41*, 2610 (1947).
597. Imperial Chemical Industries, Ltd., British Patent 586,796 (1947); C.A. *42*, 3217 (1948).
598. *Ind. Eng. Chem. 44*, 11A, 13A, 15A (1952).
599. Institute of Synthetic Org. Chem. Res., Japanese Patent 154,815 (1943); C.A. *44*, 3515 (1950).
600. Institute of Textile Technology, British Patent 732,779 (1951).
601. Ivanoff, *Chem. Ber. 87*, 1600-04 (1954).
602. Jackson, U. S. Patent 2,682,525 (1954).
603. Jacobson, U. S. Patent 2,436,926 (1948).
604. Jansen, U. S. Patent 2,440,095 (1948).
605. Janz and Duncan, *Anal. Chem. 25*, No. 9, 1410-11 (1953).
606. Janz and Duncan, *J. Am. Chem. Soc. 75*, 5389-92 (1953).
607. Janz and Duncan, *Nature 171*, 933 (1953).
608. Janz and McCulloch, *J. Am. Chem. Soc. 77*, 3143-45 (1955).
609. Jarrijon and Gossot, *Inds. plastiques 3*, 121 (1947); C.A. *41*, 4955 (1947).
610. Jenkins, *Chemistry and Industry 1955*, No. 4, 89-90.
611. Johnson and Fitzpatrick, Paper presented at the combined Southeastern and Southwestern regional A.C.S. meeting held in New Orleans, Dec. 10-12, 1953.
612. Jones, U. S. Patent 2,652,345 (1953).

613. JONES AND ERB, U. S. Patent 2,683,094 (1954).
614. JONES, KENNEDY AND SCOTT, *U. S. Bur. Mines, Rept. Investigations 3597* (1941).
615. JONES AND MELVILLE, *Proc. Royal Soc.* (London) *A187*, 37 (1946).
616. JOY, U. S. Patent 2,576,944 (1951).
617. JULIA, *Compt. rend. 237*, 913-17 (1953).
618. JUVE, U. S. Patent 2,271,125 (1942).
619. JUVE AND GARVEY, U. S. Patent 2,271,124 (1942).
620. KALB AND SAUER, U. S. Patent 2,540.736 (1951).
621. KAMBARA, *J. Soc. Chem. Ind. Japan 47*, 518 (1944); C.A. *43*, 1594 (1949).
622. KASZUBA, *J. Am. Chem. Soc. 67*, 1227 (1945).
623. KATAYAMA AND KAMBARA, *Chem. High Polymers* (Japan) *10*, 73-75 (1953).
624. KATCHMAN AND MCLAREN, *J. Am. Chem. Soc. 73*, 2124-27 (1951).
625. KEIM, U. S. Patent 2,688,609 (1954).
626. KERN, *J. Am. Chem. Soc. 77*, 1382-83 (1955).
627. KERN, *Angew. Chem. 61*, No. 12, 471-74 (1949).
628. KERN AND FERNOW, *J. prakt. Chem. 160*, 281 (1942).
629. KEYSSNER, U. S. Patent 2,163,176 (1939).
630. KHOMIKOVSKII, *Doklady Akad. Nauk S.S.S.R. 60*, 615 (1948); C.A. *43*, 437 (1949).
631. KILGORE, PB 22413; *Bib. 2*, 236.
632. KING, ACHESON AND YORKE-LONG, *J. Chem. Soc. 1948*, 1926.
633. KING AND MCMILLAN, *J. Am. Chem. Soc. 68*, 1468 (1946).
634. KINMONTH AND TAYLOR, *British Medical J.* 1406-09 (1955).
635. KIPINS AND ORNFELT, *J. Am. Chem. Soc. 71*, 3571 (1949).
636. KISSINGER, VON AND CARMACK, *J. Am. Chem. Soc. 68*, 1563 (1946).
637. KLABUNDE, U. S. Patent 2,422,556 (1947).
638. KLAGER, *J. Org. Chem. 20*, 650-55 (1955).
639. KLEINER, BAYER AND BECHT, U. S. Patent 2,643,958 (1953).
640. KLEVENS AND PLATT, *Technical Report ONR.*, Contract N6oRI-2o, Task Order IX, Project NR 019101, 1954.
641. KLIMENKOV, KARGIN AND KITAIGORODSKU, *J. Phys. Chem. U.S.S.R. 27*, 1217-27 (1953); C.A. *48*, 3106f (1954).
642. KLOETZEL AND CHUBB, *J. Am. Chem. Soc. 72*, 150-53 (1950).
643. KLOETZEL AND MERTEL, *J. Am. Chem. Soc. 72*, 4786-91 (1950).
644. KNAPSACK-GRIESHEIM A.-G., Brazilian Application 74,725 (1954).
645. KNOPF AND SCHOLZ, German Patent 707,321 (1941); C.A. *37*, 2946 (1943).
646. KOBAYASHI, *Kagaku 23*, 366 (1953); C.A. *48*, 4430f (1954).
647. KOBE AND LONG, *Petroleum Refiner 29*, No. 5, 89 (1950).
648. KOCH, *Fibres (Natural and Synthetic) 16*, No. 5, 174-76 (1955).
649. KOCH, *Fibres (Natural and Synthetic) 16*, 314-20 (1955).
650. KODAK (A/ASIA) PTY. LTD., Australian Patent 142,534 (1948).
651. KODAK, LTD., British Patent 648,926 (1951).
652. KODAK, PTY., LTD., Australian Patent 142,117 (1955).
653. KOEHLER, Canadian Patent 454,436 (1949).
654. KOELSCH, *J. Am. Chem. Soc. 65*, 57 (1943).
655. KOELSCH, *J. Am. Chem. Soc. 65*, 437 (1943).
656. KOELSCH, *J. Am. Chem. Soc. 65*, 2458 (1943).
657. KOELSCH AND WALKER, *J. Am. Chem. Soc. 72*, 346 (1950).
658. KOENECKE AND MCKAY, U. S. Patent 2,669,526 (1954).
659. KOLTHOFF AND PARRY, *J. Am. Chem. Soc. 73*, 3718-23 (1951).
660. KOLTHOFF AND SANDELL, *Textbook of Quantitative Analysis*, Revised Ed., The Macmillan Co., New York, 1945, pp. 623 ff.
661. KOLVOORT AND AKKERMAN, U. S. Patent 2,496,222 (1950).
662. KOENIG, BOCK AND TREPPENHAUER, German Patent 738,399 (1943); C.A. *38*, 3990 (1944).
663. KOENIG AND WEGNER, PB 691 (1941); *Bib. 1*, 39.
664. KOST, *Vestnik Moskov. Univ. 1947*, No. 2, 141; C.A. *42*, 3722 (1948).
665. KOST, *A. N. Uchenye Zapiski Moskov. Gosudarst. Univ. im. M.V. Lomonosova No. 131*, 39-97 (1950); C.A. *47*, 9905-06 (1953).
666. KOST AND TERENT'EV, *J. Gen. Chem. U.S.S.R. 22*, 719-21 (1952) (English Translation); C.A. *47*, 2759 (1953).
667. KOST, TERENT'EV AND YASHUNSKII, *Vestnik Moskov. Univ. 5*, No. 6, *Ser. Fiz.-Mat. i Estest. Nauk* No. 4, 41-42 (1950); C.A. *45*, 6644 (1951).
668. KOST AND YASHUNSKII, *Doklady Akad. Nauk S.S.S.R. 83*, 93-96 (1952); C.A. *47*, 2696 (1953).
669. KROPA, U. S. Patent 2,310,961 (1943).
670. KROPA, U. S. Patent 2,356,767 (1944).
671. KROPA, U. S. Patent 2,425,191 (1947).
672. KROPA AND DUNNE, U. S. Patent 2,541,927 (1951).
673. KROPA AND WELCHER, U. S. Patent 2,703,792 (1955).
674. KRZIKALLA AND FLICKINGER, PB 638 (1942); *Bib. 1*, 45.
675. KUNICHIKA, OTA AND MORIMURA, *Bull. Inst. Chem. Research, Kyoto Univ. 26*, 91 (1951); C.A. *48*, 7339c (1954).
676. KUROKI, *J. Chem. Soc. Japan, Ind. Chem. Sect., 56*, 704-07 (1953); C.A. *48*, 13226 (1954).

677. KURTZ, German Patent 707,852 (1941); C.A. *47*, 2747 (1943).
678. KURTZ, *Ann. 572*, No. 1, 23-82 (1951).
679. LADD, U. S. Patent 2,632,019 (1953).
680. LADD, Canadian Patent 512,237 (1955).
681. LANGLEY AND ADAMS, *J. Am. Chem. Soc. 44*, 2326 (1922).
682. LAPIANA AND HOUTH, U. S. Patent 2,664,365 (1953).
683. LARSSON AND THURNE, *Svensk Papperstidn. 57*, No. 3, 73-76, 77 (1954).
684. LAWTON, BUECHE AND BALWIT, *Nature 172*, 76-77 (1953).
685. LEBRAS AND COMPAGNON, *Rubber Chem. Tech. 20*, 938 (1947).
686. LEE, U. S. Patent 2,700,185 (1955).
687. LEEKLEY, U. S. Patent 2,439,308 (1948).
688. LEHMAN, *Assoc. Food and Drug Officials U. S. Quart. Bull. 15*, 82-89 (1951).
689. LEONARD, CORT AND BLEVINS, *Ind. Eng. Chem. 43*, 2500-02 (1951).
690. LESLIE AND HENZE, *J. Am. Chem. Soc. 71*, 3480 (1949).
691. LEVINA, SHUSHERINA AND KAMINSKAYA, *Doklady Akad. Nauk S.S.S.R. 86*, 79-82
       (1952); C.A. *47*, 4849F (1953).
692. LEVINA, et al., *J. Gen. Chem. (U.S.S.R.) 24*, No. 8, 1439-44 (1954).
693. LEWIS, MAYO AND HULSE, *J. Am. Chem. Soc. 67*, 1701 (1945).
694. LEWIS, WALLING, CUMMINGS, BRIGGS AND WENISCH, *J. Am. Chem. Soc. 70*, 1527
       (1948).
695. LICHTY, U. S. Patent 2,231,838 (1941).
696. LICHTY, U. S. Patent 2,328,984 (1943).
697. LICHTY AND D'IANNI, U. S. Patent 2,298,739 (1942).
698. LIESER AND KEMMNER, *Chem. Ber. 84*, 4-12 (1951).
699. LINCOLN, ELLIS AND RICHARDSON, British Patent 613,807 (1948); C.A. *43*, 5414 (1949).
700. LINDGREN AND SINCLAIR, *J. Econ. Entomol. 44*, 980-90 (1951).
701. LINDGREN AND VINCENT, *J. Econ. Entomol. 44*, 975-79 (1951).
702. LINDSAY AND CHELDELIN, *J. Am. Chem. Soc. 72*, 828-30 (1950).
703. LINDSTROM AND LAMM, *J. Phys. and Colloid Chem. 55*, 1139-46 (1951).
704. LIPSON AND SPEAKMAN, *Nature 157*, 590 (1946).
705. LOCHTE, THOMAS AND TRUITT, *J. Am. Chem. Soc. 66*, 550 (1944).
706. LODER, U. S. Patent 2,554,484 (1951).
707. LONG, U. S. Patent 2,231,363 (1941).
708. LOWE, MINSK, KENYON, U. S. Patent 2,632,704 (1953).
709. LYTTON, U. S. Patent 2,537,146 (1951).
710. MACGREGOR, British Patent 588,751 (1947).
711. MACGREGOR, U. S. Patent 2,482,011 (1949).
712. MACGREGOR, British Patent 636,020 (1950); C.A. *44*, 6624 (1950).
713. MACGREGOR, British Patent 636,295 (1950); C.A. *44*, 6624 (1950).
714. MACGREGOR, *J. Soc. Dyers and Colourists 67*, 66-73 (1951).
715. MACGREGOR AND HAPPEY, U. S. Patent 2,522,627 (1950).
716. MACGREGOR AND PUGH, *J. Chem. Soc. 1945*, 535.
717. MACGREGOR AND PUGH, *J. Soc. Dyers and Colourists 64*, 71 (1948).
718. MACGREGOR AND PUGH, *J. Soc. Dyers and Colourists 67*, 74-80 (1951).
719. MACGREGOR AND PUGH, *Proc. XIth Intern. Congr. Pure and Appl. Chem.* (London) *5*,
       123-31 (1947) (Pub. 1953).
720. MACK, U. S. Patent 2,545,963 (1951).
721. MACARTHUR AND LOGAN, U. S. Patent 2,713,044 (1955).
722. MCBEE, DINELEY AND BURCH, *J. Am. Chem. Soc. 77*, 385-87 (1955).
723. MCCARTNEY, *Modern Plastics 30*, 118 (1953).
724. MCFARLAND, *Corrosion 9*, No. 4, 1 (1953), (General News).
725. MCKINLEY, *Elec. World 124*, 52 (1945).
726. MCKINNEY, COWAN AND UHING, U. S. Patent 2,538,024 (1951).
727. MCKINNEY, UHING AND COWAN, U. S. Patent 2,517,585 (1950).
728. MCKINNEY, UHING, SETZKORN AND COWAN, *J. Am. Chem. Soc. 72*, 2599 (1950).
729. MCKINNEY, UHING, SETZKORN AND COWAN, *J. Am. Chem. Soc. 73*, 1641-44 (1951).
730. MCKINNEY, UHING, SETZKORN AND COWAN, U. S. Patent 2,562,198 (1951).
731. MCLAMORE, U. S. Patent 2,451,852 (1948).
732. MCPHEE AND LIPSON, *Australian J. Chemistry 7*, No. 4, 387-96 (1954).
733. MCQUEEN, U. S. Patent 2,424,664 (1947).
734. MCQUEEN AND WERNTZ, U. S. Patent 2,566,237 (1951).
735. MAGAT, FARIS, REITH AND SALSBURY, *J. Am. Chem. Soc. 73*, 1028 (1951).
736. MALINOWSKI, *Roczniki Chem. 26*, 85-97 (1952); C.A. *48*, 620 (1954).
737. MAMIYA, *J. Soc. Chem. Ind. Japan 44*, 860 (1941); C.A. *42*, 2108 (1948).
738. MANN AND COOKSON, *Nature 157*, 846 (1946).
739. MANN AND MILLAR, *J. Chem. Soc. 1952*, 4453-57.
740. MANN AND SMITH, *J. Chem. Soc. 1951*, 1898-1905.
741. MARCHIONNA, *Butalastic Polymers*, Reinhold Publishing Corp., New York, 1946,
       pp. 290-99.
742. MARK AND FIKENTSCHER, U. S. Patent 1,984,417 (1934).
743. MARKINA, KHOMIKOVSKII AND MEDVEDEV, *Doklady Akad. Nauk S.S.S.R. 75*, 243-46
       (1950); C.A. *45*, 2707 (1951).
744. MARPLE AND BORDERS, U. S. Patent 2,375,015 (1945).

745. MARPLE AND BORDERS, U. S. Patent 2,455,689 (1948).
746. MARPLE, EVANS AND BORDERS, U. S. Patent 2,375,016 (1945).
747. MARRA AND STINCHFIELD, U S. Patent 2,699,432 (1955).
748. MARTIN, *Soil Sci. Soc. Amer., Proc. 17*, 9-16 (1953).
749. MARTINO, U. S. Patent 2,656,376 (1953).
750. MARVEL, FRIEDLANDER, SWANN AND INSKIP, *J. Am. Chem. Soc. 75*, 3846-48 (1953).
751. MATTOCKS AND HUTCHINSON, *J. Am. Chem. Soc. 70*, 3474 (1948).
752. MAY, U. S. Patent 2,612,480 (1952).
753. MAY AND FISHER, British Patent 639,733 (1950); C.A. *44*, 9981 (1950).
754. MAY AND FISHER, U. S. Patent 2,576,959 (1951).
755. MAY AND FISHER, U. S. Patent 2,577,621 (1951).
756. MAYER, McGOVRAN, TALLEY, SMITH, SAUNDERS AND WOODWARD. *U. S. Bur. Entomol. and Plant Quarantine E-768*, 16 pp. (1949); C.A. *43*, 5893 (1949).
757. MAYFIELD, U. S. Patent 2,606,884 (1952).
758. MAYO, LEWIS AND WALLING, *J. Am. Chem. Soc. 70*, 1529 (1948).
759. MAYO AND WALLING, *Chem. Rev. 46*, 191 (1950).
760. MAYO, WALLING, LEWIS AND HULSE, *J. Am. Chem. Soc. 70*, 1523 (1948).
761. MEEK, POON AND CRISTOL, *J. Am. Chem. Soc. 74*, 761-63 (1952).
762. MEEK, POON, MERROW AND CRISTOL, *J. Am. Chem. Soc. 74*, 2669-72 (1952).
763. MEEK AND RAGSDALE, *J. Am. Chem. Soc. 70*, 2502 (1948).
764. MEISENBERG, PB 35041; *Bib. 7*, 974.
765. MERCK & CO., INC., Brazilian Application 69,224 (1953).
766. MEYER, German Patent 820,306 (1950).
767. MEYER, German Application C 692 (1950); Switzerland (1949).
768. MEYER, U. S. Patent 2,623,882 (1952).
769. MEYER, SAIKA AND GUTOWSKY, *J. Am. Chem. Soc. 75*, 4567-73 (1953).
770. MICHAELS, *Ind. Eng. Chem. 46*, No. 7, 1485-90 (1954).
771. MIGRDICHIAN, U. S. Patent 2,356,075 (1944).
772. MIKESKA, U. S. Patent 2,461,336 (1949).
773. MILLER, U. S. Patent 2,536,611 (1951).
774. MILLER AND BRADLEY, U. S. Patent 2,375,937 (1945).
775. MILLER AND BRADLEY, U. S. Patent 2,382,803 (1945).
776. MILLER AND FLOWERS, U. S. Patent 2,535,690 (1950).
777. MINTER, U. S. Patent 2,542,827 (1951).
778. MISRA AND SHUKLA, *J. Indian Chem. Soc. 29*, 201-02 (1952); *Brit. Abstr. 1953*, A II, 383.
779. MISRA AND SHULKA, *J. Indian Chem. Soc. 29.* 455 (1952).
780. MOCHEL, U. S. Patent 2,429,838 (1947).
781. MOCHEL, *International Congress of Sciences Applied to the Textile Industry* (collected papers) Ghent (1951), pp. 129-40 (in French); *Tex. Research J. 23*, No. 5, 338 (1953).
782. *Modern Plastics 33*, No. 1, 104-08, 225-28 (1955).
783. MOE, U. S. Patent 2,461,502 (1949).
784. MOE, U. S. Patent 2,520,161 (1950).
785. MOE, MILLER AND BUCKLEY, *J. Am. Chem. Soc. 74*, 1325-27 (1952).
786. MONSANTO CHEMICAL COMPANY, British Patent 640,158 (1950); C.A. *44*, 11170 (1950).
787. MONSANTO CHEMICAL COMPANY, British Patent 730,209 (1955).
788. MONSANTO CHEMICAL COMPANY, British Patent 732,912 (1952).
789. MORGAN, *Ind. Eng. Chem. 45*, 2296-2306 (1953).
790. MORRIS, U. S. Patent 2,530,362 (1950).
791. MOORE AND MOORE, U. S. Patent 2,543,187 (1951)
792. MORRISON AND NICHOLSON, *J. Chem. Phys. 20*, 1021-23 (1952).
793. MORRISON AND SHANNON, U. S. Patent 2,662,044 (1953).
794. MORTENSON, U. S. Patent 2,396,963 (1946).
795. MORTON AND LANDFIELD, *J. Am. Chem. Soc. 74*, 3523-26 (1952).
796. MORWAY, U. S. Patent 2,583,435 (1952).
797. MORWAY AND SMITH, U. S. Patent 2,612,472 (1952); U. S. Patent 2,612,473 (1952).
798. MORWAY AND YOUNG, U. S. Patent 2,467,148 (1949).
799. MOSER, *Ceramic Age 60*, No. 4, 31-33 (1952).
800. MOSS, U. S. Patent 2,524,020 (1950).
801. MOSS AND COOK, U. S. Patent 2,459,088 (1949).
802. MOUREU, *Ann. Chem. Phys.* [7], *2*, 186 (1893).
803. MOUREU AND BROWN, *Bull. soc. chim. France 27*, 901 (1920).
804. MOWRY, U. S. Patent 2,529,455 (1950).
805. MOWRY AND HEDRICK, U. S. Patent 2,625,471 (1953).
806. MOWRY AND HEDRICK, U. S. Patent 2,651,886 (1953).
807. MOWRY AND RINGWALD, U. S. Patent 2,653,975 (1953).
808. MULLER, *Angew. Chem. 61*, 179 (1949).
809. MULLER, *Collection Czechoslov. Chem. Commun. 20*, 241 (1955).
810. MUNGER, *Oil and Gas J. 50*, No. 24, 100, 103, 105-08 (1951).
811. MUNGER, *Petroleum Eng. 27*, No. 7, C-7–C-10 (1955).
812. NAKAZAWA AND MATSUURA, *J. Pharm. Soc. Japan 71*, 802-04 (1951); C.A. *46*, 8025 (1952).
813. NAKAZAWA AND MATSUURA, *J. Pharm. Soc. Japan 72*, 51-54 (1952); C.A. *46*, 11142 (1952).

814. NAZAROV AND SHVEKHGEYMER, *J. Gen. Chem. (U.S.S.R.) 24* 157-63 (1954); C.A. *49*, 3003c (1955).
815. NAZAROV AND SHVEKHGEYMER, *J. Gen. Chem. (U.S.S.R.) 24*, 163-69 (1954); C.A. *49*, 3034c (1955).
816. NAZAROV AND SHVEKHGEYMER, *Zhur. Obshchei Khim. J. Gen. Chem. (U.S.S.R.) 25*, 504 (1955); C.A. *50*, 2573f (1956).
817. NAZAROV AND ZAVYALOV, *J. Gen. Chem. (U.S.S.R.) 24*, 469-74 (1954); C.A. *49*, 6142h (1955).
818. NELLES AND LOMMEL, German Patent Application I 51,944; quoted by Bayer, see ref. 95.
819. NELSON AND VANDERBILT, *Proc. 2nd Rubber Technol. Conf. 1948*, 49.
820. NESS, U. S. Patent 2,556,885 (1951).
821. NESS, U. S. Patent 2,673,826 (1954).
822. *Neuere Methoden der preparitiven Organischen Chemie*, p. 340.
823. NEWMAN, U. S. Patent 2,594,061 (1952).
824. NICHOLS, U. S. Patent 2,683,163 (1954).
825. NICHOLS AND FLOWERS, *Ind. Eng. Chem. 42*, 292-95 (1950).
826. NIEDERHAUSER, U. S. Patent 2,577,477 (1951).
827. NIEDERHAUSER AND BRUSON, U. S. Patent 2,379,097 (1945).
828. NIELSON, LEONARD AND CORT, U. S. Patent 2,606,325 (1952).
829. NIELSEN, *J. Am. Chem. Soc. 75*, 1435-39 (1953).
830. NOGARE, PERKINS AND HALE, *Anal. Chem. 24*, 512-15 (1952).
831. NOWAK, U. S. Patent 2,281,375 (1942).
832. NOWAK, HOFMEIER AND TOBIS, U. S. Patent 2,191,580 (1940).
833. NOZAKI, *J. Polymer Sci. 1*, 455 (1946).
834. NOZAKI, U. S. Patent 2,666,025 (1954).
835. NOZAKI, U. S. Patent 2,666,042 (1954).
836. NOZAKURA AND KONOTSUNE, *Bull. Chem. Soc. Japan 29*, 322 (1956).
837. NOZAKURA AND KONOTSUNE, *Bull. Chem. Soc. Japan 29*, 326 (1956).
838. NYQUIST AND KROPA, U. S. Patent 2,468,716 (1949).
839. *Oil, Paint and Drug Reptr. 167*, No. 9, 7 (1955).
840. OKAMURA AND NAGAO, *Bull. Research Inst. Teikokw Jinzo Kenshi Kaisha Ltd. 2*, No. 1, 64-67 (1950); C.A. *45*, 898 (1951).
841. OKAMURA AND YAMASHITA, *J. Soc. Textile Cellulose Ind., Japan 9*, 444-54 (1953); C.A. *48*, 1010 (1954).
842. OKAMURA AND YAMAGATA, *Chem. High Polymers (Japan) 6*, 502-04 (1949); C.A. *46*, 1292 (1952).
843. OLIN, U. S. Patent 2,461,842 (1949).
844. OLINER AND O'NEIL, *Paper Trade J. 125*, No. 7, 55 (1947).
845. OLSON AND McMILLAN, U. S. Patent 2,632,210 (1953).
846. ORR AND WILLIAMS, *J. Am. Chem. Soc. 77*, 3715-20 (1955).
847. OSTER, *Nature 173*, 300-01 (1954).
848. OSWIN, U. S. Patent 2,618,575 (1952).
849. OWEN AND KIMBERLIN, U. S. Patent 2,414,762 (1947).
850. PALIT AND DAS, *Proc. Roy. Soc. (London) A226*, 82-95 (1954).
851. PARKER, U. S. Patent 2,456,428 (1948).
852. PARKER, U. S. Patent 2,539,385 (1951).
853. PARTS, *Nature 168*, 79 (1951).
854. PATTILLOCH, U. S. Patent 2,694,633 (1954).
855. PATTON AND JUBANOWSKY, U. S. Patent 2,580,460 (1952).
856. PAXTON AND ELKINS, U. S. Patent 2,674,547 (1954).
857. PB 824 (1943); *Bib. 1*, 37.
858. PB 3868, p. 55; *Bib. 1*, 239.
859. PB 83370, frames 2988-91; *Bib. 9*, 991.
860. PEARSON, JONES AND COPE, *J. Am. Chem. Soc. 68*, 1225 (1946).
861. PECKHAM, U. S. Patent 2,595,977 (1952).
862. PEPPER, *Quart. Rev. (London) 8*, No. 1, 88-121 (1954).
863. PERKINS AND SYLVESTER, U. S. Patent 2,685,572 (1954).
864. PETERSEN AND RAKLE, *Ind. Eng. Chem. Anal. Ed. 16*, 63 (1944).
865. PETROPOULOS, CADWELL AND HART, *Paper No. 10*, p. 183 *American Chemical Society, Division of Paint, Plastics and Printing Ink Chemistry*, New York Meeting, September 1954.
866. PETROV AND SAPOZHNIKOVA, *J. Gen. Chem. (U.S.S.R.) 18*, 424, 640 (1948); C.A. *42*, 7721 (1948); C.A. *43*, 558 (1949).
867. PETROV AND SOPOV, *J. Gen. Chem. (U.S.S.R.) 17*, 2228 (1947); C.A. *42*, 4957 (1948).
868. PETROV AND VLADIMIROVA, *J. Gen. Chem. (U.S.S.R.) 17*, 1543 (1947); C.A. *42*, 2238 (1948).
869. PHIBBS, *J. Phys. Chem. 59*, No. 4, 346-53 (1955).
870. PIETRA, *Bull. sci. fac. chim. ind. Bologna 11*, 78-82, 83-85 (1953).
871. PIETRUSZA AND COSBY, U. S. Patent 2,608,576 (1952).
872. PINTELL, U. S. Patent 2,711,380 (1955).
873. PISTOR, German Patent 857,637 (1952); C.A. *47*, 11239 (1953).
874. PISTOR AND PLIENINGER, *Ann. 562*, 239 (1949).

875. PITZL, U. S. Patent 2,541,157 (1951).
876. PITZL, U. S. Patent 2,570,478 (1951).
877. PITZL, U. S. Patent 2,606,894 (1952).
878. PLAUT, U. S. Patent 2,701,809 (1955).
879. PLAUT AND RITTER, *J. Am. Chem. Soc. 73*, 4076-77 (1951).
880. POKROVSKII, *Gigiena, i Sanit. 1954*, No. 7, 22-26; C.A. *48*, 13262 (1954).
881. POLLARD, RIETZ AND ROBBINS, *J. Am. Chem. Soc. 75*, 2989-90 (1953).
882. POLONOWSKI, PESSON AND ZELNIK, *Compt. rend. 241*, 215-17 (1955).
883. POLSON, U. S. Patent 2,579,451 (1951).
884. PORTER AND NESTY, U. S. Patent 2,445,693 (1948).
885. POZHIL'TSOVA AND ARBUZOV, *Doklady Akad. Nauk S.S.S.R. 91*, No. 2, 269-70 (1953).
886. PREVOT, *Compt. rend. 230*, 288-90 (1950).
887. PREVOT, *Compt. rend. 233*, 366-68 (1951).
888. PREVOT, CHAPIRO, COUSIN, LANDLER AND MAGAT, *Disc. Faraday Soc.*, No. 12, 98-109 (1952) (Discussion 110-32).
889. PREVOT, *Compt. rend. 237*, 1686-88 (1953).
890. PRICE AND ZOMLEFER, *J. Org. Chem. 14*, 210 (1949).
891. PRILL, *J. Am. Chem. Soc. 69*, 62 (1947).
892. PRITCHARD, OPHEIM AND MOYER, *Ind. Eng. Chem. 47*, No. 4, 863-66 (1955).
893. PUDOVIK AND ARBUZOV, *Zhur. Obshchei Khim.* (*J. Gen. Chem.*) *21*, 1837-47 (1951); English Translation *21*, 2035-39 (1951); C.A. *46*, 6082e (1952).
894. PUDOVIK AND LEBEDEVA, *Zhur. Obshchei. Khim. 22*, 2128-32 (1952); English Translation *22*, 2183-86 (1952).
895. QUIG, *Can. Textile J. 66*, 42 (1949).
896. RADI, U. S. Patent 2,582,160 (1952).
897. RAPOPORT, SMITH AND NEWMAN, *J. Am. Chem. Soc. 69*, 693 (1947).
898. RATERINK AND BRUSON, U. S. Patent 2,466,739 (1949).
899. REED, *Modern Plastics 27*, No. 4, 117 (1949).
900. REHBERG, U. S. Patent 2,559,660 (1951).
901. REHBERG AND SICILIANO, *Ind. Eng. Chem. 44*, 2864-66 (1952).
902. REHBERG AND DIXON, *J. Am. Chem. Soc. 74*, 1095 (1952).
903. REICH AND BECKER, *J. Am. Chem. Soc. 71*, 1834 (1949).
904. REICHERT, *Faserforsch. und Textiltech. 5*, 204-10 (1954).
905. REID, U. S. Patent 2,514,222 (1950).
906. REID AND BEST, U. S. Patent 2,713,549 (1955); U. S. Patent 2,713,550 (1955).
907. REID, U. S. Patent 2,713,562 (1955); U. S. Patent 2,713,566 (1955).
908. REILLY, U. S. Patent 2,614,092 (1952).
909. REILLY, U. S. Patent 2,664,373 (1953).
910. REIN, *Angew. Chem. 60*, 159 (1948).
911. REITZ AND SABATHY, *Monatsh. Chem. 71*, 131 (1938).
912. REPPE, PB 75390 (1936); *Bib. 6*, 868.
913. REPPE AND HOFFMANN, U. S. Patent 1,891,055 (1932).
914. REPPE, KUTEPOW AND LEICHTLE, U. S. Patent 2,668,175 (1954).
915. REPPE, LEICHTLE AND KUTEPOW, Canadian Patent 513,607 (1955).
916. RETTER AND FRANKE, PB 35112; *Bib. 7*, 981.
917. RETTER AND FRANKE, PB 35113; *Bib. 7*, 981.
918. REZNIKOVA, VOYUTSKII AND ZAIONCHKOVSKII, *Kolloid Zhur. 16*, No. 3, 204 (1954); C.A. *48*, 11834 (1954).
919. REZNIKOVA, ZAIONCHKOVSKII AND VOYUTSKII, *Kolloid Zhur. 15*, 108-16 (1953); C.A. *47*, 7815 (1953).
920. RICHARDSON AND CASANGES, *J. Econ. Entomol. 35*, 664 (1942).
921. RICKERT, unpublished results; quoted by Bayer, see ref. *95*.
922. RITCHIE, JONES AND BURNS, U. S. Patent 2,183,357 (1939).
923. RITTER, U. S. Patent 2,573,673 (1951).
924. RITTER AND MINIERI, *J. Am. Chem. Soc. 70*, 4045 (1948).
925. ROBINSON, U. S. Patent 2,429,031 (1947).
926. ROCHOW AND ROCHOW, *Science 111*, 271 (1950).
927. ROCHOW AND ROWE, *Anal. Chem. 21*, 461 (1949).
928. RODIONOV AND YARTSEVA, *Bull. acad. sci. U.S.S.R., Classe sci. chem. 1948*, 251; C.A. *42*, 4942 (1948).
929. ROE AND SWERN, *J. Am. Chem. Soc. 75*, 5479-81 (1953).
930. ROGERS, *J. Am. Chem. Soc. 69*, 2544 (1947).
931. ROGERS, U. S. Patent 2,460,536 (1949).
932. ROGERS, *Composition and Properties of Oil-Well Drilling Fluids*, p. 427-28 (1953).
933. ROGERS, *J. Chem. Soc. 1955*, 769-72.
934. ROHM AND HAAS, German Patent Application R 120,526; ADPA *6*, 319.
935. ROHM AND HAAS, British Patent 719,315 (1954).
936. ROMEYN AND McCLEARY, U. S. Patent 2,597,951 (1952).
937. ROSS (Roy. Cancer Hosp., London), *J. Chem. Soc. 1950*, 2257-72.
938. ROWLAND, U. S. Patent 2,543,601 (1951).
939. R. T. VANDERBILT CO., *The Vanderbilt Rubber Handbook*, p. 51 (1948).
940. RUBIN AND WISHINSKY, *J. Am. Chem. Soc. 68*, 828 (1946).
941. RUGELEY, FEILD AND PETROKUBI, U. S. Patent 2,420,565 (1947).

942. RUST, U. S. Patent 2,448,005 (1948).
943. RUST, U. S. Patent 2,471,456 (1949).
944. RUST, U. S. Patent 2,484,962 (1949).
945. SALOMON, Rec. trav. chim. 68, 903-14 (1949) (in English).
946. SANDS AND TURNER, Anal. Chem. 24, 791-93 (1952).
947. SANTAPPA, Current Sci. (India) 23, 145-47 (1954); C.A. 48, 12561 (1954).
948. SANTAPPA, J. Sci. Ind. Research (India) 13, No. 12, 819-24 (1954).
949. SARBACH, U. S. Patent 2,325,984 (1943).
950. SAUER AND HADSELL, J. Am. Chem. Soc. 70, 4258 (1948).
951. SAUER AND REED, U. S. Patent 2,388,575 (1945).
952. SAUNDERS, Nature 160, 179 (1947).
953. SAUNDERS, Ind. Eng. Chem. 43, 121-26 (1951).
954. SCATTERGOOD AND MACLEAN, J. Am. Chem. Soc. 71, 4153 (1949).
955. SCHAFFEL, U. S. Patent 2,609,361 (1952).
956. SCHAFFEL AND WOLLISON, U. S. Patent 2,617,788 (1952).
957. SCHAEFGEN AND FLORY, J. Am. Chem. Soc. 70, 2823 (1948).
958. SCHENCK AND DANISHEFSKY, J. Org. Chem. 16, 1683-89 (1951).
959. SCHEYER, unpublished results; quoted by Bayer, see ref. 95.
960. SCHIEFER, APPEL, KRASNY AND RICHEY, Textile Research J. 23, No. 7, 489-94 (1953).
961. SCHMELZLE AND EASTWOLD, U. S. Patent 2,607,710 (1952).
962. SCHMIDLE AND MANSFIELD, Ind. Eng. Chem. 44, 1388 (1952).
963. SCHMIDT, TREPPENHAUER AND ALBRECHT, PB 75258; Bib. 6, 855.
964. SCHMIEDER AND WOLF, Kolloid Z. 134, No. 2/3, 149-89 (1954).
965. SCHMITZ AND LAWTON, Science 113, 718 (1951).
966. SCHMUTZLER, U. S. Patent 2,590,653 (1952).
967. SCHMUTZLER, U. S. Patent 2,590,654 (1952).
968. SCHMUTZLER, U. S. Patent 2,636,015 (1953).
969. SCHOUTEDEN, Chimie and Industrie 74, No. 4, 167 (1955).
970. SCHREYER, U. S. Patent 2,564,131 (1951).
971. SCHREYER, U. S. Patent 2,640,082 (1953).
972. SCHUERCH, J. Am. Chem. Soc. 74, 5061-67 (1952).
973. SCHULE, U. S. Patent 2,605,247 (1952).
974. SCHULTZ, J. Am. Chem. Soc. 70, 2666 1948).
975. SCHULZ AND PUFAHL, U. S. Patent 2,562,583 (1951).
976. SCHULZ AND PUFAHL, Canadian Patent 510,228 (1955).
977. SCHULZE AND CROUCH, U. S. Patent 2,469,132 (1949).
978. SCHULZE AND MAHAN, U. S. Patent 2,425,267 (1947).
979. SCHULZE AND MAHAN, U. S. Patent 2,447,600 (1948); U. S. Patent 2,464,723 (1949).
980. SCHWOEGLER, U. S. Patent 2,403,686 (1946).
981. SCHWOEGLER, U. S. Patent 2,615,820 (1952).
982. SEGRO AND MELCHORE, French Patent 1,100,638.
983. SEMON, U. S. Patent 2,374,841 (1945).
984. SENVAR, Comm. fac. sci. univ. Ankara 4, B, 66-81 (1952).
985. SENVAR AND AKIN, Comm. fac. sci. univ. Ankara 4, B, 82-93 (1952).
986. SEYMOUR, U. S. Patent 2,681,877 (1954).
987. SEYMOUR AND BUTLER, U. S. Patent 2,471,785 (1949).
988. SEYMOUR AND KISPERSKY, U. S. Patent 2,439,227 (1948).
989. SHANNON, U. S. Patent 2,381,371 (1945).
990. SHANTA, U. S. Patent 2,694,700 (1954).
991. SHECHTER, CONRAD, DAULTON AND KAPLAN, J. Am. Chem. Soc. 74, 3052-56 (1952).
992. SHERWOOD, Petroleum Processing 7, 1632, 1804-07, 1809-10 (1952).
993. SHERWOOD, Petroleum Processing 9, 384-89 (1954).
994. SHIRLEY AND ALSOBROOK, J. Am. Chem. Soc. 73, 2963-64 (1951).
995. SHOSTAKOVSKII AND BOGDANOVA, Zhur. Priklad. Khim. 24, 495-501 (1951); C.A. 46, 1961 (1952).
996. SIGNER, U. S. Patent 2,658,048 (1953).
997. SIGNER AND BEAL, U. S. Patent 2,658,051 (1953).
998. SIMONS, U. S. Patent 2,510,761 (1950).
999. SIMRIL AND HERSHBERGER, Modern Plastics 27, No. 10; 97, 98, 100, 102, 150-52, 154, 156, 158 (1950).
1000. SINGH AND SINGH, J. Indian Chem. Soc. 25, 227 (1948); C.A. 43, 7937 (1949).
1001. SKEIST, J. Am. Chem. Soc. 68, 1781 (1946).
1002. SKINNER, Ind. Eng. Chem. 47, 222-29 (1955).
1003. SKINNER AND THOMPSON, J. Chem. Soc. 1955, 487-89.
1004. SMALLMAN, J. Econ. Entomol. 42, 596-601 (1949).
1005. SMELTZ AND DYER, J. Am. Chem. Soc. 74, 623-28 (1952).
1006. SMITH, J. Am. Chem. Soc. 72, 4313-14 (1950).
1007. SMITH, J. Org. Chem. 16, 415-18 (1951).
1008. SMITH AND YU, J. Am. Chem. Soc. 74, 1096-98 (1952).
1009. SMITH, MIKESKA AND PAPKIN, U. S. Patent 2,601,063 (1952).
1010. Soil Sci. 73, 419-93 (1952).
1011. SOENNERSKOG, Acta Chem. Scand. 8, 579-84 (1954).
1012. SOUTHER, U. S. Patent 2,386,363 (1945).

1013. SPAULDING AND BROCKWAY, U. S. Patent 2,502,678 (1950).
1014. SPENCE, U. S. Patent 2,385,550 (1945).
1015. SPENCE, BUTTERBAUGH AND KROEKER, U. S. Patent 2,385,551 (1945).
1016. SPILLANE AND KAYSER, U. S. Patent 2,557,703 (1951).
1017. SPRAGUE AND LAND, U. S. Patent 2,580,476 (1952).
1018. STALLINGS, U. S. Patent 2,390,032 (1945).
1019. STALLINGS, U. S. Patent 2,473,308 (1949).
1020. STANTON AND LOWRY, U. S. Patent 2,482,073 (1949).
1021. STANTON AND LOWRY, U. S. Patent 2,538,737 (1951).
1022. STAUDINGER AND FAULKNER, U. S. Patent 2,484,760 (1949).
1023. STECK, HALLOCK AND SUTER, *J. Am. Chem. Soc. 70*, 4063 (1948).
1024. STEINBECHNER, PB 73553, frames 7055-57; *Bib. 8*, 770.
1025. STEINER AND SCHINZ, *Helv. Chim. Acta 34*, 1176-83 (1951).
1026. STETTER AND COENEN, *Chem. Ber. 87*, 869-72 (1954).
1027. STETTER AND COENEN, *Chem. Ber. 87*, 990-93 (1954).
1028. STEWART AND CLARK, *J. Am. Chem. Soc. 69*, 713 (1947).
1029. STEWART AND MATHES, *J. Org. Chem. 14*, 1111 (1949).
1030. STILBERT, CUMMINGS AND GUERRANT, U. S. Patent 2,684,953 (1954).
1031. STINCHFIELD AND KAULAKIS, U. S. Patent 2,685,538 (1954).
1032. STONE AND EMELEUS, *J. Chem. Soc. 1950*, 2755-59.
1033. STORK, TERRELL AND SZMUSZKOVICZ, *J. Am. Chem. Soc. 76*, 2029-30 (1954).
1034. STOVER, U. S. Pat. 2,518,397 (1950).
1035. STOWELL, *India Rubber World 122*, No. 3, 315 (1950).
1036. STRAIN, U. S. Patent 2,135,443 (1938).
1037. STROH, German Patent 894,244 (1953); C.A. *48*, 12789 (1954).
1038. STULL, *Ind. Eng. Chem. 39*, 517 (1947).
1039. SUMNER, U. S. Patent 2,390,470 (1945).
1040. SURREY AND HAMMER, *J. Am. Chem. Soc. 72*, 1814-15 (1950).
1041. SURREY, U. S. Patent 2,555,944 (1951).
1042. SURREY, SUTER AND BUCK, *J. Am. Chem. Soc. 74*, 4102-03 (1952).
1043. SUSICH, *Textile Research J. 23*, 545-72 (1953).
1044. SUZUKI, *Kagaku 23*, 535-36 (1953); C.A. *47*, 11892 (1953).
1045. SWINDELLS, U. S. Patent 2,698,235 (1954).
1046. SYMONS, *Research (London) 6*, Suppl. No. 1, 55-65 (1953).
1047. SZABO AND STILLER, *J. Am. Chem. Soc. 70*, 3667 (1948).
1048. TACHIKAWA, SASHIO AND YOSHIDA, *J. Soc. Org. Synthetic Chem. (Japan) 11*, 265-68 (1953); C.A. *48*, 9903 (1954).
1049. TAKAMATSU, Japanese Patent 6942 (1951); C.A. *47*, 5167 (1953).
1050. TALAT-ERBEN AND BYWATER, *Paper presented at Symposium on Macromolecules, Milan, Italy*, Sept.–Oct. 1954.
1051. TAMAYO AND MARTINEZ, *Anales real soc. espan. fis. y quim. (Madrid) 48B*, 81-88 (1952); *Brit. Abstr. A II, 1952*, 1165.
1052. TANNER, et al., PB 81638, *B.I.O.S. Final Report*, 1480.
1053. TARBELL AND FUKUSHIMA, *J. Am. Chem. Soc. 68*, 2499 (1946).
1054. TARBELL AND NOBLE, *J. Am. Chem. Soc. 72*, 2657-61 (1950).
1055. TARBELL, SHAKESPEARE, CLAUS AND BUNNETT, *J. Am. Chem. Soc. 68*, 1217 (1946).
1056. TAWNEY, U. S. Patent 2,504,054 (1950).
1057. TAWNEY AND PRILL, *J. Am. Chem. Soc. 70*, 2828 (1948).
1058. TAYLOR AND MARTIN, *Agr. Eng. 34*, 550-54 (1953).
1059. TAYLOR AND TOMLINSON, *J. Chem. Soc. 1950*, 2724-25.
1060. TENHET, *J. Econ. Entomol. 38*, 449 (1945).
1061. TEPPEMA AND MANNING, U. S. Patent 2,367,629 (1945).
1062. TERENT'EV AND BUTSKUS, *Zhur. Obshchei Khim. 23*, 1230-34 (1953); C.A. *47*, 12237 (1953).
1063. TERENT'EV AND BUTSKUS, *Doklady Akad. Nauk S.S.S.R. 97*, 851 (1954); C.A. *49*, 10312e (1955).
1064. TERENT'EV, BUTSKUS AND YASHUNSKY, *J. Anal. Chem. U.S.S.R. 9*, 162-65 (1954).
1065. TERENT'EV, CHURSINA AND KOST, *J. Gen. Chem. (U.S.S.R.) 20*, 1073-78 (1950); C.A. *44*, 9349 (1950).
1066. TERENT'EV AND GURVICH, *Vestnik Moskov. Univ. 5*, No. 5, Ser. Fiz. Mat. i Estest. Nauk No. 3, 47-51 (1950); C.A. *45*, 7005 (1951).
1067. TERENT'EV AND GURVICH, *Zhur. Obshchei Khim.21*, 1632-37 (1951); C.A. *46*, 4474(1952).
1068. TERENT'EV AND KOST, *J. Gen. Chem. (U.S.S.R.) 16*, 859 (1946); C.A. *41*, 1609 (1947).
1069. TERENT'EV AND KOST, *J. Gen. Chem. (U.S.S.R.) 17*, 1632 (1947); C.A. *42*, 2578 (1948).
1070. TERENT'EV AND KOST, *J. Gen. Chem. (U.S.S.R.) 18*, 510 (1948); C.A. *42*, 7297 (1948).
1071. TERENT'EV AND KOST, U.S.S.R. Patent 78,376 (1949); C.A. *47*, 10000 (1953).
1072. TERENT'EV AND KOST, *Vestnik Moskov. Univ. 5*, No. 8, Ser. Fiz. Mat. i Estest. Nauk No. 5, 41-42 (1950); C.A. *45*, 8443 (1951).
1073. TERENT'EV AND KOST, *J. Gen. Chem. (U.S.S.R.) 20*, 2141-43 (1950); C.A. *46*, 11105 (1952).
1074. TERENT'EV AND KOST, *Zhur. Obshchei Khim. 21*, 1867-69 (1951); C.A. *46*, 6589(1952).
1075. TERENT'EV, KOST AND CHURSINA, *J. Gen. Chem. (U.S.S.R.) 21*, 268-70 (1951); C.A. *45*, 7008 (1951).

1076. TERENT'EV, KOST AND GURVICH, *Vestnik Moskov. Univ. 6*, No. 12, Ser. Fiz. Mat. i Estest. Nauk No. 8, 79-83; C.A. *47*, 6877 (1953).
1077. TERENT'EV, KOST AND GURVICH, *J. Gen. Chem. (U.S.S.R.) 22*, 1977-86 (1952).
1078. TERENT'EV, KOST AND POTAPOV, *J. Gen. Chem. (U.S.S.R.) 18*, 82 (1948); C.A. *42*, 4942 (1948).
1079. TERENT'EV AND TERENT'EVA, *J. Gen. Chem. (U.S.S.R.) 12*, 415 (1942); C.A. *37*, 3095 (1943).
1080. TETER AND MERWIN, U. S. Patent 2,388,507 (1945).
1081. TETER AND MERWIN, U. S. Patent 2,433,306 (1947).
1082. TETER AND SHAND, U. S. Patent 2,588,056 (1952).
1083. *Textile Inds. 118*, No. 12, 101 (1954).
1084. THIELE AND FRANKE, PB 35103; *Bib. 7*, 980.
1085. THIELE AND FRANKE, PB 35106; *Bib. 7*, 980.
1086. THOMAS, GLEASON AND PELLON, *J. Polymer Sci. 17*, 275-90 (1955).
1087. THOMAS AND PELLON, *J. Polymer Sci. 13*, 329-53 (1954).
1088. THOMPSON AND TARKINGTON, *J. Chem. Soc. 1944*, 597.
1089. THURSTON, Canadian Patent 443,713 (1947).
1090. TIMBEKOV AND SODYKOV, *Zhur. Obshchei Khim. 25*, 786 (1955); C.A. *49*, 10983h (1955).
1091. TIMM AND MECKE, *Z. Physik 97*, 221 (1935).
1092. TISCH, *Modern Plastics 32*, No. 11; 119, 120, 122, 124, 126, 128, 130, 132-34, 207 (1955).
1093. TOMUNAK, U. S. Patent 2,571,075 (1951).
1094. TONG AND KENYON, *J. Am. Chem. Soc. 69*, 2245 (1947).
1095. TORKINGTON, *Proc. Roy. Soc. (London) A206*, 17-39 (1951).
1096. TREPPENHAUER, KOENIG AND BOCK, German Patent 734,221 (1943); C.A. *38*, 1246 (1944).
1097. TREPPENHAUER, KOENIG, BOCK AND SCHROETER, German Patent 734,475 (1943); C.A. *38*, 2966 (1944).
1098. TSURUTA, KUROKI AND NISHIO, *Chem. High Polymers (Japan) 7*, 129-31 (1950); C.A. *46*, 420 (1952).
1099. TUCKER, *J. Chem. Soc. 1952*, 803-07.
1100. TUERCK AND LICHTENSTEIN, U. S. Patent 2,394,644 (1946).
1101. TUERCK AND LICHTENSTEIN, U. S. Patent 2,417,024 (1947).
1102. TUERCK AND LICHTENSTEIN, Canadian Patent 456,891 (1949).
1103. UFER, PB 58775, frames 401-04.
1104. UFER, German Patent 670,357 (1939); C.A. *33*, 2907 (1939).
1105. UTERMOHLEN AND HAMILTON, *J. Am. Chem. Soc. 63*, 156 (1941).
1106. UTERMOHLEN, *J. Am. Chem. Soc. 67*, 1505 (1945).
1107. U. S. RUBBER Co., British Appln. 18,753/48.
1108. U. S. RUBBER Co., British Patent 647,382 (1950).
1109. U. S. RUBBER Co., British Patent 696,118 (1953).
1110. VALENTINE, *J. Textile Inst., Trans. 46*, No. 4, T270-83 (1955).
1111. VAN BUSKIRK, *Modern Plastics 33*, No. 1, 246 (1955).
1112. VAN BUSKIRK, *India Rubber World 122*, 184 (1950).
1113. VAN DER BURG, *Rec. trav. chim. (Pays-Bas) 41*, 21 (1922).
1114. VANDERBILT AND BASCOM, U. S. Patent 2,527,162 (1950).
1115. VAN DER KERK, LUIJTEN AND NOLTES, *Chemistry and Industry 1956*, 352.
1116. VAUGHAN, U. S. Patent 2,618,634 (1952).
1117. VAUGHAN, U. S. Patent 2,618,635 (1952).
1118. VAUGHAN, U. S. Patent 2,633,456 (1953).
1119. VIERHAUS, PB 35101; *Bib. 7*, 980.
1120. VOGEL, et al., *J. Chem. Soc. 1952*, 514-49 (1952).
1121. VON LEIBITZ-PIWNICKI, PB 683 (1943); *Bib. 1*, 47.
1122. WAGNER AND DUGGER, *J. Am. Chem. Soc. 77*, 227-31 (1955).
1123. WALKER, U. S. Patent 2,352,671 (1944).
1124. WALKER, U. S. Patent 2,409,086 (1946).
1125. WALKER, *J. Applied Chem. (London) 2*, 470-81 (1952).
1126. WALTON, U. S. Patent 2,535,557 (1950).
1127. WARNER, U. S. Patent 2,662,932 (1953).
1128. WATKINS, *Oil Gas J. 51*, No. 49; 100-01, 120, 123 (1951).
1129. WEBBER, *Gas 30*, No. 2, 44-46 (1954).
1130. WEBER AND POWERS, U. S. Patent 2,518,509 (1950).
1131. WEBER AND LEIMULLER, German Patent 902,009 (1954); C.A. *49*, 3244 (1955).
1132. WEEKS AND COLTER, *Soil Sci. 73*, 473-84 (1952).
1133. WEGLER, German Patent 734,725 (1943); C.A. *38*, 3671 (1944).
1134. WEGLER, German Patent 735,771 (1943); C.A. *38*, 3992 (1944).
1135. WEGLER, PB 693; *Bib. 1*, 39.
1136. WEGLER, unpublished results; quoted by Bayer, see ref. *95*.
1137. WEGLER AND BALLAUF, *Chem. Ber. 81*, 527 (1948).
1138. WEISGERBER, U. S. Patent 2,535,245 (1950).
1139. WEISGERBER, U. S. Patent 2,683,173 (1954).
1140. WEITH, *Chem. Eng. News 31*, No. 27, 2763-65 (1953).
1141. WEITH, *Can. Chem. Processing 38*, No. 8, 66, 68 (1954).
1142. WERNTZ, U. S. Patent 2,566,272 (1951).

1143. WHETSTONE, U. S. Patent 2,445,652 (1948).
1144. WHITBY, "Synthetic Rubber," John Wiley and Sons, N. Y. (1954).
1145. WIDEGVIST, Arkiv Kemi 3, 59-67 (1951); C.A. 45, 10217 (1951).
1146. WHITMORE, et al., J. Am. Chem. Soc. 66, 725 (1944).
1147. WIEDEMAN AND MONTGOMERY, J. Am. Chem. Soc. 67, 1944 (1945).
1148. WIEST AND GLASER, U. S. Patent 2,396,626 (1946).
1149. WIEST AND GLASER, U. S. Patent 2,403,570 (1946).
1150. WILCOX, GOLDSTEIN AND SIMMONS, J. Chem. Phys. 22, 516-18 (1954).
1151. WILES AND ELAM, U. S. Patent 2,602,785 (1952).
1152. WILEY, J. Am. Chem. Soc. 73, 4205-09 (1951).
1153. WILEY AND BRAUER, Rubber Chem. and Technol. 22, 402-04 (1949).
1154. WILEY AND NESTY, U. S. Patent 2,526,310 (1950).
1155. WILEY, U. S. Patent 2,607,748 (1952).
1156. WILEY AND NESTY, Canadian Patent 513,465 (1955).
1157. WILEY, SMITH, JOHNSON and MOFFAT, J. Am. Chem. Soc. 76, 4933-35 (1954).
1158. WILLIAMS, U. S. Patent 2,684,350 (1954).
1159. WINANS, U. S. Patent 2,334,140 (1943).
1160. WINGFOOT CORP., British Patent 571,750 (1945); C.A. 41, 3114 (1947).
1161. WINGFOOT CORP., British Patent 581,994 (1946); C.A. 41, 2074 (1947).
1162. WINGFOOT CORP., British Patent 593,475 (1947); C.A. 42, 2138 (1948).
1163. WINKELMANN, U. S. Patent 2,473,319 (1949).
1164. WITSCHONKE, Anal. Chem. 26, 562-64 (1954).
1165. WOHNSIEDLER AND KROPA, U. S. Patent 2,582,303 (1952).
1166. WOLFE, U. S. Patent 2,217,632 (1940).
1167. WOLK, U. S. Patent 2,407,861 (1946).
1168. WOLZ, German Patent 741,156 (1943).
1169. WOODING AND HIGGINSON, J. Chem. Soc. 1952, 774-79.
1170. WOODS, J. Am. Chem. Soc. 74, 3959 (1952).
1171. WOODWARD, U. S. Patent 2,681,366 (1954).
1172. WOODWARD, et al., J. Am. Chem. Soc. 73, 2403-04 (1951).
1173. WOOLDRIK, British Patent 732,421 (1955).
1174. WRIGHT AND MINSK, J. Am. Chem. Soc. 75, 98-101 (1953).
1175. WROBEL, Roczniki Chem. 25, 255-56 (1951).
1176. WULFF, HOPFF AND WIEST, German Patent 728,531 (1942); C.A. 38, 376 (1944).
1177. WUERSTLIN, Kunststoffe 40, 158-60 (1950).
1178. WUERSTLIN, Kolloid Z. 120, No. 1-3, 84-103 (1951).
1179. YASHUNSKII, et al., J. Gen. Chem. (U.S.S.R.) 23, No. 5, 753 (1953).
1180. YOHO AND LEVINE, J. Am. Chem. Soc. 74, 5597-99 (1952).
1181. YOSHIDA AND OKAJIMA, J. Pharm. Soc. (Japan) 73, 171-73 (1953); C.A. 47, 11198 (1953).
1182. YOUNG, BUCKLEY, NEWBERG AND TURNER, Ind. Eng. Chem. 41, 401 (1949).
1183. YOUNG AND NEWBERG, U. S. Patent 2,657,185 (1953).
1184. YOUNG, STILBERT AND LALK, U. S. Patent 2,593,236 (1952).
1185. ZELLARS AND LEVINE, J. Org. Chem. 13, 911 (1948).
1186. ZERNER AND POLLOCK, U. S. Patent 2,559,835 (1951).
1187. ZERNER AND POLLOCK, U. S. Patent 2,615,887 (1952); U. S. Patent 2,615,888 (1952); U. S. Patent 2,615,889 (1952).
1188. ZERWECK AND MUELLER, Ger. appln. C 2483, Cl. 120, 21 (Sept. 25, 1942); Patent-blatt 72, No. 29,1757 (1952).
1189. ZERWECK AND MUELLER, Ger. appln. C 2503, Cl. 120, 21 (Dec. 14, 1942); Patent-blatt 72, No. 41, 2601 (1952).
1190. ZIEGLER, Brennstoff-Chem. 30, 181-84 (1949).
1191. ZIEGLER, DEPARADE AND KUEHLHORN, Ann. 567, 151-79 (1950).
1192. ACHMATOWICZ AND MICHALSKI, Roczniki Chem. 30, 243 (1956); C.A. 51, 1064b (1957).
1193. AIMONE AND BOOTH, U. S. Patent 2,740,522 (1956).
1194. ALBISETTI, et al., J. Am. Chem. Soc. 78, 2637 (1956).
1195. ALLEN AND HUNTER, Chem. and Ind. (London), 756 (July 28, 1956).
1196. ALLEWELT, U. S. Patent 2,748,110 (1956).
1197. Am. Textile Reptr. 71, No. 1, 8 (1957).
1198. ANGIER AND WATSON, J. Polymer Sci. 20, 235-50 (1956).
1199. BAINTON, JR., U. S. Patent 2,768,146 (1956).
1200. BALLANTINE, Modern Plastics 35, No. 1, 171-76 (1957).
1201. BALLANTINE, J. Polymer Sci. 19, 219-24 (1956).
1202. BARNEY AND CAIRNS, J. Am. Chem. Soc. 72, 3193 (1950).
1203. BARRETT, U. S. Patent 2,812,317 (1957).
1204. BASDEKIS, U. S. Patent 2,812,314 (1957).
1205. BATES, et al., J. Chem. Soc. 1956, 388.
1206. BEKHLI, Doklady Akad. Nauk S.S.S.R., 113, No. 3, 588-89 (1957).
1207. BEKHLI, Zhur. Obshchei Khim. 27, 698 (1957); C.A. 51, 16347c (1957).
1208. BENSASSON AND PREVOT-BERNAS, J. chim. phys. 53, 93-95 (1956).
1209. BENSASSON AND PREVOT-BERNAS, J. chim. phys. 54, 479-82 (1957).
1210. BEVINGTON AND EAVES, Nature 178, 1112-13 (1956).
1211. BEYER, LAESSIG AND SCHUDY, Chem. Ber. 90, No. 4, 592-98 (1957).

1212. BIKALES, BLACK AND RAPOPORT, *Textile Research J. 27*, 80 (1957).
1213. BIKALES, GRUBER AND RAPOPORT, *Ind. Eng. Chem. 50*, 87 (1958).
1214. BIRUM AND KERN, U. S. Patent 2,769,777 (1956).
1215. BOCHIVIC, MICHALSKI, *Roczniki Chem. 26*, 593 (1952); C.A. *49*, 2345h (1955).
1216. BOOTH AND HEDLEY, U. S. Patent 2,729,557 (1956).
1217. BRISKIN AND CHAPIN, U. S. Patent 2,772,252 (1956).
1218. BUC, U. S. Patent 2,809,984 (1957).
1219. BUC, U. S. Patent 2,809,985 (1956).
1220. CALDWELL AND HILL, U. S. Patent 2,732,369 (1956).
1221. CALLINAN, *J. Electrochem. Soc. 103*, No. 5, 292-96 (1956).
1222. CAMPBELL AND STEVENS, *J. Chem. Soc. 1956*, 959.
1223. CAROSELLI, U. S. Patent 2,754,223 (1956).
1224. CASON AND CHANG, *J. Org. Chem. 21*, 449-54 (1956).
1225. CHAPIN, U. S. Patent 2,772,253 (1956).
1226. CHAPIRO, *Industrie des Plastiques Modernes*, 67-71 (November, 1956).
1227. CHAPIRO, *J. Polymer Sci. 23*, 377-86 (1957).
1228. *Chem. Week 78*, 40 (1956).
1229. *Chem. Week 80*, 112, 114, 116 (1957).
1230. CHINSOLI, MINISCI AND QUILICO, *Gazz. Chim. Ital. 87*, No. 1, 100-08 (1957).
1231. CHRISTOPHER, CARPENTER AND SPECTOR, U. S. Patent 2,798,882 (1955).
1232. CHRISTOPHER, CARPENTER AND SPECTOR, U. S. Patent 2,798,884 (1955).
1233. COFFIELD, et al., *J. Am. Chem. Soc. 79*, 5019 (1957).
1234. COHEN AND WITKOP, *J. Am. Chem. Soc. 77*, 6595 (1955).
1235. COHEN AND HEAPS, U. S. Patent 2,794,736 (1957).
1236. COMPTON, *Textile Research J. 27*, 222 (1957).
1237. COMPTON, MARTIN, WORD AND BARBER, *Textile Research J. 26*, 47 (1956).
1238. COOVER, JR. AND DICKEY, U. S. Patent 2,763,621 (1956).
1239. COOVER, JR. AND SHEARER, JR., U. S. Patent 2,798,061 (1957).
1240. CRAGOE, JR. AND PIETRUSKIEWICZ, *J. Org. Chem. 22*, 1338 (1957).
1241. CRITCHFIELD, *Anal. Chem. 28*, 76-79 (1956).
1242. CRITCHFIELD AND JOHNSON, *Anal. Chem. 28*, 73-75 (1956).
1243. INSTITUTE OF TEXTILE TECHNOLOGY, MONSANTO CHEMICAL COMPANY AND AMERICAN
        CYANAMID COMPANY, *Joint Report on "Cyanoethylation of Cotton"* (September, 1956).
1244. CYMERMAN-CRAIG, et al., *J. Chem. Soc. 1955*, 3628.
1245. DAUES AND HAMNER, *Anal. Chem. 29*, 1035-37 (1957).
1246. DEAN AND MANUNAPICHU, *J. Chem. Soc. 1957*, 3112.
1247. DEANIN, U. S. Patent 2,783,166 (1957).
1248. DELABY, DAMIENS AND SEYDEN-PENNE, *Compt. rend. 242*, 910-13 (1956).
1249. DEMALDE, et al., *Chim. e ind. (Milan) 38*, 371 (1956).
1250. DENO, EDWARDS AND PERIGGOLO, *J. Am. Chem. Soc. 79*, 2108 (1957).
1251. DE PAUW, *Compt. rend. 27e Congr. chim. ind. Brussels III*, 363-66 (1954).
1252. DICKERMAN AND SIMON, *J. Org. Chem. 22*, 259 (1957).
1253. DOMBROVSKII, *Zhur. Obshchei Khim. 24*, 610 (1954); C.A. *49*, 5484c, 11537h (1955).
1254. DOMBROVSKII, et al., *Zhur. Obshchei Khim. 26*, 3214 (1956); C.A. *51*, 8038e (1957).
1255. DOMBROVSKII, et al., *Zhur. Obshchei Khim. 27*, 419 (1957); C.A. *51*, 15454eg (1957).
1256. EMBREE, MITCHELL AND WILLIAMS, *Can. J. Chem. 29*, 253 (1951).
1257. FARBENFABRIKEN BAYER, British Patent 735,048 (1955).
1258. FARBENFABRIKEN BAYER, British Patent 773,807 (1957).
1259. FEGLEY, et al., *J. Am. Chem. Soc. 79*, 4736-37 (1957).
1260. FIESSELMANN AND RIBKA, *Chem. Ber. 89*, No. 1, 27-39 (1956).
1261. FORDEMWALT AND KOURTZ, *Textile Research J. 25*, 84 (1955).
1262. FOUST AND SEEMS, U. S. Patent 2,762,784 (1956).
1263. FOWLER, JR. AND HELLMANN, U. S. Patent 2,798,063 (1957).
1264. FORDHAM AND WILLIAMS, *Ind. Eng. Chem. 47*, 1714-24 (1955).
1265. FRAISSE AND JACQUIER, *Bull. soc. chim. (France)* [8-9], 986 (1957).
1266. FREEDMAN, *J. Am. Chem. Soc. 77*, 6003 (1955).
1267. GAYLORD, *Interchemical Review 15*, 91 (1956-1957).
1268. GENERAL ELECTRIC COMPANY, British Patent 762,953 (1956).
1269. GILMAN, CAROLAN AND RESNICK, *Modern Plastics 34*, No. 1, 176-80, 185 (1956).
1270. GODEFROI AND WITTLE, *J. Org. Chem. 21*, 1163-68 (1956).
1271. GOODMAN, SILVERSTEIN AND BENITEZ, *J. Am. Chem. Soc. 79*, 3073 (1957).
1272. GREATHOUSE, et al., *Ind. Eng. Chem. 48*, 1263 (1956).
1273. GREGORY AND TOMLINSON, *J. Chem. Soc. 1956*, 795.
1274. GRUBER AND BIKALES, *Textile Research J. 26*, 67 (1956).
1275. GUILLET AND MORRISH, *Proc. Roy. Soc. (London) A. 233*, 172-183 (1955).
1276. HARDY AND ADAMS, U. S. Patent 2,766,229 (1956).
1277. HAERING AND WAGNER-JAUREGG, *Helv. Chim. Acta 40*, No. 3, 852-71 (1957).
1278. HEALY, JR., U. S. Patent 2,816,135 (1957).
1279. HEININGER, *J. Org. Chem. 22*, 1213 (1957).
1280. HEININGER, *J. Org. Chem. 22*, 704 (1957).
1281. HEININGER, U. S. Patent 2,792,296 (1957).
1282. HEININGER, U. S. Patent 2,726,945 (1955).
1283. HEININGER, U. S. Patent 2,802,021 (1957).

1284. HEININGER, U. S. Patent 2,809,988 (1957).
1285. HINMAN AND ROSENE, *J. Org. Chem. 21*, 1539-40 (1956).
1286. HOFFMAN, et al., *J. Am. Oil Chemists' Soc. 33*, 410-14 (1956).
1287. HOFFMANN, KEBRLE AND SCHMID, *Helv. Chim. Acta 40*, No. 2, 387-94 (1957).
1288. HUENIG AND KAHANEK, *Chem. Ber. 90*, No. 2, 238-45 (1957).
1289. HUNYAR AND GROBE, *Faserforsch. u. Textiltech. 6*, No. 12, 548-53 (1955).
1290. IMMERGUT AND MARK, *Makromol. Chem. 18/19*, 322-41 (1956).
1291. IMOTO AND TAKEMOTO, *J. Polymer Sci. 18*, 377-87 (1955).
1292. ITTYERAH AND MANV, *J. Org. Chem. 21*, 3179 (1956).
1293. JACKSON, *J. Org. Chem. 21*, 1374-75 (1956).
1294. JANSSEN, et al., *Ind. Eng. Chem. 50*, 76 (1958).
1295. JOHNSTON, U. S. Patent 2,754,320 (1956).
1296. JOHNSTON, U. S. Patent 2,789,995 (1957).
1297. JOHNSTON AND GROSS, *J. Org. Chem. 22*, 1264 (1957).
1298. JONES, U. S. Patent 2,734,915 (1956).
1299. JONES AND CANTERINO, U. S. Patent 2,731,439 (1956).
1300. JUMAR AND SCHULZE, *J. prakt. Chem. 5* [4], No. 1-2, 83-90 (1957).
1301. KENDALL AND DUFFIN, U. S. Patent 2,726,248 (1955).
1302. KERN, U. S. Patent 2,773,822 (1956).
1303. KIRMSE AND HORNER, *Chem. Ber. 89*, No. 7, 1674-80 (1956).
1304. KLEIN, et al., *Textile Research J. 27*, 50 (1957).
1305. KLEIN, et al., *Ind. Eng. Chem. Data Series 2*, 72 (1957).
1306. KNUNYANTS AND VYAZANKIN, *Isvest. Akad. Nauk. S.S.S.R., Otdel. Khim. Nauk. 1957*, 238; C.A. *51*, 11235a (1957).
1307. KOBAYASHI, *J. Polymer Sci. 26*, 230-33 (1957).
1308. KOCHI, *J. Am. Chem. Soc. 79*, 2942 (1957).
1309. KOCHI, *J. Am. Chem. Soc. 78*, 1228 (1956).
1310. KOCHI, *J. Am. Chem. Soc. 77*, 5090 (1955).
1311. KOELSCH AND HOOD, *J. Org. Chem. 20*, 1282 (1955).
1312. KOSMIN AND HEININGER, Australian Patent 207,326 (1957).
1313. KOST, SHCHEGOLEVA AND YUDIN, *Zhur. Obshchei Khim. 25*, 2464-69 (1955); C.A. *50*, 9410e (1956).
1314. KOST AND TERENT'EV, *Zhur. Obshchei Khim. 26*, 1992-93 (1956); C.A. *51*, 5067e (1957).
1315. KRIMM, U. S. Patent 2,768,962 (1956).
1316. KRIMM, German Patent 948,157 (1956).
1317. KRIMM, German Patent 951,568 (1956).
1318. KRIMM, German Patent 1,002,342 (1957).
1319. KURUKI, et al., *Chem. High Polymers (Japan) 11*, 201-05 (1954); C.A. *50*, 1320 (1956).
1320. KURUKI AND WAKAMATSU, *Chem. High Polymers (Japan) 11*, 205-11 (1954); C.A. *50*, 1320 (1956).
1321. LAGUCHEVA AND PETROV, *Sbornik Statei Obshchei Khim. 2*, 1347 (1953); C.A. *49*, 528ıh (1955).
1322. LAMANT, *Compt. rend. 242*, 380-82 (1956).
1323. LAMANT, *Bull. soc. chim. France 23* [5], 562 (1956).
1324. LEWIS AND HOGLE, *J. Polymer Sci. 21*, 411 (1956).
1325. LOWE AND GATES, U. S. Patent 2,691,582 (1954).
1326. LUKES AND BLAHA, *Coll. Czech. Chem. Communs. 22*, No. 2, 626-28 (1957).
1327. LUSKIN, et al., *J. Am. Chem. Soc. 78*, 4042 (1956).
1328. MAEDER, U. S. Patent 2,753,318 (1956).
1329. MALINOWSKI AND BENBENEK, *Rocznicki Chem. 27*, 379 (1953); C.A. *49*, 1034h (1955).
1330. MANN AND WILKINSON, *J. Chem. Soc. 1957*, 3336.
1331. MARIELLA, CLUTTER AND EBNER, *J. Org. Chem. 20*, 1702 (1955).
1332. MARVEL, et al., *J. Polymer Sci. 20*, 437 (1956).
1333. MARVEL, TWEEDY AND ECONOMY, *J. Org. Chem. 21*, 1420-22 (1956).
1334. MASTAGLI, LAMBERT AND FRANCOIS, *Bull. soc. chim. France* [10], 1108 (1957).
1335. MCKINNEY, COWAN AND EVANS, U. S. Patent 2,775,565 (1956).
1336. MCMASTER, *Modern Textiles Mag. 38*, No. 8, 59-62 (1957).
1337. MEEK, et al., *J. Am. Chem. Soc. 78*, 5413 (1956).
1338. MELCHORE, *Modern Plastics 33*, No. 7, 163-64, 166, 250, 252 (1956).
1339. MELCHORE, *SPE Journal 13*, No. 7, 33-37 (1957).
1340. MERKER AND SCOTT, *J. Polymer Sci. 25*, 115-18 (1957).
1341. METZGER AND HELD, U. S. Patent 2,759,016 (1956); Canadian Patent 547,263 (1957).
1342. MILLER, *Can. J. Chem. 36*, No. 2 (1958).
1343. MILLER, *Can. J. Chem. 36*, No. 2 (1958).
1344. MILLER, et al., *J. Am. Chem. Soc. 78*, 5299 (1956).
1345. MILLS, JR. AND STACK, JR., *Ind. Eng. Chem. 48*, 260-62 (1956).
1346. MIRONOV, et al., *Isvest. Akad. Nauk S.S.S.R., Otdel. Khim. Nauk 1955*, 768; C.A. *50*, 7075d (1956).
1347. MIRONOV AND POGONKINA, *Isvest. Akad. Nauk S.S.S.R., Otdel. Khim. Nauk 1956*, 707; C.A. *51*, 7819a (1957).
1348. MISRA AND ASTHANA, *J. prakt. Chem. 4* [4], 270 (1957).
1349. MISRA AND ASTHANA, *Ann. 609*, No. 1-3, 240-46 (1957).
1350. MISRA AND ASTHANA, *J. prakt. Chem. 3*, 4-12 (1956).

1351. MOHRBACHER AND CROMWELL, *J. Am. Chem. Soc. 79,* 401 (1957).
1352. MONTGOMERY, U. S. Patent 2,816,129 (1957).
1353. MORTENSEN AND MARTIN, *Soil Sci. 81,* No. 1, 33-46 (1956).
1354. MUGNO AND BORNENGO, *Gazz. Chim. Ital. 86,* 451 (1956).
1355. NAZAROV AND MAKIN, *Zhur. Obshchei Khim. 27,* 499 (1957); C.A. *51,* 15520b (1957).
1356. NAZAROV, MAKIN AND GRAPOV, *Zhur. Obshchei Khim. 27,* 101 (1957); C.A. *51,* 12903f (1957).
1357. NAZAROV AND SHVEKHGEIMER, *Isvest. Akad. Nauk S.S.S.R., Otdel. Khim. Nauk 1956,* 199; C.A. *50,* 13902f (1956).
1358. NAZAROV AND SHVEKHGEIMER, *Isvest. Akad. Nauk S.S.S.R., Otdel. Khim. Nauk 1956,* 1378-82; C.A. *51,* 8046e (1957).
1359. NAZAROV, et al., *Zhur. Obshchei Khim. 24,* 319 (1954); C.A. *49,* 4651e, 8241h (1955).
1360. NAZAROV, et al., *Zhur. Obshchei Khim. 24,* 329 (1954); C.A. *49,* 4514h (1955).
1361. NAZAROV AND ZAV'YALOV, *Zhur. Obshchei Khim. 24,* 466 (1954); C.A. *49,* 6139f (1955).
1362. NAZAROV AND ZAV'YALOV, *Isvest. Akad. Nauk S.S.S.R., Otdel. Khim. Nauk 1957,* 325; C.A. *51,* 14597b (1957).
1363. NAZAROV, et al., *Isvest. Akad. Nauk S.S.S.R., Otdel. Khim. Nauk 1956,* 205; C.A. *50,* 13762d (1956).
1364. OGATA, et al., *J. Am. Chem. Soc. 78,* 5426 (1956).
1365. OGDEN, U. S. Patent 2,726,220 (1955).
1366. OLDHAM AND KROPA, U. S. 2,718,497 (1955).
1367. ONYON, *J. Polymer Sci. 22,* 13-18 (1956).
1368. ORR AND WILLIAMS, *Can. J. Chem. 33,* 1328 (1955).
1369. OSTER AND MIZUTANI, *J. Polymer Sci. 22,* 173 (1956).
1370. PETROV, et al., *Doklady Akad. Nauk S.S.S.R. 100,* 81 (1955); C.A. *50,* 1573f (1956).
1371. PETROV, et al., *Isvest. Akad. Nauk S.S.S.R., Otdel. Khim. Nauk 1956,* 256; C.A. *50,* 13726c (1956); C.A. *51,* 2536c (1957).
1372. PETROV AND VDOVIN, *Zhur. Obshchei Khim. 27,* 45 (1957); C.A. *51,* 12044f (1957).
1373. PIERCE, U. S. Patent 2,737,434 (1956).
1374. PIETRA, *Boll. sci. fac. chim. ind. Bologna 11,* 78 (1953); C.A. *49,* 13975g (1955).
1375. PIETRA, *Boll. sci. fac. chim. ind. Bologna 11,* 83 (1953); C.A. *49,* 13976b (1955).
1376. PIKE AND BAILEY, *J. Polymer Sci. 22,* 55-64 (1956).
1377. PINNER AND WYCHERLEY, *Plastics (London) 22,* 456-58 (1957).
1378. PINNER AND WYCHERLEY, *Plastics (London) 22,* 503-06 (1957).
1379. POLCH, U. S. Patent 2,769,699 (1956).
1380. PREVOT-BERNAS, *J. chim. phys. 53,* 418-21 (1956).
1381. POOLEY, U. S. Patent 2,757,147 (1956).
1382. PRICE AND SCHWAN, *J. Polymer Sci. 16,* 577 (1955).
1383. PROCTOR AND THOMSON, *J. Chem. Soc. 1957,* 2302.
1384. PROCTOR AND THOMSON, *J. Chem. Soc. 1957,* 2312.
1385. PROFFT, *Chem. Ber. 90,* No. 9, 1734-37 (1957).
1386. PUDOVIK AND LEBEDEVA, *Zhur. Obshchei Khim. 25,* 1920 (1955); C.A. *50,* 8442c (1956)
1387. PUDOVIK AND LEBEDEVA, *Zhur. Obshchei Khim. 25,* 2235 (1955); C.A. *50,* 9280d, 11977g (1956).
1388. PUDOVIK AND PLAKATINA, *Sbornick Statei Obshchei Khim. 2,* 831 (1953); C.A. *49,* 6821b (1955).
1389. PUDOVIK AND POLOZNOVA, *J. Gen. Chem. U.S.S.R. 25,* 745 (1955) (English translation); C.A. *50,* 2417e (1956).
1390. REYNOLDS AND KOLTHOFF, *J. Phys. Chem. 60,* 969-974 (1956).
1391. RICE AND GROGAN, *J. Org. Chem. 20,* 1687 (1955).
1392. RODIONOV AND BELIKOV, *Doklady Akad. Nauk S.S.S.R. 93,* 827 (1953); C.A. *49,* 1550i (1955).
1393. ROSENBERG AND GREENBERG, *Modern Plastics 35,* No. 4, 173-74, 176, 178, 253-54, 256 (1957).
1394. SADOV AND SOKOLOVA, *Tekstil. Prom. 16,* No. 5, 33-36 (1956); C.A. *50,* 12485 (1956).
1395. SANDERS, U. S. Patent 2,787,561 (1957).
1396. SANDERS, U. S. Patent 2,787,603 (1957).
1397. SCHMIDT-NICKELS, U. S. Patent 2,794,805 (1957).
1398. SCHOEBERL AND LANGE, *Ann. 599,* 140 (1956); C.A. *51,* 2549 (1957).
1399. SCHOUTEDEN, *Chimie and industrie 78,* No. 3A, 102 (1957).
1400. SCHOUTEDEN, *Makromol. Chem. 24,* No. 1, 25-49 (1957).
1401. SHEERAN, U. S. Patent 2,785,975 (1957).
1402. SHERWOOD, *Am. Dyestuff Reptr. 44,* 262-64 (1955).
1403. SHONO AND ODA, *Kogyo Kagaku Zasshi, 59,* 385 (1956); C.A. *51,* 11324d (1957).
1404. STAEHLE, U. S. Patent 2,751,315 (1956).
1405. STAEHLE, U. S. Patent 2,776,236 (1957).
1406. STETTNER AND COENEN, *Chem. Ber. 87,* 869 (1954); *Angew. Chem. 67,* 775 (1955).
1407. STICKLES, U. S. Patent 2,744,846 (1956).
1408. STILBERT, et al., U. S. Patent 2,755,260 (1956).
1409. STREPIKHEEV AND BOGDANOV, *Sbornik Statei Obshchei Khim. 2,* 1462 (1953); C.A. *49,* 4551i (1955).
1410. SUBRAMANIAN AND SANTAPPA, *Makromol. Chem. 22,* No. 1/2, 147-62 (1957).

1411. SUMITOMO AND HACHIHAMA, *J. Chem. Soc. Japan, Ind. Chem. Sect. 60*, No. 7, 840-43 (1957).
1412. SURREY AND LESHER, *J. Am. Chem. Soc. 78*, 2573 (1956).
1413. SUTTON, U. S. Patent 2,767,153 (1956).
1414. SVETLIK, et al., *Ind. Eng. Chem. 48*, No. 6, 1084-89 (1956).
1415. SYMONS, *J. Chem. Soc. 1955*, 2794-96.
1416. TEETER, et al., *J. Org. Chem. 22*, 512 (1957).
1417. TERENT'EV AND BUTSKUS, *Zhur. Obshchei Khim. 27* [10], 2884 (1957).
1418. TERENT'EV AND GURVICH, *Sbornik Statei Obshchei Khim., Akad. Nauk S.S.S.R. 1*, 404 (1953); C.A. *49*, 1047i (1955).
1419. TERENT'EV AND GURVICH, *Sbornik Statei Obshchei Khim., Akad. Nauk S.S.S.R. 1*, 404 (1953); C.A. *49*, 1047e (1955).
1420. TERENT'EV AND KOST, *Zhur. Obshchei Khim. 27*, 262 (1957); C.A. *51*, 12907e (1957).
1421. TERENT'EV, et al., *Zhur. Obshchei Khim. 26*, 719 (1956); C.A. *50*, 14586c (1956).
1422. TERENT'EV, et al., *Zhur. Obshchei Khim. 25*, 1613 (1955); C.A. *50*, 4911b (1956).
1423. TERENT'EV, et al., *Zhur. Obshchei Khim. 26*, 2925-28 (1956); C.A. *51*, 8010i (1957).
1424. TERENT'EV, et al., *Zhur. Obshchei Khim. 25*, 1959 (1955); C.A. *50*, 4910f, 12025c (1956).
1425. TERENT'EV, et al., *Zhur. Obshchei Khim. 26*, 557 (1956); C.A. *50*, 13871h (1956).
1426. THOMAS, et al., *J. Polymer Sci. 24*, 43-56 (1957).
1427. THOMPSON, *J. Polymer Sci. 19*, 373 (1956).
1428. TOUEY AND COOVER, JR., U. S. Patent 2,805,205 (1957).
1429. TREIBS AND MICHL, *Ann. 589*, 163-73 (1954); C.A. *49*, 15858g (1955).
1430. TREIBS, et al., *J. prakt. Chem. 2*, 1-30 (1955).
1431. TOMITA, et al., *J. Pharm. Soc. Japan 74*, 742-46 (1954); C.A. *49*, 11661i (1955).
1432. TUTWILER, et al., U. S. Patent 2,803,599 (1957).
1433. UMHOEFER, U. S. Patent 2,720,532 (1955).
1434. VALENTINE, *J. Textile Inst. Trans. 47*, No. 1, 1-15 (1956).
1435. VAN DER KERK, et al., *J. Appl. Chem. (London) 7*, 356 (1957).
1436. VEBRA, U. S. Patent 2,785,176 (1957).
1437. VEREINIGTE GLANZSTOFFE FABRIKEN, A. G., British Patent 752,893 (1956).
1438. VICTOR CHEMICAL WORKS, British Patent 759,329 (1954).
1439. WALBORSKY AND HORNYAK, *J. Am. Chem. Soc. 77*, 6026 (1955).
1440. WALKER, *J. Am. Chem. Soc. 78*, 3698 (1956).
1441. WALKER, U. S. Patent 2,816,100 (1957).
1442. WASSERMAN, et al., *J. Am. Chem. Soc. 78*, 2808 (1956).
1443. WEAVER, et al., *Textile Research J. 26*, 518 (1956).
1444. WEBSTER, *Agr. Chemicals 10*, No. 8, 44-46, 99 (1955).
1445. WEYLORD AND SULLIVAN, U. S. Patent 2,742,491 (1956).
1446. WEISBERG, U. S. Patent 2,724,632 (1955).
1447. WILEY, et al., *J. Am. Chem. Soc. 77*, 5105 (1955).
1448. WITNAUER, et al., *J. Polymer Sci. 20*, 213 (1956).
1449. WITTIG AND WITTENBERG, *Ann. 606*, No. 1-3, 1-23 (1957).
1450. WOLFRAM, et al., U. S. Patent 2,790,822 (1954).
1451. YASHUNSKAYA, et al., *Zhur. Priklad. Khim. 29*, 105-10 (1956).
1452. YASHUNSKII, et al., *Zhur. Obshchei Khim. 25*, 2457 (1955); C.A. *50*, 9428d (1956).
1453. ZAHN AND GERSTNER, *Ber. 88*, 1731-37 (1955).
1454. ZELNICK, et al., *Bull. soc. chim. France 23* [5], 888 (1956).

INDEX